An Introduction to **Physical Organic Chemistry**

An Introduction to Physical Organic Chemistry

Edward M. Kosower

Department of Chemistry
State University of New York
Stony Brook

John Wiley & Sons, Inc.   *New York · London · Sydney*

Library of Congress Catalog Card Number: 67–28947
Printed in the United States of America

To those who provided the counterpoint:

Nechama, Ariel, Daria

—my parents

—Marita

Preface

שלום! Shalom! Peace! Chance favors the prepared mind, and tranquillity (I hope) will predispose the reader toward an acceptance of the unfamiliar organization of the subject of physical organic chemistry utilized in this book. A primary object of the development is to convey a broad perspective useful even for specific reactions that have not been covered.

The subject matter has been presented to both seniors and first-year graduate students in one-semester courses. The text is easily sufficient for a one-year course with appropriate supplementation on theory, stereochemistry, and conformational analysis and photochemistry. Chemists who have completed their training should find the book useful for a review of recent developments. Superior students in the second semester of organic chemistry will find portions of the book interesting as background.

The volume is divided into three parts: Substituent Effects, Medium Effects, and Intermediates. The first part is, in turn, divided into groups of sections characterized by the relationship of the transition states to the initial states: polar transition states (separation of charge different in initial and transition states), radical transition states, and isopolar transition states (no important difference in charge separation for transition and initial states). New schemes for the classification of substitution and radical reactions are presented. The choice of illustrative material is always a difficult one; I should appreciate comments from those who have more pertinent or more felicitous examples.

Many friends and colleagues have contributed valuable comments and criticisms, including Professors Teddy G. and Patricia S. Traylor, David M. Lemal, William D. Closson, Edward M. Arnett, Thomas J. Katz, William D. Saunders, Andrew Streitwieser, Jr., Noboru Hirota, Harold L. Friedman, V. J. Shiner, Cyril A. Grob, Paul v. R. Schleyer, Roald Hoffmann, Gary

Griffin, Theodore S. Sorensen, John I. Brauman and Drs. Stanley Seltzer and Eric S. Albone.

The preparation of the manuscript was aided immensely by the efforts of Mrs. Grace Stephens and Mrs. Nancy Mullen.

Edward M. Kosower

Huntington, New York
April 29, 1967

Sections and Problems

Contents

Brønsted acidity. Proton-transfer rates. Relationship of log k for proton-transfer to log K for proton dissociation. Expected versus actual behavior for log k versus log K. Brønsted catalysis. Molecular interpretation of Brønsted coefficients.
Proton exchange and hydrocarbon acidity. pK_a scale for very weak acids. Isotope effects. Mechanism of exchange reactions. Anion stabilization: hybridization, delocalization, and inductive effects. $C^{13}H$ coupling constants. Hybridization and bond distances. Hetero-substituted carbon acids. Fluorocompound acidities. Lewis acids: hard and soft acids and bases.

Radical Transition States

(electron-transfer reactions) ($E_+R\cdot$, E_+RH, E_+R^+, $E_-R\cdot$, E_-RH, E_-R^-) and S (substitution reactions) (S_IR, S_DR, S_AR). Techniques for studying radicals. Stable free radicals. Radical-dimer equilibrium. Peroxy radicals. Fragmentation to radicals. Comparison of azo compound decompositions. Symmetrical and unsymmetrical decomposition. Triplet radical pair in cage at 77°K. Stereospecific cage recombination. Ring strain in radical formation. Electron-transfer reactions. Franck-Condon principle. S_DR (atom-transfer) reactions on halogen with pentacyano-cobaltate(II), chromium(II), and 1-ethyl-4-carbomethoxypyri-dinyl. Solvent effect on radical halogen abstraction. Hydrogen transfer reactions.

Definition of complex. Charge-transfer transition. Donors. Acceptors. Ground state charge-transfer contribution. Criteria for charge-transfer transitions. Selected charge-transfer maxima. Reactions through charge-transfer complexes. Reaction cate-gories: **C, G, S, D, T, L**. Potential energy curves for D,A and D^+,A^- complexes. Some photochemical and thermal electron transfers. Chemiluminescence as a result of an electron-transfer reaction. Cyclodimerization via diradical ion-pairs.

Isopolar Transition States

[2 + 2] cycloadditions. Diradical intermediates. Stereospecificity of collapse of singlet and triplet diradicals. [2σ + 2] cyclo-addition of bicyclobutanes. Molecular orbitals for simple cases. Symmetry (S) and antisymmetry (A) of orbitals. Molecular orbital correlation diagrams. Photo[2 + 2]cycloaddition. [2 + 3] cycloaddition. The three major groups of "1,3-dipoles." Solvent effect and stereo-specificity of [2 + 3] cycloaddition. Molecular orbital correlation diagrams for [2 + 3] cyclo-addition. [2 + 4] cycloaddition. Secondary hydrogen isotope effect on the reverse of [2 + 4] cycloaddition. Some cyclo-addition reactions of cyclobutadiene. Molecular orbital correla-tion diagrams for [2 + 4] cycloaddition.

Electrocyclic reactions. Cyclobutene ring opening. Conrotatory and disrotatory ring opening. Thermal and photochemical ring openings and closures. Trienes and cyclohexadienes. Cyclopropyl cations, radicals, carbanions, and ring opening. Concerted solvolysis and ring opening of cyclopropyl derivatives. [5 → 4 + 1] fragmentation. Atom transfer reactions defined. Sigmatropic changes of order. [i,j]. [1,j] hydrogen migrations. Antarafacial and suprafacial migrations. [3,3] sigmatropic changes of order. "Cope" and "Claisen rearrangements." Divinylcycloalkanes. Geometry of [3,3] sigmatropic changes of order on the basis of molecular orbital correlation diagrams and steric strain in transition state. Degenerate [3,3] sigmatropic changes of order. Bullvalene and barbaralone.

PART TWO *Medium Effects*

      Discontinuous character of solvents. Effect of solute on solvent molecule arrangements. First coordination shell. Cybotactic region. Dielectric constants. Macroscopic and microscopic levels. Local environment.
      Distortion polarization and orientation polarization. Relation of dielectric constant to polarizability. Corrections to Debye–Clausius–Mosotti equation. Macroscopic solvent parameters.
      Frequency dependence of dielectric constant. Refractive index and dynamic dielectric constant.
      General treatment of relaxation processes and relaxation times. Perturbation of a chemical equilibrium and its relaxation. Dielectric relaxation. Dielectric relaxation times. Spin-lattice relaxation and spin-lattice relaxation times, T_1. Correlation times.
      Radial distribution function. Structure of water and ice. Theories of liquid water. Structure of liquid alcohols. Mixing of ethanol and water. Excess functions for mixing.

PART THREE   *Intermediates and Unusual Molecules*

GENERAL REMARKS

The impact of the intellectual approach practiced by the physical organic chemist on the subject of organic chemistry has been enormous and decisive. From a level that might have readily been understood by Escoffier (*256*) who said, "C'est par la chimie qu'on est arrivé à connaître les diverses propriétés des substances alimentaires," organic chemistry has grown into a subject with deep roots in theoretical and physical chemistry. There is scarcely a branch of organic chemistry, including that concerned with synthesis, that could not be treated within the context of physical organic chemistry. Textbooks written for undergraduate organic chemistry have been strongly influenced by the physical organic approach to the subject. It is thus difficult to define the limits of physical organic chemistry, expanded (as it is) so far beyond the original treatment of Hammett (*2*). Two complementary approaches may be used to provide some background in physical organic chemistry. A thorough development of theoretical concepts, like that offered by Wiberb (*1*) or in more specialized books like that of Streitwieser (*65*), can make the student responsive to the abstract elements in the problems of organic chemistry. We might call this the *physical* approach. In contrast, the *organic* approach tries to group the phenomena of organic chemistry in a way that reveals the resemblances and analogies between them. The latter method permits individual topics to be developed at whatever level seems most suitable. Like its excellent predecessors, Hine (*257*), Gould (*258*), and Ingold (*59*), this book utilizes the organic approach. For the most part, the discussion is directed at students who have had both undergraduate organic and physical chemistry.

The book consists of three somewhat unequal parts: (1) substituent effects, (2) medium effects, and (3) intermediates. Explicit discussions of steric and conformational effects have not been included, since excellent summaries are available (*52, 247, 249*). Although most of the discussion in the book is concerned with carbon compounds, a good many of the ideas and correlations can be applied to the chemistry of other elements. Our representations of organic molecules are conventional, even though it is clear that some modifications could be made. If we think of formulas as ways of expressing the geometric relationship of electrons and atoms, the application of the principles of topological mapping to organic structures (see Lederberg, *250*) might well bring us to new concepts about molecules and their transformations.

A brief review of some formal notions about chemical reactions will be

1

useful in providing a common basis for later discussions. Consider two reactants, A and B. The *initial state* of the system, A + B, is the energy of the system before any reaction has occurred. If the initial state includes meaningful participation by the medium (for example, the solvent), we might write it as $A_{(m)} + B_{(m)}$, but we normally exclude the bulk of the medium from our description. Collisions of the A and B molecules with molecules of the medium permit a few of the A + B combinations to acquire enough energy to assume the molecular arrangement of the *transition state*, the least energetic arrangement which allows A + B to form the *products* of the reaction. (The energy "hill" which must be climbed to form the transition state is also called a *barrier*. It is sometimes possible, if the barrier is narrow enough, for *tunneling* through the barrier to occur. Electrons and hydrogen atoms are the only chemical species for which tunneling is worth considering.) A free energy versus reaction coordinate diagram is illustrated in Fig. 0.1.

A free energy versus reaction coordinate diagram is a convenient way of representing how we *believe* the free energy of the A + B system changes as A and B react to form products. The product (or products) of a reaction may be unstable with respect to conversion to other compounds. Depending on the conditions under which the reaction was carried out, an unstable product might be isolated or might serve only as an *intermediate*. Two diagrams indicating the participation of intermediates in reactions are shown in Figs. 0.2 and 0.3. Figure 0.2 describes a reaction in which the *rate-determining step*

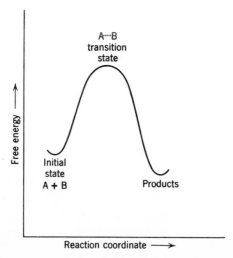

Figure 0.1   Free energy versus reaction coordinate diagram for the reaction of A and B.

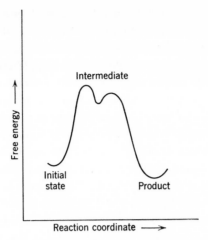

Figure 0.2 A free energy versus reaction coordinate diagram for a reaction proceeding via one intermediate.

(the highest transition state in the diagram) occurs before the first inter-mediate; Fig. 0.3 indicates a reaction in which two intermediates are involved, and the transition state occurs after the first intermediate.

We should note that the use of free energy in the description presumes that

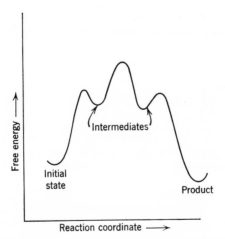

Figure 0.3 A free energy versus reaction coordinate diagram for a reaction proceeding via two intermediates and for which the rate-determining step occurs in the conversion of the first intermediate into the second.

there is thermodynamic equilibrium between the A + B system and all the states accessible to it. This condition is probably fulfilled in most thermal reactions, but it is certainly not met in photochemical reactions because the electronic transition occurs much more rapidly than molecular motion can establish thermal equilibrium. The energies in thermal systems are usually given by a Boltzmann distribution for which the number of molecules, N_i, with an energy, E_i, above the lowest state, can be expressed as $N_i = N_0 \exp(-E_i/kT)$ with N_0 equal to the number of molecules in the lowest state. In contrast, the study of reactions in molecular beams does not involve molecules with a Boltzmann distribution of energies.

In order to ascertain whether or not the diagram we have drawn is an appropriate one for the reaction under consideration, we carry out experimental tests that may include some or all of the following: the kinetic dependence of the reaction on the reactants, the identification of the products, the use of isotopic atoms as labels and their location in the products, the measurement of the effect of isotopic substituents on the rate of the reaction, elucidation of the stereochemistry of the reaction, studies of the effect of substituent and solvent change on the rate and products of the reaction, and a search for possible catalytic influences on the rate and products of the reaction. The details of the final description will vary according to the number of experimental criteria we are able to apply, and we cannot therefore expect a "final" description to survive beyond the time at which new criteria are applied to a reaction. The description of the reaction is usually referred to as the *mechanism* of the reaction. One of the chief concerns of modern chemistry, and especially physical organic chemistry, is the mechanism of chemical reactions.

The transition states, through which organic reactions may proceed, can be loosely grouped into three classes: polar, free radical, and isopolar. Polar transition states often differ considerably in charge separation from the initial state, as shown in the examples A1, 2, and 4. Displacement reactions (A3) sometimes involve charge separation in the transition state, but very often they have transition states in which the charge is more dispersed than in the initial state. Free radical transition states are reached through creation of spin or transfer of spin (Examples B1–4). Isopolar transition states (C1, 2) normally differ very little in charge distribution from the corresponding initial states. Illustrative examples are shown in the following equations.

(A) Reactions through Polar Transition States
(1) $AB \rightarrow A^+ \cdots B^-$ (A^+ = carbonium ion)

(2) $AB \rightarrow A^- \cdots B^+$ (A^- = carbanion)

(3) $Y + AB \rightarrow Y \cdots A \cdots B$ (displacement)

(4) $Z-A-B-C-X \rightarrow Z^+ \cdots A \cdots B \cdots C \cdots X^-$ (fragmentation)

(*B*) *Reaction through Free Radical Transition States*

(1) $AB \rightarrow A^\cdot \cdots B^\cdot$ (radical pair formation)

(2) $A^\cdot + BC \rightarrow A^\cdot \cdots B \cdots C^\cdot$ (atom transfer)

(3) 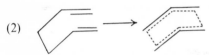   [2 + 2] cycloaddition via charge-transfer through diradical ion-pair

(4)   [2 + 2] cycloaddition via diradical (text discussion under Isopolar Reactions)

(*C*) *Reactions through Isopolar Transition States*

(1)   [2 + 4] cycloaddition

(2)   [3, 3] sigmatropic change

Most of the techniques used to investigate mechanism fall into two broad groups. Changes in the structure of the reactants will affect both the initial state and the transition state. The effect observed for a given structural change will usually vary in magnitude as the distance between the reaction center and the changed portion of the molecule is increased. There are, however, important exceptions to this generalization (neighboring groups, conformer-stabilizing groups like *t*-butyl). All of the changes that fall into the first category can be treated as *substituent effects,* and thus the first broad group of investigative measures involves the study of the effect of intramolecular changes. The second broad group includes all extramolecular changes, for which we use the description *medium effects.* We count *cage effects* with the second group. Medium effects must also be considered in light of changes in both the initial state and the transition state.

The study of the kinetics and products of a reaction and a consideration of substituent and medium effects on that reaction constitute a substantial portion of physical organic chemistry. Within this organizational pattern for the subject, we have selected areas which are of significance to those interested in physical organic chemistry. Numerous topics—even important ones—have only been lightly touched. It is hoped that the approach used in this text will lend itself intellectually to the facile incorporation of new material and that the framework provided for the student will provide appropriate means for development.

Problems

1. Prepare a free energy versus reaction coordinate diagram for each of the general reactions used to illustrate the different types of transition states, including the portion of the curve which describes the product or products.

2. For each diagram written above, show the effect on the curve if the substituent near the reaction center is changed from (a) electron-supplying to electron-withdrawing (CH_3O to CF_3, for example) and (b) small to large (H to *t*-butyl, for example). (Note that a concrete example would make it easier to answer this question. Later sections of the book may be consulted for appropriate reactions if necessary.)

3. For each of the reactions described in Problem 2, indicate the following:
   (a) The kinetic dependence on the reactants.
   (b) The nature of the products.
   (c) How the products would be separated.
   (d) How the products would be identified.
   (e) Usefulness of isotope labeling (deuterium, carbon-13, etc.).
   (f) The usefulness of a study of the stereochemistry.
   (g) The solvent effect on the reaction.
   (h) What catalysts (H^+, OH^-, etc.) might be expected to influence the reaction.

The student should make a serious attempt to answer these questions. After completing his study of Parts 1 and 2 of the book, it would be useful to review the answers prepared for these questions.

PART ONE

Substituent Effects

And then I glanced at the clock again. This time it
read 12:28, which led me to exclaim, "My God, so much
has happened in the last three minutes."

It seems, then, that until new methods of communication
are devised, we must make do with what we have.

The Drug Experience, Paul Moser

1.0   Introduction

The effect of a substituent is evaluated by a measurement of how the introduction of the substituent into a substrate affects a physical or chemical property of the substrate. The nature of the substrate is important with respect to the changes elicited by a particular substituent. If we define the *reaction center* as consisting of those atoms that actually undergo changes in bonding on forming the transition state, we can understand that substituent changes at the reaction center will generally have more influence than substituent changes at a more distant atom. We shall include with substituent changes those variations that might at first sight be thought of as *structural* as, for example, in the comparison of the reactivities of bridgehead halides and alkyl halides. It will also become clear that the geometric and electronic relationship of the substituent to the reaction center is more important than whether the substituent is separated from that center by a certain number of other atoms.

We have chosen to divide the discussion of substituent effects into classes, based on the probable nature of the transition states for the reactions in which they are observed. Even though there are some reactions that do not fall cleanly into one of the three broad classes (reactions through polar transition states, reactions through free radical transition states, and reactions through isopolar transition states), we believe that this classification easily accommodates a great amount of physical organic chemistry.

One of the earliest methods for evaluating substituent effects was based on the measurement of acid strengths. We shall begin our discussion of substituent effects with a section on acidity in which we shall also bring forward the Brønsted equation for the correlation of the effects of acids on reactions, the notion of linear free energy relationships (including some general ideas about the limitations on their range of usefulness) and the importance of rate measurements on fast reactions like proton transfer.

The strengths of very weak acids like aromatic hydrocarbons have been approximately known for a long time, but it is only recently that techniques for reasonably accurate measurement of these acidities have permitted further insights into the understanding of these acid strengths to be developed (Section 1.2).

The best known linear free energy relationship is that of Hammett and much of our knowledge of substituent effects, as we shall see in Section 1.3, comes from the $\rho\sigma$-correlation originally based on the acidities of benzoic acids.

Two sections on nucleophilic replacement (or substitution) reactions explore the effects of structural (and substituent) change on both displacement and ionization reactions that involve the replacement of one group by another at a carbon atom (Sections 1.4 and 1.5).

In the discussion on free radical reactions, one section (1.6) will concern radical reactions explicitly and a second (1.7) will cover charge-transfer reactions in which either the initial reactants or the products must be free radicals.

Many of the reactions discussed under isopolar transition states in Sections 1.8 and 1.9 have been called by other terms, for example, thermal rearrangement reactions, 1,3-dipolar additions, "no-mechanism" reactions, etc. Theoretical developments in the treatment of these reactions suggest that a new general term might be appropriate, occasionally along with different designations for the reactions themselves. In this way, we hope to bring out the similarities in the courses of superficially different reactions.

Limitations in space and time have made it impossible to do more than touch here and there upon the chemistry of excited states, but we think that many of the ideas developed for ground-state species will be applicable to these highly energetic species if proper account is taken of the much greater variety of transition states accessible to such species. We might expect that singlet excited states (except for charge-transfer complexes in which the separation of charge is much greater than that within a molecule after excitation) will follow many of the rules for polar transition states, and that triplet excited states will resemble radicals in their reactions. The relationship of excited states to the chemistry of molecules undergoing isopolar reactions is indicated in the discussion on isopolar transition states (Sections 1.8 and 1.9).

It is not possible to avoid all mention of medium effects in any discussion of substituent effects, but medium effects have been invoked only when necessary because Part 2 of the book is devoted entirely to such effects.

POLAR TRANSITION STATES

1.1 Acidity

Brønsted (259) defined acids as species which had a tendency to lose a proton and bases as species which had a tendency to gain a proton. Persuasive arguments for the currency and generality of this definition have been given by Bell (4). An acid-base pair

$$(1) \qquad BH^+ = B + H^+$$

consists of the acid (BH$^+$) and its conjugate base (B) or, alternatively, of the base (B) and its conjugate acid (BH$^+$). The equilibrium of Eq. 1 cannot be observed; all reactions of an acid involve the transfer of the proton to a base which may be the solvent.

$$(2) \qquad BH^+ + S = B + SH^+$$

Aqueous solution is an important and convenient solvent for the study of acids, with the water molecule acting as a base for the removal of the proton from the acid.

$$(3) \qquad BH^+ + H_2O = H_3O^+ + B$$

Although the equilibrium constant for the reaction shown in Eq. 3 is formally given by

$$(4) \qquad K = \frac{[H_3O^+][B]}{[H_2O][BH^+]}$$

it is usual to omit the water term because in dilute aqueous solution, the change in concentration of the water due to the formation of the hydronium ion, H_3O^+, is negligible. The commonly used expression for the acid dissociation constant, K_a, is given as:

$$(5) \qquad K_a = \frac{[H_3O^+][B]}{[BH^+]}$$

The wide range over which K_a varies makes it more convenient to express the information in logarithmic form. Thus, $pK_a = \log K_a$.

Only strong acids can protonate the molecules of weakly basic solvents. Perchloric acid, hydrogen bromide, sulfuric acid, p-toluenesulfonic acid, and hydrogen chloride form a series of decreasing acid strength in acetic acid, although they are of apparently equal strength in the more basic solvent,

9

water. Meaningful comparisons of acid strengths must be made in a single solvent or under such conditions that medium effects (for example, ion-aggregation) are minimized. For acids and solvent molecules, which are both neutral, the dissociation process produces two ions. The effect of the solvent on the ions is an important component of the interactions that determine the extent of dissociation in such cases.

(6) $BH + S = B^- + SH^+$

The factors that affect the strength of acids will be described in the next section (Section 1.2) along with data on the pK_a values for many acids. Additional pK_a data are included in the survey of substituent constants (Section 1.3), and others may easily be found in the literature (4).

Eigen and his co-workers (260) have changed the whole perspective of chemists on the rates and mechanisms of proton-transfer reactions by discovering the usefulness of *relaxation methods* in measuring the rates of reactions up to the diffusion controlled limit. (For an excellent summary of the methods used to study fast reactions, see Caldin, 74.) We might illustrate the principle of relaxation as follows: suppose we had a solution of an acid, BH, in equilibrium with its conjugate base, B^- at $25°$, and that the anion B^- had a characteristic light absorption which could be measured for our solution at a given wavelength. If the temperature of the solution is suddenly changed (in microseconds by the discharge of a large condenser through the solution), the components of the solution will no longer be in equilibrium. The time required for the solution to change $1/e$ of the way toward the new equilibrium composition is called the *relaxation time*, τ. The relaxation time is equal to the reciprocal of the first-order rate constant if only one chemical process occurs in the reaction system [see Section 2.4]:

(7) $$\ln \left[\frac{a_0}{\dfrac{a_0}{e}} \right] = kt_{1/e} = k\tau; \qquad \tau = 1/k$$

In addition to temperature-jump ("*T*-jump"), several other methods [pressure jump ("*P*-jump"), electric field pulse, etc.] can be used to change the equilibrium condition. The change in composition that occurs to meet the new equilibrium condition may be monitored by spectrophotometry, conductance, fluorescence, polarized light rotation, etc. Details on the treatment of the data may be found in the book by Amdur and Hammes (421) and the papers of Eigen (260). The rate constants found for many proton-transfer reactions approach the diffusion-controlled limit. The fastest reaction in aqueous solution is the reaction of the hydronium ion with the hydroxide ion for which the rate constant is 1.3×10^{11} l. mol.$^{-1}$ sec.$^{-1}$. The rate is unusually high because of the special mechanisms that transfer these species through structured water (see Fig. 2.10). Some rate constants for proton-transfer reactions are listed in Table 1.1. Note that the rate constant for the combination of the proton with the hydroxide ion in ice is the highest of all, probably limited by the rate of generation of the reactant species and rapid because of the ice structure, which favors cooperative transfer of the reactants.

Consider a simple mechanism for proton transfer in which an intermediate (hydrogen-bonded) complex is formed between the acid and base (Eq. 8) (260)(421) (k_1 and k_{-2} are characteristic of diffusion-controlled processes so that, for example, k_{-2} can be ignored for the forward reaction.)

$$(8) \qquad BH^+ + Y \underset{k_{-1}}{\overset{k_1}{\rightleftharpoons}} BHY^+ \underset{k_{-2}}{\overset{k_2}{\rightleftharpoons}} B + YH^+$$

Using the steady-state treatment, the forward (k_f) and reverse (k_r) rate constants can be derived (Eqs. 9–13).

$$(9) \qquad \frac{d(BHY^+)}{dt} = k_1(BH^+)(Y) - k_{-1}(BHY^+) - k_2(BHY^+) = 0$$

$$(10) \qquad (BHY^+) = \frac{k_1}{k_{-1} + k_2}(BH^+)(Y)$$

$$(11) \qquad \frac{dB}{dt} = k_2(BHY^+) = k_2 \frac{k_1}{k_{-1} + k_2}(BH^+)(Y)$$

$$(12) \qquad k_f = \frac{k_1}{(k_{-1}/k_2) + 1}$$

$$(13) \qquad k_r = \frac{k_{-2}}{1 + k_2/k_{-1}}$$

It is easy to see that if Y binds the proton more strongly than B, there will be little tendency for the intermediate to return to BH^+ and Y. If $pK_{YH^+} \gg pK_{BH^+}$, $k_{-1} \ll k_2$, and the reaction rate is controlled by the value of k_1. The reaction rate will thus be diffusion controlled, and k_f will be a constant. Using the definition of equilibrium constants, we can write the identity:

$$(14) \qquad \log k_f - \log k_r \equiv pK_{YH^+} - pK_{BH^+} \equiv \Delta(pK)$$

The rate constant k_f thus bears a relationship to the quantity $\Delta(pK)$. Formally, we may write this as

$$(15) \qquad \frac{\partial \log k_f}{\partial \Delta(pK)} = \alpha$$

TABLE 1.1 *Rates of Proton-transfer Reactions*[a]

Acid	Conjugate Base	pK_a	k_{H^+} [b,d]	k_{OH^-} [c,d]
H_2O	OH^-	15.75	1.4×10^{11}	
H_2O(solid)(ice)	OH^-	21.4	8.6×10^{12}	
D_2O	OD^-	16.5	8.4×10^{10} [g]	
$H\cdot$	e^-_{aq}	9.7[e]	2.1×10^{10} [e]	
C_6H_5OH	$C_6H_5O^-$	9.98		$\sim 1.4 \times 10^{10}$
$CH_3COCH=C(OH)CH_3$	$[CH_3COCHCOCH_3]^-$	8.24	3.1×10^{10}	1.9×10^7
$1,2\text{-}(CH_3)_2NC_6H_4COOH$	$1,2\text{-}(CH_3)_2NC_6H_4COO^-$	8.42		1.1×10^7
HCN	CN^-	9.1		3.7×10^9
CH_3COCH_3	$[CH_3COCH_2]^-$	~ 20	$\sim 5 \times 10^{10}$	2.7×10^{-1}
$CH_3COCH_2COCH_3$	$[CH_3COCHCOCH_3]^-$	9.0	1.2×10^7	4×10^4
$CO_2(+H_2O)$	HCO_3^-	6.35	5.6×10^4	1×10^4
$C_7H_7^+(+H_2O)$[f]	C_7H_7OH	4.75	6.6×10^4	

[a] From Ref. 260 except as noted. [b] For the reaction of the conjugate base with H^+ in l. mol.$^{-1}$ sec.$^{-1}$. [c] For the reaction of the acid with OH^- in l. mol.$^{-1}$ sec.$^{-1}$. [d] Most measurements refer to 298°K. [e] Ref. 261. [f] Tropylium ion. [g] k_{D^+}.

12

for which it is clear that the quantity α is zero if $\Delta(pK)$ has a positive value and one if $\Delta(pK)$ has a substantial negative value. If $\Delta(pK) = 0$, the intermediate complex has an equal chance of decomposing to reactants or to products and, in the ideal case, the rate constant k_f is one half as large as the maximum possible. The α must change from a value of one to a value of zero in a *transition region*. The ideal cases are illustrated in Figs. 1.1a and 1.1b.

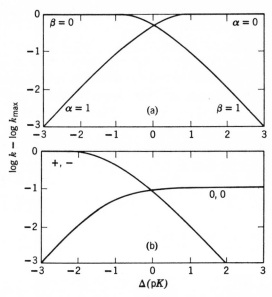

Figure 1.1   Idealized diagrams depicting the relationship of $\log k$ and $\Delta(pK)$ in "normal" acid–base systems. (a) Diagram for the symmetrical charge type, as for $BH^+ + Y \rightleftharpoons B + YH^+$. (b) Diagram for the unsymmetrical charge type, as in the reverse of neutralization $HX + B \rightleftharpoons BH^+ + X^-$. The slopes for the forward reactions are shown as α, and the corresponding slopes for the reverse reactions are symbolized by β (cf. Eq. 15). (Neutral particles that react to form charged pairs will do so at a rate of about one-tenth that of "normal" reactants due to electrostatic retardation of the separation of the reaction partners) (adapted from Ref. 260 with the permission of the author and *Angewandte Chemie*).

"Normal" behavior is defined as showing a narrow transition region for the change in the slope (α) of the plot of $\log k$ versus $\Delta(pK)$, as in the case of the reaction of imidazole with proton donors:

(16) $HN\overset{\frown}{\underset{\smile}{}}N + BH \longrightarrow \left[HN\overset{\frown}{\underset{\smile}{}}NH \right]^+ + B^-$

illustrated in Fig. 1.2. In contrast, the transition region for the plot of the log k for the reaction of acetylacetonate anion (**1**) with proton donors versus $\Delta(pK)$ is very broad (Fig. 1.2). In addition, the rate of the reaction of **1** with a proton donor as strong as the hydronium ion is much slower than the rate for diffusion-controlled reaction (Eq. 17) in the formation of the *ketone*, acetylacetone (**2**).

Eigen (*260*), following earlier arguments of Bell (*4*), has rationalized deviations from theoretically expected behavior by lack of parallelism in the potential energy curves which describe a series of proton-transfer reactions. We should like to present a molecular view which rationalizes the broad transition region and offers some insight into proton-transfer reaction rates.

Free energy versus reaction coordinate diagrams may be constructed from data on the reactions of acetylacetonate anion (**1**) with proton donors, with the aid of transition state theory. The transition state theory equation for the

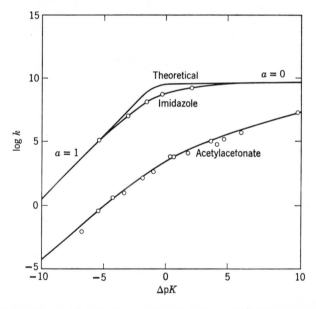

Figure 1.2 Log k versus $\Delta(pK)$ plots. The theoretical curve like that shown in Fig. 1.1*a*. The curve marked imidazole represents the reaction shown in Eq. 16 and that marked acetylacetonate for the reaction shown in Eq. 17. (The donors for imidazole are glucose, phenol, $Hp_2O_7^{3-}$, *p*-nitrophenol, and acetic acid. The donors for acetylacetonate are water, glycerol, mannose, glucose, trimethylphenol, phenol, *o*-chlorophenol, *m*-nitrophenol, *p*-nitrophenol, dimedone, acetic acid, benzoic acid, chloroacetic acid, and hydronium ion) (adapted from Ref. 421: *Chemical Kinetics: Principles and Selected Topics* by I. Amdur and G. G. Hammes, McGraw-Hill Book Co.) (used with permission of the authors and the publishers).

(17)

$$\left[\begin{array}{c} \text{structure: } CH_3\text{-C(=O)-CH-C(=O)-CH}_3 \text{ enolate anion} \end{array} \right]^{-} + \text{HB} \longrightarrow \left[\begin{array}{c} \text{Transition state with } \delta^{-} \text{ on oxygens and } H\text{----}B^{\delta-} \end{array} \right]$$

Transition state

$$\downarrow$$

$$CH_3\text{-C(=O)-CH}_2\text{-C(=O)-CH}_3 + B^{-}$$

2

rate constant (Eq. 18) may be rearranged (Eq. 19) in order to calculate the heights of the transition state barriers. To refresh his knowledge of transition state theory, the student should consult Amdur and Hammes (*421*). A concise summary of the limitations and assumptions of transition state theory is also given.

(18)
$$k = \frac{kT}{h} \exp\left(-\Delta F^{*}/RT\right)$$

ΔF^{*} = transition state free energy (above initial state from which the transition state was derived)

k_r = rate constant for reaction

k = Boltzmann constant, 1.3804×10^{-16} erg molecule^{-1} $^{\circ}$K^{-1}

T = temperature in $^{\circ}$K

h = Planck's constant, 6.6252×10^{-27} erg-sec.

R = gas constant, 1.9872 cal. mole^{-1} $^{\circ}$K^{-1}

(19)
$$\Delta F^{*} = 2.3RT \log \frac{kT}{h} - 2.3RT \log k_r$$

Free energy versus reaction coordinate curves for the reaction of **1** with hydronium ion and phenol are shown in Fig. 1.3. It is striking that the transition state for the reaction of the hydronium ion is much closer to the initial state than the transition state for the reaction of phenol. If the shapes of the curves varied with height above the initial state, we would expect that the transition state free energy differences would not correspond exactly to those for the initial states. Is the variation in shape a property of the hydrogen–oxygen bond of the donor? The potential energy curves for hydrogen–oxygen bonds are not particularly *anharmonic* (pp. 111–115, *263*), and good parallelism would be expected for the potential energy curves at low vibrational quantum numbers. The transition state for proton transfers certainly corresponds to vibrational states of hydrogen–oxygen (or hydrogen–nitrogen or hydrogen–carbon), which are not very far above the ground vibrational state. Good parallelism between changes in initial state and changes in the transition state levels would thus be expected. The *ad hoc* arguments of Eigen (*260*) and Bell (*4*) about the variation in shape of the potential energy curves from one compound to another are probably insufficient to explain the broad transition range for the quantity α (Eq. 15 and Fig. 1.2). We might also ask whether the hydrogen bond formed by the compact hydronium ion has any unusual property which could "explain" its behavior. The length of the shortest hydrogen bond in the hydronium perchlorate crystal ($H_3O^+ClO_4^-$) is 2.9 A (*262*), a distance that is actually greater than the distance found for the hydrogen bonds between phenols (2.6–2.8 A, *263*). The hydronium ion is thus not specially favored with respect to the formation of unusually tight hydrogen bonds.

In order to explain the broad transition region for α, we think that it is necessary to postulate a primary role for the solvent. The broad transition region is really a way of describing the failure of a proton acceptor to take advantage of availability of a proton offered by a proton donor. (Otherwise, we would have the situation for which $\alpha = 1$.) If we compare the transition states for the two reactions of the anion **1** (shown in Fig. 1.3) and remember

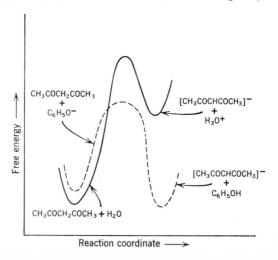

Figure 1.3   A free energy versus reaction coordinate diagram for ------ the reaction of acetylacetonate anion with hydronium ion and ——— the reaction of acetylacetonate anion with phenol. The data used to construct the diagram are from Ref. 160. The relative positions of the two curves are arbitrary.

that the initial charge at the carbon in the acetylacetonate anion is much less than the charge at an oxygen atom in, for example, the methoxide ion, we can infer that the solvent is organized at the hydronium ion proton-transfer transition state in a way that is much less suitable for the product than for the phenol proton-transfer transition state (Fig. 1.4).

Brønsted and Pedersen (*3*) discovered that a simple equation (Eq. 20) could be used to relate the rate of decomposition of nitramide catalyzed by acids (Eq. 21) to the dissociation constant of the acid. An analogous equation can be written for base-catalyzed reactions. Small statistical corrections for the numbers of atoms involved in proton transfers can be made but will not be considered here (see Bell, *4*).

$$(20) \qquad\qquad k = GK^{\alpha}$$

(*G* and α are constants which depend upon the nature of the substrate, the class of acids, the solvent, the temperature, etc. The usual designation for the exponent in a base-catalyzed reaction is β.)

TABLE 1.2   *Brønsted Coefficients for Base-Catalyzed Halogenation*[a]

Substrate	$\log k_2$[b]	β	pK_s[c]
CH_3COCH_3	-8.56	0.88	20.0
$CH_3COCH_2CH_2COCH_3$	-7.85	0.89	18.7
CH_3COCH_2Cl	-5.29	0.82	16.5
CH_3COCH_2Br	-5.03	0.82	16.1
$CH_3COCHCl_2$	-3.78	0.82	14.9
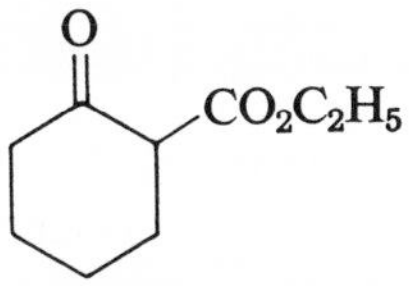 (cyclohexanone with $CO_2C_2H_5$)	-1.76	0.64	13.1
$CH_3COCH_2CO_2C_2H_5$	-1.06	0.59	10.5
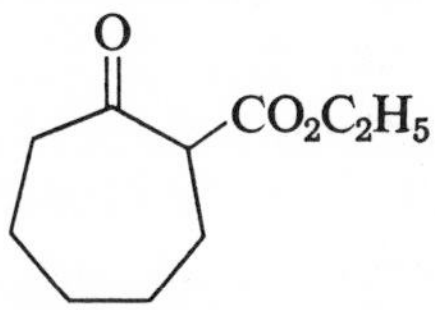 (cycloheptanone with $CO_2C_2H_5$)	-0.60	0.58	10.0
$CH_3COCH_2COC_6H_5$	-0.45	0.52	9.7
$CH_3COCH_2COCH_3$	-0.24	0.48	9.3
$CH_3COCHBrCOCH_3$	$+0.26$	0.42	8.3

[a] From Ref. 4.   [b] For a hypothetical carboxylic acid of $pK_a = 4$ in liters mole^{-1}sec.$^{-1}$.   [c] pK_a of substrate.

(21) [Reaction scheme: nitrous oxide / diazotization pathway]

H₂N–N⁺(=O)(O⁻) ⇌ H(–N=N⁺)(OH)(O⁻) —HB→ [H(–N=N⁺)(OH)(Ö⁻---H----B)] Transition state

H⁺ ↓   [Possible pathway]

N_2O + H_3O^+ ←H₂O— N≡N⁺(OH) + H₂O ←v. fast— H(–N=N⁺)(OH)(OH) + B⁻

The close relationship of Eq. 20 and Eq. 15 is better shown if an expression for $\log k$ is written (Eq. 22). The remarks made above about the behavior of α and β therefore apply to the "Brønsted equation":

(22)
$$\log k = \alpha \log K + \log G$$

According to the theoretical curves shown in Fig. 1.1, the slower the reaction catalyzed by acid (or base), the more likely it is for the Brønsted coefficient α (or β) to approach unity. Data on the halogenation of ketones

$$CH_3\overset{O}{\overset{\|}{C}}CH_2{-}H + B \longrightarrow \left[CH_3\overset{O}{\overset{\|}{C}}CH_2\cdots H\cdots B \right] \longrightarrow BH^+ +$$
Transition state

(23)

$$X^- + CH_3\overset{O}{\overset{\|}{C}}CH_2X \xleftarrow[\text{v. fast}]{X_2} \left[CH_3\overset{O}{\overset{\|}{C}}CH_2 \right]^-$$

support this prediction, as shown in Table 1.2. Decreasing the polarity of the solvent (see Part 2) would probably decrease the Brønsted coefficient because the transition state free energy would depend much more on the solvent than the initial state free energy. If, for example, the solvent contributed only one charged atom to the region of the transition state, as in the case of the very weak acids we shall examine in the next section, the position of that charged atom would have a large effect on the transition state free energy.

The Brønsted equation in the form shown as Eq. 22 has considerable utility as an equation of correlation. This equation is a *linear free energy relationship*, one which depends upon the proportionality of changes in rate (activation free energy) to changes in equilibrium constants (initial state free energies). It is a particularly clear case of the shortcomings of such relationships: the range of its application is limited, and it is possible to interpret the

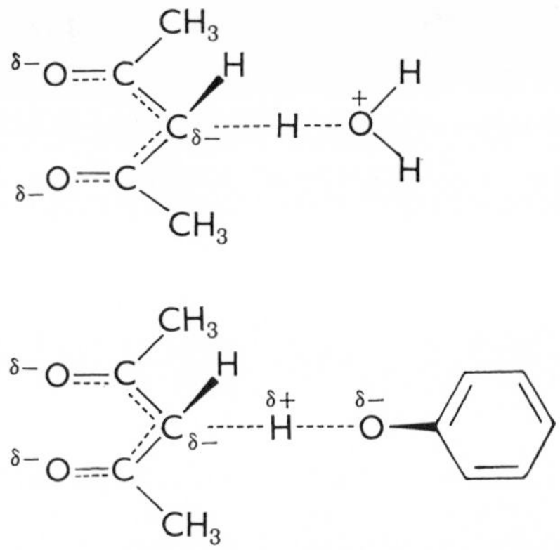

Figure 1.4 Transition states for the reaction of acetylacetonate anion (**1**) with hydronium ion or phenol. Although charge distributions are only qualitatively indicated, it is likely that there is much more "bond formation" between the acceptor and the proton in the case of the phenol proton transfer than in the case of the hydronium ion proton transfer. The net charge on the oxygens of the anion **1** would thus be different in the two cases. The solvation of the two transition states is *certain to be different.*

slopes of the relationship (α) in molecular terms only in a very qualitative way. We shall come across a number of other linear free energy relationships (the Hammett $\rho\sigma$-correlation, Y-values, Z-values) in this book. In each case, we shall find it important to understand the molecular basis for the correlations that are found in order to properly evaluate the range and applicability of these relationships, which are extremely useful when used with discrimination and taste.

The wide range of conformity of the hydration of carbonyl compounds to the Brønsted relationship has led to the suggestion by Bell (*264*) that a cyclic transition state involving several water molecules should be written for the reaction:

(24)

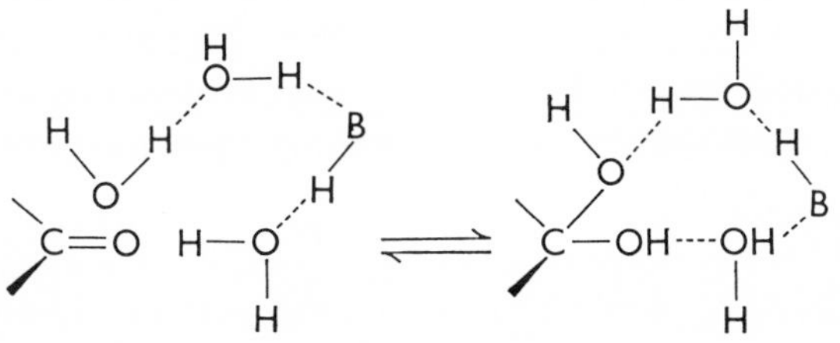

Although the full benefit of an increase in acidity would not be expected to be reflected in a corresponding increase in rate, the solvent composition of the transition state should not vary much with acid strength and thus should not show the differences expected for the transition states illustrated in Fig. 1.4.

Other aspects of Brønsted correlations have been discussed by Bruice and Benkovic (*265*).

Problems

1. Arrange the following acids in order of increasing strength (solvent—benzene): H_2SO_4, H_2O, H_2S, C_6H_5COOH, CH_3COOH, $HClO_4$, $CF_3C_6H_4SO_3H$, $CH_3OC_6H_4SO_3H$, HCl, $(CH_3)_3COH$, CF_3COOH.
2. Design an experiment which could be used to check the order assigned in Problem 1.
3. Compare the relaxation time, τ, to the half-life, $t_{1/2}$, of a first-order reaction.
4. Compare the rates, k_{H^+} (for $H^+ + OH^-$) and k_{D^+} (for $D^+ + OD^-$), and devise a qualitative explanation for the difference.
5. In Table 1.2 are recorded Brønsted coefficients for the base-catalyzed halogenation of acetone and 2-bromo-1,3-pentanedione. Write the transition states for the reactions of these two compounds and explain the marked difference in the two transition states.

1.2 Very Weak Acids

Removal of the hydrogen bonded to a particular atom as a proton

$$(25) \qquad B + HA \longrightarrow BH^+ + A^-$$

offers the opportunity for learning how well the atom can accommodate negative charge. By establishing quantitative criteria for the accommodation of charge (measurement of the acidity of HA, for example), we may be able to evaluate the relative effectiveness of different mechanisms for charge accommodation and to correlate these with calculations on anion stability. The ability of an atom to accommodate negative charge in a given structural situation is an important measure of how that structure interacts with the atom in question. We can thus utilize measurements like acidity to provide information about the chemical properties of organic molecules.

Acids for which the dissociation constants can be measured in aqueous solvents should be familiar to the student. Some of these will be taken up in connection with quantitative measures of substituent effects (Section 1.3). We have limited this section to very weak acids (roughly speaking, acids that do not dissociate in aqueous solution) for two reasons. First, very weak acids are usually not treated in elementary texts and yet are important in both physical organic chemistry and organic synthesis. Second, very weak acids may be studied under conditions in which the influence of the solvent is minimal. Differences in acidity under these conditions in which highly electronegative atoms (for example, oxygen) and the solvent are important factors in controlling the magnitude of acid dissociation constants.

Conant and Wheland (5) introduced, and McEwen (6) developed, the measurement of the equilibrium constants for dissociation of very weak acids by means of ion-pair equilibria:

$$(26) \qquad RH + R_1^- M^+ \rightleftharpoons R^- M^+ + R_1 H$$

Establishing the position of the equilibrium (the anions usually differ in ultraviolet or visible spectrum) is equivalent to the measurement of a pK_a difference (Eqs. 27–29). Given a suitable starting point, such as a compound acidic enough to be measured by ordinary methods in aqueous solution, a scale of acidities can be developed.

$$(27) \qquad K = \frac{[R^-][R_1 H]}{[R_1^-][RH]}$$

(28)
$$K = \frac{[R^-][SH^+][R_1H][S]}{[RH][S][R_1^-][SH^+]} = \frac{K_a^{RH}}{K_a^{R_1H}}$$

(29)
$$\Delta pK_a(RH - R_1H) = pK_a^{RH} - pK_a^{R_1H}$$

Other equilibria, like lithium–halogen interchange between lithium organic compounds and organoiodine derivatives (Eq. 30, *266*) and the organo-mercury–organomagnesium compound exchange (Eq. 31, *267*) can be used to rank carbanions in order of relative stability.

(30)
$$RLi + R_1I \rightleftharpoons RI + R_1Li$$

(31)
$$R{-}Mg{-} + R_1{-}Hg{-} \rightleftharpoons R_1Mg{-} + R{-}Hg{-}$$

Methods based on the evaluation of the position of an equilibrium become less and less practical as the acids studied become weaker and weaker. Shatenshteïn (*7*) introduced a procedure based on a Brønsted correlation between the rate of hydrogen exchange and the pK_a determined by the equilibrium method. Most studies were carried out with potassium dideutero-amide ($K^+ND_2^-$) in deuteroammonia (ND_3). Streitwieser and his co-workers (*8, 9*) have greatly extended the utility of this approach by measuring the rates of tritium exchange from tritiated hydrocarbons as catalyzed by lithium or cesium cyclohexylamide in cyclohexylamine. The weakest acid for which a pK_a has been obtained is cyclohexane with a pK_a of 49.

The Brønsted correlation used by Streitwieser and his co-workers (*9, 13*) is based on the rate of exchange observed in methanol with sodium methoxide and the pK_a obtained by the equilibrium method with cesium cyclohexyl-amide in cyclohexylamine. The structures of the hydrocarbons used in the correlation (Fig. 1.5) do not vary very much from the range of fluorene and diphenylmethane, and this fact might pose some problems in considering how general the correlation might be. The coefficient (α) for the line in Fig. 1.5 is 0.58. Shatenshteïn found a value for α of about 0.5 for potassium amide in liquid ammonia, using the pK_a values derived by McEwen. The similarity of the two coefficients derived from rather different rate measurements and different equilibrium values suggests that we should examine our expectations for Brønsted correlation coefficients in relatively nonpolar solvents.

The details of the exchange process (hydrogen for deuterium or tritium) in hydrocarbons have been summarized by Streitwieser and Hammons (*156*) and may be illustrated with some data for the case of alkylbenzenes and lithium cyclohexylamide in cyclohexylamine.

A comparison of the rate of exchange of toluene-α-*d* (**3**) and toluene-α-*t* yielded a k_D/k_T ratio of 3, corresponding to a k_H/k_D of 12. An isotope effect

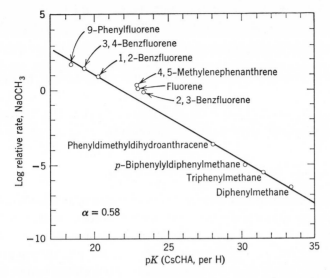

Figure 1.5 Plot of the log k for the tritium exchange rate versus the pK_a determined for the same hydrocarbons in cyclohexylamine with cesium cyclohexyamide as base (Ref. 9, used by permission of Professor A. Streitwieser) (k_H for fluorene is ca. 1×10^{-5} sec.$^{-1}$).

of this size implies that the hydrogen–carbon bond is almost completely broken at the transition state.

An effect produced by the substitution of an isotope for an atom involved in the bond-breaking or bond-making process is called a *primary isotope effect*. Consider the two processes (proton-transfer, Eq. 32, deuteron-transfer, Eq. 33) with the initial states, AH + B and AD + B and the transition states, A---H---B and A---D---B.

(32) $$\text{AH} + \text{B} \longrightarrow \underset{\text{Transition state}}{\text{A---H---B}} \longrightarrow \text{A} + \text{HB}$$

(33) $$\text{AD} + \text{B} \longrightarrow \underset{\text{Transition state}}{\text{A---D---B}} \longrightarrow \text{A} + \text{DB}$$

The difference in initial state free energies between Eq. 32 and Eq. 33 resides in the difference in the *zero-point vibrational energies* of the AH and AD bonds, which is equal to $\frac{1}{2}h\nu(1 - \sqrt{m_H/m_D})$ as a ROUGH approximation (m_H = mass of hydrogen atom, m_D = mass of deuterium atom). In the simplest case, the bonds in the transition state are equal in strength to both A and B and the zero-point energy of a transition state A---H(or D)---B bond is negligible. The rate difference between the reaction with AH and the reaction with AD is given by Eq. 34. A more complete development of hydrogen isotope effects will be found in Ref. 4, Chapter 11.

$$(34) \qquad \frac{k_{AH}}{k_{AD}} = \exp \frac{h\nu}{2kT} \left(1 - \sqrt{\frac{m_H}{m_D}} \right)$$

in which ν = the stretching frequency for the carbon–hydrogen bond. This equation assumes a very large mass for the rest of the molecule. Approximate maximum values for kinetic isotope effects are presented in Table 1.3.

TABLE 1.3 *Approximate Maximum Values for Kinetic Isotope Effects*[a]

	Temperature (°C)	Ratio
k_{CH}/k_{CD}	0	8.2
k_{CH}/k_{CD}	25	6.9
k_{CH}/k_{CD}	100	4.6
k_{CH}/k_{CD}	500	2.1
k_{NH}/k_{ND}	25	9.2
k_{OH}/k_{OD}	25	11.5
k_{CH}/k_{CT}	25	16
$k_{C^{12}H}/k_{C^{14}H}$	25	1.041
$k_{C^{12}H}/k_{C^{13}H}$	25	1.022
$k_{C^{12}C^{12}}/k_{C^{12}C^{14}}$	25	1.092
$k_{CO^{16}}/k_{CO^{18}}$	25	1.063

[a] From Ref. 257.

The exchange reaction proceeds with retention of configuration. A study of the exchange of optically active ethylbenzene-α-d (**4**) indicated that each exchange of an α-hydrogen resulted in 82% retention of configuration.

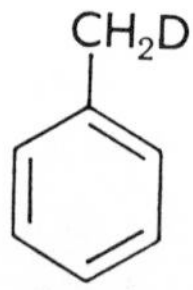

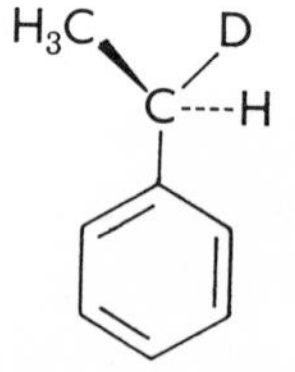

On the basis of these and other data (for example, the exchange rates are a function of the concentration of monomeric lithium cyclohexylamide), the exchange reaction can be represented as a *front-side replacement* of hydrogen (or deuterium) through a transition state in which there is considerable loss of bonding between the carbon and hydrogen.

(35)

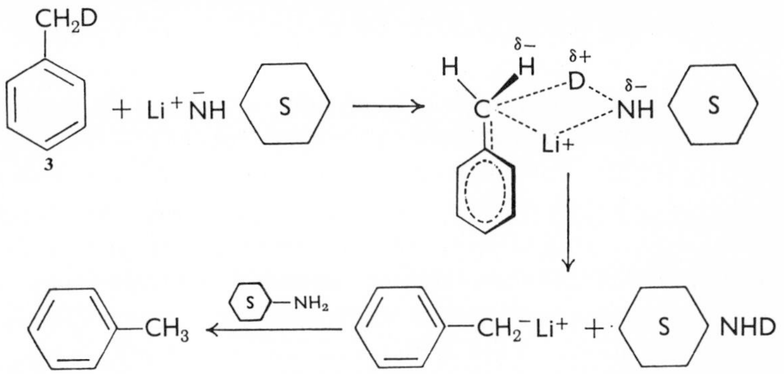

Reprotonation of arenemethide ions (for example, benzyllithium, Eq. 35) occurs on the side chain rather than on the ring (*11*) although n.m.r. measurements on triphenylmethide ions (*14*) indicate that there is considerable delocalization of charge into the rings. According to the idea formalized by Hammond (*12*), the transition state for the reaction of an unstable species is quite close in structure to that species. The transition state for the reprotonation of an unstable ion is similar to that ion:

(36)

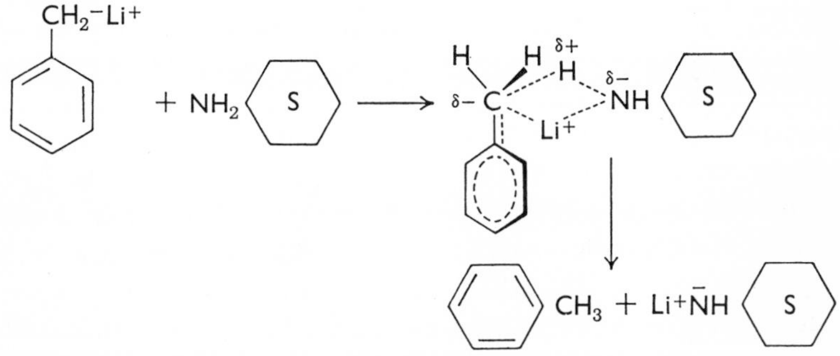

In certain systems, reprotonation can take place at positions other than that from which the original proton was removed.

We can now return to the question of the magnitude and constancy of the Brønsted coefficient, α. In Section 1.1, we indicated that α should decrease as solvent polarity was decreased. Rates of exchange using cyclohexylamide salts should probably be correlated by a somewhat lower α than rates of exchange in methanol with sodium methoxide as catalyst. If such a trend in the value of α did exist, the values of the pK_a for the weakest acids would be the most seriously affected. We would not expect the magnitude of the change in α to be great. The constancy of α over a large range of pK_a (and $\log k$) seems reasonably certain since the correlations used by Streitwieser are all over the range of $\log k$ which should in principle be correlated by an α of unity [$\Delta(pK_a)$ is very large]. We can make the surmise that the range of $\log k$ covered is below the transition range for α (see Fig. 1.1).

Cram (*10*) has combined information from equilibrium and kinetic measures of hydrocarbon acidity into a scale called the McEwen–Streitwieser– Applequist–Dessy (MSAD) pK_a scale. The reference compound was 9-phenyl-fluorene with a pK_a of 18.5 in aqueous sulfolane. Relative acidities are very much closer together in dimethyl sulfoxide than in the ether or amine solvents used for most measurements, and care must be taken not to confuse results obtained in either type of solvent. The MSAD scale of pK_a values modified by Streitwieser (*9*) is shown in Table 1.4.

The acidities of hydrocarbons can be interpreted in terms of the three most important factors that control the ability of a carbon atom to accommodate negative charge. These are (1) *hybridization* of the orbital (or orbitals) that carries the negative charge, (2) *delocalization* of the charge, and (3) stabilization of the charge through the *inductive* (or *field*) effect.

Hybridization refers to the relative proportion of *s*- and *p*-orbitals deemed appropriate for a particular carbon orbital. (In these terms, we might recall that the orbitals of the carbons of ethylene include three sp^2 and one *p*.) The *s*-electrons are, on the average, closer to the nucleus than the *p*-electrons and therefore experience a greater interaction with the nucleus. This is equivalent to saying that *s*-orbitals have a higher electronegativity than *p*-orbitals. The larger the contribution of *s*-character to a hybrid orbital, the greater the electronegativity of that hybrid orbital. The more electronegative an orbital, the more effectively can that orbital accommodate negative charge. Hydrogens attached to carbons through orbitals which have appreciable *s*-character should be removed more easily as protons than hydrogens bonded to carbons through orbitals with small amounts of *s*-character. The acidity order of the hydrocarbons, ethane, ethylene, and acetylene (see Table 1.4), is easily understood in terms of the hybridization of the orbitals of the anions. (For further insight into the problem of electronegativity of orbitals, see Coulson, *15*).

An alternative explanation for the acidity of ethylene and acetylene is that a special resonance stabilization contributes to the stability of the anion. The

TABLE 1.4 *The pK_a Values of Hydrocarbons*[a,b,d]

Compound	pK_a	Compound	pK_a	Compound	pK_a
Fluoradene	11	Cyclopentadiene	15	9-Phenylfluorene	18.5[d]

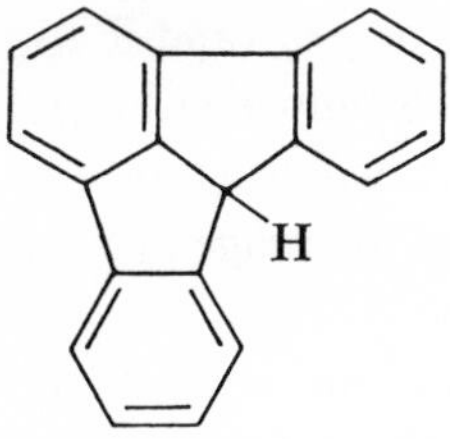

(5)

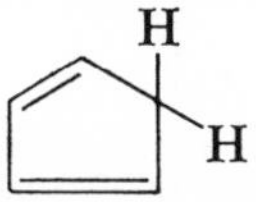

(6)

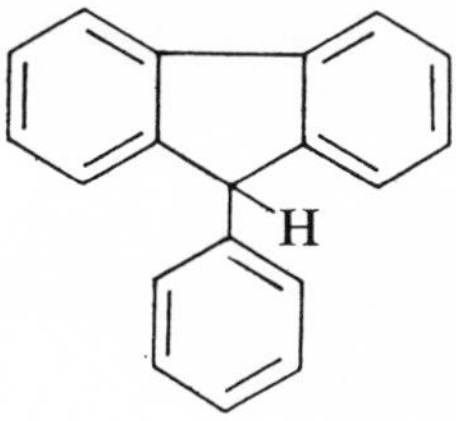

(7)

Compound	pK_a	Compound	pK_a	Compound	pK_a
Indene	20	Phenylacetylene	20	Fluorene	22.8

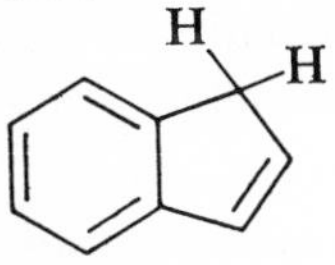

(8)

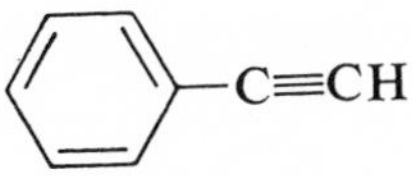

(9)

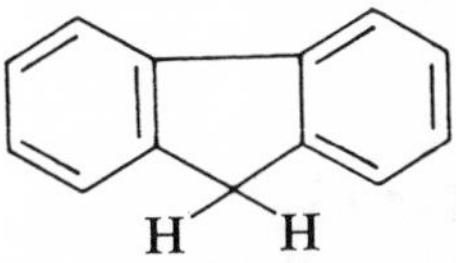

(10)

Compound	pK_a	Compound	pK_a	Compound	pK_a
Acetylene	25	1,3,3-Triphenyl-propene	26.5	Triphenylmethane	31.5
Ethylene	42				

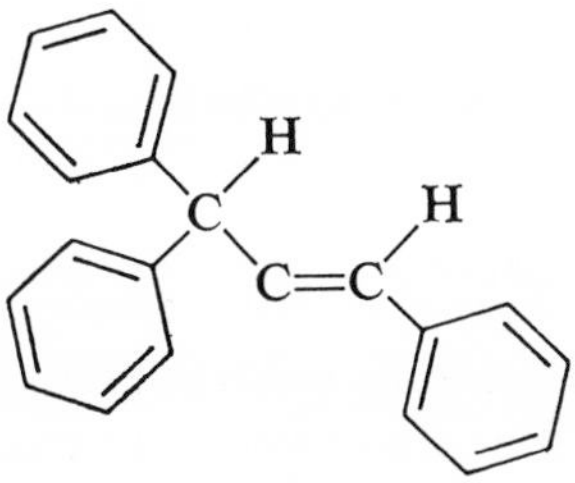

(12)

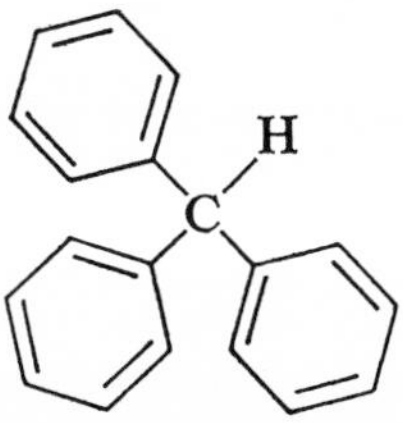

(13)

Compound	pK_a	Compound	pK_a	Compound	pK_a
Diphenylmethane	33.1	Toluene (α-)	39[c]	Propene (α-)	~40

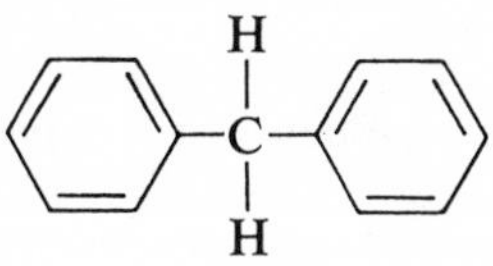

(15)

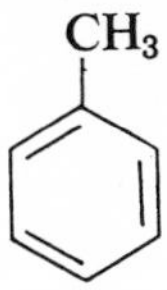

(16)

Compound	pK_a	Compound	pK_a	Compound	pK_a
Cycloheptatriene	36?	Ethylbenzene (α-)	40	Benzene	41

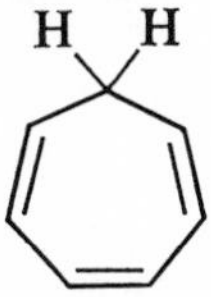

(18)

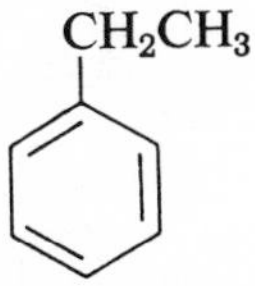

(19)

(20)

TABLE 1.4 (*Continued*).

Compound	pK_a	Compound	pK_a	Compound	pK_a
Cumene (α-)	41	Tryptycene	41.6	Cyclopropane	44
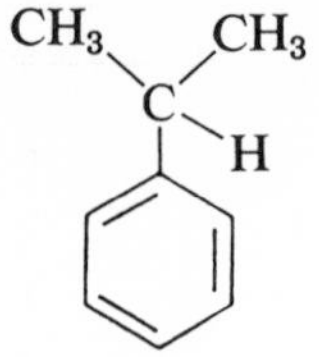 (21)		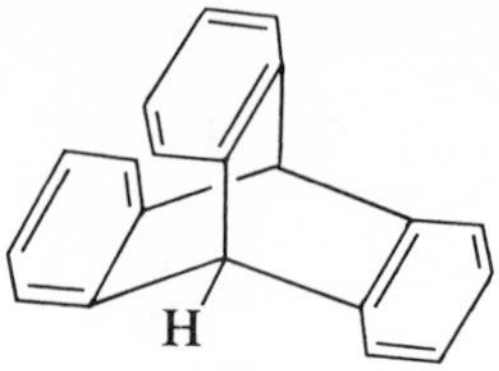 (22)		 (23)	
Cyclobutane	47	Methane	47	Ethane	48
		(24)			
Neopentane	48	Propane (2-)	49	Cyclopentane	48
		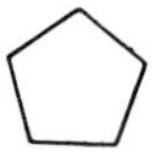 (29)			
Cyclohexane	49				
		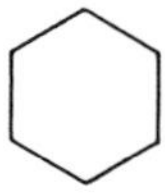 (30)			

[a] From Ref. 10 and Ref. 9.   [b] No attempt has been made to adjust values to the same absolute scale.   [c] Ref. 10 gives 35 for the α-position of toluene.   [d] Ritchie and Uschold (Ref. 786) have suggested that the pK_a for the primary reference compound for most of the entries, 9-phenylfluorene(7) is better taken as 16.4 in cyclohexylamine. Use of the lower pK_a value would lower most of the pK_a values listed by 2 units.

stabilization of the acetylene anion can be written with a "methylenoid" form, **11b**.

$$HC\equiv C:^- \quad \longleftrightarrow \quad H\ddot{C}^-=C:$$
$$\text{11a} \qquad\qquad\qquad \text{11b}$$

This formulation can be rejected on several grounds. First, form **11b** corresponds to the singlet form of a methylene which, in most cases, is not the ground state of a methylene (see Part 3, Section 3.2). Resonance forms should be comparable in stability in order to contribute substantially to the stabilization of a particular species. Second, there is little evidence that negative charge generated in **11b** at the second carbon atom can be further delocalized. A phenyl substituent at the 4-position of benzene relative to a hydrogen, which is being removed as a proton, does not enhance the acidity of the hydrogen as we might have expected (**20a** ↔ **20b** in comparison to **31a** ↔ **31b**) (*18*).

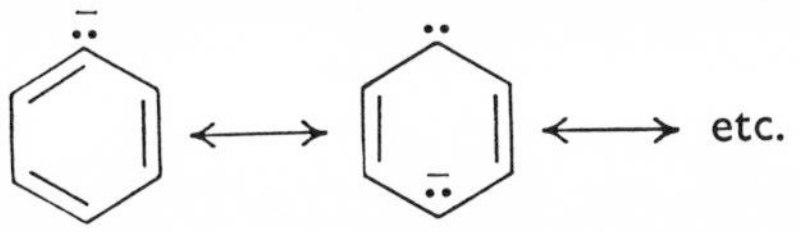

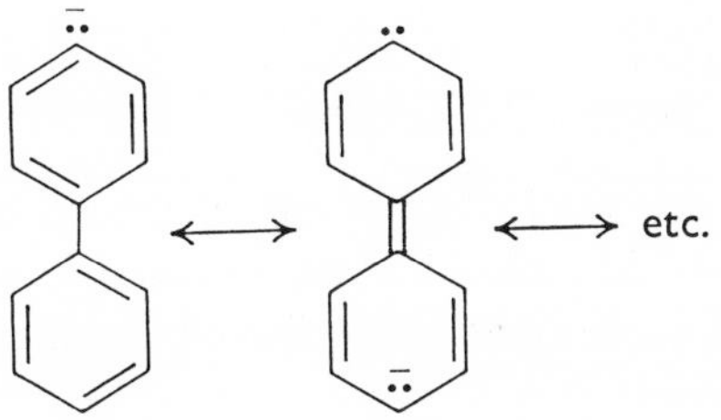

Furthermore, the 3- and 4-isomers of 1-methylpyridiniumcarboxylic acid betaines lose carbon dioxide at comparable rates and much more slowly than the 2-isomer (*19*).

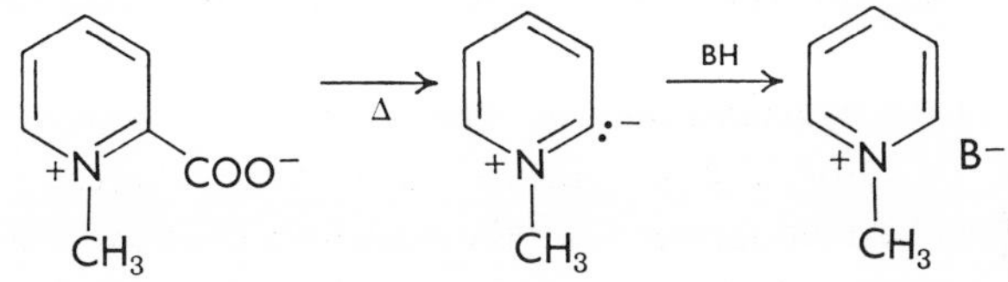

"Methylenoid" resonance should be specially favored for the intermediates derived from the 2-(**32a** ↔ **32b**) and 4-betaines (**33a** ↔ **33b**) and no more favorable for the 3-isomer than for a benzene anion (**34a** ↔ **34b**). The failure of the rates of decarboxylation to reflect any extra stabilization in the anions at the transition state, so that the 4- and 2-isomers would decompose at similar rates, suggests that "methylenoid" resonance is unimportant.

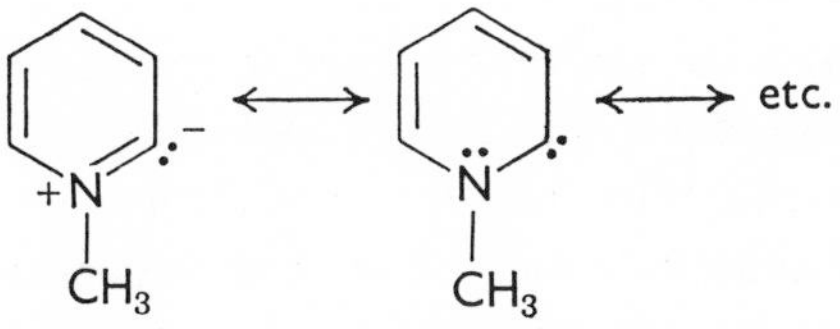

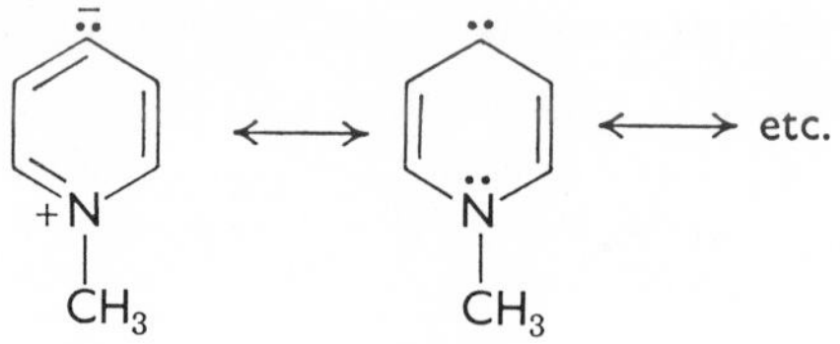

33a   33b

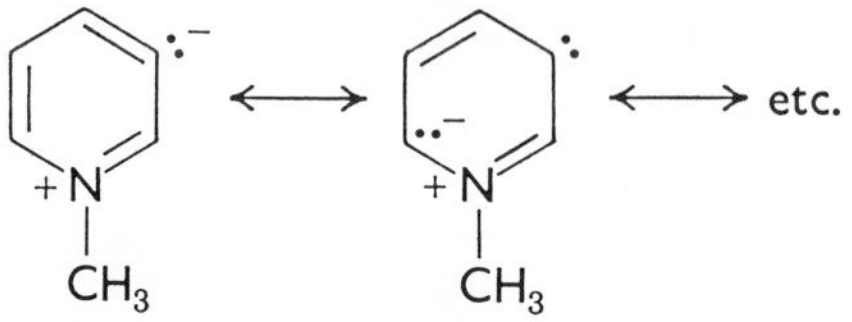

34a   34b

If hybrid orbitals are valid descriptions of the distribution of bonding electrons around atoms in molecules, experimental measures should reveal differences in bond properties that we ascribe to hybridization. Let us examine a carbon–hydrogen bond:

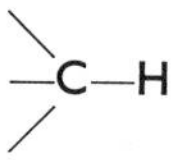

35

The nature of the carbon orbital that overlaps with the hydrogen s-orbital to form the bond should affect the length of the bond, the strength of the bond, and how readily a nuclear spin of a carbon nucleus interacts with the nuclear spin of the hydrogen nucleus. The s-orbital is spherically symmetric around the carbon atom and the p-orbital has a preferred direction. It follows that p-orbital will extend farther from the nucleus, a conclusion supported by the fact that it is easier to remove an electron from a p-orbital than from an s-orbital of the same quantum number. Bonds between carbon and hydrogen formed with a carbon orbital of high s-character will be shorter than those formed with carbon orbitals of high p-character. Although the range of bond lengths is not large, the trend from acetylene (1.059 A) to methane (1.094 A) is clear. Analysis of spectroscopic data further shows that a carbon–hydrogen bond formed with an orbital that is probably pure p (in methyne, CH) is 1.120 A long. These bond lengths are listed in Table 1.5.

The strength of the bond can be measured in two somewhat indirect ways. Analysis of the vibrational spectrum of a molecule leads to the assignment of stretching force constants (in units that indicate how much force is required to stretch the bond an Angstrom) (269). The frequencies observed in the infrared spectra of hydrocarbons for the carbon–hydrogen bond vary from

TABLE 1.5 *Effects of Hybridization*

Compound (Carbon Hybridization)	pK_a	C—H Bond Length, A	Stretching Force Constant (Millidynes/A)	Bond Energy kcal./mole	$J_{C^{13}H}$, Coupling Constant in C.p.s.
Acetylene(sp)	25	1.059[e]	5.88	125[j]	248[g]
Ethylene(sp^2)	42[m]	1.085[e]	5.05	103[j]	156.4[f]
Methane(sp^3)	47[a,m]	1.094[e]	4.88	104[j]	125[h]
Methyne(p)[b]	~(70)[c]	1.120	4.09	81[k]	0[i]
Cyclopropane($sp^{2.27}$)[d]	44	1.094[l]	—	—	161[h]

[a] The pK_a for ethane (**48**) would probably be more appropriate as a comparison for the first two compounds listed in Table 1.5. [b] It is almost certain that the hybridization of a carbon orbital in a bond for a molecule like methyne would be p. [c] Based on the linear relationship between percent s-character and pK_a. [d] Ref. 272. [e] Ref. 16. [f] Ref. 30. [g] Ref. 31 for methylacetylene. [h] Ref. 31. [i] Ref. 32 (see Fig. 1.6). [j] Bond dissociation energy (see Table 1.32). [k] Bond dissociation energy (see Table 1.31). [l] Ref. 251 for bicyclopropyl. [m] See footnote d, Table 1.4.

3300 cm.$^{-1}$ for alkynes through 3050 cm.$^{-1}$ for alkenes to 2900 cm.^{1} for alkanes. The stretching force constants depend mostly on these frequencies— in the case of bonds to an element as light as hydrogen. Some of these constants are listed in Table 1.5.

The second way to measure the bond strength is to find out how much energy is required to make the bond break.

$$A—B \longrightarrow A\cdot + B\cdot$$

The bond energies for the carbon–hydrogen bond in a few hydrocarbons are shown in Table 1.5. (Other bond energies are listed later in the book in Tables 1.31, 1.32, etc.) Both measures of bond strength show that the greater the amount of s character, the greater the bond strength.

The nucleus of carbon-12 has no magnetic moment and therefore does not affect proton absorptions in *nuclear magnetic resonance spectrometry*. About 1.1% of natural carbon is the isotope carbon-13 that has a nuclear spin of 1/2. The degree of coupling between the carbon nucleus and an adjacent hydrogen nucleus depends very much on the electrons in the bond joining the two atoms. The coupling is described by a constant called the coupling constant, $J_{C^{13}H}$, and can be obtained in favorable cases from the proton magnetic resonance spectrum by finding the carbon-13 satellites (*270, 318, 442*). The coupling constants for a few carbon–hydrogen bonds are listed in Table 1.5 and the relationship between *s*-character (defined by the geometry) and $J_{C^{13}H}$ is shown to be linear in Fig. 1.6. Although the hybridization of the carbon orbital bonded to the hydrogen is very important in controlling the coupling constant, other factors also have an influence (*271*). The considerable range of $J_{C^{13}H}$ obtained for carbon–hydrogen bonds of presumably constant hybridization, but with substituents on the carbon of widely different electronegativities, is illustrated in Table 3.5.

The idea of hybridization is also useful in explaining bond lengths between carbons in many organic molecules. From resonance theory, for example, it might have been predicted that the bond distances in long chain polyenes would all become equivalent. In fact, alternation of the short carbon–carbon double bond and the long carbon–carbon single bond is found even for highly conjugated polyenes. Bernstein (*16*) has summarized bond length data (much of it derived from highly accurate microwave spectra analysis) to illustrate the relationship between carbon–carbon bond length and the hybridization of the orbitals participating in the bond. Dewar and Schmeising (*17*) have considered not only the bond lengths but the possibility that stabilization energies of conjugated molecules (related to resonance energies) might be largely due to hybridization rather than delocalization. Some bond length data are listed in Table 1.6.

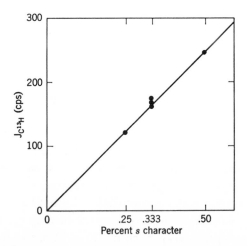

Figure 1.6 Dependence of $J_{C^{13}H}$ on *s*-character (adapted from Ref. 32 and used with the permission of the author and the *Journal of Chemical Physics*).

TABLE 1.6 *Bond Lengths for Different Bond Types*[a]

Bond Type	Bond Length (C—C), A	Molecule
sp^3-sp^3	1.534	Ethane [b,c,d]
sp^3-sp^2	1.488	Propene
sp^3-sp	1.459	Methylacetylene
sp^2-sp^2	1.470	Butadiene
sp^2-sp	1.426	Vinyl cyanide
sp-sp	1.376	Cyanoacetylene
Multiple Bonds		
sp^2-sp^2	1.397	Benzene
sp^2-sp^2	1.421	Graphite
sp^2-sp^2	1.338	Ethylene
sp^2-sp	1.309	Allene
sp-sp	1.285	Butatriene
sp-sp	1.205	Acetylene

[a] Ref. 16.   [b] In hexachloroethane, the C—C distance is 1.564 ± 0.014 A (Ref. 273).   [c] In bicyclopropyl, external and internal C—C distances are identical at 1.517 A (Ref. 251).   [d] The bridgehead-bridgehead bonds in 1,1′-*bis*-

norbornyl

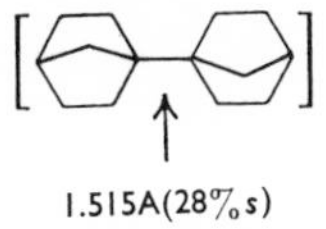

1.515A(28% s)

and 1,1′-*bis*-adamantyl

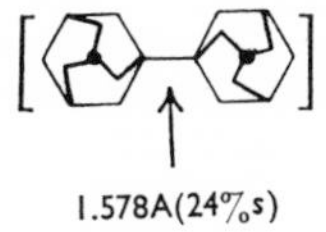

1.578A(24% s)

have been determined by X-ray crystallography (Ref. 784).

If the carbon atom which must acquire the charge in the change from the acid to anion can distribute the charge to other atoms, the effectiveness of that carbon atom for the accommodation of charge is increased. The two mechanisms for passing along part of the charge to other atoms are *delocalization* and the *inductive* (or *field*) effect.

Delocalization is achieved by overlap of the orbital which carries the charge with a π-electron system. We can illustrate the interaction by a comparison of methide ion (**25a**) and allyl anion (**17a, 17b, 17c, 17d**). The allyl anion is shown in two ways: with the *p*-orbitals drawn to show π-overlap, and with resonance forms.

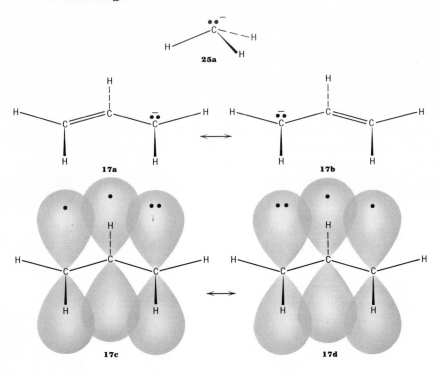

25a

17a   17b

17c   17d

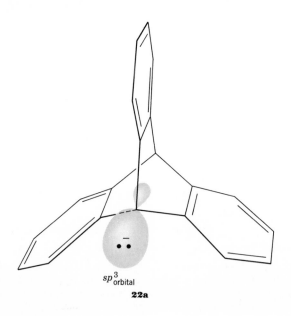

sp^3_{orbital}

22a

The molecular orbitals for the allyl anion may be formed by a linear combination of the atomic *p*-orbitals (LCAO) as shown in Fig. 1.7. [The student is referred to Streitwieser (*65*), or the book by Murrell, Kettle, and Tedder (*791*) for the background and development of the theoretical aspects of organic chemistry. Careful attention to the simple applications made in this text will provide valuable qualitative insight into many physical organic chemical problems. This is particularly true in Sections 1.8 and 1.9.] The fact that the charge is equally distributed over two atoms in the allyl anion should make it easier to generate that anion since each carbon has to accommodate only half of the charge carried on the central carbon of the methide ion (**25a**). Delocalization is even more effective at the stabilization of the anion than might be surmised from a comparison of the pK_a values of propene and methane, since the orbitals that carry the charge in the allyl anion are *p*-orbitals, and these are less electronegative than the *sp³*-orbitals that carry the charge in saturated hydrocarbon anions. It is also probable that the inductive effect of the vinyl group in propene increases the ease of ionization of the methyl-hydrogens in comparison to ethane. Thus, even in the simple case of

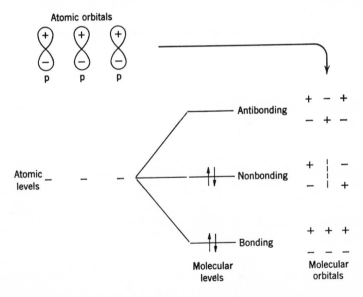

Figure 1.7 LCAO (Linear Combination of Atomic Orbitals) construction of orbitals and levels for allyl anion. (The same levels apply to the allyl carbonium ion and allyl radical, which are seen to have approximately the same stabilization energy because the middle level, into which the added electrons are placed, is nonbonding).

propene, a variety of factors contribute to raising the pK_a of the 3-hydrogen about 8 units above that of ethane (Table 1.4).

The most effective overlap of p-orbitals occurs when the orbitals are parallel to each other. The less parallel the orbitals, the less effective is the delocalization achieved through use of these orbitals. The importance of over-lap in the stabilization of the anion is demonstrated by a comparison of the pK_a values of triphenylmethane (31.5) and fluoradene (11). Substitution of three phenyl groups into methane (pK_a 47) produces an increase in acidity equivalent to 15.5 pK_a units. If we remove the *ortho*-hydrogens from the phenyl substituents and join the rings, the anion can assume a planar con-figuration, and a further increase of acidity by 20.5 pK_a units is noted. It would seem that parallel orientation of the p-orbitals is quite important for de-localization.

Delocalization is not responsible for all of the increase in acidity between methane and triphenylmethane. The compound triptycene (**22**) forms an anion **22a** in which the p-orbital carrying the charge is perpendicular to the π-orbitals of the benzene rings of the molecule. The fact that the pK_a of **22** is 41.6 (methane pK_a 47) must be traced to the inductive effect of the benzene rings operating through the sp^2-orbitals with which they are bonded to the "methane" carbon.

We might have expected cycloheptatriene (**18**) to be slightly more acidic than cyclopentadiene (**6**). In fact, **6** is at least 20 pK_a units more acidic than **18**, a difference which is largely due to the special stability of the anion of **6**, **6a**. The anion **6a**, like benzene, has 6 electrons in a cyclic π-electron system. Cyclic π-electron systems which have filled molecular orbital levels according to rule proposed by Hückel are unusually stable and possess the chemical property of persistence through chemical reactions. The Hückel rule for filled shells in cyclic systems is that they contain $4n + 2$ π-electrons in which n is an integer with values 0, 1, 2,..., etc. The unusual stability of systems with filled shells means that even if the system is disrupted (by addition of atoms or electrons), there is considerable driving force toward regeneration of the original system. These systems are often described as "aromatic" in type since it was with aromatic hydrocarbons like benzene that the unusual stability of these systems was first noted and interpreted. The pK_a of cyclo-nonatriene is estimated to be between 16 and 21 and the high acidity is no doubt due to the special stability of the 10 π-electron system of the cyclono-natrienide ion (*20, 21*).

One extremely important substitution which enhances the effectiveness of delocalization as a mechanism for removing charge from a carbon which forms an anion is that of placing atoms more electronegative than carbon at the positions to which charge must be delocalized. Both nitrogen and oxygen are very suitable in this regard as shown by the trend of the pK_a data listed in Table 1.7.

TABLE 1.7 pK_a *Values Heterosubstituted Carbon Acids*[a]

Compound	pK_a	Compound	pK_a
CH_3COCH_3	20	CH_3NO_2	11
$CH_2(COCH_3)_2$	9	$CH_2(NO_2)_2$	4
$CH(COCH_3)_3$	6	$CH(NO_2)_3$	0[h]
$CH(CHO)_3$	2.3[b]		
		CH_3CN	25
$CH_3SO_2CH_3$	23	$CH_2(CN)_2$	12
$CH_2(SO_2CH_3)_2$	14	$CH(CN)_3$	−5[c,h]
$CH(SO_2CH_3)_3$	0	$BrCH(CN)_2$	~5[c]
	15		−6.1[d,e,f]
	9.78[d,e]		−7.2[d,e,f,g]
	2.52[d,e]		~ −8.9[d,e,f]
	1.11[d,e]		< −11[d,e,g]

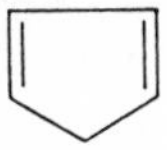

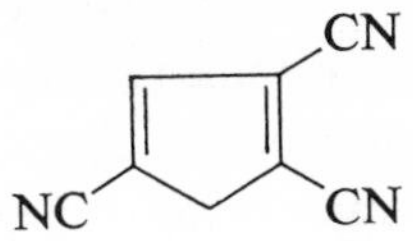

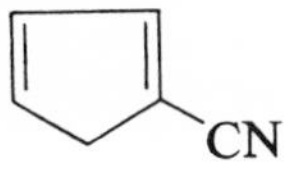

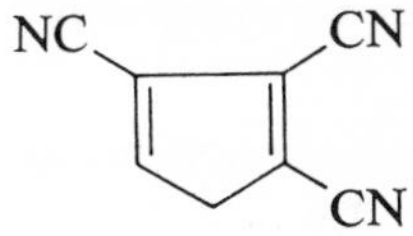

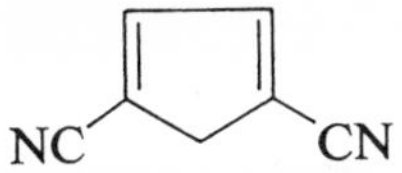

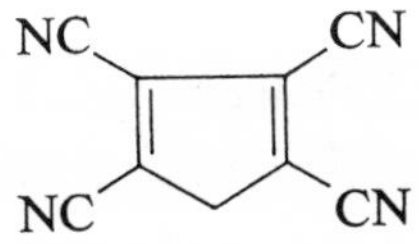

[a] Ref. 22. [b] Ref. 23. [c] Ref. 157. [d] Ref. 254. [e] Position of proton arbitrary. [f] Estimated from data in CH_3CN. [g] Not detectably protonated by perchloric acid in acetonitrile. [h] The trinitromethyl (nitroform) anion is not planar, a fact which helps to explain why cyanoform is more acidic than nitroform (*783*).

6a **6a**

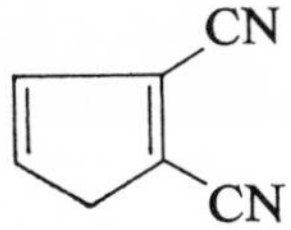

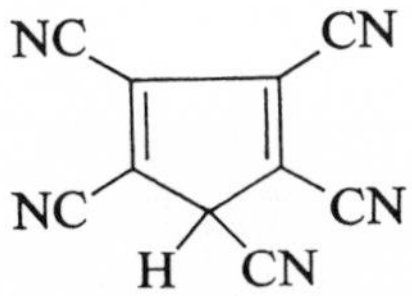

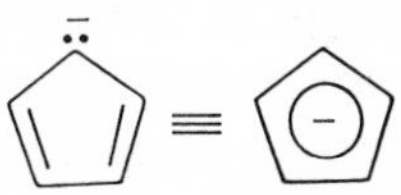

The *inductive effect* operates through the bonds connecting the carbon bearing the negative charge to the rest of the molecule. Inductive effects are usually negligible if more than three bonds separate a substituent which could exert such an effect from the carbon which must bear the charge. An inductive effect which might be overlooked arises from the difference in the electronegativities of the orbitals connecting two atoms. An sp^2-orbital will attract electrons from an sp^3-orbital, for example. It is sometimes difficult to separate the operation of the inductive effect from that of the *field effect* which involves direct electrostatic interaction through space or through the polarizable medium represented by the solvent or compound, or both.

Streitwieser and Lawler (*18*) discovered a striking variation in the acidities of aromatic polycyclic hydrocarbons with structures ranging from benzene to anthracene. The acidities were reflected in the deuterium exchange rates, and the $\log k$ (anthracene) $- \log k$ (benzene) was about 1.5. Application of the same methods to the corresponding arenemethyl compounds (for example, methylanthracene and toluene) revealed a $\log k$ difference of about 2. Since it might have been expected that delocalization would have had a strong effect upon the acidities of the arenemethyl compounds, it was concluded that the inductive effect was responsible for a large part of the acidity in both series.

Compounds in which a positively charged group is attached directly to the center which must bear the charge should show large inductive effects. Presumably the inductive effect (and/or field effect) accounts for the pK_a of the acid forms of pyridinium cyclopentadienide (**36**) (*24*) and trimethylammoniocyclopentadienide (**37**) (*25*).

36   37

The pK_a of these acids is about 10 in contrast to a pK_a of 15 found for the parent hydrocarbon **6**. The augmentation of acidity is less than might have been expected from estimates of the extra stabilization arising from the interaction of opposite charges (which may be estimated from Eq. 38). Decreased acidity augmentation is due to *electrostatic inhibition of delocalization* (cf. Saunders and Gold, Ref. 274), since the cyclopentadienide ion in the betaines **36** and **37** is no longer symmetrical and not stabilized to the same extent as **6a**.

$$(38) \qquad E = \frac{330q_1q_2}{Dr} \text{ in kcal./mole}$$

q_1, q_2 = charges on ions engaged in interaction

$\quad D$ = dielectric constant of medium between charges. Usually must be estimated as an *effective dielectric constant*. (For further details, see Part 2, Section 2.2.)

$\quad r$ = distance between charges in Angstroms

Further information on inductive and delocalization effects on acidity can be obtained from measurements on halocarbons, particularly fluorocarbons. The exchange rates for a few monohydrofluorocarbons were measured by Andreades (*26*) and the pK_a values, which may be estimated from these rate data, are listed in Table 1.8, along with data showing that chlorine, bromine, and iodine are far more effective than fluorine for stabilizing anions. Also listed are pK_a values determined in aqueous solution for some dinitro-methane derivatives. These show that an α-fluorine decreases the acidity of dinitromethane in contrast to an α-fluorine in fluoroform that is far more acidic than methane. Although the effects of β-fluorines on acidity have been ascribed to "negative hyperconjugation" in the anion (for example, **38a**$\leftrightarrow$ **38b**), the role of such hyperconjugation has been questioned by Sheppard (*37*). (See footnote f, Table 1.8.) The interpretation of the results is severely hampered by the lack of information on exchange rates (pK_a values) for hydrogens in systems with β-chlorine, bromine, or iodine. These systems would require careful study because of the possibility of elimination reactions (Eq. 39).

(For an example, see Ref. 282.)

Allinger, Tai, and Miller (*275*) have carried out some calculations on inter-actions in α-haloketones; these calculations suggest that something akin to β-hyperconjugation should increase in importance in the order: fluorine, chlorine, bromine, and iodine.

TABLE   1.8   *Acidities   of   Fluorine   Derivatives*[a,b,c]

Compound	pK_a
HCF_3	29
$HCF_2(CF_2)_5CF_3$	27
$HCF(CF_3)_2$	16
$HC(CF_3)_3$	11[f]
$HCCl_3$	ca. 16
$HCBr_3$	ca. 12
HCI_3	ca. 12
$H_2C(NO_2)_2$	3.57[d,e]
$HC(NO_2)_2Cl$	3.80[d]
$HC(NO_2)_2F$	7.70[d,e]

[a] Ref.   26.   [b] Ref.   555.   [c] Ref.   276.
[d] In H_2O at 25°.   [e] Ref. 268.   [f] The
compound   1-H-undecafluorobicyclo-
[2.2.1]heptane (**T1.8A**) is five times
faster in methoxide-methanol catalyzed
tritium exchange than *tris*(trifluoromethyl)methane.

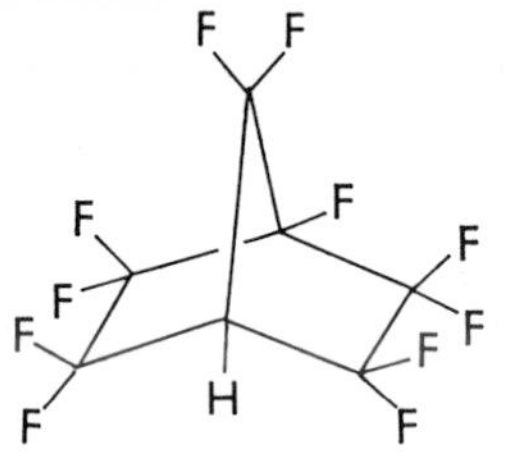

T1-8A

Although ring strain can apparently
increase acidity by several orders of
magnitude, the inductive effect must be
the major means by which fluorine
increases the acidity of the bridgehead
hydrogen in **T1.8A**.

    Another definition of acids and bases has been advanced by Lewis as a
generalization of the Brønsted proton-transfer concept (*277*). Acids are
species that can accept a pair of electrons, and bases are species that donate a
pair of electrons. Proton donating compounds (the acids of the Brønsted
scheme) would not be regarded as acids in the Lewis classification. The usefulness and generality of the proton-transfer concept is so patent and the

application of the Lewis definition to such acids so unclear that it does not seem wise to reject the former at the expense of the latter. Nevertheless, the Lewis scheme has provided an extremely general approach to acceptor-donor interactions (Lewis acid–Lewis base) like the one investigated by Brown and co-workers (278):

$$(CH_3)_3N + B(CH_3)_3 \rightleftharpoons (CH_3)_3\overset{+}{N}:\overset{-}{B}(CH_3)_3$$

Pearson (27) has extended the pattern by dividing Lewis acids and bases into two groups: "*hard*" and "*soft*" (28). Hard acids and bases are those derived from small atoms and generally have low polarizability. Soft acids and bases are usually derived from large atoms and are usually polarizable. The usefulness of this division arises from the generalization that hard acids prefer to associate with hard bases and soft acids with soft bases. A tabulation of the two kinds of Lewis acids is made in Table 1.9. The importance of hard Lewis acids in organic chemistry will be especially apparent in Part 3, Section 3.1, in the discussion on the generation of carbonium ions.

TABLE 1.9 *Classification of Lewis Acids*[a]

Hard	Soft
H^+, Li^+, Na^+, K^+	Cu^+, Ag^+, Au^+, Tl^+, Hg^+, Cs^+
Be^{2+}, Mg^{2+}, Ca^{2+}, Sr^{2+}, Sn^{2+}	Pd^{2+}, Cd^{2+}, Pt^{2+}, Hg^{2+}, CH_3Hg^+
Al^{3+}, Sc^{3+}, Ga^{3+}, In^{3+}, La^{3+}	Tl^{3+}, $Tl(CH_3)_3$, BH_3
Cr^{3+}, Co^{3+}, Fe^{3+}, As^{3+}, Ir^{3+}	RS^+, RSe^+, RTe^+
Si^{4+}, Ti^{4+}, Zr^{4+}, Th^{4+}, Pu^{4+}, VO^{2+}	I^+, Br^+, HO^+, RO^+
$Be(CH_3)_2$, BF_3, BCl_3, $B(OR)_3$	I_2, Br_2, ICN
$Al(CH_3)_3$, $Ga(CH_3)_3$	M^0(metal atoms)
R_3C^+, RCO^+	

Borderline
Fe^{2+}, Co^{2+}, Ni^{2+}, Cu^{2+}, Zn^{2+}, Pb^{2+}
$B(CH_3)_3$, SO_2, NO^+

[a] Ref. 27.

Problems

1. From the correlation shown in Fig. 1.5, calculate the rates of exchange for cyclohexane, cyclopropane, and benzene. (Cesium cyclohexylamide in cyclohexylamine is used but we shall assume that the Brønsted coefficient is the same as that in sodium methoxide in methanol.)

2. What isotope-effect correction in the rate constants should be made if tritiated hydrocarbons were used, that is, cyclohexane-t, cyclopropane-t, and benzene-t?

3. Would the corrected rate constant found in Problem 2 be changed if cyclohexane-1,1-t_2 were used? (The student should find out what a secondary hydrogen isotope effect is.)

4. Devise an experimental approach to the measurement of the rates estimated in Problem 1.

5. Compare the following pairs of hydrocarbon acids (Table 1.4) and select the factor or factors responsible for the difference in acidity.
   (a) Cyclopentadiene(**6**) and fluorene(**10**).
   (b) Acetylene(**11**) and phenylacetylene(**9**).
   (c) Cyclopropane(**23**) and cyclohexane(**30**).
   (d) Triphenylmethane(**13**) and 9-phenylfluorene(**7**).
   (e) Cycloheptatriene(**18**) and cyclopentadiene(**6**).

6. Write a molecular level scheme and the molecular orbitals for a linear arrangement of the following:
   (a) Two p-orbitals.
   (b) Three p-orbitals.
   (c) Four p-orbitals.
   (d) Five p-orbitals.

7. Discuss the species derived from each of the orbital-systems mentioned in Problem 6 with (a) the same number of electrons as p-orbitals, (b) one less electron than p-orbitals, and (c) one more electron than p-orbitals.

8. Calculate the energy of interaction in betaine **36** (or **37**) using Eq. 38 (Part 1), assuming that (a) the charge is localized at the carbon next to the nitrogen, and (b) the center of negative charge is at the center of the five-membered ring. (Assume that the dielectric constant D is 2, 5, or 10.) What difference in pK_a should each of these stabilization energies lead to, using cyclopentadiene as the reference acid? Is cyclopentadiene an appropriate reference acid?

9. Saunders and Gold (*274*) have determined some rates of exchange for quaternary ammonium ions as shown in Table P9, using 1 N sodium hydroxide in water. Rationalize the relative rates in terms of the factors which have been discussed in Section 1.2.

10. Divide the list of nucleophiles in Ref. 29 into hard and soft Lewis bases.

11. Camphenilone, an optically active ketone with the structure **39**, undergoes deuterium exchange and racemization when heated in t-butyl alcohol-O-d at 185°. Racemization and exchange proceed at about the same rate and are about 50% complete after 24 hours. Write a mechanism for the exchange which also explains the racemization. Estimate a pK_a for the acidic hydrogen (assume a rate factor of 10^3–10^4 to correct to 45°) (in Fig. 1.5, assume that the rate of exchange of fluorene is ca. 1×10^{-5} sec.$^{-1}$ at 45° with sodium

TABLE P9

Compound	Temperature °C	k, 1. mole^{-1} sec.$^{-1}$	Calcd. Relative k, 50° [a]
$(CH_3)_4N^+$ [b]	100	2.29×10^{-8}	1.0
$(CH_3)_3\overset{+}{N}CH_2C=CH_2$ with CH_3	101	3.00×10^{-5}	1400
(structure: cyclohexenyl ring, H_3C–$\overset{+}{N}$–CH_3)	101	1.10×10^{-4}	5700
$(CH_3)_3N^+CH_2CH=CH—CH=CH_2$	85	3.00×10^{-4}	1.2×10^5
(structure: cyclohexadienyl ring, H_3C–$\overset{+}{N}$–CH_3)	35	0.132	1.8×10^{10}

[a] Calculated using measured activation energies.
[b] Ref. 279.

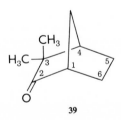

39

methoxide in methanol). Compare the pK_a estimated in this way with that for acetone (Ref. 280).

12. Explain why fluorine hyperconjugation cannot account for the acidity of the hydrogen acid, **T1-8A** (see Table 1.8, footnote f).

TABLE P9

Compound	Temperature °C	k, l. mole^{-1} sec.$^{-1}$	Calcd. Relative k, 50° [a]
$(CH_3)_4N^{+}$ [b]	100	2.29×10^{-8}	1.0
$(CH_3)_3\overset{+}{N}CH_2C{=}CH_2$ $\quad\quad\quad\quad\lvert$ $\quad\quad\quad\quad CH_3$	101	3.00×10^{-5}	1400
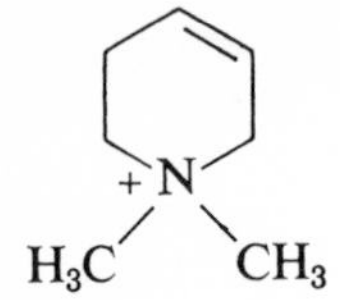	101	1.10×10^{-4}	5700
$(CH_3)_3N^{+}CH_2CH{=}CH{-}CH{=}CH_2$	85	3.00×10^{-4}	1.2×10^5
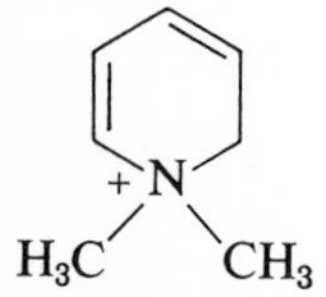	35	0.132	1.8×10^{10}

[a] Calculated using measured activation energies.
[b] Ref. 279.

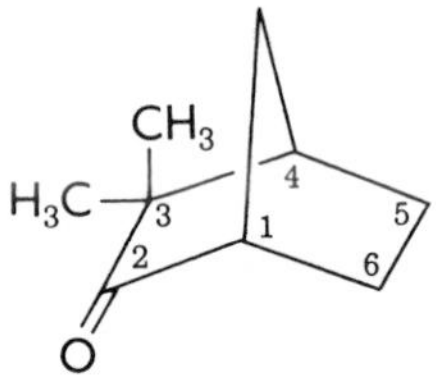

39

methoxide in methanol). Compare the pK_a estimated in this way with that for acetone (Ref. 280).

12. Explain why fluorine hyperconjugation cannot account for the acidity of the hydrogen acid, **T1-8A** (see Table 1.8, footnote f).

1.3 Substituent Constants

Intuition about organic reactions still plays a role in our choice of suitable reaction systems for intensive study, but it is intuition immensely sharpened by qualitative and quantitative insights into the behavior and properties of organic molecules. One of the most important steps in the development of physical organic chemistry was the realization by Hammett (2) that certain extrathermodynamic relationships could provide much insight into the effects of substituents.

Two similar relationships were proposed. The first was that equilibria for various reactions could be quantitatively related to the equilibrium for the ionization of benzoic acids (Eqs. 40, 41).

(40) $$C_6H_5COOH + H_2O \rightleftharpoons C_6H_5COO^- + H_3O^+$$

(41) $$m\text{- or } p\text{-}XC_6H_4COOH + H_2O \rightleftharpoons m\text{- or } p\text{-}XC_6H_4COO^- + H_3O^+$$

A substituent constant, σ, was defined as shown in Eq. 42 and represents the effect of that substituent on the ionization of benzoic acid.

(42) $$\log \frac{K}{K_0} \equiv \sigma \text{ (at 25°)}$$

K is the equilibrium constant for ionization of a benzoic acid bearing the substituent for which the constant σ is to apply. K_0 is the ionization constant for unsubstituted benzoic acid.

If we consider another equilibrium, let us say the ionization of phenylacetic acids (Eqs. 43, 44), we find that the effect of the substituent on the new equilibrium is proportional to the effect of the substituent on the ionization of benzoic acids. We call the proportionality constant when defined as in Eq. 45 a *reaction constant*, ρ.

(43) $$C_6H_5CH_2COOH + H_2O \rightleftharpoons C_6H_5CH_2COO^- + H_3O^+$$

(44) $$m\text{- or } p\text{-}XC_6H_4CH_2COOH + H_2O = m\text{- or } p\text{-}XC_6H_4CH_2COO^- + H_3O^+$$

(45) $$\log \frac{K(XC_6H_5CH_2COOH)}{K_0(C_6H_5CH_2COOH)} = \rho \log \frac{K(XC_6H_4COOH)}{K_0(C_6H_5COOH)}$$

The relationship shown in Eq. 45 is clearly a *linear free energy relationship* and may be expressed as Eq. 46 with the aid of the definition of Eq. 42.

(46) $$\log \frac{K(XC_6H_4CH_2COOH)}{K(C_6H_5CH_2COOH)} = \rho\sigma$$

The free energy versus reaction coordinate diagram of Fig. 1.8 shows two equilibria characterized by the free energy changes, ΔF_0 and ΔF_1. Hammett adopted a reaction as standard (for defining σ, the substituent constant) because he hoped that a substituent would have an effect on the stabilization of the benzoic acids and a proportional effect on the stability of the anion derived from that benzoic acid. Similar expectations were necessary for any reaction to be compared to the *standard* or *model reaction*.

The second relationship put forward by Hammett was that the rate of various reactions of benzene derivatives could be quantitatively related to the equilibrium for the ionization of benzoic acids. For example, the rates of hydrolysis of benzoic acid esters can be related to the substituent constant σ by means of the reaction constant ρ:

$$(47) \qquad \log \frac{k(\mathrm{XC_6H_4COOR})}{k(\mathrm{C_6H_6COOR})} = \rho\sigma$$

An equation of this type implies that the effect of the substituent on the transition state is proportional to its effect on the initial state (and to its effect on the ionization of benzoic acids). Substitution on the reactant produces a change in ΔF^* (see Fig. 1.9) which is the net result of an effect on the initial state and the transition state. As long as the changes are each proportional to

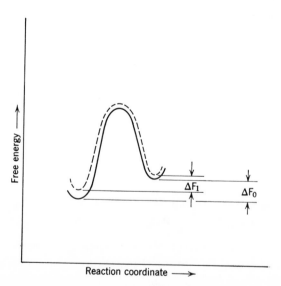

Figure 1.8 Free energy versus reaction coordinate diagram for two related equilibria, for example, the ionizations of two benzoic acids.

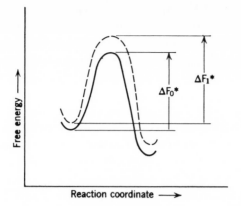

Figure 1.9 A free energy versus reaction coordinate diagram for two related reactions, for example, the hydrolysis of benzyl chlorides.

the changes in the stability of benzoic acids as a result of substitution, the changes in rate ($\Delta\Delta F^*$) will be directly related to changes in the position of the ionization equilibrium (that is, to σ).

Hundreds of rates and equilibria have been correlated through the $\rho\sigma$-treatment, and the approach is rather successful considering that four states (see Figs. 1.8 and 1.9) must be related in order for the correlations to hold. It is wise, however, to remember that substituent constants are only a form of information about a model reaction. Within the constants are summed the effect of solvent on the initial and final states, the effect of temperature, and the second-order effect of the substrate on the nature of the solvent around the molecule (the local region). (See Part 2 of this book.)

Substituents interact with benzene rings by both inductive and delocalization (*resonance*) mechanisms. In order to examine the inductive effect (mixed with the field effect) of substituents, Roberts and Moreland (*33*) placed the substituent at the other end of a rigid, saturated cyclic structure from the carboxylic acid group for which measurements of pK_a were desired. Additional data were obtained by Holtz and Stock (*34*) on 4-substituted bicyclo-[2.2.2]octane-1-carboxylic acids

(48)

$$\text{(40)} \quad + \; H_2O \; \rightleftharpoons \quad \text{(40a)} \quad + \; H_3O^+$$

and are listed in Table 1.10 in order to convey some notion of the response of the equilibrium constant to changes in substitution. The substituent constants, which can be defined with the aid of Eq. 48, are not listed, but they are almost the same as the σ_I-constants listed in Table 1.11. We have followed the suggestions of Ritchie and Sager in retaining only a few of the many substituent constants that have been suggested for use in correlating chemical phenomena (*35*).

TABLE 1.10   *Dissociation Constants of 4-X-Bicyclo[2.2.2]-octane-1-carboxylic Acids in 50% Ethanol-Water[a] at 25°[b]*

Substituent	$10^7 K_{12}$	pK_a
H	1.34 ± 0.09	6.87 ± 0.03
CH_3	1.30 ± 0.04	6.89 ± 0.01
CH_3CH_2	1.28 ± 0.01	6.89 ± 0.01
$HOCH_2$	1.59 ± 0.04	6.80 ± 0.01
HO	3.24 ± 0.24	6.50 ± 0.03
CH_3O	3.97 ± 0.12	6.40 ± 0.02
CH_3CH_2OCO	3.98 ± 0.18	6.40 ± 0.02
Cl	7.34 ± 0.44	6.13 ± 0.03
Br	7.30 ± 0.22	6.14 ± 0.01
NO_2	15.30 ± 0.50	5.82 ± 0.01
CN[c]		5.94
$N(CH_3)_3{}^{+}$ [d]		5.37

[a] 50% ethanol by weight.   [b] Ref. 34.   [c] Ref. 33 with result corrected for change of solvent by comparison of ρ-values.   [d] Ref. 34, footnote 18, cites unpublished results by C. F. Wilcox and J. S. McIntyre, which were corrected as in footnote c.

Another approach to the problem of evaluating the inductive effects of substituents in chemical environments for which both inductive and resonance effects should be expected is that of Taft (*36*). Following an early idea of Ingold, a substituent constant, σ^*, is defined by Eq. 49, which represents the difference in activation free energy changes produced by a substituent in base- and acid-catalyzed hydrolyses of *m*- and *p*-substituted benzoic acid esters. The transition states for the two types of hydrolysis are shown in Eqs. 50 and 51. The comparison is based on the assumptions that (1) steric and resonance effects are the same in both types of hydrolysis, and (2) polar (inductive + field) effects are significant only in base-catalyzed hydrolysis.

TABLE 1.11   *Substituent Constants*[a]

Substituent	$\sigma_I{}^b$	σ_m	σ_p	$\sigma_p{}^+$	$\sigma_p{}^-$
CH_3	0.00	−0.07	−0.17	−0.31	—
CF_3	0.41	0.43	0.54	0.52	—
CHO	0.31[c]	0.35	0.22	—	1.13
$COCH_3$	0.28	0.38	0.50	—	0.87
$CONH_2$	0.21[c]	0.28	—	—	0.62
COOR	0.30	0.37	0.45	0.48	0.68
C_6H_5	0.10	0.06	−0.01	−0.17	—
COO^-	0.05[c]	−0.10	0.00	−0.03	—
CN	0.56	0.56	0.66	0.66	0.90
$N(CH_3)_3{}^+$	0.92	0.88	0.82	0.41	—
NO_2	0.63	0.71	0.78	0.79	1.24
$NHCOCH_3$	0.28	0.21	0.00	0.00	—
$N{=}NC_6H_5$	0.25[c]	—	0.64	—	—
$NHNH_2$	0.15	−0.02	−0.55	—	—
$N(CH_3)_2$	0.10	−0.21	−0.83	−1.7	—
NH_2	0.10	−0.16	−0.66	−1.3	—
N_3	0.44[d]	0.33	0.08	—	0.11
OCF_3	0.55[c]	0.47	0.28	—	—
OCH_3	0.25	0.12	−0.27	−0.78	−0.2
OH	0.25	0.12	−0.37	−0.92	—
$OCOCH_3$	0.39	0.39	0.31	—	—
O^-	−0.16[c]	−0.17	−0.52	—	−0.81
$N_2{}^{+e}$	—	1.76	1.91	—	—
F	0.52	0.34	0.06	−0.07	−0.02
Cl	0.47	0.37	0.23	0.11	—
Br	0.45	0.39	0.23	0.15	—
I	0.38	0.35	0.18	0.13	—
$SOCH_3$	0.52	0.52	0.49	—	—
SO_2CH_3	0.60	0.60	0.72	—	1.05
SCH_3	0.19	0.15	0.00	−0.60	—
SCF_3	0.35[d]	0.46	0.64	—	—
$B(OH)_2$	−0.08[c]	0.01	0.45	—	—
$C{\equiv}CH^f$	—	0.205	0.233	0.179	—

[a] Taken from Ref. 35 except as noted.   [b] σ_I-Aliphatic.   [c] N.m.r. value.
[d] Derived indirectly from σ_m and σ_p, cf. Ref. 41.   [e] Ref. 42.   [f] Ref. 255.

$$(49) \quad \left[\log\left(\frac{k(XC_6H_4COOR)}{k(C_6H_5COOR)}\right)_B - \log\left(\frac{k(XC_6H_4COOR)}{k(C_6H_5COOR)}\right)_A\right] = 2.48\sigma^*$$

The reason for the use of the factor 2.48 in Eq. 49 is to scale the magnitude of the substituent constants so that they are comparable to σ. The comparison of hydrolysis rates under basic and acidic conditions need not be limited to benzoic acid derivatives, and a more general equation can be written and has been used on purely aliphatic esters, with the reference level established for acetate esters so that $\sigma^* = 0.00$ (Eq. 53).

$$
(50) \quad
\begin{array}{c}
\text{O} \\ \parallel \\ \text{RCOR}'
\end{array}
+ \text{OH}^-
\rightleftharpoons
\begin{array}{c}
\text{O}^- \\ | \\ \text{RC}-\text{OR}' \\ | \\ \text{OH}
\end{array}
\longrightarrow
\begin{array}{c}
\text{O}^{\delta-} \\ |\vdots \\ \text{RC}\!=\!\!=\!\text{OR}'^{\delta-} \\ | \\ \text{OH}
\end{array}
$$

Transition states

$$
(51) \quad
\begin{array}{c}
\text{O} \\ \parallel \\ \text{RCOR}'
\end{array}
+ \text{H}_3\text{O}^+
\rightleftharpoons
\begin{array}{c}
\text{OH} \\ | \quad \text{H}^+ \\ \text{RC}-\text{OR} \\ | \\ \text{OH}
\end{array}
\longrightarrow
\begin{array}{c}
{}^{\delta+}\text{OH} \\ |\vdots \quad \text{H} \\ \text{RC}\!=\!\!=\!\text{OR}^{\delta+} \\ | \\ \text{OH}
\end{array}
$$

$$
(52) \quad
\begin{array}{c}
\text{O}^{\delta-} \\ |\vdots \quad {}^{\delta-} \\ \text{RC}\!=\!\!=\!\text{OR}' \\ | \\ \text{OH}
\end{array}
\longrightarrow
\begin{array}{c}
\text{O} \\ \parallel \\ \text{RCOH}
\end{array}
+ \text{OR}^- ;
\begin{array}{c}
{}^{\delta+}\text{OH} \\ |\vdots \quad \text{H} \\ \text{RC}\!=\!\!=\!\text{OR}'^{\delta+} \\ \diagdown\text{OH}
\end{array}
\longrightarrow
\begin{array}{c}
\text{H}\overset{+}{\text{O}} \\ \parallel \\ \text{RCOH}
\end{array}
+ \text{R}'\text{OH}
$$

$$
(53) \quad \left[\log\left(\frac{k(\text{RCOOR}')}{k(\text{CH}_3\text{COOR}')} \right)_{\text{B}} - \log\left(\frac{k(\text{RCOOR}')}{k(\text{CH}_3\text{COOR}')} \right)_{\text{A}} \right] = 2.48\sigma^*
$$

Although mutual interaction between a substituent and a given organic structure must be a function of both the structure and the substituent, it is convenient to divide the total effect of a substituent into several contributions. Taft (*36, 38*) has utilized division into inductive and resonance effects:

$$
(54) \qquad\qquad \sigma = \sigma_\text{I} + \sigma_\text{R}
$$

The chief source for the substituent constants σ_I is a simple proportion between these constants and the σ^*-constants derived from a study of hydrolyses in which the group in question is separated from the ester group by a methylene:

$$
(55) \qquad\qquad \sigma_\text{I}(\text{X}) = 0.45\sigma^*(\text{XCH}_2)
$$

Thus far we have considered two types of substituent constants, σ and σ_I (σ_R can be obtained by subtracting σ_I from σ). Two additional substituent constants have been proposed for use in reactions not well correlated by σ. These are denoted σ^+ (for reactions in which electron demand on the substituent is so strong that the resonance contribution of the substituent is greater than usual) and σ^- (for reactions in which electron withdrawal by the substituent is greater than can be accounted for by the usual resonance interaction).

Brown and Okamoto (*39*) devised the scheme for defining the σ^+-constants. By utilizing the solvolysis of *t*-cumyl chlorides in 90% acetone–water as the standard reaction, a reaction constant was derived from a study of the *m*-substituted chlorides. It was thought that the resonance contribution from *m*-substituents should be negligible and that the usual σ_m-constants could be used for correlation of the rate constants for the solvolysis reaction.

(56)

Transition state

The reaction constant (ρ-value) obtained was then used to evaluate the substituent constant for *p*-substituents which had caused the rate constants for certain compounds to be quite different from the values expected from a $\rho\sigma$-correlation. The σ^+-constants were thus obtained.

An analogous procedure was used to define σ^--constants, using the ionization of phenols as the standard reaction (*40*):

(57)

A selected group of substituent constants are listed in Table 1.11.

Nuclear magnetic resonance shielding parameters should provide an excellent method for investigating substituent effects because the measurement depends on a transition that does not change the chemical character of the molecule. The usual methods for determining substituent constants really depend on the difference between the substituent effects on two chemically different states, the initial state, and either the transition state or the product state. For a "suitable" substituent, a second group might affect the electron density around the substituent in a way which reflects the electrical character of the second group. To avoid complications of geometric relationship of the two substituents, the ideal connection between them should be a simple, rigid group of atoms with a π-system capable of transmitting substituent effect over a modest distance. The "suitable" substituent, which we might call the *probe* substituent, should be as small and symmetric as possible to avoid unecessary interference with solvent structure and last, but not least, it should have a nuclear spin, preferably 1/2, so as to be detectable by n.m.r. spectroscopy. All these requirements are neatly met in fluorine. Taft (*43*) has made the delightful observation that "the fluorine atom may be regarded as a distant but sensitive observer removed from the confusion of the 'battle-field' (that is, field of interaction of solvent and substituent) by the rigid benzene ring." The disadvantage of n.m.r. measurements is that they are usually carried out with solutions of moderate concentration ($\sim 5\%$) although Taft (*43*) has claimed that this corresponds to infinitely dilute solution for most of the measurements.

Taft (*38*) found that fluorine chemical shift measurements by Gutowsky and co-workers (*44, 45*) (which were only roughly correlated by σ_m and σ_p constants) could be treated much more effectively by using σ_I for the *m*-substituents and a different blend of σ_I and σ_R constants for the *p*-substituents than that shown in Eq. 54. A plot of fluorine shielding parameters, desig-

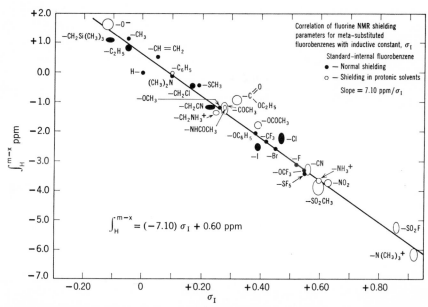

Figure 1.10 The correlation of fluorine n.m.r. shielding parameters for *m*-substituted fluorobenzenes with the inductive substituent constant, σ_I. The reference n.m.r. absorption line is established by an internal standard, fluorobenzene. ● designates "normal" shielding. ○ designates the mean shielding (indicating a variation in position of the resonance line due to the influence of solvent) in protonic solvents no more acidic than formic acid. (Reprinted with permission of the authors and the *Journal of the American Chemical Society* from Ref. 43.)

nated as $\int_H^{m-x}$ and given as the difference in p.p.m. from the hydrogen substituent, versus σ_I is shown in Fig. 1.10 (*43*). The relationship between δ_F and
σ_I and σ_R is given in Eq. 58 for *para*-substituents. This relationship is not
general, but it illustrates that different modes of measuring substituent effects
can elicit different composite electrical effects. This can be shown by a plot
of shielding parameters for *para*-substituents against those for *meta*-sub-
stituents; it is clear that no single equation can encompass the responses of
all substituents in all situations (Fig. 1.11) (*46*).

$$(58) \qquad \delta_{F(p)} = 0.58\sigma_I + 1.88\sigma_R$$

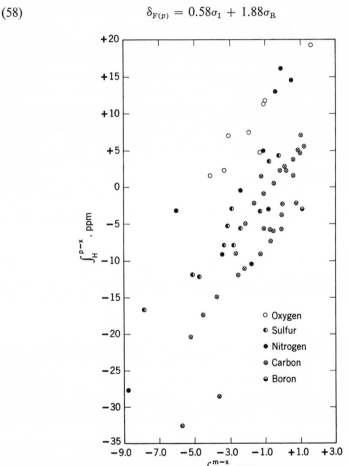

Figure 1.11 Relationship between the shielding parameters for *p*- and *m*-substituted
benzenes. The first atom of the substituent is designated. (Reprinted with permission of
the authors and the *Journal of the American Chemical Society* from Ref. 46.)

The theoretical basis for understanding substituent effects does not yet exist (Ehrenson, *47*). There is a serious concern about the separability of inductive, field, and conjugative effects, but there is little doubt that such separations are empirically useful. Correlations based on the constants shown in Table 1.11 have contributed materially to our understanding of many reactions and equilibria.

We may now utilize the substituent constants obtained in the ways described to correlate data on rates, equilibria, and other chemical properties. As long as we appreciate the fact that substituent constants are the reflection of a number of interactions between the substituent and the standard structure in a model reaction, we shall find them useful in interpreting data. It should be clear that the reaction constant ρ is a measure of the extent of electron demand at a reaction center upon the rest of the molecule. Four cases, for which our interpretations of ρ are strengthened by other evidence on the nature of the process under study, will be presented. These are (1) the ionization of benzyl radicals, for which electron demand from the substituent should be strong (Eq. 59), (2) solvolysis of benzyl halides, in which electron demand should be less than in the case of the ionization of benzyl radicals (Eq. 60), (3) dissociation of diaroyl peroxides, for which electron supply and electron demand should both be minimal (Eq. 61), and (4) charge-transfer transition of pyridinium iodides, in which electron withdrawal by the substituent on the electron acceptor should have a strong influence (Eq. 62).

(59)

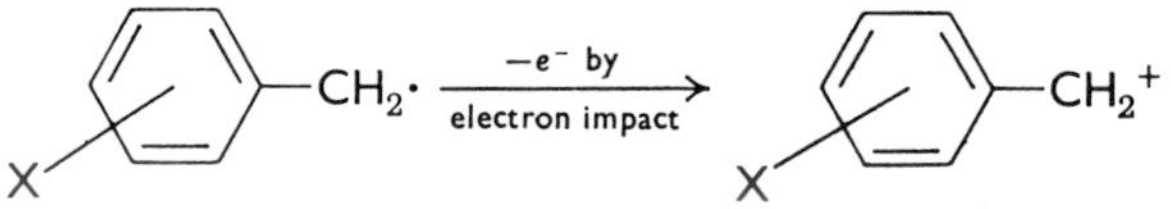

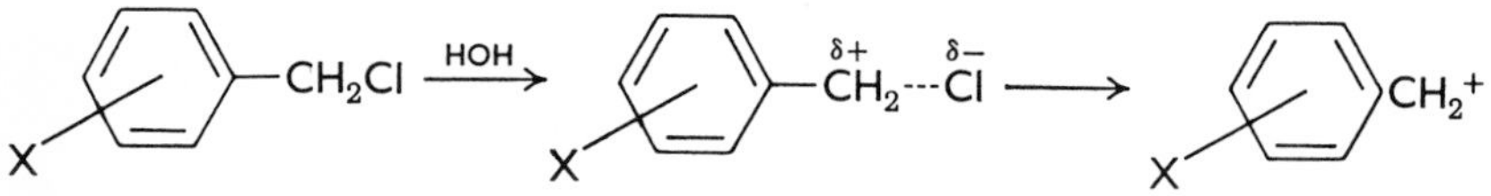

(60)

(61)

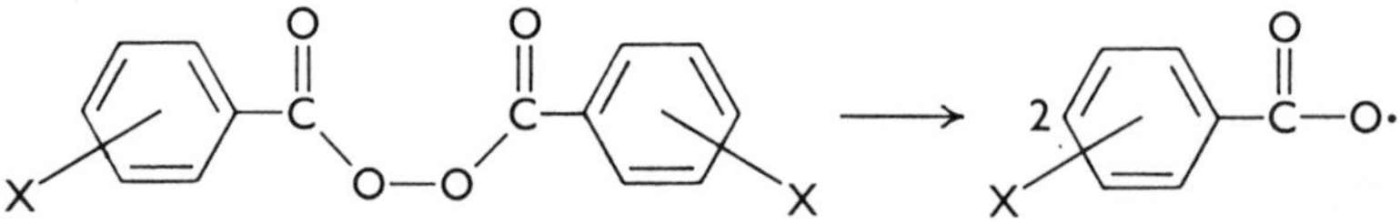

(62)

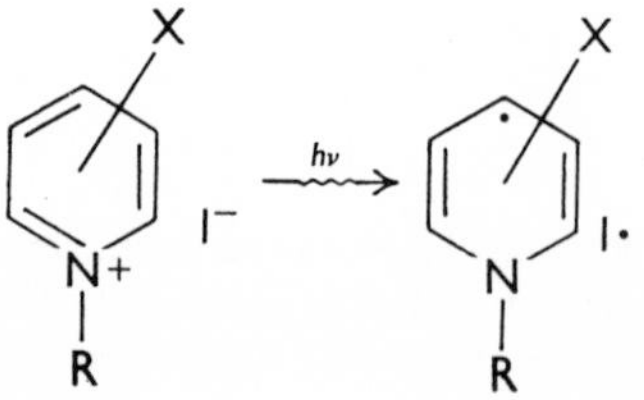

Lossing and his co-workers (*48*) have examined the ionization potentials of benzyl radicals (Table 1.12) generated by passage of the benzyl bromide through an 800° zone, from which they were admitted into a mass spectrometer. A different procedure was used to generate the *p*-methoxybenzyl radical because it was unstable at 800°, decomposing into methyl radical and quinomethane.

(63) 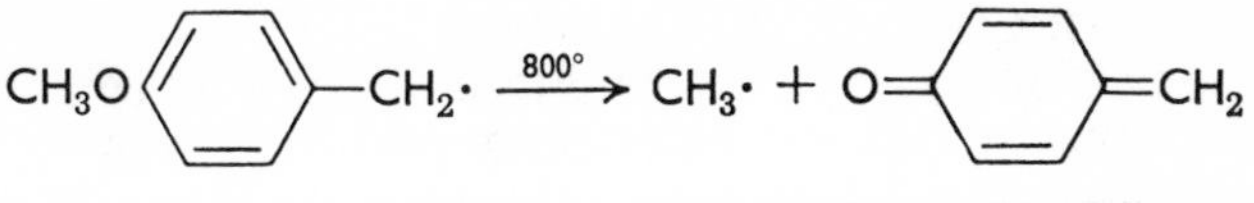 CH_3O—⟨benzene ring⟩—$CH_2\cdot$ $\xrightarrow{800°}$ $CH_3\cdot$ + $O{=}$⟨ring⟩${=}CH_2$

The nitrite ester of 2-*p*-methoxyphenylethanol decomposes at 400° to nitric oxide and the alkoxy radical. The alkoxy radical is unstable and forms *p*-methoxybenzyl radical and formaldehyde (Eqs. 64, 65).

(64) 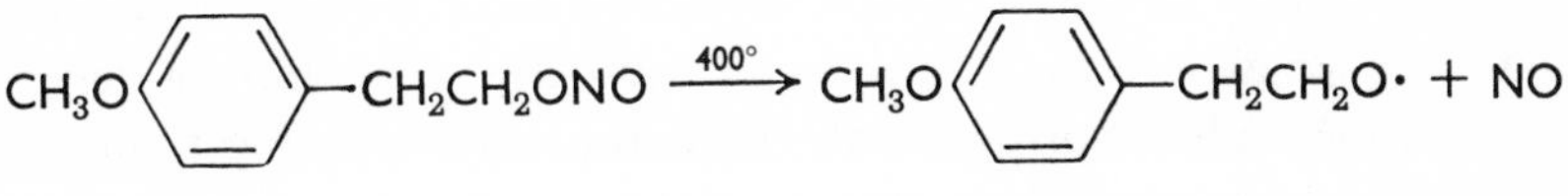 CH_3O—⟨ring⟩—CH_2CH_2ONO $\xrightarrow{400°}$ CH_3O—⟨ring⟩—$CH_2CH_2O\cdot$ + NO

(65) 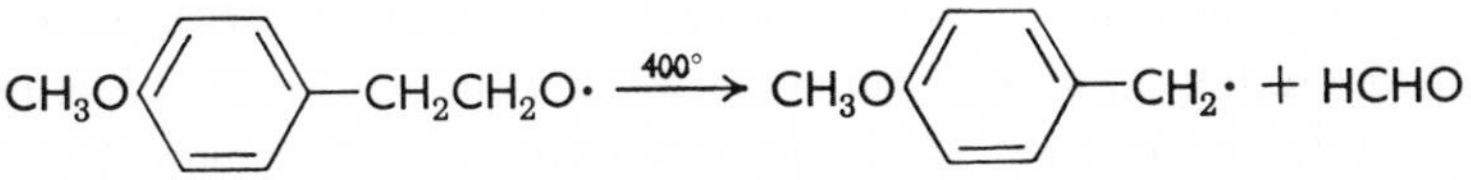 CH_3O—⟨ring⟩—$CH_2CH_2O\cdot$ $\xrightarrow{400°}$ CH_3O—⟨ring⟩—$CH_2\cdot$ + HCHO

The ionization potentials are listed in Table 1.12 for a number of the benzyl radicals. A ρ value can be obtained from the data by converting the potentials from electron-volts into kcal./mole (1 e.v. = 23.06 kcal./mole), dividing by $2.303RT$ and plotting against σ^+. The form of the Hammett correlation shown in Eq. 66 shows why this procedure is followed.

(66) $$\log \frac{K}{K_0} = \rho\sigma = \frac{\Delta\Delta F}{2.303RT}$$

TABLE 1.12   *Ionization Potentials of Benzyl Radicals*[a]

Substituent	Ionization Potential (in e.v.)
4-CN	8.36 ± 0.1
4-F	7.78 ± 0.1
H	7.76 ± 0.08
4-CH_3	7.46 ± 0.03
4-CH_3O	6.82 ± 0.1

[a] Ref. 48.

TABLE 1.13   *Charge-Transfer Bands for Pyridinium Iodides*[a]

Substituent	$\lambda_{max}(\epsilon_{max})$	E_T[b]
4-CH$_3$	3590(1230)	79.64
3-CH$_3$	3700(1310)	77.27
H	3738(1200)	76.49
3-COOCH$_3$	4070(1850)	70.25
4-COOCH$_3$	4489(1230)	63.69
4-CN	4912(922)	58.20

[a] Ref. 50.   [b] Transition energy in kcal./mole.

The ρ derived from these data is -19.1, a value much more negative than that observed in most reactions. The electron demand by a bare carbonium ion is very high and leads to a considerable degree of electron delocalization. By the study of solvolysis rates of derivatives that yield carbonium ions as intermediates, we can examine the electron demand by a developing carbonium ion center at the transition state. The transition state is probably fairly close to the carbonium ion in charge (*12*) but we should expect that its sensitivity to substituent change might be somewhat less than that of the carbonium ion itself. The ρ-value found (-2.18) for the hydrolysis of benzyl chlorides is, however, far less than the ρ for the ionization of benzyl radicals in the gas phase, and we must conclude that solvation of the carbonium ion center materially reduces the demand for charge donation by substituents. For benzyl chlorides bearing electron-withdrawing substituents, it is possible that the ionization reaction competes with a nucleophilic displacement by solvent water. The ρ values for the solvolysis of more highly substituted benzyl halides are more negative but still smaller than that of the gas phase ionization, with -4.62 for *t*-cumyl chloride (90% acetone–water) and -5.09 benzhydryl chlorides (ethanol).

The highest substituent sensitivity ever observed for any process is that found by Taft, Martin, and Lampe (*54*) for the reaction shown in Eq. 67. In this case, the substituent is directly attached to the methyl cation carbon which makes the electron demand. No ordinary substituent constant serves to correlate all the results, but there is a rough correlation with σ^+. The data are shown in Table 1.14 as stabilization energies and appearance potentials relative to methyl cation as 0.0. The ρ value (based on σ^+) is about -45.

Stabilization of radicals apparently depends less on the nature of the substituent than the stabilization of carbonium ions and, in general, radical

TABLE 1.14   *Relative Stabilization Energies for Mono-substituted Methyl Cations*[a]

Ion	ΔA, e.v.[b]	Stabilization Energy, kcal./mole[b]
$^+CH_2CN$	$+0.4$	-10
$^+CH_3$	(0.0)	(0)
$^+CH_2F$	-1.1	26
$^+CH_2Cl$	-1.4	32
$^+CH_2CH_3$	-1.5	35
$^+CH_2SCN$	-1.8	42
$^+CH_2Br$	-2.2	51
$^+CH_2I$	-2.3	53
$^+CH_2C_6H_5$	-2.4	55
$^+CH_2OH$	-2.6	60
$^+CH_2SH$	-2.8	64
$^+CH_2OCH_3$	-3.0	69
$^+CH_2SCH_3$	-3.2	74
$^+CH_2P(CH_3)_2$	-3.4	79
$^+CH_2NH_2$	-4.1	95
$^+CH_2NHCH_3$	-4.3	99
$^+CH_2N(CH_3)_2$	-4.6	106

[a] From Ref. 54.   [b] Relative to methyl.

reactions show considerably smaller substituent effects than ionic reactions. The rates of decomposition of diaroyl peroxides to arylcarboxylate radicals (Eq. 61) has a reaction constant of -0.38, using the sum of the σ-constants for the substituents in both rings to evaluate the substituent effect (*53*). Many radical reactions have ρ-values of less than 1.6. The reaction of diphenyl-picrylhydrazyl with phenols, however, has been reported to have a ρ of -2.72 [(*51*), compare with (*49*)].

(67) $$CH_3X\ (g) + e^- \longrightarrow\ ^+CH_2X + 2e^- + H$$

The light absorption process which produces charge-transfer within the pyridinium iodide ion-pair has a ρ of 13.4. The maxima from which the "reaction constant" was calculated are listed in Table 1.13 (Kosower, *50*). This transition is discussed in detail in Sections 1.7 and 2.6.

Considerable caution must be exercised in applying the concept of linear free energy relationships with substituent constants to electronic transitions (*55, 56*). The resemblance of the ultraviolet absorption curves for *o-* and *m*-disubstituted benzene derivatives (and the great difference between these and the curve for the *p*-derivative) has been explained by Grinter and Heilbronner (57) as primarily a result of the similarity of the molecular orbitals for the *o*- and *m*-derivatives (Fig. 1.12). The longest wavelength absorption band is due to a transition from the highest filled molecular orbital to the lowest empty molecular orbital. The wave function for the lowest empty molecular orbital is illustrated for *o*-, *m*-, and *p*-derivatives. The two major factors that militate against the use of substituent constants for the correlation of most electronic transitions are (1) the vertical character of the electronic transition whereby a vibrationally excited upper state is produced, and (2) the electronic structure of the upper state possibly interacting with the substituent in an entirely different way from the way in which the ground state interacts.

Most reactions have ρ-values much lower than most of those we have discussed thus far. However, extreme cases provide us with a good sense of the maximum effect we might expect from a given substituent and, through our knowledge of the details of the extreme cases (for example, ionization), offer us the opportunity for judging the degree of charge separation change from the initial state to the transition state in the more common reactions.

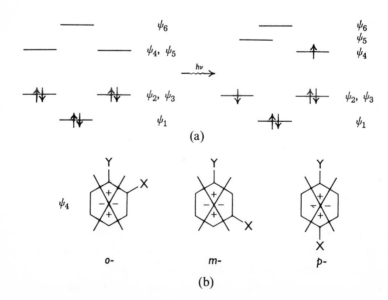

Figure 1.12   (*a*) An electronic transition in a benzene derivative. (*b*) The lowest empty molecular orbital for *o*-, *m*-, and *p*-disubstituted benzene derivatives.

Reaction	Solvent	T, °C	
ArCOOH ⇌ ArCOO⁻ + H⁺	H_2O	25	1.000
	CH_3OH	25	1.761
	EtOH	25	2.278
	n-C_4H_9OH	25	1.502
ArCH₂COOH ⇌ ArCH₂COO⁻ + H⁺	H_2O	25	0.562
ArCH₂CH₂COOH ⇌ ArCH₂CH₂COO⁻ + H⁺	H_2O	25	0.237
ArCH=CHCOOH ⇌ ArCH=CHCOO⁻ + H⁺	H_2O	25	0.418
ArC≡CCOOH ⇌ ArC≡CCOO⁻ + H⁺	50% EtOH—H_2O	24	0.625
ArB(OH)₂ + H₂O ⇌ ArB(OH)₃⁻ + H₃O⁺	25% EtOH—H_2O	25	2.177
ArPO₃H₂ ⇌ ArPO₃H⁻ + H⁺	H_2O	25	0.754
ArOH ⇌ ArO⁻ + H⁺	30% EtOH—H_2O	25	2.522
	95% EtOH—H_2O	21	3.141
ArNH₃⁺ ⇌ ArNH₂ + H⁺	30% EtOH—H_2O	25	3.186
	CH_3OH	25	4.027
	EtOH	25	4.496
ArCOOCH₃ + OH⁻ → ArCOO⁻ + CH₃OH	60% Me_2CO—H_2O	25	2.382
ArCOCl + EtOH → ArCOOEt + HCl	EtOH	0	1.735
ArO⁻ + C₂H₅I → ArOC₂H₅ + I⁻	EtOH	43	-0.99
ArCH₂ONO₂ + OEt⁻ → ArCHO + NO₂⁻	EtOH	30	3.4
ArCN + SH⁻ → ArC(SH)=NH	EtOH	61	2.15
Ar(C₆H₅)CHCl + EtOH → Ar(C₆H₅)CHOEt + HCl	EtOH	25	-5.09
ArH + NO₂⁺ → ArNO₂ + H⁺	Ac_2O	25	-7.29
ArB(OH)₂ + Br₂ → ArBr + B(OH)₃	20% AcOH—H_2O	25	-3.82
Ar₃C⁺ + H₂O ⇌ Ar₃COH + H₃O⁺	dil. H_2SO_4	25	3.97
ArH + Br₂ → ArBr + HBr	AcOH	25	-12.1 [c]
ArH + Cl₂ → ArCl + HCl	AcOH	25	-8.06 [c]
ArSi(CH₃)₃ + H₃O⁺ → ArH + [(CH₃)₃Si]₂O	dil. AcOH	25	-4.60 [c]

[a] Ref. 1.   [b] Ref. 58.   [c] Versus σ^+.

The ρ-values for a variety of reactions are listed in Table 1.15. Ritter and Miller (86) have discussed the comparison of ρ-values.

Although we shall not deal directly with the important topic of steric effects in this book, a substituent constant, E_s, which reflects the steric effect of a group, is worthy of mention. Taft (36) pointed out that the negligible effect of the polarity of substituents on the rates of acid-catalyzed hydrolyses made it possible to utilize such hydrolyses to define quantitative measures of the steric effect of a group on the rate of a reaction. The constants are defined with Eq. 68.

$$(68) \qquad\qquad \log \frac{k}{k_0} = E_s$$

Eliel (52) has developed the study of conformer ratios of cyclohexane derivatives as a measure of steric effects, the principle being that the larger the group is, the less it will accept an axial orientation in a cyclohexane ring.

Steric substituent constants based on Eq. 68 are listed in Table 1.16.

TABLE 1.16   *Steric Substituent Constants*[a,b]

Substituent ortho-Substituted Benzoates	E_s	Substituent Aliphatic Esters, RCOOR'	E_s
		R	
CH_3O	+0.99	H	+1.24
C_2H_5O	+0.90	CH_3	0.00
F	+0.49	$ClCH_2$, FCH_2	−0.24
Cl	+0.18	$BrCH_2$	−0.27
Br	0.00	ICH_2	−0.37
CH_3	0.00	F_2CH	−0.67
I	−0.20	F_3C	−1.16
NO_2	−0.75	Cl_3C	−2.06
C_6H_5	−0.90	$(C_2H_5)_3C$	−3.8

[a] Note that $E_s = 0.00$ for CH_3.   [b] Ref. 36.

Problems

1. Define σ, σ_m, σ_p, σ_I, σ_R, $\sigma_p{}^+$, $\sigma_p{}^-$, ρ, E_s and indicate the standard reaction which provided the prime source of information about the constant.
2. Why is the ρ-value for the ionization of benzyl radicals (a) larger than the ρ-value for the solvolysis of t-cumyl chlorides and (b) smaller than the ρ-value for the stabilization of methyl cations by substituents?

3. Explain the differences between the following pairs of substituent constants in terms of the factors with which you are familiar.
   (a) CH_3: σ_I and σ_p
   (b) C_6H_5: σ_m and σ_p^+
   (c) $N(CH_3)_2$: σ_I and σ_p^+
   (d) $\sigma_p(OCF_3)$ and $\sigma_p(OCH_3)$
   (e) $\sigma_p^+(F)$ and $\sigma_p^+(Cl)$
   (f) $\sigma_I(N_3)$ and $\sigma_I(NH_2)$
   (g) $\sigma_p(NO_2)$ and $\sigma_p[N^+(CH_3)_3]$

4. Interpret the ρ-values for the following reactions (Table 1.15) in terms of probable mechanism of reactions and possible charge distribution in the transition state.
   (a) $ArCOCl + EtOH \rightarrow ArCOOEt + HCl$
   (b) $ArCN + SH^- \rightarrow ArC(SH)=NH$
   (c) $ArH + Br_2 \rightarrow ArBr + HBr$
   (d) $ArSi(CH_3)_3 + H_3O^+ \rightarrow ArH + [(CH_3)_3Si]_2O$

5. Interpret the ρ-values given for the ionization of benzoic acids in four different solvents (Table 1.15).

6. Consider the following pK_a data for substituted anilines (Eqs. P6a and P6b) (Table P6).

   (P6a)　　　$C_6H_5NH_2 + NH_2^- \underset{NH_3(l)}{\rightleftharpoons} C_6H_5NH^- + NH_3$

   (P6b)　　$XC_6H_4NH_2 + C_6H_5NH^- \underset{NH_3(l)}{\rightleftharpoons} XC_6H_4NH^- + C_6H_5NH_2$

TABLE P6

Substituent	pK_a $(XC_6H_4NH_2)$	pK_a $(XC_6H_4NH_3^+)$
2,5-Cl_2	0	1.52
3,5-$(CF_3)_2$	0.06	
4-CN	0.34	1.74
2,4-Cl_2	1.16	2.01
3,4-Cl_2	2.45	2.96
3-CF_3	3.22	3.49
4-Cl	4.34	3.89
—	5.65	4.60
4-F	5.88	4.65
3,5-$(CH_3)_2$	6.22	4.91
2,5-$(CH_3)_2$	6.26	4.61
4-CH_2CH_2	6.43	
4-CH_3	6.58	5.08

Anilide ions were generated by the reaction shown in Eq. P6a. pK_a values were obtained through the use of Eq. 29 (Part 1). Compare the ρ-values for the two sets of pK_a values. What σ-constant should be used for the 4-CN group? Is the procedure of using sums of σ-constants for disubstituted anilines valid? What difficulties could arise from such correlations? (Ref. 281.)

1.4   Nucleophilic Displacement Reactions

The recognition by Hughes and Ingold (59) that there were two classes of nucleophilic *substitution* reactions was a major advance in physical organic chemistry. Certain alkyl halides yielded products in nucleophilic substitution reactions by an ionization mechanism (Eqs. 69 and 70) called S_N1 because the kinetics of disappearance of alkyl halide depended only on the concentration of the alkyl halide (Eq. 71).

(69) $RX \longrightarrow R^+ + X^-$

(70) $R^+ + N \longrightarrow RN^+$

(71) $v = -\dfrac{d(RX)}{dt} = k(RX)$

Other alkyl halides reacted at a rate dependent on both the concentration of alkyl halide and that of added nucleophile (S_N2) (Eqs. 72 and 73).

(72) $N + RX \longrightarrow NR^+ + X^-$

(73) $v = -\dfrac{d(RX)}{dt} = k(RX)(N)$

If the nucleophile is bonded covalently to the molecule which contains a carbon–halogen linkage, certain structural arrangements will lead to *intramolecular "S_N2"* attack and yet the kinetics will follow Eq. 71. Some reactions which conform to Eqs. 69 and 70 will follow the kinetic pattern described by Eq. 73 in nonpolar solvents. The original nomenclature is no longer suitable for all cases, most especially in defining the role of the solvent.

In proposing a classification of reaction mechanisms, we must ask the question of how useful and general our proposal is. In the case of substitution reactions

(74) $A + BC \longrightarrow AB + C$

in which A replaces C, what we really want to know is what happened between the time we mixed the reactants and the time at which we isolated the products. If bonding to B by A is concerted with the loosening of the bond to C, and *no intermediate is detected or inferred* from studies of the reaction, the transition state for the reaction can be written A···B···C, and the free energy versus reaction coordinate diagram can be drawn as shown

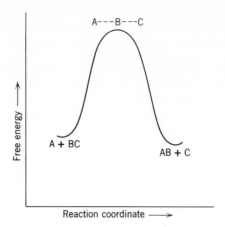

Figure 1.13 Free energy versus reaction coordinate diagram for S_D substitution mechanism.

in Fig. 1.13. Let us call this mechanism S_D or direct substitution. We might note that at least three types of S_D mechanisms exist: $S_D N$ (direct nucleophilic substitution), $S_D E$ (direct electrophilic substitution), and $S_D R$ (direct radical substitution). For $S_D R$ reactions, remember that the substitution is at atom B which is the atom "transferred" from C to A in a common way of describing such reactions. Thus, for concerted processes, the classification scheme seems fairly general.

In many reactions it is necessary to propose that an intermediate is formed during the course of the substitution reaction. There are two important pathways for the formation of intermediates. The first involves cleavage of the BC molecule into two fragments, B and C:

(75) $$BC \longrightarrow B + C$$

The second proceeds by the association of A with BC to form an intermediate with the composition ABC:

(76) $$A + BC \longrightarrow ABC$$

The intermediate B forms the final product by reaction with A, and the intermediate ABC decomposes to form AB and C. In either case, the free energy versus reaction coordinate diagram is the same and is shown in Fig. 1.14. Although we might group reactions that proceed by dissociation into fragments or by association into a complex intermediate together, we choose to label these as different mechanisms. For reactions through intermediates of the type B, the designations S_IN (substitution through an intermediate that reacts with a nucleophile), S_IR (substitution through an intermediate that reacts with a radical), and S_IE (substitution through an intermediate that reacts with an electrophile) seem appropriate. For reactions through intermediates like ABC, we utilize the terms S_AN (substitution through association of a nucleophile), S_AR (substitution through association of a radical), and S_AE (substitution through association of an electrophile).

Our classification of substitution mechanisms bears a resemblance to that put forward by Langford and Gray for inorganic substitution reactions (*283*).

Examples of these mechanisms will be presented to make the classification more concrete.

The reaction of radioactively labeled iodide ion with optically active *sec*-octyl iodide in acetone

$$(77) \qquad (+)\text{CH}_3\overset{|}{\text{C}}\text{H}(\text{CH}_2)_4\text{CH}_3 \xrightarrow[\text{acetone}]{\text{NaI}} (-)\text{CH}_3\overset{|}{\text{C}}\text{H}(\text{CH}_2)_4\text{CH}_3$$

gave data which showed that the initial rate of introduction of radioactivity was equal to the rate of inversion at the asymmetric center (*284*). Each act of replacement of iodide ion was therefore accompanied by an inversion. For a symmetrical case (that is, in which A = C in A + BC), inversion with every

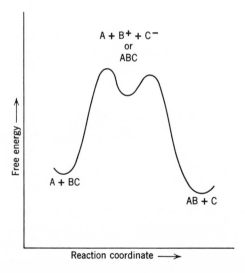

Figure 1.14 Free energy versus reaction coordinate diagram for S_I substitution mechanism.

act of substitution precludes the intervention of an intermediate. The pathway from starting material to products must thus be described as a *direct nucleophilic substitution* (S_DN) on carbon (Eq. 78).

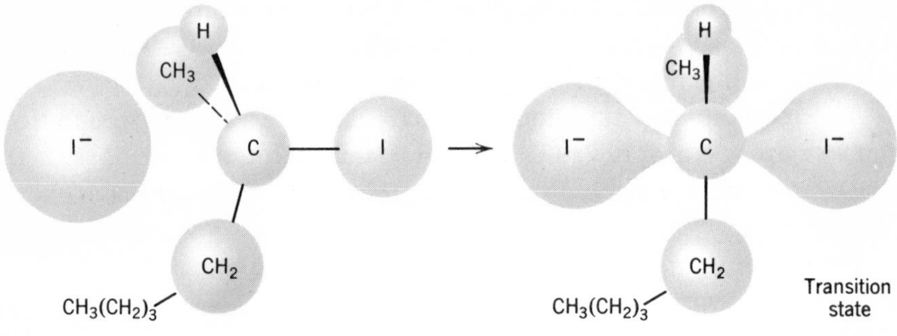

Transition state

There are many examples of direct substitution by radicals on atoms which are singly bonded to other atoms (for example, hydrogen, halogen). There are few examples of substitution on atoms which are bonded to two other atoms (for example, the sulfur in disulfides), unless we count addition reactions of the type $A\cdot + B{=}C \rightarrow ABC\cdot$. There are no examples which come readily to mind of radical substitution by the direct route on atoms that are bonded to three or four other atoms. We can cite very few examples of the S_DR mechanism for carbon [Eq. 78a, Applequist and Searle (792)], but a typical S_DR reaction on chlorine is illustrated in the reaction of phenyl radical with tetrachloromethane (Eq. 79).

(78a)

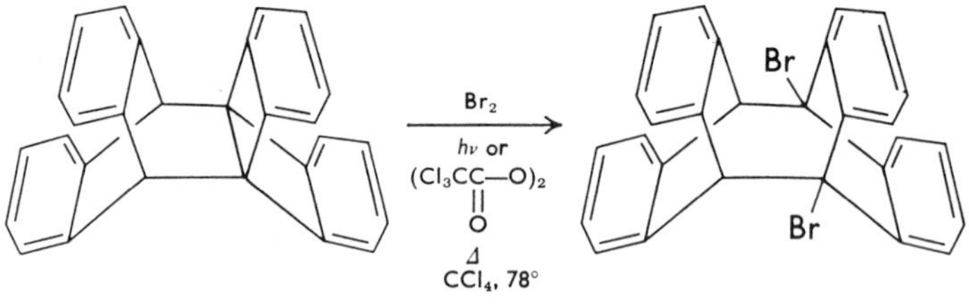

(79) $C_6H_5\cdot + CCl_4 \longrightarrow C_6H_5Cl + CCl_3\cdot$

(The product trichloromethyl radical may disappear by dimerization or reaction with another phenyl radical.)

The reaction of either *cis*- or *trans*-4-methylcyclohexylmercuric bromides with bromine under polar conditions produces the corresponding *cis*- or *trans*-4-methylcyclohexyl bromides with retention of configuration (Eq. 79a). Under free radical-forming conditions, no stereospecificity is observed, the reaction probably proceeding through the 4-methylcyclohexyl radical (*793*).

(79a)

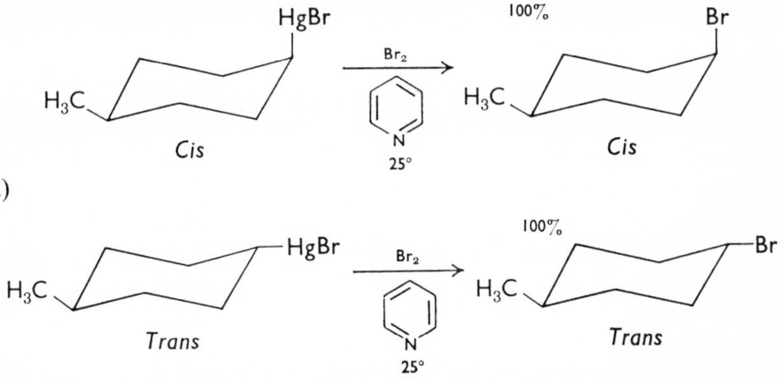

The attack of a positively charged (electrophilic) species on carbon appears to proceed with retention as shown by the reaction of mercuric chloride with R-(—)-dibutyl 1-phenylethane boronate to yield R-(—)-1-phenylethyl mercuric chloride (*285*) (Eq. 80). [R is a designation for absolute configuration, see p. 92 of Ref. 52.]

(80)

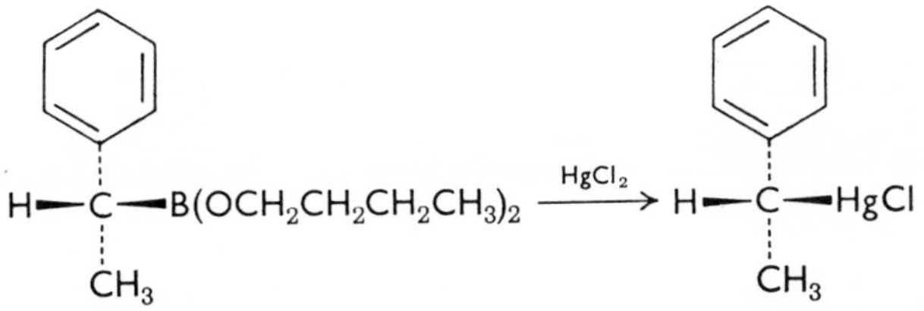

The hydrolysis of *t*-butyl bromide (Eq. 81) is a typical S_1N reaction.

(81)
$$(CH_3)_3CBr \longrightarrow (CH_3)_3C^+ + Br^-$$
$$\downarrow H_2O$$
$$(CH_3)_3\overset{+}{C}OH_2 \longrightarrow (CH_3)_3COH$$

In some cases, as in the methanolysis of 2,4-dimethyl-4-hexyl phthalate (Fig. 1.15), the stereochemical result is not 100% racemization as predicted for a mechanism of reaction through a "free" carbonium ion (*60*). The predominance of inversion for this solvolysis under certain experimental conditions is no doubt related to the intervention of a "cage effect" (Section 2.10

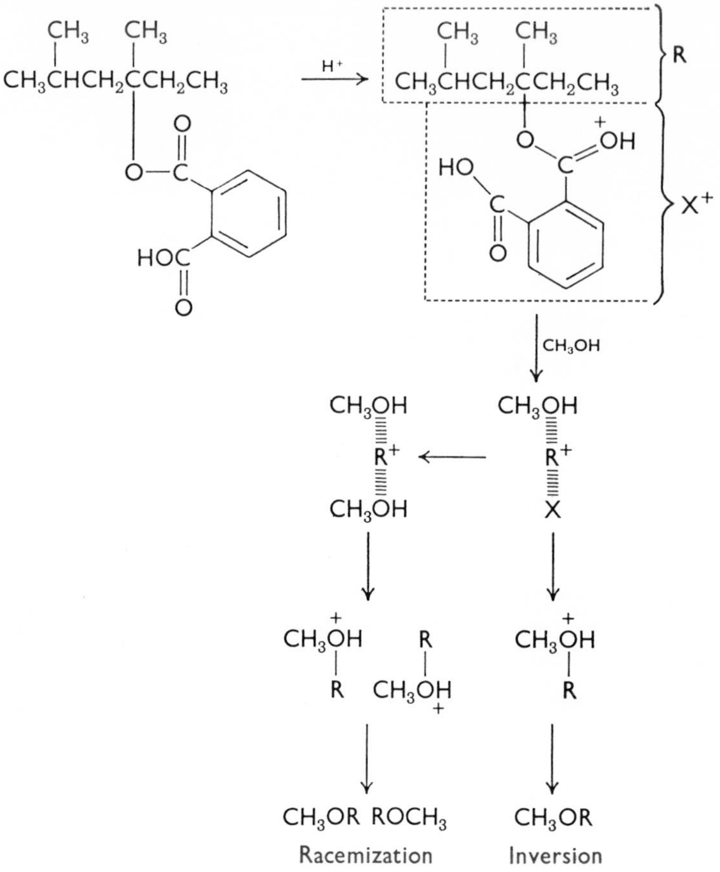

Figure 1.15 Acid-catalyzed solvolysis of 2,4-dimethyl-4-hexyl acid phthalate. In pure methanol, the product is 60% inverted and 40% racemized (or 80% inverted and 20% retained). Note that the solvolysis fits the equation $RX^+ \rightarrow R^+ + X$.

on "reaction partners") and implies that more than one carbonium ion-like intermediate occurs along the reaction pathway (Fig. 1.16). It is convenient, nevertheless, to regard a reaction of the type shown in Fig. 1.15 as an S_IN reaction. It is probable that most reactions in this category proceed through multiple intermediates, and we shall consider some of the evidence for such intermediates in the next section (Section 1.5).

The role of reaction partners (Section 2.10) in determining the ultimate products of reaction is particularly important in the case of radicals. A stable

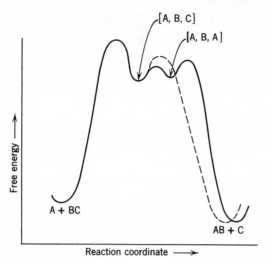

Figure 1.16 A free energy versus reaction coordinate diagram for the reaction of a compound via the S_I mechanism by way of closely related intermediates.

free radical, BIP (2,3′,5′,6-tetra-*t*-butylindophenoxyl) (*287*) (**41**), reacts with AIBN (azoisobutyronitrile) (**42**) in a reaction that proceeds by the formation

(82)

$$CH_3\overset{\overset{\displaystyle CH_3}{|}}{\underset{\underset{\displaystyle CN}{|}}{C}}-N{=}N-\overset{\overset{\displaystyle CH_3}{|}}{\underset{\underset{\displaystyle CN}{|}}{C}}-CH_3 \xrightarrow{\Delta} 2CH_3\overset{\overset{\displaystyle CH_3}{|}}{\underset{\underset{\displaystyle CN}{|}}{C}}\cdot \ + \ N_2$$

42

(83)

Adduct (?)

of free radicals from the AIBN, followed either by recombination of the free radicals or reaction ("trapping") by the BIP (*286*) (Eqs. 82, 83). This reaction can be regarded as an S_IR reaction.

It may be remarked that a carbonium ion intermediate or a carbanion intermediate (both S_I) could react with a radical. In the latter case, electron transfer is the only possible reaction. In the former example, a product could form according to Eq. 84. Although such a reaction is formally an example of the S_IR mechanism, we do not consider it further.

(84) $$B^+ + R\cdot \longrightarrow BR\cdot^+$$

Base-catalyzed exchange of deuterium for hydrogen in acetone is an example of an S_IE reaction (Eqs. 85, 86).

(85) $$CH_3COCH_3 + OD^- = CH_3COCH_2^- + HDO$$

(86) $$CH_3COCH_2^- + D_2O = CH_3COCH_2D$$

Nucleophilic aromatic substitution and ester hydrolysis are two reactions which follow S_AN mechanisms. The kinetics of the reaction of dimethylamine and 4-nitrophenylphosphate (**43**) depend on base up to a limit, after which the rate is independent of base. Base thus increases the rate of conversion (probably by shifting an equilibrium) up to the point at which the final step becomes rate-limiting (*288*).

(87)

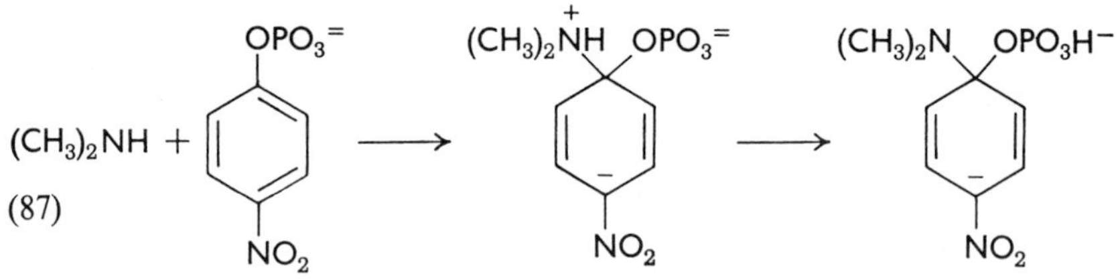

43

(88)

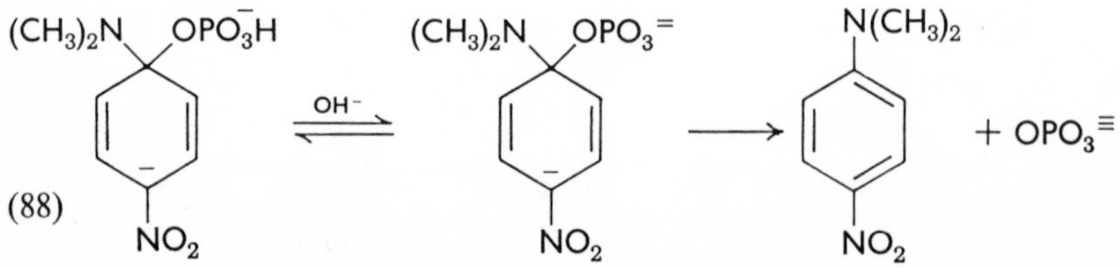

From many experiments, but especially from the decisive oxygen-18 exchange experiments carried out by Bender (*501*), the intervention of the "tetrahedral intermediate" in ester hydrolyses and other reactions of esters is well known (Eqs. 89, 90).

(89)

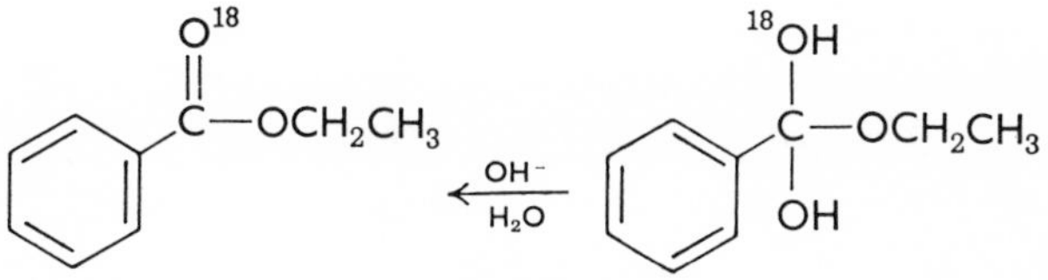

(90)

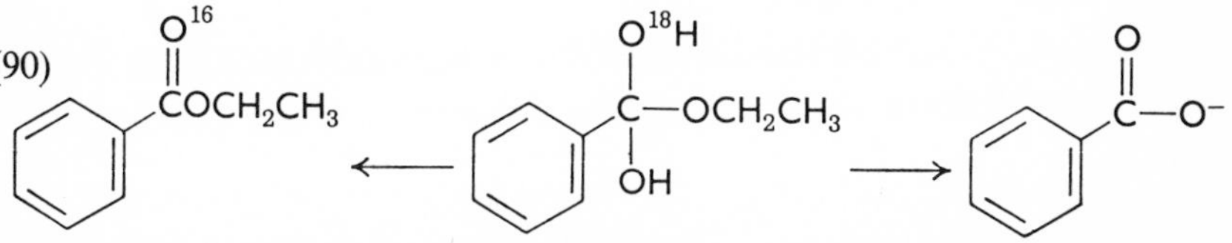

Arylation of aromatic rings by free radicals goes by way of an $S_A R$ mechanism, as in the formation of diphenyl from the reaction of phenylazo-triphenylmethane (**44**) and benzene (Eqs. 91–93) (*289*).

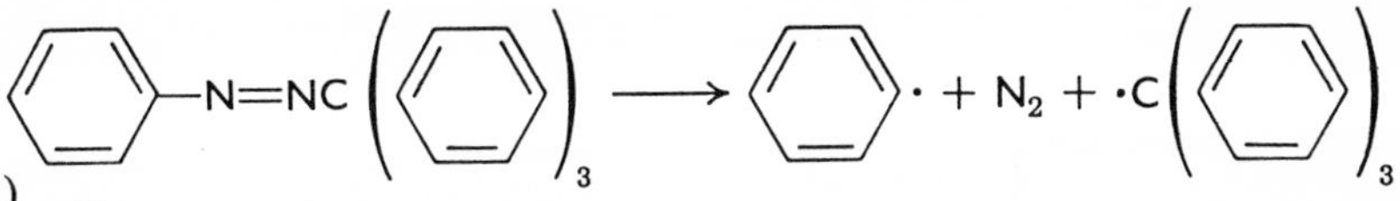

(91) **44**

(92)

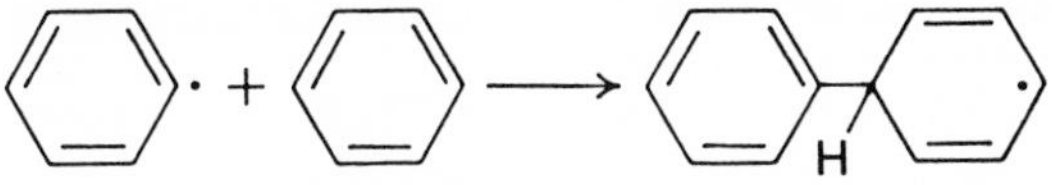

(93)

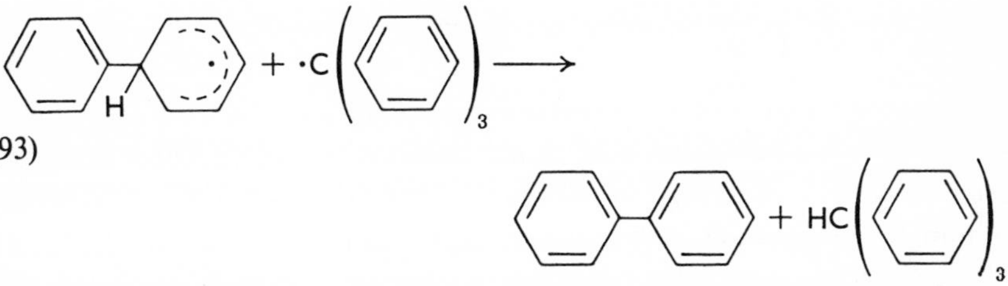

Pentamethylbenzene and nitronium fluoroborate react to form a complex, probably **45**, which decomposes to form pentamethylnitrobenzene in a reaction which may be classed as $S_A E$ (Eqs. 94, 95) (*290*).

(94)

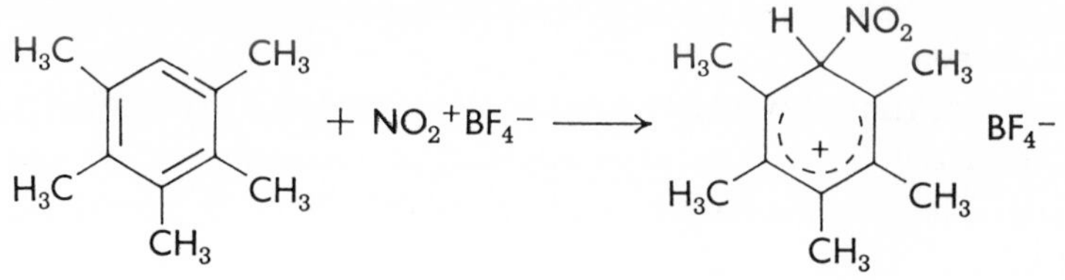

(95)

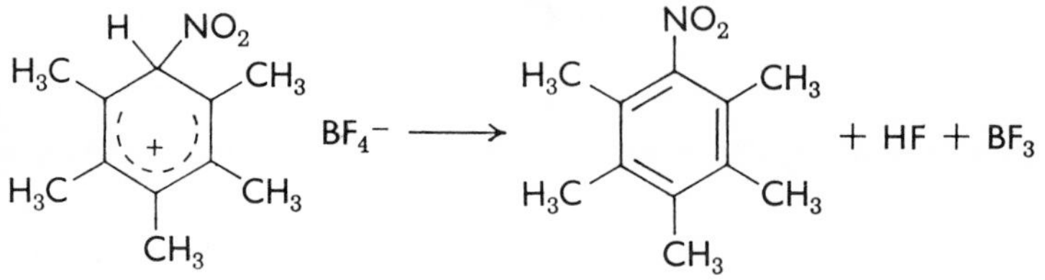

We may now return to the question of the usefulness and generality of the proposed scheme, which can be organized in the form of a small table (Table 1.17). From our discussion, it is clear that we must remember that N, R, and

TABLE 1.17

Substitution	Attacking Reagent		
	Nucleophilic	Radical	Electrophilic
Direct	$S_D N$	$S_D R$	$S_D E$
Intermediate	$S_I N$	$S_I R$	$S_I E$
Associated intermediate	$S_A N$	$S_A R$	$S_A E$

E refer to the nature of the attacking reagent (the A in A + BC), that it is an overall substitution reaction on a certain kind of atom which is always referred to (for example, on carbon, on hydrogen, on sulfur, etc.), that nothing is specified about the pathway (Is the direct transition state very far above the initial state? Are there two or three intermediates? etc.), that the scheme could in principle be extended to addition and elimination reactions, and that the kinetic criteria, which are applicable, will depend on the case. The charm of the scheme is that it is easy to remember, that it is more general than the older terms which are usually used in this connection (that is, S_N1 and S_N2), and that it is easy to imagine its extension to many elements besides carbon.

The stereochemical consequences of one act of direct substitution may be summarized as follows: S_DN: inversion, S_DR: unknown for carbon, and S_DE: retention. The transition state in an S_D reaction may be considered as a molecule

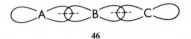

46

for which three molecular orbitals can be constructed from the three atomic orbitals of the species A, B, and C. [Streitwieser (60) has pointed out that there is little evidence for **46** as an unstable intermediate for substitution on carbon.] The three molecular orbitals are, in order of increasing energy, bonding, nonbonding, and antibonding. Berson and co-workers (656) (see also p. 484, 249) have made some rough calculations on the molecular orbitals of **46** and concluded that the total energy of the system is lower for four electrons when the A and C orbitals are as far apart as possible (backside approach resulting in inversion), primarily because the system

47

leads to a nonbonding orbital of an energy greater than the stabilization of the bonding orbital can compensate for. The two-electron case (electrophilic substitution S_DE) leads naturally to frontside replacement (retention) because of the favorable overlap of the orbitals belonging to A and C. The three-electron case (S_DR) cannot be compared to any actual examples but may be surmised to go with either retention or inversion unless other factors favor a particular result. (Equation 78a illustrates a probable S_DR inversion by bromine atom at carbon. However, the substrate utilized does not seem capable of reacting by any pathway with a different stereochemistry.)

To form the transition state **46**, the orbital on the attacking nucleophile A, which will eventually bond to B, must overlap with an orbital of B. Overlap integrals, as a measure of the degree of interaction of two atoms through a particular pair of orbitals, vary very much with distance. For overlap through p-orbitals, in which the electron density is symmetrically distributed around the axis joining the two atoms of the bond (σ-overlap), the overlap also varies

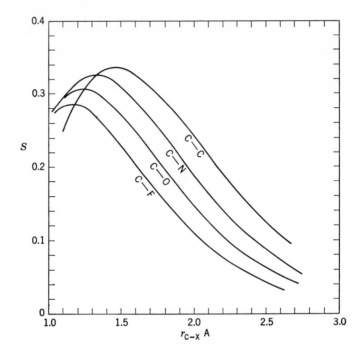

Figure 1.17 Slater overlap integrals for $p_\sigma p_\sigma$-bonds. (Reprinted with permission of the author and John Wiley and Sons, Inc. from Ref. 65.)

with the nature of the nuclei being bonded as shown in Fig. 1.17. Examination of these curves provides some justification for the statement that the transition state distance between B and C is about 0.5 A more than the bond distance, and that the transition state distance between A and B is about 0.5 A more than the normal bond distance. The total bonding energy of the portion of the molecule symbolized by A---B---C is thus not terribly different from the bonding energy of B—C, and the energy required to drive a typical reaction forward can be expended in bending bonds, rearranging solvent structure, etc. The transition state **46** should form less and less easily as the approach of A to the backside of B is hindered. Indeed, S_DN reactions are characterized by a considerable sensitivity to steric effects for the approach of A to BC. Some average relative rates for various alkyl systems collected by Streitwieser are summarized in Table 1.18. The most striking quantity listed is that for neopentyl derivatives which, on the average, undergo S_DN reactions about 10^{-5} as rapidly as ethyl derivatives [S_DN data for *t*-butyl halides

TABLE 1.18 *Average Relative Rates of Alkyl Systems*[a]

Alkyl group	Relative Rate	Log Relative Rate
CH_3	30	1.5
CH_3CH_2	1.0	0.0
$CH_3CH_2CH_2$	0.4	−0.4
$CH_3CH_2CH_2CH_2$	0.4	−0.4
$(CH_3)_2CH$	0.025	−1.6
$(CH_3)_2CHCH_2$	0.03	−1.5
$CH_2{=}CHCH_2$	40	1.6
$C_6H_5CH_2$	120	2.1
$(CH_3)_3CCH_2$	0.00001	−5.0

[a] From Ref. 60.

actually refers to an elimination reaction (*62, 63*)]. In bridgehead halides (for example, 1-bromotryptycene):

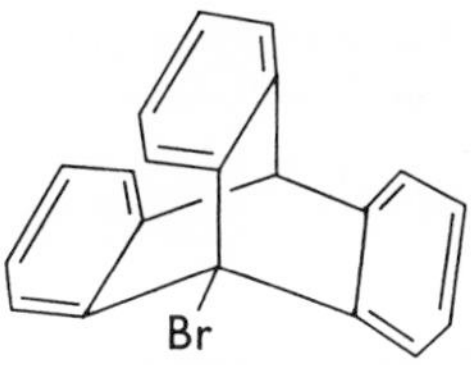

48

the backside is completely blocked and the molecule does not undergo S_DN reactions at all. No S_DN reactions are known for *t*-butyl halides, although such transition states are, in principle, possible.

The rate pattern shown in Table 1.18 constitutes a useful criterion of mechanism. Both bonding and nonbonding (steric) effects contribute to the overall pattern, as indicated by the calculations of Hughes, Ingold, and co-workers (*291*) on the halogen exchange reaction. Fava and Iliceto (*64*) have applied the criterion to the interpretation of the rates of exchange of radio-active sulfite with alkyl thiosulfates:

(96) $$RSSO_3^- + {}^*SO_3^{=} \rightleftharpoons RS{}^*SO_3^- + SO_3^{=}$$

The pattern shown by the relative rates listed in Table 1.19 is so similar to S_DN reactions on carbon that it was concluded that the mechanism of the exchange involved an S_DN reaction on sulfur.

Pryor and Guard (*66*) have utilized the rate pattern criterion in an effort to establish the S_DR mechanism on sulfur (they refer to the mechanism as S_H2). Phenyl radicals were generated from phenylazotriphenylmethane (Eq. 91) and allowed to react with a mixture of dialkyl disulfides and tetrachloromethane. The ratio of phenyl alkyl sulfide (Eq. 97) to chlorobenzene (Eq. 98) in the product was determined.

(97) $C_6H_5 \cdot + RSSR \longrightarrow C_6H_5SR + RS \cdot$

(98) $C_6H_5 \cdot + CCl_4 \longrightarrow C_6H_5Cl + \cdot CCl_3$

The relative rates for a series of disulfides, RSSR, in which R was varied from methyl to *t*-butyl, are directly ascertained from the rate ratios, k_{97}/k_{98}, which are obtained from the product analyses. The ratios, k_{97}/k_{98}, are 31.0 (R = CH_3), 17.4 (R = CH_3CH_2), 16 (R = $CH_3CH_2CH_2$), 3.3 [R = $(CH_3)_2CH$], and 0.23 [R = $(CH_3)_3C$]. Although the rate ratio $k_{97}(CH_3)/k_{97}[(CH_3)_3C]$ of about 150 is impressive, the decrease in rate is far less than might have been expected on the basis of data like that in Table 1.19. We should regard the

TABLE 1.19   *Relative Rates for the Exchange of Sulfite with Alkyl Thiosulfates*[a,b,c]

Alkyl	k_{rel}
CH_3	100
CH_3CH_2	50
$(CH_3)_2CH$	0.7
$(CH_3)_3C$	0.0006 [d]

[a] From Ref. 64. [b] $RSSO_3^- + {}^*SO_3^=$. [c] k_2 for $CH_3SSO_3^=$ at 25°, pH 7.9, $\mu = 0.5$, H_2O is about 2.2×10^{-1} l. mol.$^{-1}$ sec.$^{-1}$. [d] Extrapolated from data at 60° and 90°.

conclusion of Pryor and Guard (that reaction via Eq. 97 is an example of an S_DR mechanism) with due caution.

The S_DN rate pattern criterion was successfully applied by Wiley and co-workers to the novel preparative procedure which they developed for alkyl bromides through the reaction of an alcohol and triphenylphosphine dibromide. The first step is the reaction of the dibromide with the alcohol to form an alkoxytriphenylphosphonium bromide (Eq. 99), followed by a slower reaction in which bromide ion displaces the phosphine oxide in an S_DN reaction (Eq. 100).

(99) $ROH + (C_6H_5)_3PBr_2 \longrightarrow (C_6H_5)_3POR^+Br^-$

(100) $(C_6H_5)_3POR^+Br^- \longrightarrow (C_6H_5)_3PO + RBr$

The neopentyl halide is formed about 10^{-5} as fast as the butyl halide (*67, 68*).

The orbital picture of the transition state shown as **46** suggests that delocalization might stabilize the transition state and result in acceleration of S_DN reactions. Data, demonstrating that this effect can be substantial in magnitude, are listed in Table 1.20. Potassium iodide in acetone reacts with

TABLE 1.20 *Relative Rates of S_DN Reaction of Iodide Ion with Alkyl Chlorides*[a]

Alkyl Group	Relative Rate
CH_3	200
CH_3CH_2	2.5
$1-C_4H_9$	1.00
$CH_2{=}CHCH_2$	79
$C_6H_5CH_2$	200
ICH_2	0.1
$NCCH_2$	3000
$C_6H_5COCH_2$	100000
CH_3COCH_2	36000
CH_3OCH_2	1000000[b]
$FerCH_2Cl$[c]	8600000[b]

[a] From Ref. 257 except as noted.   [b] From Ref. 292 for the reaction of ethoxide ion in 50% ether–ethanol.   [c] Ferrocenylmethyl chloride (**49**), a reactive compound first studied kinetically in Ref. 292.

phenacyl chloride, for example, about 10^5 as rapidly as with 1-propyl chloride. The reaction with phenacyl chloride is shown in Fig. 1.18 to illustrate the overlap of the orbital on the carbon atom at which displacement takes place with the π-orbital of the carbonyl group.

Tidwell and Traylor (*292*) have utilized the delocalization criterion (acceleration of S_DN processes) to establish that ferrocenylmethyl chloride

(**49**) reacts with ethoxide ion by an S_DN mechanism. Their data are listed in Table 1.20.

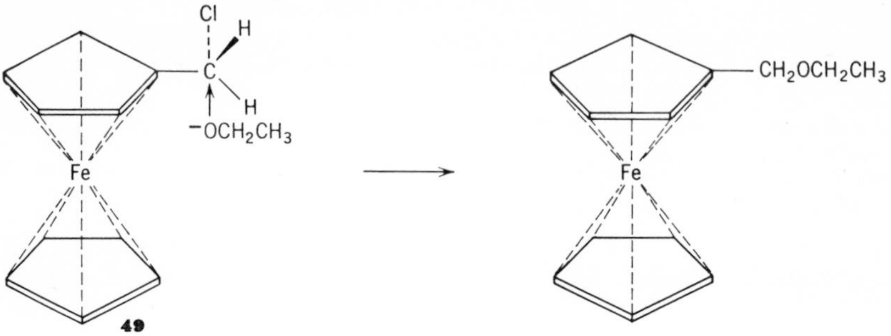

The foregoing discussion suggests that steric effects and delocalization are the chief structural influences (in the organic moiety at B in A + BC) on the rates of S_DN reactions. We can now briefly consider the properties of A as a nucleophile which favor S_DN reactions.

A number of attempts have been made to understand the behavior of nucleophiles by constructing correlations of nucleophilic reactivities with other parameters. Swain and Scott suggested the two-parameter equation,

(102) $$\log \frac{k}{k_0} = sn$$

s = constant characteristic of substrate

k_0 = rate constant for water as nucleophile

n = nucleophilicity of nucleophile

which emphasized that rates were a function both of the character of the substrate and the attacking reagent (*293*). Edwards (*29*) tried to relate nucleophilicity to basicity and oxidation-reduction potential with a four-parameter equation. Another attempt by Edwards (*294*) is similar, depending on basicity and molar refractivity:

(103) $$\log \frac{k}{k_0} = \alpha P + \beta H$$

$P = \log \dfrac{R_N}{R_{H_2O}}$, R = molar refractivity

$H = pK_a + 1.74$

α, β = constants characteristic of substrate

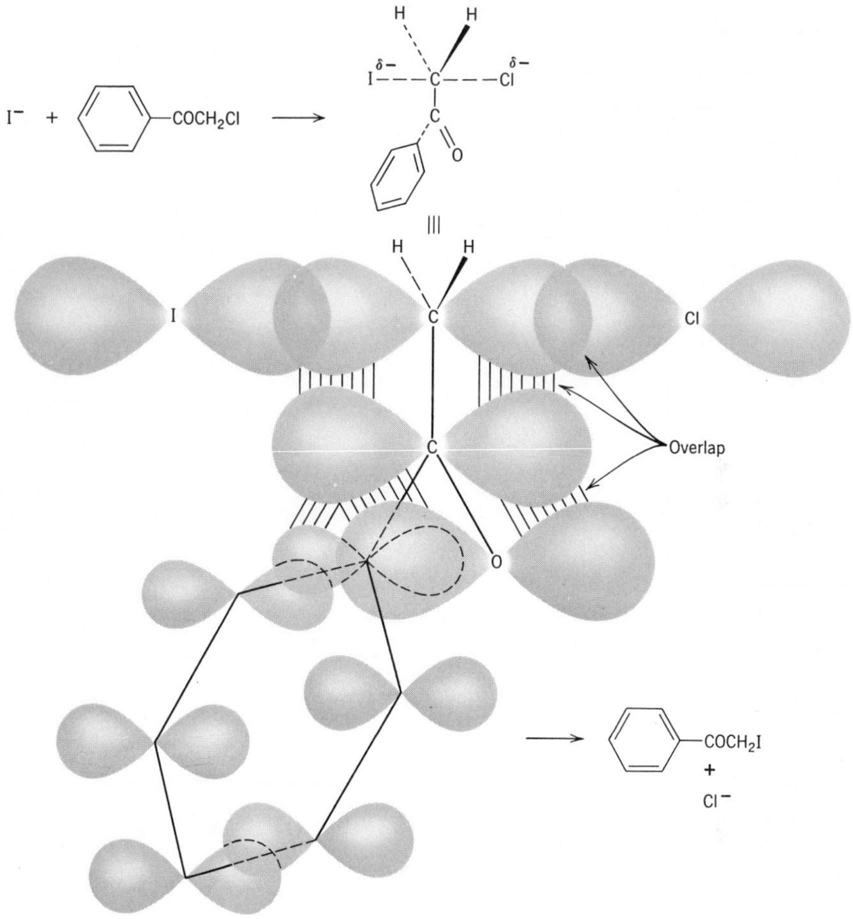

Figure 1.18 The reaction of phenacyl chloride with iodide ion.

Although correlation equations are useful for prediction of rates and for judging whether particular rates are anomalous, they are only qualitatively useful for the purpose of understanding what *nucleophilicity towards carbon* really is. Oxidation-reduction potentials and refractivities are measures of how available electrons are in a molecule, but they cannot in themselves inform us of reactivity toward carbon compounds. Edwards and Pearson (*295*) have summarized "the factors determining nucleophilic reactivities." We shall refer to these more conservatively as factors which underlie a relationship to nucleophilicity. Since it is important to have some notion

TABLE 1.21   *Rates of Nucleophilic Replacements*[a,b]

		Substrates	
Nucleophile	pK_{HA}	Carbonyl Carbon[c]	Tetrahedral Phosphorus[d]
HOO$^-$	11.5	3.3×10^3	1.6×10^3
Acetoximate	12.4	60	—
Salicylaldoximate	9.2	53	25
OH$^-$	15.7	15	27
$C_6H_5O^-$	10.0	1.7	0.57
NH_2OH	6	1.7	2.2×10^{-2}
OCl$^-$	7.2	27	11
$CO_3^=$	10.4	1.7×10^{-2}	1.3
NH_3	9.2	0.27	—
CN$^-$	10.4	0.18	—
$C_6H_5S^-$	6.4	—	1.2×10^{-4}
$C_6H_5NH_2$	4.6	2.5×10^{-4}	—
C_5H_5N	5.4	1.7×10^{-3}	—
NO_2^-	3.4	2.2×10^{-5}	—
$CH_3CO_2^-$	4.8	8.3×10^{-5}	—
F$^-$	3.1	1.7×10^{-5}	Very reactive[e]
$S_2O_3^=$	1.9	1.7×10^{-5}	Unreactive
H_2O	-1.7	1×10^{-8}	1.7×10^{-8}

	Saturated[f] Carbon	Peroxide[g] Oxygen	Platinum(II)[h]
$SO_3^=$	2.3×10^{-4}	2×10^{-1}	—
$S_2O_3^=$	1.7×10^{-4}	2.5×10^{-2}	—
$SC(NH_2)_2$	2.5×10^{-5}	Very fast	8×10^{-1}
I$^-$	1.2×10^{-5}	6.9×10^{-1}	2×10^{-1}
CN$^-$	1×10^{-5}	1.0×10^{-3}	—
SCN$^-$	3.2×10^{-6}	5.2×10^{-4}	4×10^{-1}
NO_2^-	1.8×10^{-6}	5×10^{-7}	4×10^{-3}
OH$^-$	1.2×10^{-6}	i	i
N_3^-	8×10^{-7}	—	8×10^{-3}
Br$^-$	5×10^{-7}	2.3×10^{-5}	(5×10^{-3})[e]
NH_3	2.2×10^{-7}	—	(8×10^{-4})[e]
Cl$^-$	1.1×10^{-7}	1.1×10^{-7}	9×10^{-4}
C_5H_5N	9×10^{-8}	—	3×10^{-3}
H_2O	1×10^{-10}	i	5×10^{-7}

[a] From Ref. 295.   [b] Rate constants in l. mole^{-1} sec.$^{-1}$.   [c] *p*-Nitrophenyl acetate as substrate.   [d] Isopropyloxy-methyl-fluoro-oxyphosphorane as substrate.   [e] Estimated from other compounds.   [f] Substrate is hypothetical methyl compound for which the rate of reaction with chloride ion is the same as that for the reaction of peroxide with chloride ion.   [g] Substrate is hydrogen peroxide.   [h] Substrate is bromodiethylenetriamino-platinum(II), Pt(dien)Br$^+$.   [i] Rate is too low to measure.

about relative nucleophilicities, and it is difficult to set forth in any simple way the role of the substrate in eliciting nucleophilicity from an attacking reagent, we must be content with data on relative reactivities as shown in Table 1.21. Depending on the substrate, basicity, polarizability, and "the α-effect" (possession of a pair of electrons on the atom next to the one performing the nucleophilic attack) appear to deserve recognition as those factors which are related to nucleophilicity towards carbon.

The role of the group which is displaced (the "leaving group") in an $S_D N$ reaction has not yet been well defined. The leaving group must accommodate a pair of electrons, often as a negative charge, and it is natural that a relationship should be found between the acidity of the compound from which the leaving group is derived and the facility with which that group departs from the substrate in a nucleophilic displacement reaction. The rate constant for the solvolysis of methyl perchlorate is about 1.2×10^{-3} sec.$^{-1}$ at 25° in 81% acetone—10% benzene—9% water, much higher than one might expect for the corresponding iodide (*296*). If we could measure the rate of reaction for methyldiazonium ion under the same conditions, the rate would no doubt exceed that of the perchlorate by a comfortable factor. Rough leaving group activities have been reported by Streitwieser (*60*) based on averaging results from a number of displacement reactions. These are listed in Table 1.22;

TABLE 1.22 *Relative Leaving Group Ability*[a,b]

Leaving Group	Relative Rate
N_2	High
$OSOCl$	High
$OClO_3$	~ 2000[a]
$OSO_2C_6H_5$	6
I	3
Br	1
$OH_2{}^+$	1[c]
$S(CH_3)_2{}^+$	0.5[c]
Cl	0.02
ONO_2	0.01
F	0.0001

[a] From Ref. 60. [b] In displacement reactions relative to bromide ion. [c] In ethanol. [d] An estimate quoted by E. R. Thornton in "Solvolysis Mechanisms," p. 165, Ronald Press, New York, 1964.

nitrogen and chlorosulfite are added at the beginning on the basis of their high activity as leaving groups.

Problems

1. Write example of the following kinds of reactions:
   (a) An S_DN reaction on carbon.
   (b) An S_DN reaction on hydrogen.
   (c) An S_DN reaction on sulfur.
   (d) An S_DN reaction on phosphorus.
   (e) An S_DN reaction on nitrogen.
   (f) An S_DN reaction on silicon.
   (g) An S_IN reaction on carbon.
   (h) An S_DN reaction on iodine.
   (i) An S_AN reaction on carbon.
2. Show that the initial rate of racemization in the S_DN reaction of an iodide with an alkyl iodide is twice the rate of substitution.
3. Identify the probable mechanistic class of each of the following reactions:

(a)

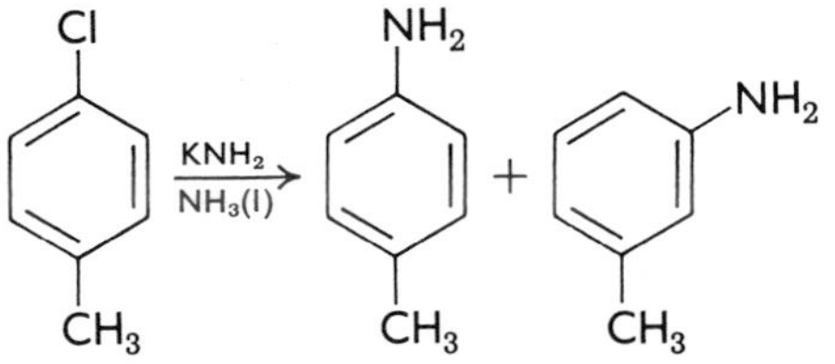

(b)

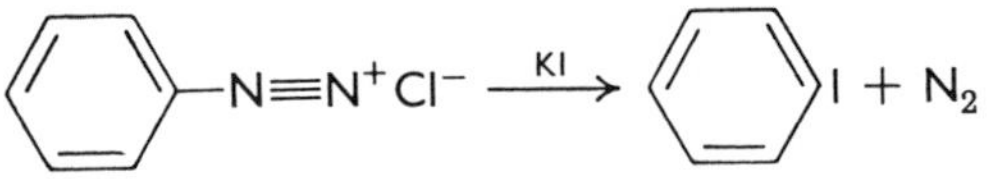

(c)

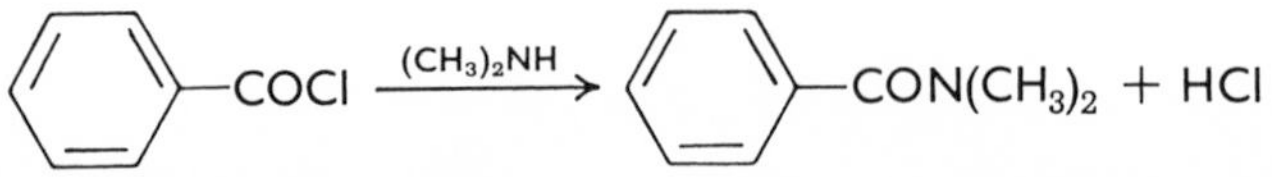

(d) $CH_3CH_2CH_2CH_2OH + SOCl_2 \longrightarrow CH_3CH_2CH_2CH_2OSOCl + HCl$

(e) $CHCl_3 + OH^- \longrightarrow COCl_2 + H_2O + Cl^-$

4. The two phenacyl derivatives, **50** and **51**, react at quite different rates with iodide ion, according to the equations (P4*a* and P4*b*) shown.

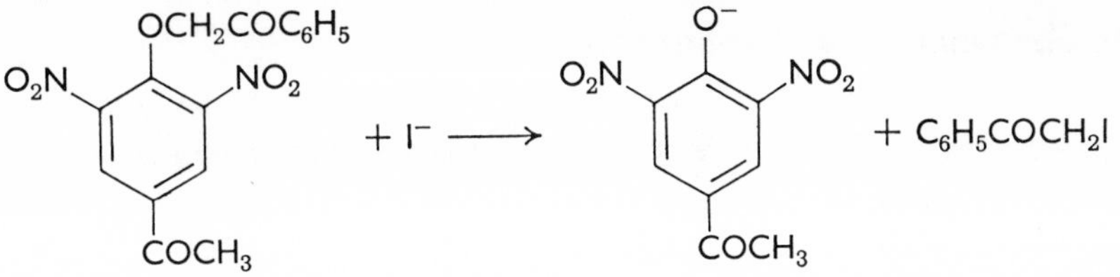

The rates of reaction, enthalpies, of activation, and entropies of activation for these reactions are listed in Table P4.

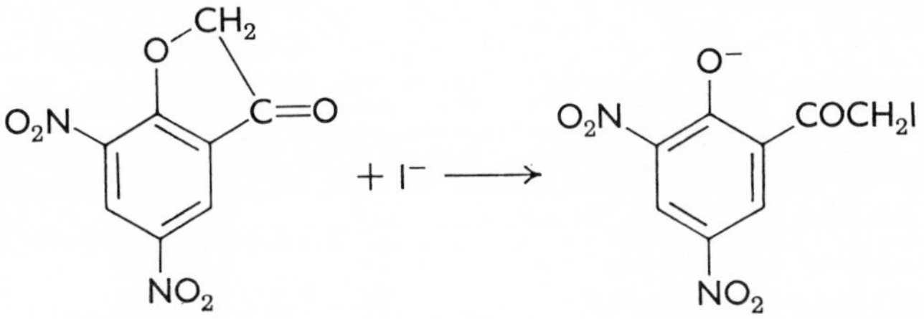

TABLE P4

Compound	Temperature °C	$10^3 k$ l. mole^{-1} sec.$^{-1}$	ΔH^* kcal./mole	ΔS^* e.u.
50	0	11.0	10.2	−30
51	0	0.0012 estimated		
	49	1.6	31.3	25

Construct models or diagrams with which the difference between the reactivities of **50** and **51** can be explained (Ref. 298).

1.5 Carbonium Ion Reactions

The process that we have labeled S_IN proceeds by way of carbonium ion or carbonium ion-like intermediates. The transition state for the formation of carbonium ion intermediates reflects to some extent the nature of the intermediates that will be formed. The accommodation of the positive charge on the carbon atom, which releases the atoms to which it was bonded in the initial state, is a sensitive function of the nature of the system within which the accommodation must take place. Any molecular characteristic that facilitates the acquisition of charge by the carbon atom will make the transition state more accessible and increase the rate of reaction of the compound from its initial state. The investigation of the ways in which the positive charge can be accommodated by an organic structure has been and still is one of the most fruitful endeavors in physical organic chemistry. The chief factors contributing to the stabilization of the transition state and the intermediate in a S_IN reaction are depicted in Fig. 1.19. The presence of a gegenion (counterion, or ion of opposite charge) can provide a considerable stabilization by electrostatic interaction with the positively charged species. The free energy for this interaction may be calculated with Eq. 38. Evidence that ion-pairs intervene in many, if not all, carbonium ion reactions will be mentioned in many places in this book. Specific data favoring the idea that some reactions proceed through two distinct ion-pair intermediates will be taken up in Section 2.10. A set of equilibria, which represents a slightly more complicated situation than that shown in Fig. 1.19, is given in Eq. 104, along with some of the terms used in this book and by Winstein and co-workers to describe the intermediates.

$$(104) \qquad RX \rightleftharpoons R^+X^- \rightleftharpoons R^+ \,\|\, X^- \rightleftharpoons R^+ + X^-$$

	Intimate ion-pair	Solvent-separated ion-pair	Carbonium ion
	Cage ion-pair	Extended cage ion-pair	

The "ideal" carbonium ion will have three sp^2-orbitals at $120°$ angles in a plane perpendicular to that of an empty p-orbital. [This is at least an effective way of viewing the electron distribution and can be expected, on the basis of doing the least promotion (of electrons from s to p) and the maximization of overlap between the central carbon and the groups to which it is attached.] We shall see that the hybridization of the central carbon has a considerable influence on the stability of the carbonium ion intermediate, as reflected in

84

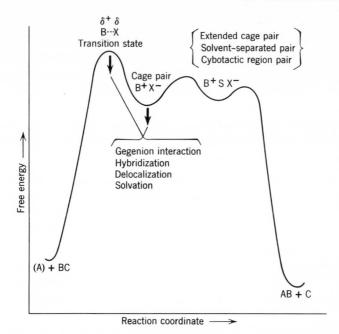

$$\delta^+ \; \delta$$
$$B\text{-}\text{-}X$$
Transition state

Extended cage pair
Solvent–separated pair
Cybotactic region pair

Cage pair
$B^+ X^-$

$B^+ S X^-$

Gegenion interaction
Hybridization
Delocalization
Solvation

Free energy ⟶

(A) + BC

AB + C

Reaction coordinate ⟶

Figure 1.19 Free energy versus reaction coordinate diagram for the formation of a carbonium ion-pair intermediate and the subsequent formation of another kind of carbonium ion-pair intermediate. The arrows represent the lowering of the curves by various kinds of stabilization (listed below) with the relative sizes reflecting the idea that more stabilization is to be expected in the intermediate than in the transition state to that intermediate.

the ease with which transition states can be reached from compounds which, for structural reasons, cannot go to a planar carbonium ion.

Delocalization of the charge at the central carbon is probably the most important mechanism for making it easy to generate a positive charge at a particular carbon atom. Transferring or sharing the charge may be achieved through the inductive effect, conjugation, or nucleophilic assistance from a group within the molecule. Solvation can aid in satisfying the demand of a positive charge at a particular carbon atom for interaction with counter-charges, usually by supplying appropriate dipoles. The solvent is extremely important in the departure of the leaving group by interacting with the anion or neutral molecule, so that the transition state to the intermediate is made easier to attain.

An extreme measure of the ability of an organic structure to accommodate positive charge is provided by the ionization potential of organic radicals.

The ionization potential may be measured by extrapolation of the voltage versus intensity plot for a suitable peak in the mass spectrometer to zero intensity. The method of electron-impact (the process by which species are ionized in the mass spectrometer) is probably the most convenient for radicals, but a number of other methods can be used for more stable species, including the remarkable technique of photoelectron spectroscopy. A general review has been published by Turner (*299*). The ionization potentials of alkyl and fluoroalkyl radicals are listed in Table 1.23. Substitution has a profound

TABLE 1.23   *Ionization Potentials of Substituted Methyl Radicals*[a,b]

Radical	I, kcal./mole[f]
H	313
CH_3	229
CH_3CH_2	202
$(CH_3)_2CH$	182
$(CH_3)_3C$	171
$(CH_3)_2CHCH_2$	193
$CH_2{=}CHCH_2$	188
$CH_3CH{=}CHCH_2$	178
$C_6H_5CH_2$	179[c]
$(C_6H_5)_2CH$	169
C_6H_5	223[d]
CF_3	220[e]
CF_3CF_2	231[e]
$(CF_3)_2CF$	243[e]

[a] From p. 181, Ref. 60, except as noted.   [b] Phenyl radical is included for comparison.   [c] This value differs somewhat from that implied in Table 1.14.   [d] Ref. 70.   [e] Ref. 69.   [f] ±2–3 kcal./mole.

effect on the ease with which an electron may be removed from a radical, as we have already discovered from the data in Table 1.12. The extremely large effect of substitution on the stability of methyl carbonium ions was illustrated in Table 1.14. A comparison of the data on stabilization energies for methyl cations and the ionization potentials for methyl radicals indicates that radicals are also stabilized by substitution, but to a much lesser extent than carbonium ions. The comparison of methyl and ethyl radical ionizations is

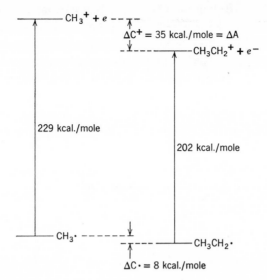

Figure 1.20 A comparison of the ionization potentials for methyl and ethyl radicals. The stabilization energy comes from Table 1.15, and the ionization potential data from Table 1.23. The stabilization of the carbonium ion is shown as ΔC^+ (or ΔA) and that of the radical as ΔC.

shown in Fig. 1.20. Carbonium ion stabilization by a methyl group is equal to 35 kcal./mole, in comparison to radical stabilization by the methyl substituent of 8 kcal./mole. It is interesting to note that the stabilization of perfluoroalkyl carbonium ions by perfluorosubstituents decreases with increasing substitution (*69*).

The magnitude of the energies required to generate carbonium ions from radicals might have suggested that alkyl halides could not undergo an ionic reaction without the stabilization of the transition state produced by solvation. However, the interaction of the gegenion with the carbonium ion in the intermediate and of the partial changes in the transition state is so great that ionic transition states are possible *even in the gas phase*. The interaction energies are estimated by means of Eq. 38. Maccoll (*71*) has made an extensive study of the gas-phase decomposition of alkyl halides. The overall reaction is one of elimination, as in the conversion of isopropyl bromide to propene and hydrogen bromide:

(105) $CH_3CHBrCH_3 \longrightarrow CH_3CH{=}CH_2 + HBr$

The rates for a number of gas-phase elimination reactions are listed in Table 1.24. The criterion which suggests that the reactions may be *quasi-heterolytic*

TABLE 1.24   *Gas-phase Elimination Reactions*[a]

Substance	$\log k_{600°K}$	$\log k_{300°K}$	E (kcal./mole)	$\log k_{373}^{El}$[b]
EtBr	-6.05	-25.6	53.9	
i-PrBr	-4.69	-22.0[d]	47.8	-6.80[c]
t-BuBr	-1.21	-16.4[e]	42.0	-2.51
EtCl	-6.97	-37.6	56.9	
i-PrCl	-4.89	-23.2	50.5	
t-BuCl	-2.49	-19.4	46.6	

[a] Rates are calculated from the equation $k = Ae^{-E/RT}$ using the data of Ref. 71.   [b] Log k^{El} is the log of the rate of elimination of hydrogen bromide from an alkyl bromide in acetonitrile at 373°K, Ref. 72.   [c] Actually the value for *sec*-BuBr.   [d] Log k_{373} (*sec*-BuBr) of -13.7 cited in Ref. 72.   [e] Log k_{373} of -10.6 cited in Ref. 72.

(heterolytic = separation of BC into B$^+$ and C$^-$) is the sensitivity of the rate of elimination to the substitution on the carbon which bear the leaving group. The activation energies for the elimination reactions were used to estimate rates for 300°K. The pattern at 300°K is similar to that at 600°K and the data are useful in developing an appreciation for the remarkably increased rate of reaction observed for the same compounds in more polar media. The rates of elimination in acetonitrile for two compounds are cited in Table 1.24 and show that the solvent is very important in developing the charge-separation required for the transition state (*72*). The transition state for the elimination of hydrogen bromide from *t*-butyl bromide may be written:

Transition state

The maximum rate effect that might be expected for the substitution of a methyl for hydrogen on a carbon attached to a leaving group is given by the extra stabilization introduced by the methyl substituent. From Fig. 1.20, we see that the maximum stabilization is 35 kcal./mole or a factor of $10^{25.7}$ in the rate of carbonium ion formation from the methyl-substituted compound over the compound bearing a hydrogen. We must make a correction for the fact that not all of the extra stabilization will be effective at the transition state. If we assume that half of the maximum is available at the transition state for stabilization, we should then predict that *t*-butyl compounds would react 10^{13} as rapidly as isopropyl derivatives. Using the definition of *Limiting* (*Lim.*) solvolysis as the reaction of an alkyl halide or equivalent derivative with a solvent having the minimal nucleophilic participation by solvent at the transition state (*61*) (S_lN) we find that *Lim.* solvolyses are accelerated by a factor of 10^6, through the introduction of a methyl group for a hydrogen at the carbon bonded to the leaving group (*60, 73, 474*). The availability of rapid reaction rate measuring techniques (*74*) makes it practical to consider the comparison of two halides (for example, isopropyl and *t*-butyl bromides) under conditions for which the mechanism is *Lim.* We may conclude from a consideration of the effect of a methyl substituent on solvolysis rates and gas-phase eliminations that we might expect 25% at most of the maximum stabilization of a carbonium ion to be reflected in an increased rate in an S_lN reaction. The proximity of the gegenion to the developing positive charge at the transition state no doubt diminishes the electron demand.

The gas-phase is not routinely utilized by most investigators for studying the effect of structure on reactivity because such studies are experimentally difficult. We might ask whether or not it is possible to examine the behavior of carbonium ions under nonpolar conditions in solution. The discovery of aprotic diazotization by Friedman and Logullo (*475*) in the generation of benzyne

(107)

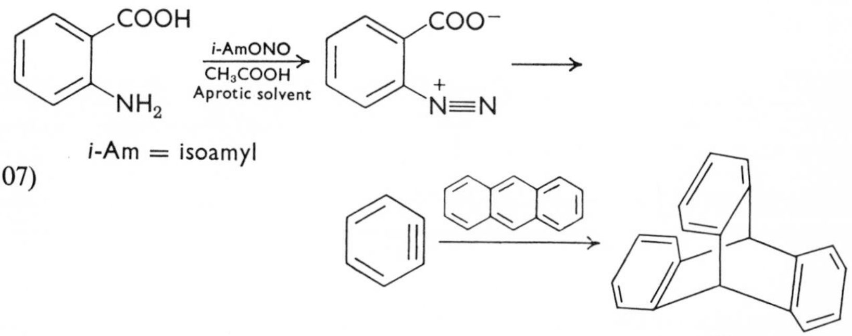

by the route of Stiles and Miller (*476*) led to experiments on the generation of diazonium ions in aprotic media (aprotic save for the equivalent of acetic acid used in the reaction and the equivalent of water produced in the formation of diazonium ion). Aliphatic and suitable aromatic diazonium ions (see Eq. 107) are unstable in nonsolvating media and readily decompose to yield products which are often quite different from these observed for diazonium ions in more polar media. The reaction of cyclopropylcarbinylamine (52) with isoamyl nitrite and acetic acid under aprotic conditions yields almost exclusively the highly strained hydrocarbon, bicyclo[1.1.0]butane (403), as shown (477):

(108)

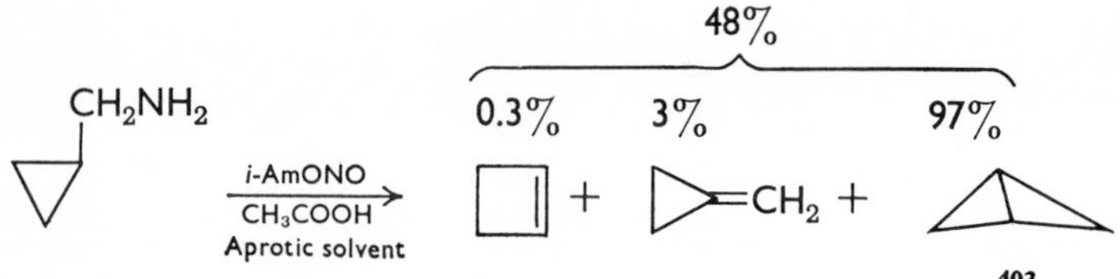

Formation of the cyclopropane rings under these conditions almost certainly does *not* involve prior formation of the cyclopropyl-methylene (see Part 3, Section 3.2), as shown by the almost perfect parallelism in the deuterium contents of methylcyclopropane and 1-butene derived from the aprotic diazotization of isobutylamine-1,1-d_2 (Eq. 109) (478). Later in this section we shall illustrate the fact that solvolysis of cyclopropylcarbinyl derivatives (that is, generation of cyclopropylcarbinyl carbonium ion under protic conditions) yields a mixture of cyclopropylcarbinyl, cyclobutyl, and allylcarbinyl derivatives.

(109)

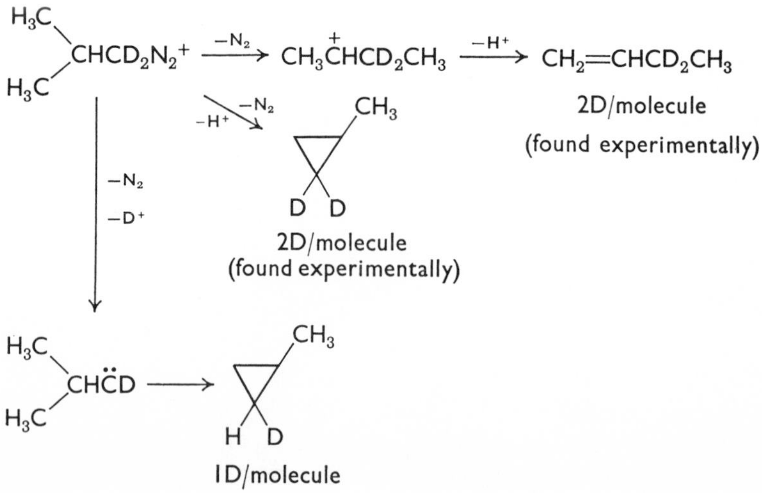

Data on the reaction of primary amines with nitrous acid have been reviewed by Streitwieser (*479*) and present some interesting comparisons for the results from arpotic diazotization (*480*).

Two factors control the degree of stabilization of a transition state (relative to some standard like methyl derivatives) for carbonium ion-pair formation. First, the ability of the groups attached to the carbon which will bear the positive charge to donate charge to that carbon will determine how well the charge can be distributed among other atoms in the molecule. Second, the ability of the central carbon to accept the charge will control how well donor groups can function in a particular molecular situation.

The coplanarity of the groups attached to the central carbon is important in two ways to the operation of the second factor, charge acceptation. Overlap of π-orbitals in the donor groups is most efficient if the p-orbitals are all parallel. In addition, for the reasons we mentioned at the beginning of this section, a planar carbonium ion is intrinsically more stable than a tetrahedral, nonplanar carbonium ion. The first experimental investigation of this point was carried out by Bartlett and Knox (*75*) through a study of the reactivity of apocamphyl chloride (**53**). Although tertiary chlorides normally react very rapidly with silver nitrate in ethanol, **53** showed no sign of reaction after 48 hours at 78°. The reactivity of **53** was far lower than that of tertiary chlorides like *t*-butyl chloride.

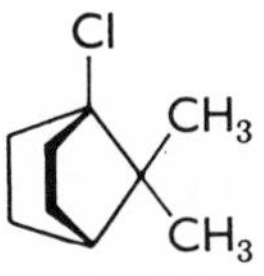

53

Doering and his co-workers (*252, 253*) compared the reactivities of 1-bromobicyclo[2.2.1]heptane (**54**) and 1-bromobicyclo[2.2.2]octane (**55**).

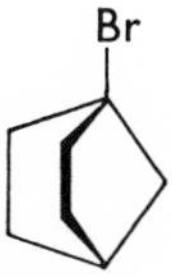

54 　　　**55** 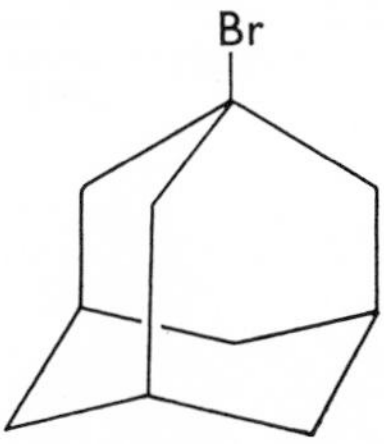　　　**56**

The former, like **53**, was quite unreactive and yielded the corresponding alcohol only after treatment with aqueous silver nitrate at 150° for two days. The latter, compound **55**, produced the alcohol after reaction with aqueous silver nitrate at room temperature for four hours. We can estimate the rate factor for the hydrolysis reaction, k_{55}/k_{54}, as at least 10^7. In all three cases, **53**, **54**, and **55**, backside nucleophilic participation in the formation of the transition state is excluded. The reactivity of **55** must be due to the fact that the transition state for ionization may achieve a greater degree of planarity than is possible for **54**. The *bridgehead* halide, 1-bromoadamantane (**56**), is much more reactive than **55**, with k_{56}/k_{55} of about 10^3. An ordinary tertiary bromide like *t*-butyl bromide (**57**) is still more reactive than **56**, and k_{57}/k_{56} is about 10^3 (*76*).

$$CH_3 - \underset{\underset{CH_3}{|}}{\overset{\overset{CH_3}{|}}{C}} - Br$$

57

If we accept the notion that carbonium ions prefer a coplanar arrangement of the groups attached to central carbon atom, we might briefly examine the reasons why a bridgehead cation cannot achieve such a coplanar arrangement. Bridgehead cations can certainly be prepared and studied: the 1-adamantyl cation (**58**) has been generated from 1-adamantyl fluoride in antimony pentafluoride (*77*). A planar 1-adamantyl cation (**59**) would have angles quite a bit smaller than the 109° 28′ expected for tetrahedral carbon atoms using sp^3 orbitals for bonding and would be less stable than **58** because of angle strain.

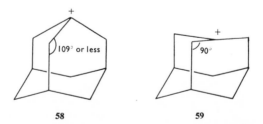

58   59

The extra energy required to assemble a ring with bond angles quite different from those preferred for saturated hydrocarbons is called the *ring strain energy*. A tabulation of data on heat of formation of carbocyclic rings is shown in Table 1.25. *Ring strain* in cyclopropane is smaller than might have been expected, probably because rehybridization of the orbitals causes the ring bonds to be relatively less strained (*272*). Ring strain arises from angle

TABLE 1.25 *Strain Energies in Carbocyclic Rings*[a]

Ring Size	$\Delta H_c/n$[b] kcal./mole	$\Delta H_c/n - 157.4$ kcal./mole	Ring Strain $n(\Delta H_c/n - 157.4)$ kcal./mole
3	166.6	9.2	27.6
4	164.0	6.5	26.4
5	158.7	1.3	6.5
6	157.4	0.0	0.0
7	158.3	0.9	6.3
8	158.6	1.2	9.6
9	158.8	1.4	12.6
10	158.6	1.2	12.0
11	158.4	1.0	11.0
12	157.7	0.3	3.6
13	157.8	0.4	5.2
14	157.4	0.0	0.0
15	157.5	0.1	1.5
16	157.5	0.1	1.6
17	157.2	−0.2	−3.4

[a] From Ref. 249, p. 193.   [b] Heat of combustion divided by the number of methylene groups.

strain and from hydrogen–hydrogen repulsion, of the type that occurs in completely eclipsed ethane (compare **60** and **61**). Hydrogen–hydrogen repulsions cost about 1 kcal./mole/eclipsed pair of hydrogens.

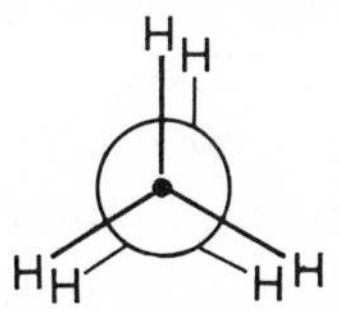

60

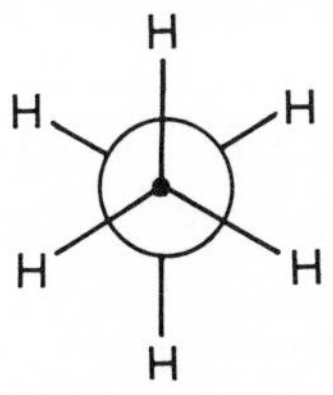

61

Ring strain is apparently responsible for destabilizing the tertiary 3-homo-adamantyl ion (**62**) to the point at which it is comparable in stability to the isomeric *primary* carbonium ion, the 1-adamantylcarbinyl carbonium ion (**63**) (*474*). In the solvolysis of 1-adamantylcarbinyl *p*-toluenesulfonate (**64**) in acetic acid, 94% tertiary acetate (**65**) and 6% primary acetate (**66**) are formed (Eq. 110). The rate of the acetolysis of **64** is about the same as that of neopentyl *p*-toluenesulfonate, and the solvent effect (see Part 2) suggests that ionization to **63** is the pathway followed by the reaction. (By **63**, we mean **63** or ion-pairs of **63**) (Table 1.26).

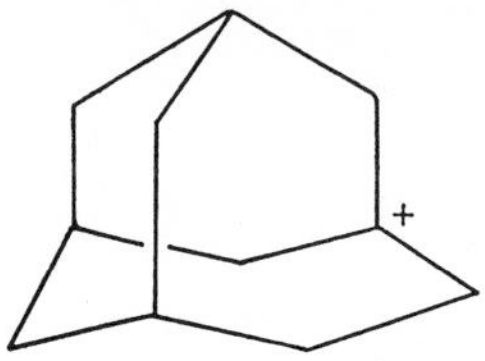

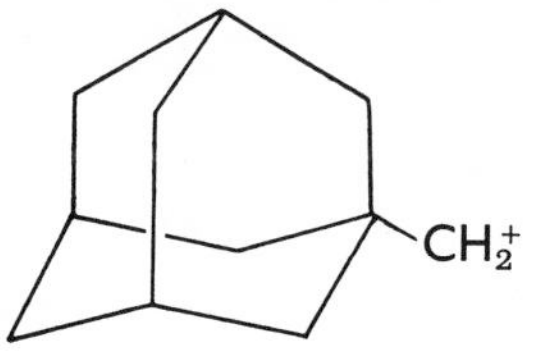

The discussion thus far of how charge may be accommodated in the intermediate for the S_1N mechanism has touched only upon those cases in which the charge left behind by the departure of C (from BC) is localized at the atom to which it was originally bonded. Grob (*87*) recognized a general mechanism for accommodating the charge on an atom or set of atoms other than the "original" one called *fragmentation*. Fragmentation may occur after the rate-determining ionization (Eq. 111) or may provide driving force for the reaction and occur in a fashion concerted with the departure of X (Eq. 112).

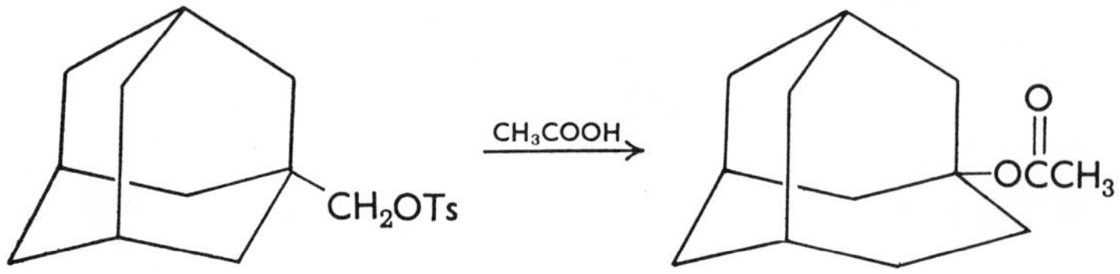

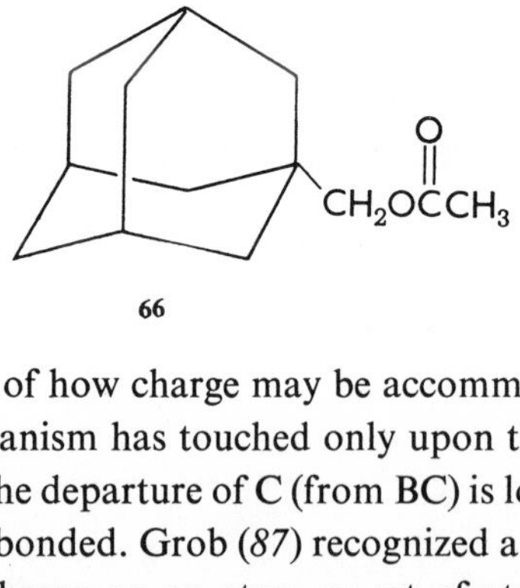

(111)   a—b—c—d—X $\longrightarrow$ a—b—c—d$^+$ + X$^-$

$$\overbrace{\text{a—b}^+ + \text{c} = \text{d}}$$

(112) $\overset{\curvearrowright}{\text{a}}$—b—$\overset{\curvearrowleft}{\text{c}}$—d—$\overset{\curvearrowleft}{\text{X}}$ $\longrightarrow$ a—b$^+$ + c$=$d + X$^-$

a, b, c, d may be carbon, nitrogen, oxygen, phosphorus, or other atoms capable of forming double bonds.

TABLE 1.26   *Rates of Reaction of Neopentyl-Type p-Toluenesulfonates*[a]

Compound	Solvent	Temperature (°C)	k_1, sec.$^{-1}$
$(CH_3)_3CCH_2OTs$ (67)	CH_3COOH	100	1.74×10^{-6}
		75	8.32×10^{-8}
	$HCOOH$	75	1.89×10^{-5}
1-Adamantylcarbinyl OTs (64)	CH_3COOH	100	2.18×10^{-6}
		75	1.38×10^{-7}
	$HCOOH$	75	5.76×10^{-5}

[a] Ref. 474.

"Driving force" can be recognized if the rate of a reaction is faster than expected and is most often assumed to represent stabilization of the transition state of the derivative as compared with a model. The model usually chosen is an alkyl halide of the appropriate structure lacking in those substituents that are supposed to be responsible for the increase in rate. For example, we might estimate the driving force due to an α-methyl group by comparing the rates of ionization of isopropyl halide with ethyl halide and conclude that the driving force is about 8.2 kcal./mole (at 25°C, from $\Delta\Delta F^*$).

The increase in the rate of reaction of a molecule which fragments over that for the model compound is called *frangomeric* acceleration. In the solvolysis of γ-amino chlorides in aqueous solution, fragmentation is favored by the introduction of substituents on the atoms *a* or *d* (Eq. 112), as shown by the fragmentation yields indicated in Eqs. 113–115.

(113)
$$(CH_3)_2NCH_2CH_2\overset{\displaystyle CH_3}{\underset{\displaystyle |}{C}}HCl \xrightarrow[H_2O]{OH^-} \text{No fragmentation}$$

(114) $H_2NCH_2CH_2\overset{\displaystyle CH_3}{\underset{\displaystyle CH_3}{\overset{|}{\underset{|}{C}}}}-Cl \xrightarrow[H_2O]{OH^-}$ (20%)$H_2N=CH_2{}^+ + CH_2=C(CH_3)_2 + Cl^-$

(115) $(CH_3)_2NCH_2CH_2\overset{\displaystyle CH_3}{\underset{\displaystyle CH_3}{\overset{|}{\underset{|}{C}}}}-Cl \xrightarrow[H_2O]{OH^-}$ (43%)$(CH_3)_2N=CH_2{}^+$
$+ CH_2=C(CH_3)_2 + Cl^-$

Delocalization of charge through *p*-orbital overlap is enhanced if the *p*-orbitals are parallel to one another. A stereoelectronic factor is clearly important in fragmentation, as will be illustrated by a number of cases. One *γ*-amino halide that gives rise exclusively to fragmentation products is 4-bromoquinuclidine (**68**). The solvolysis of **68** is almost 10^5 faster than that of 1-bromo[2.2.2]bicyclooctane **55** in 80% ethanol at 40°, and the solvolysis products are remarkable in that they would be rather unexpected in the solvolysis of a tertiary halide:

(116)

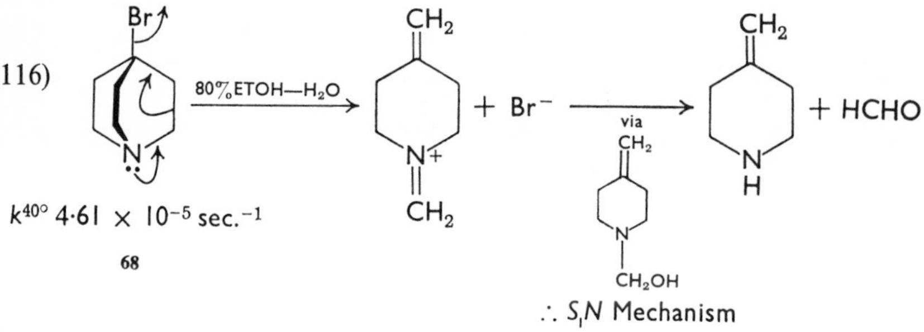

$k^{40°}$ 4·61 × 10^{-5} sec.$^{-1}$

68

∴ S$_i$N Mechanism

(117)

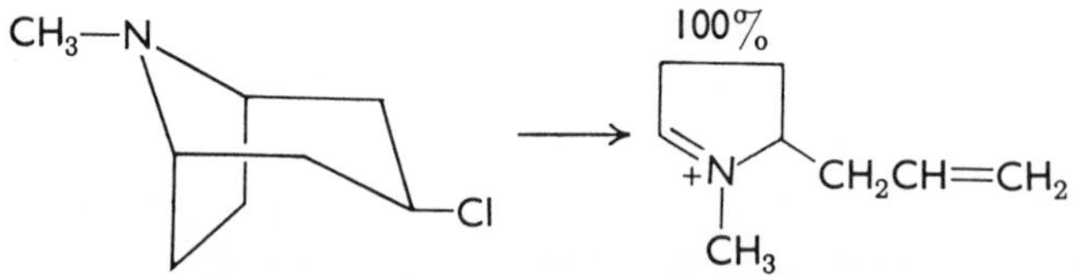

69

The spatial relationship required for the orbitals participating in fragmentation is shown quite clearly by the contrasting behavior of *β*-tropanyl chloride (**69**) and its epimer, *α*-tropanyl chloride (**70**). The *β*-isomer solvolyzes with exclusive formation of fragmentation products, and the rate of reaction is 13,500 times greater than the equatorial 3-chlorobicyclo[3.2.1]octane (**71**) in 80% ethanol–water at 62° (Eq. 117). The α-isomer (**70**) reacts at approximately the same rate as the axial *homomorphic* 3-chlorobicyclo[3.2.1]octane (**72**) and about 645 times as rapidly as cyclohexyl chloride (**73**). [A homomorph is a molecule with a shape almost identical to the molecule with which it is compared. Homomorphic molecules are generally desirable as model

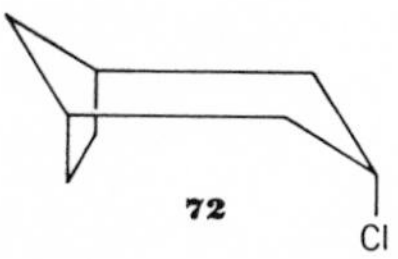

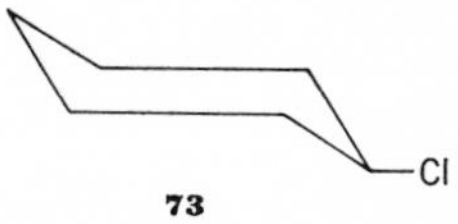

(118)

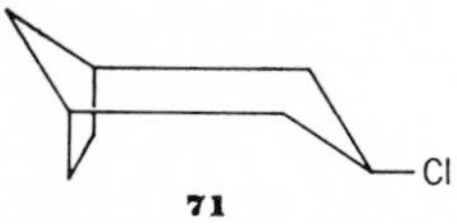

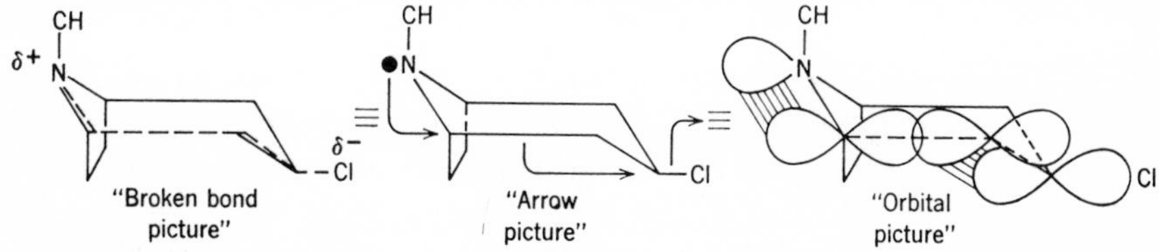

substances or as reference systems for rate comparisons because many structural features of the substrate-solvent interaction are comparable.] The products from the α-isomer are shown in Eq. 118. The transition state for the concerted fragmentation assumed to account for the rate acceleration found for the process of Eq. 117 is depicted as **74**. The reason for the large degree of retention in the solvolysis product of the α-isomer **70** is left as a question to be answered by the student after he has completed reading this section (*726*).

Even with free rotation possible for the amino group attached to the γ-carbon, the rigid relationship of the b—c—d—X portion of the molecule in certain adamantane derivatives leads to complete fragmentation along with a modest degree of frangomeric acceleration over the rates of reaction found for the homomorphic compounds (*88*) (Fig. 1.21). Three arrangements, which one might call staggered, skew, and eclipsed, describe the relationship of the nitrogen attached to the γ-carbon and the rest of the fragmenting system (Fig. 1.22).

Although we have chosen to restrict our illustrations of fragmentation to γ-amino halides, such reactions occur even in all carbon systems and the chemist must be alert for the possibility of fragmentation in a complicated substrate at all times. The aptness of nitrogen in the **a**-position of a molecule capable of undergoing fragmentation is exhibited most effectively when certain steric relationships between the donor and departing groups exist. Favored stereochemical relationships (see the transition state shown in **74**) will lower the transition state for fragmentation as opposed to other reaction pathways in other cases.

Delocalization of the charge into π-systems conjugated with the cationic center is the most effective manner of redistributing charge and results in the

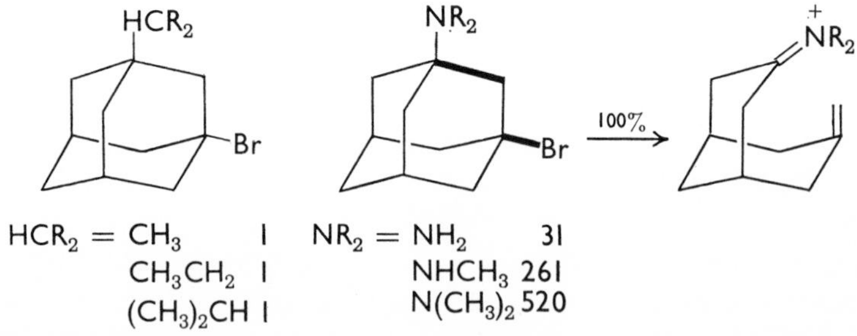

$$HCR_2 = CH_3 \quad 1 \qquad NR_2 = NH_2 \quad 31$$
$$CH_3CH_2 \quad 1 \qquad \qquad NHCH_3 \quad 261$$
$$(CH_3)_2CH \quad 1 \qquad \qquad N(CH_3)_2 \, 520$$

Figure 1.21 Rates and products of reaction of some aminoadamantane derivatives compared with their homomorphs (courtesy of Professor C. A. Grob).

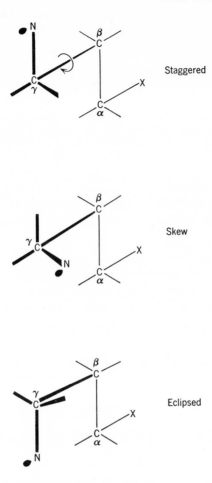

Figure 1.22   Some anticoplanar arrangements of X, C_α, C_β, C_γ and C_β, C_γ, N● (● = pair of electrons) (Courtesy of Professor C. A. Grob).

greatest rate effects in comparisons with a standard system. Indeed, the rate differences between compounds of varying degrees of substitution are so great that it is difficult to obtain comparisons under the same conditions. Table 1.27 presents some rough estimates of relative rates for a number of halides, with structure ranging from 1-propyl chloride to triphenylmethyl chloride. The latter is at least 10^{12} as reactive as the former. However, the rate factor is certainly a lower limit inasmuch as there is no certainty that 1-propyl chloride solvolysis is truly *Lim.* and that the solvolysis of triphenylmethyl chloride under the conditions used was unaccompanied by *ion-pair return*. If

TABLE 1.27 *Effects of Delocalization on Solvolysis Rates*[a]

Compound	Relative k
$CH_3CH_2CH_2Cl$	~ 0.04[b]
$HC{\equiv}CCH_2Cl$	~ 0.01
$CH_2{=}CHCH_2Cl$	1.0
trans-$CH_3CH{=}CHCH_2Cl$	$\sim 2 \times 10^3$
trans-$C_6H_5CH{=}CHCH_2Cl$	$\sim 2 \times 10^5$
$(CH_3)_2C{=}CHCH_2Cl$	$\sim 3 \times 10^6$
$CH_2{=}CHC(CH_3)_2Cl$	$\sim 1 \times 10^7$
$(CH_3)_2CHCl$	~ 0.1
$(CH_3)_3CCl$	$\sim 4 \times 10^4$
$C_6H_5CH(CH_3)Cl$	$\sim 8 \times 10^4$
$(C_6H_5)_2CHCl$	$\sim 4 \times 10^7$
$(C_6H_5)_3CCl$	$\sim 2 \times 10^{10}$

[a] Rough estimates based on comparison given in Ref. 60.
[b] Probably not limiting.

the rate of reaction of an alkyl chloride is followed by the rate of appearance of chloride ion, only those species which reach the stage of alcohol product ROH from separated carbonium ions and chloride ions (see Eq. 104) will actually be counted. The actual rate of ionization may be considerably higher, and it is the rate of ionization to the cage ion-pair which really reflects the degree of stabilization afforded by the substituents to the transition state.

A vinyl group raises the rate of solvolysis far more than a methyl group, presumably because the partial transfer of charge reduces the charge concentration on a single carbon atom. The transition states for *t*-butyl chloride and α,α-dimethylallyl chloride are compared as **75** and **76**. A phenyl substituent is also more effective at raising the rate of solvolysis than a methyl group. Triphenylmethyl chloride is extremely reactive, in spite of the fact that coplanarity of the phenyl groups is not achieved in the carbonium ion, much less in the transition state to the carbonium ion (**77** and **78**).

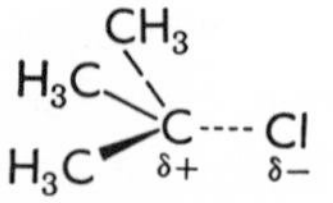

75 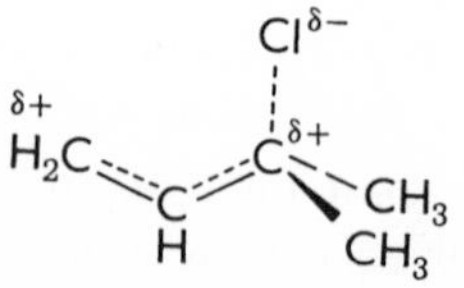   **76**

Direct evidence that the charge is actually transferred or distributed to other atoms from the original center is obtained from the n.m.r. spectrum of carbonium ions and carbanions (see Part 3, Section 3.1). Steric effects must also play a role in favoring the formation of **77**.

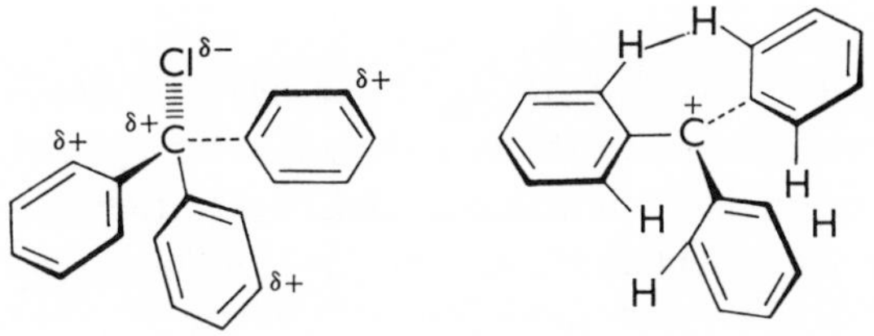

77   **78**

One of the most significant advances in the study of reaction mechanisms was the recognition by Winstein and Lucas (*89*) that substituents which were not directly connected to the carbon atom that would bear the positive charge in an S_IN reaction could play a major role in determining the rate and stereochemistry of the reaction. The only requirement for a group to behave as a *neighboring group* is that the group **G** be located in the molecule in a position which enables it to interact with the backside of the carbon that will bear the positive charge. The *neighboring group effect* results from the *participation* of the group **G** in the reaction. If the participation occurs with an increase in rate over that expected, the rate is said to show *anchimeric acceleration*. We may formulate the behavior of the system GC_nCX as shown in Eq. 119, with k_Δ representing the rate constant for the cyclic reaction (the reaction involving neighboring group participation) and k_c as the rate constant for the reaction without participation.

(119)

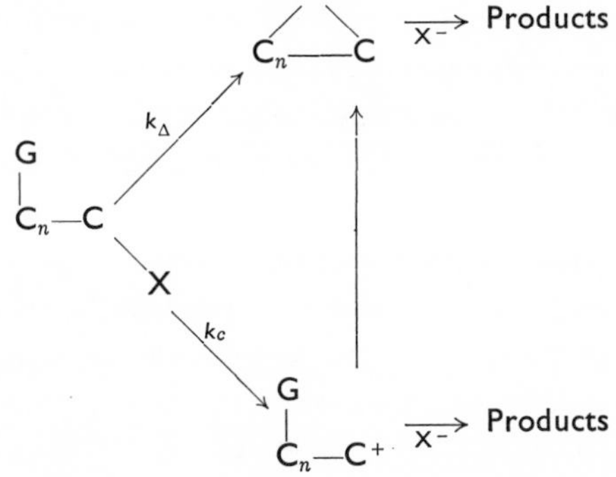

Winstein has proposed that a quantity **L** defined by the difference in transition state free energies for the cyclic and noncyclic processes (Eq. 120) be used to evaluate the extent of interaction of **G** with the carbon attached to the leaving group. **L** is thus the anchimeric acceleration produced by the group **G**.

$$(120) \qquad\qquad \mathbf{L} = RT \ln \frac{k_\Delta}{k_c}$$

We have referred several times to *model compounds* or *reference systems*. Judicious use of models to establish our expectations for a given reaction has been at the heart of much of our understanding of the effects of substituents. The bases of the substituent constants described in Section 1.3 are a few reactions, including the acid dissociation equilibria for benzoic acids. Reaction constants (ρ) are then a measure of how much more (or less) sensitive a particular reaction is to a change in substituent than the reference reaction used to define the substituent constant.

In a parallel fashion, our attempts to understand the rate of S_1N reactions are based on understanding all the factors that contribute to the stabilization of the transition state or the initial state. There is no method known, at present, by which the rate could be estimated, in the absence of all contributing factors for the solvolysis of a molecule which was exactly the same as the molecule of interest, except that it did not exercise its internal ability to affect the rate of the reaction. The current approach to this problem is to choose reference compounds that *resemble as much as possible* the system for which we desire a comparison. However, it is more difficult to do this properly than might seem to be the case. The saturated homomorphic alkyl halides, used as reference compounds for the aminoadamantyl bromide rate comparisons (see Fig. 1.21), cannot have the same solvent shell around the hydrophobic (see Part 2) alkyl groups as exists around the dialkylamino group for which hydrogen bonding to the nitrogen is an important factor. Such hydrogen bonding would actually oppose the development of charge at the nitrogen, and we might surmise that a protic solvent would not elicit the maximum possible response of the amino group in accelerating fragmentation. We shall consider some examples later in this section, which emphasize the difficulty of finding a really suitable reference compound. In the meantime, we must emphasize that the estimates for quantities like k_c must be regarded with caution, no matter how useful and convenient they may be in rationalizing some data about a limited set of reactions. Interactions may be present in the model compound, for example, which are not operative when the neighboring group is attached (cf. *79*). The student should always ask, when faced with a statement about how fast a certain compound reacts: faster than what? How appropriate is the comparison? Are there any factors that do not appear in the molecule being studied, which may affect the rate of the reference system?

In spite of these *caveats*, we shall, for the most part, utilize the reference rates reported or estimated in the literature.

For reactions of the type shown in Eq. 119, there are no specific restrictions on either **G** or n. Experience shows that **L** is largest for $n = 1$, 3, or 4, that is, for the formation of three-, five-, or six-membered rings. The neighboring groups indicated by the symbol **G** can in principle be almost anything from saturated bonds to alkoxide oxygens. Three major classes of neighboring groups can be chosen on the basis of the kind of electrons available for participation. The n-electrons, or nonbonding pairs, are the most effective for anchimeric assistance, followed in effectiveness by the π-electrons. The poorest neighboring groups are the σ-electrons of a saturated bond. A partial list of neighboring groups divided among the three classes, n, π, and σ, is given in Table 1.28.

The probability of ring closure decreases with increasing ring size, since longer chains can be arranged in more ways than shorter chains, and only a few of these arrangements are suitable for ring closure. Thus, the decrease in

TABLE 1.28 *Partial List of Neighboring Groups*

n	π	σ
H_2N	$C{=}C$	$C{-}C$
RCONH		
O^-		
CH_3O		
HO		
CO_2^-		
ROCO	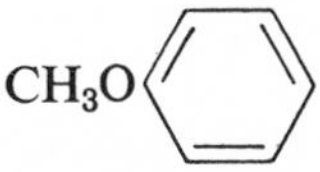 CH_3O—	
RCO		
S^-		
CH_3S	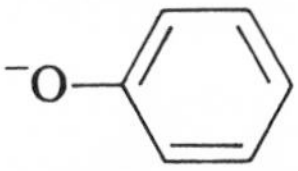 ^-O—	
HS		
Cl		
Br	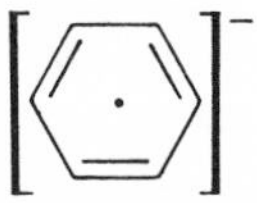	
I		

entropy, on going from the initial state to the transition state, becomes larger as the chain length increases for the process of ring closure. On the other hand, the three-membered ring is more strained than a five- or six-membered ring (see Table 1.25). The formation of rings with seven through eleven atoms is disfavored by both entropy and ring strain, and neighboring group effects, which must proceed through rings of this size, are generally small. The ring strain in rings with seven through eleven atoms (*medium rings*) arises mostly from hydrogen–hydrogen repulsion, because no conformation of any of these rings can avoid some of these interactions in the way that the six-membered ring does with six equatorial and six axial hydrogens (**79**). However, it is important to realize that strain is always distributed through an alteration of many bond angles so as to minimize the energy of the molecule.

H Equatorial hydrogen
H Axial hydrogen

79

The balance of energetic and entropic factors favors neighboring group effects for the formation of three-, five-, and six-membered rings. Rate data illustrating this point is shown in Table 1.29. The rates listed in the table for

TABLE 1.29 *Rates of Neighboring Group Reactions: Effect of Ring Size*[a]

$NH_2(CH_2)_nBr \xrightarrow[25°]{H_2O}$ Products

Ring size ($n + 1$)	3	4[d]	5	6	7
$10^4 k$, sec.$^{-1}$	6.0	0.083	5000	83	0.17

$CH_3O(CH_2)_nOBs^b \xrightarrow[25°]{CH_3COOH}$ Products

Ring size ($n + 1$)	3	4[d]	5	6	7
rel. k^e	0.28	0.63	657	123	1.16

$\langle\!\langle\ \rangle\!\rangle S(CH_2)_nCl \xrightarrow[100°]{20\% \ H_2O\text{-dioxane}}$ Products

Ring size ($n + 1$)	3	4[d]	5	6
$10^5 k$, sec.$^{-1}$	9.2	0.048	1.8	0.025[c]

[a] From Ref. 79.   [b] *p*-Bromobenzenesulfonate from Ref. 80.   [c] Estimated from data in 50% H_2O-acetone.   [d] These rates probably do not properly reflect the rates of ring-closure reactions.   [e] Relative to the rate for *n*-butyl *p*-bromobenzene sulfonate.

the reaction of the compound, which should give rise to the four-membered ring, are maximal, since they probably include a contribution from solvolysis without interaction with the neighboring group.

TABLE 1.30 *Rates of Neighboring Group Reactions Effect of Substituent*[a,b]

$$\begin{array}{c} G \\ | \\ CH_2CH_2X \end{array} \longrightarrow \text{Products}$$

G	L_0[c,d] (kcal./mole)	k/k_H
$HOCH_2CH_2S$	13	10^7
I	8.7	1600
NH_2	8	10^4
O^-	6	10^{10}
Br	4.6	0.4
HO, CH_3O	1.3	0.1

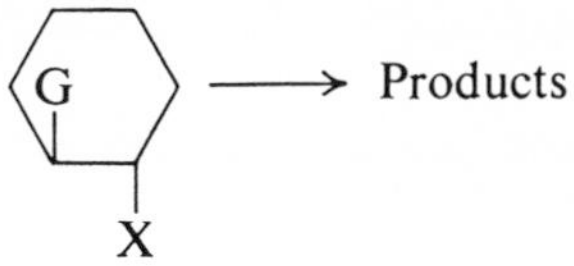

$\longrightarrow$ Products

	(L)[c]	
Cl	0	10^{-4}
Br	3.5	0.1
I	8.5	1100
CH_3O	0.9	0.05
CH_3COO	4.6	0.3[e]

[a] Ref. 78. [b] Ref. 81. [c] Includes both rate data and the calculated dipole–dipole repulsion for the generation of an ionic transition state without participation. [d] Corrected for substitution on the carbons bearing both the leaving group and the neighboring group. [e] $k_{trans}/k_{cis} \sim 10^3$.

The driving force provided by the neighboring group (the anchimeric assistance) varies greatly with the nature of the group (and with the assumptions used to estimate the rate without acceleration, k_c). The driving force L is tabulated for two different molecular situations in Table 1.30. In applying these values of **L** to other molecular situations, we should keep in mind the observations that increased substitution (at the carbon which must formally bear the positive charge) decreases the degree of anchimeric assistance that a neighboring group may provide. Substitution at the carbon carrying the neighboring group may increase the extent of anchimeric assistance. One of the sets of **L** values listed in Table 1.30 is formally L_0, that is, corrected for the effects of substitution at the two carbon atoms just mentioned.

Given the values that we have listed for **L**, we may then look into the relationship of these values to other known bonding properties of the different groups. One straightforward suggestion is that the driving force reflects the strength of the bond that forms upon ring closure, so that we might find a relationship between bond energies of bonds formed between the group

TABLE 1.31   *Selected Bond Dissociation Energies: Diatomic Species*[a]

Species	DH° [b] (kcal./mole)	Species	DH° (kcal./mole)
H_2	104.2	H_2^+	62
D_2	106.0		
He_2	0?	He_2^+	50
N_2	226	N_2^+	200
O_2	119.2	O_2^+	168
F_2	38	F_2^+	> 60
Na_2	18.7	K_2	12.2
C_2	143	Si_2	81 ± 9
Cl_2	58	Cl_2^+	94
Br_2	46.0	Br_2^+	74
I_2	36.1	I_2^+	61
H—O	102.4	H—C	81
H—F	135.8	H—N	86
H—Cl	103.0	H—S	85
H—Br	87.5	C—F	116
H—I	71.3	Cl—F	61
N—O	151.0	Br—F	60
C—O	256.9	I—F	58
Si—O	190 ± 4	I—Cl	50
B—O	187 ± 12	Br—Cl	52
P—O	141	B—Cl	119
$H—O^+$	118	$H—C^+$	85

[a] From Ref. 82.   [b] Enthalpy of dissociation at 25°C.

G and carbon and the driving force L. A comparison of the L_0 values for NH_2 and I shows that they are almost the same, but the bond dissociation energies for CH_3I and CH_3NH_2 differ by 23 kcal./mole. In order to appreciate the meaning of this comparison and the usefulness of bond energies in many physical organic problems, we can consider a few bond energies.

Bond energies represent a way of assigning the total energy given up when a molecule is formed. At one time, the total heat of formation of a molecule like methane was divided by four to obtain the "average bond energy" for a carbon–hydrogen bond, but "average bond energies" are now known to be quite far from the values obtained if a molecule is taken apart step by step, and such average energies are not very useful. The most useful approach chemically is to define "bond dissociation energies" as the energy required to effect a specific chemical reaction under certain standard conditions. For example, the bond energy of the molecule AB is the energy required to dissociate AB into the fragments A· and B·. At 25°C, the bond dissociation energy is DH°. Selected values compiled by Benson (*82*) are listed in Tables 1.31, 1.32, and 1.33. The paper of Benson should be consulted for a critical

TABLE 1.32   *Selected Bond Dissociation Energies: Effect of Molecular Environment*[a,b]

Species RO—H	DH° (kcal./mole)	Species C—H	DH° (kcal./mole)	Species C—C	DH° (kcal./mole)
HO—H	119	CH_3—H	104	CH_3—CH_3	88
CH_3CO_2—H	112	CH_3CH_2—H	98	CH_3CH_2—CH_3	85
CH_3OO—H	102	$(CH_3)_2CH$—H	94.5	$(CH_3)_2CH$—CH_3	80
O_2NO—H	101	$(CH_3)_3C$—H	91	$(CH_3)_3C$—CH_3	80
HO_2—H	90	C_6H_5—H	103	$(CH_3)_3C$—$C(CH_3)_3$	67.5
C_6H_5O—H	85	CH_2=CH—H	103	$C_6H_5CH_2$—CH_3	72
ONO—H	79	HC≡C—H	125	CH_3CO—CH_3	82
ClO—H	78	NC—H	130	CH_3CO—$COCH_3$	70
		$C_6H_5CH_2$—H	85	$HOCH_2$—CH_3	83
		$(C_6H_5)_3C$—H	75	$(C_6H_5)_3C$—$C(C_6H_5)_3$	15[c]
		Cl_3C—H	96	HC≡C—C≡CH	150
		F_3C—H	104	NC—CN	144
		$HOCH_2$—H	93	CH_2=CH—CN	128
				CH_3—CN	122
				CH_3—C≡CH	117
				CH_2=CH—CH=CH_2	100
				C_6H_5—CH_3	93

[a] From Ref. 82.   [b] Broken bond is indicated by a long bond.   [c] Estimated for gas phase. Solution value 11.5 kcal./mole.

TABLE 1.33   *Selected Bond Dissociation Energies Isoelectronic Sequences*[a]

Triple bonds	DH° (kcal./mole)	Double bonds	DH° (kcal./mole)	Single bonds	DH° (kcal./mole)
$N{\equiv}N$	226	$CH_2{=}CH_2$	163	$CH_3{-}CH_3$	88
$HC{\equiv}CH$	230	$CH_2{=}O$	175	$H_2N{-}NH_2$	58 ± 4
$HC{\equiv}N$	224	$O{=}O$	119	$HO{-}OH$	51
$^-C{\equiv}O^+$	257	$HN{=}O$	115	$F{-}F$	38
		$HN{=}NH$	$109 (\pm 10)$	$CH_3{-}Cl$	83.5
		$CH_2{=}NH$	(154 ± 5)	$H_2N{-}Cl$	(60 ± 6)
				$HO{-}Cl$	60
				$F{-}Cl$	61
				$CH_3{-}I$	56
				$NH_2{-}I$	(56)
				$HO{-}I$	56
				$F{-}I$	58

[a] From Ref. 82.

and interesting appreciation of the difficulties in assigning bond dissociation energies.

In general, the anchimeric assistance provided by a neighboring group is related to its nucleophilicity (*29, 85, 293*), but some G groups are so poor as nucleophiles in intermolecular reactions that it is not possible to make any comparisons (for example, σ-bonds).

A neighboring bromine (an *n* group) exerts considerable control over the stereochemistry of the reaction of the bromobutanols. Optically active *erythro*-3-bromo-2-butanol (**80**) yields via a bromonium ion (**81**) the *meso*-2,3-dibromobutane (**82**) (*89*).

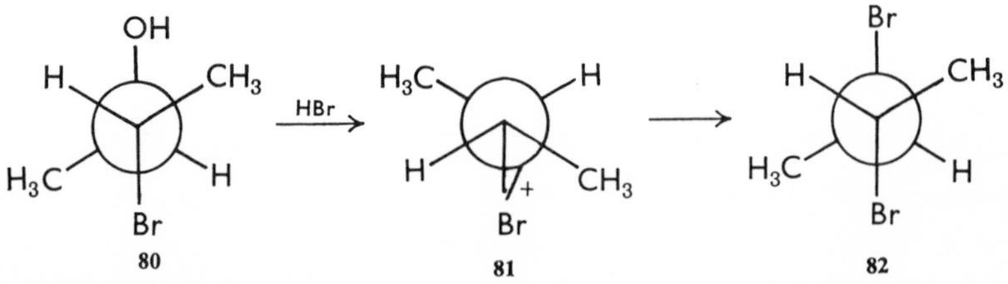

The bromonium ion **81** is the intermediate formed by participation of the bromine in the departure of the hydroxyl group as water. The value of L_0 for bromine affords us some measure of confidence that some anchimeric assistance aided in forming the transition state to the bromonium ion. Optically active *threo*-3-bromo-2-butanol (**83**) via a *cis*-bromonium ion (**84**) formed *dl*-2,3-dibromobutane (**85**) by reaction with hydrobromic acid.

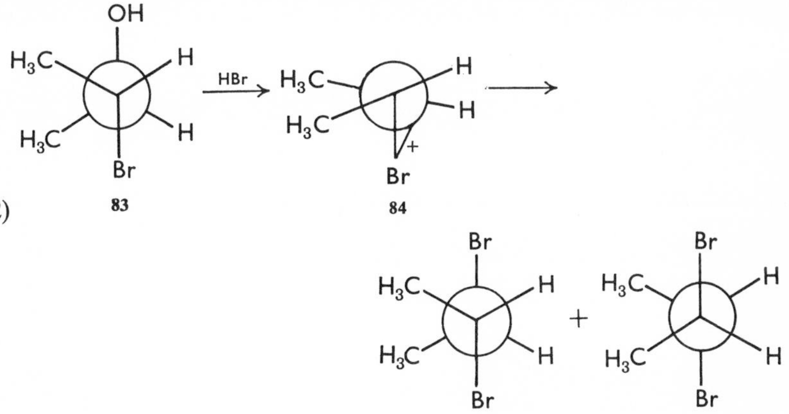

(122)

Typical of the neighboring groups that form a five-membered ring inter-mediate is the acetoxy group. Solvolysis of *trans*-2-acetoxycyclohexyl *p*-bromobenzenesulfonate (**86**) in *anhydrous* acetic acid yields the diacetate of *trans*-1,2-cyclohexanediol (**90**). If optically active starting material is used, the diacetate is racemic. [It has been shown that ion-pair return (Eq. 104) is not responsible for the racemization (*90*)]. Addition of a small amount of water to the acetic acid, used as the solvolysis medium, changes the product com-pletely to the monoacetate of *cis*-1,2-cyclohexanediol (**92**). These observa-tions are readily explained by postulating the formation of an acetoxonium ion intermediate (**88**) (*91*). Participation should be sensitive to the geometric relationship of the neighboring group to the backside of the carbon bearing the leaving group, and it is likely that the diaxial form of **86** (**87**) is an inter-mediate in the formation of **88**. Water apparently reacts with the acetoxonium ion **88** at the acetate carbon forming the *ortho*-acid **91**. The *ortho*-acid **91** undergoes acid-catalyzed hydrolysis to yield the monoacetate **92**. If the solvolysis is carried out in ethanol, the intermediate can be trapped as a moderately unstable *ortho*-ester **93** (*92*). These conversions are outlined in Fig. 1.23. The ion **88** can also be generated by protonation of the ketene acetal **94** (*83*).

If the neighboring group contains a sufficiently basic atom, the inter-mediate may be isolated as a stable salt. Winstein and Boschan (*93*) converted

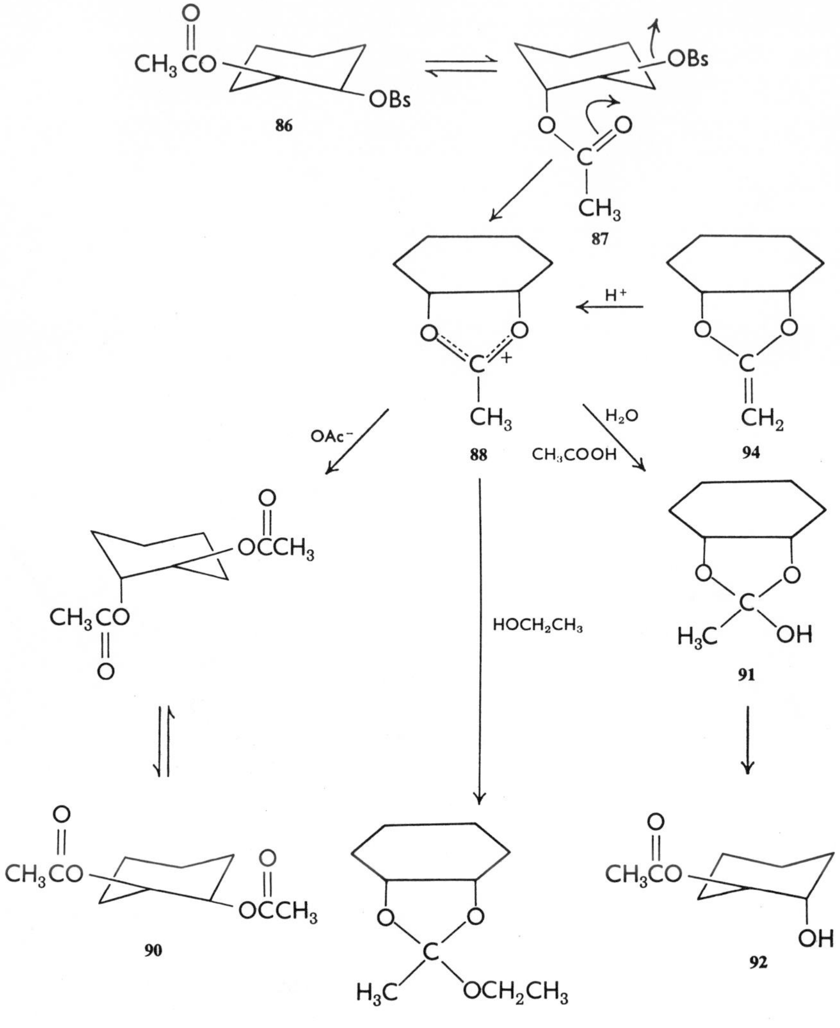

Figure 1.23 Some reactions of *trans*-2-acetoxycyclohexyl *p*-bromobenzenesulfonate with participation.

trans-2-benzamidocyclohexyl *p*-toluenesulfonate (**A**) into 2-phenyl-4,5-tetramethyleneoxazoline *p*-toluenesulfonate (**B**). Hydrolysis of the heterocyclic compound formed *cis*-2-benzamidocyclohexanol (**C**).

One of the earliest examples of a chemical consequence resulting from the participation of the π-electrons of a double bond in the solvolysis of an alkyl

(123)

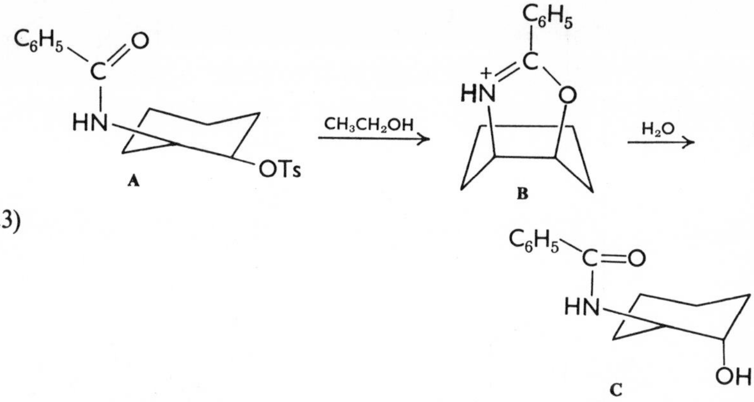

halide through an S_IN mechanism is the formation of cyclopropyl dimethyl-carbinol (96) through the treatment of 4-methyl-3-pentenyl chloride (95) with water and calcium carbonate (84).

(124)

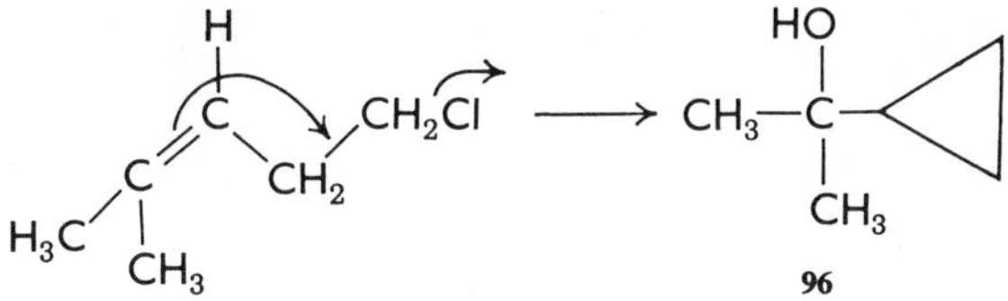

The cholesteryl system is convenient for the study of the participation of the π-electrons of the double bond in solvolysis reactions. Treatment of cholesteryl *p*-toluenesulfonate (97) with buffered methanol produces a mixture of cholesteryl methyl ether (98) and 3,5-*cyclo*cholestan-6β-yl methyl ether (99). (95) The use of buffered aqueous acetone in place of methanol led to the corresponding alcohols, cholesterol (100), and 3,5-*cyclo*cholestan-6β-ol ("*i*-cholesterol") (101). The *cyclo*-alcohol 101 may be converted to the trichloracetate (102) and the latter solvolyzed to yield the same mixture of products obtained from the cholesteryl derivative 97. In addition, the 6α-epimer of 102, the trichloracetate 103, and the *p*-toluenesulfonate of 3β-hydroxymethylene-A-norcholest-5-ene (104) (96) form the same mixture of alcohols as those obtained from 102 and 97 by hydrolysis in buffered aqueous media. These results imply that a common intermediate, shown as the homo-allylic ion 105, occurs in all of these transformations. A homoallylic ion is the

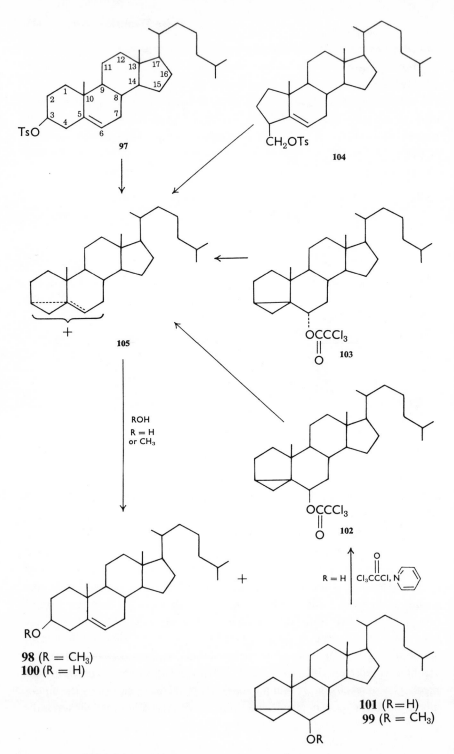

Figure 1.24 Some interconversions of cholesteryl derivatives.

112

*homo*logue of an *allylic* ion and has an additional methylene group between the double bond and the carbon bearing the leaving group. Figure 1.24 indicates the chemical relationships described above.

A series of sterol *p*-toluenesulfonates have been compared in reactivity in order to estimate the driving force due to the participation of the double bond in the solvolysis of cholesteryl *p*-toluenesulfonate, **97**. Rates are recorded in Table 1.34 for **97**, its epimer, epicholesteryl tosylate **(106)**, and the two corresponding saturated tosylates, the β- **(107)** and the α- **(108)**.

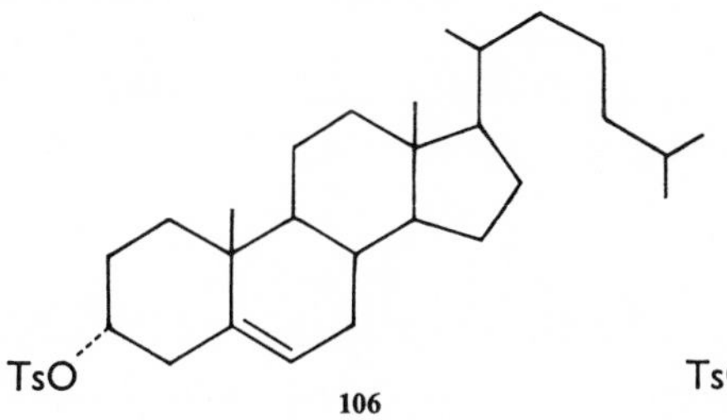

106

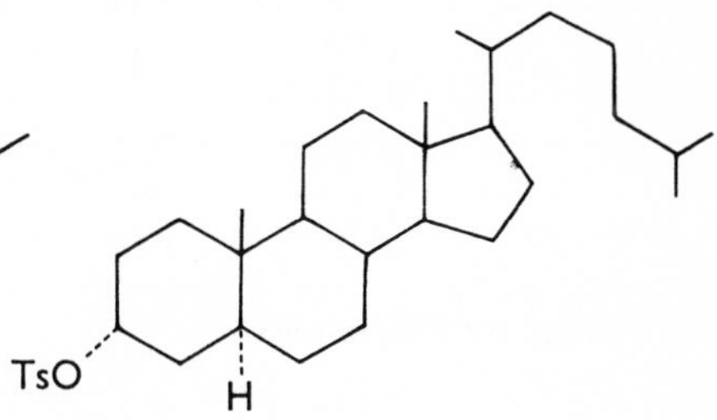

107

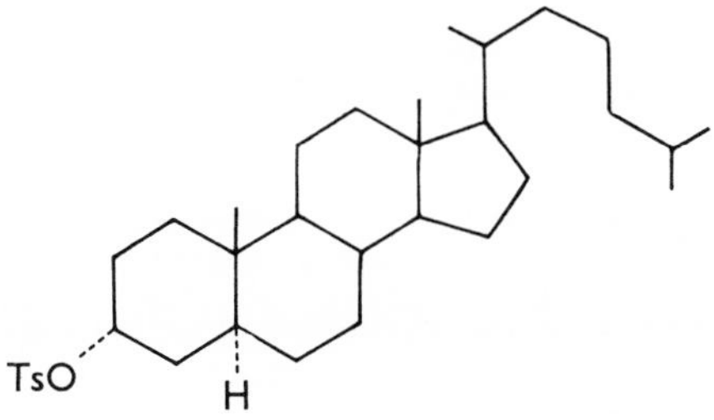

108

Assuming that **107** is an appropriate reference compound and allowing for a possible reduction in rate because of the inductive effect of the double bond (factor of 10?), we may estimate the driving force for the double bond in **97** as 4.3 kcal./mole. For a C_3—C_5 separation of 2.5 A, an interaction of this magnitude is reasonable in comparison to what might be expected on the basis of the ratio of overlap integrals for this separation and the integral at normal C—C bond distances (ca. 1.52 A) (see Fig. 1.17). The transition state for ionization of **97** is shown as **109**. The ion which arises from **109**, the homoallylic ion **105**, is shown again as **110** to indicate the stereospecificity with which it forms products. Only the products of attack from the upper side (the β-side) are found.

TABLE 1.34   *Acetolysis Rates for Sterol p-Toluenesulfonates*

Compound	$10^5 k$, sec.$^{-1}$ (at 50°)
97[a]	13.2
106[b]	3.02
107[c]	0.107
108[d]	0.707

[a] Ref. 101. [b] Ref. 102. Also reported as 2.55×10^{-5} sec.$^{-1}$ in Ref. 103. [c] A. H. Schlesinger, unpublished results communicated by Prof. S. Winstein. [d] N. J. Holness, unpublished results communicated by Prof. S. Winstein.

The ease with which the trichloroacetate esters **102** and **103** solvolyze to the cation **105** implies that the cyclopropyl group is extremely effective at promoting the ionization of leaving groups from the carbon next to the cyclopropyl ring. The high reactivity of cyclopropylmethyl chloride (**111**) was discovered by Roberts and Mazur (*97*), who found that the products of solvolysis were cyclopropylmethanol (**112**), cyclobutanol (**113**), and 3-butenol (**114**) (Eq. 125). The tertiary ester, *tris*-cyclopropyl methyl *p*-nitrobenzoate (**115**), is estimated to react about 10^7 faster than *tris*-isopropylmethyl *p*-nitrobenzoate (**116**) (*98, 99*). The product of solvolysis of **115** is the tertiary alcohol (**118**), and the presumed intermediate in the solvolysis, the carbonium ion (**117**), is stable enough to be generated and examined in moderately concentrated sulfuric acid (*100*) (Eq. 126).

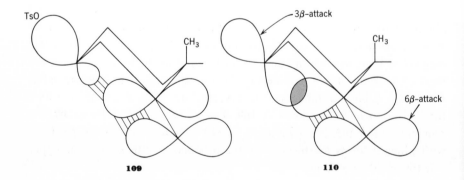

$$(125) \quad \underset{111}{\overset{CH_2Cl}{\triangle}} \xrightarrow[\text{buffer}]{H_2O} \underset{112}{\overset{CH_2OH}{\triangle}} + \underset{113}{\square^{OH}} + \underset{114}{CH_2{=}CHCH_2CH_2OH}$$

(126)

$$\underset{115}{\triangle{-}\underset{\triangle}{\overset{\triangle}{C}}{-}O\overset{O}{\overset{\|}{C}}{\bigcirc}NO_2} \longrightarrow \underset{117}{\triangle{-}\underset{\triangle}{\overset{\triangle}{C^+}}} \underset{H^+}{\rightleftarrows} \underset{118}{\triangle{-}\underset{\triangle}{\overset{\triangle}{C}}{-}OH}$$

$$\underset{116}{(CH_3)_2CH{-}\underset{CH(CH_3)_2}{\overset{CH(CH_3)_2}{C}}{-}O\overset{O}{\overset{\|}{C}}{\bigcirc}NO_2}$$

With the rate factor just cited, *tris*-cyclopropylmethyl derivatives should be more reactive than triphenylmethyl derivatives (relative $k \sim 4 \times 10^{11}$ or more for the former versus $\sim 2 \times 10^{10}$ for the latter, Table 1.27). In qualitative agreement with this expectation, the equilibrium between the alcohol **118** and the carbonium **117** in sulfuric acid (Eq. 126 right half) results in equal quantities of **117** and **118** in 22% sulfuric acid. Equivalent quantities of triphenylmethyl cation **78** and the alcohol **119** are established only at 50% sulfuric acid (*518*).

$$(127) \qquad (C_6H_5)_3COH + H_3O^+ = (C_6H_5)_3C^+ + 2\,H_2O$$
$$\qquad\qquad \underset{119}{} \qquad\qquad\qquad \underset{78}{}$$

The interaction of the cyclopropyl group with an α-cationic center has a preferred geometry for maximum effect. Kosower and Ito (*104*) examined the $\pi \to \pi^*$ transitions of two different cyclopropyl ketones, **120** and **121**. Formula **120**, with the plane of the cyclopropyl ring parallel to the π-orbital of the carbonyl group, absorbs light at a considerably longer wavelength (λ_{max} 1945 A, isooctane) than **121** (λ_{max} 1880 A, isooctane). The ground state for **121** should be higher than that of **120** in energy due to ring strain. The electronic transition should transfer charge from a region of bond strain to an unstrained region and we might have predicted that **121** should absorb at longer wavelengths than **120**. The greater substitution on the cyclopropyl ring of **121** should also favor a lower energy transition. We conclude that the favorable geometric arrangement in **120** for interaction between the cyclopropyl ring and the carbonyl group outweigh these other considerations. We may write the transition as **120** → **122**.

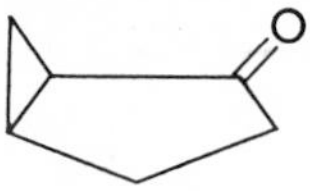

| 121 | 120 | 122 |

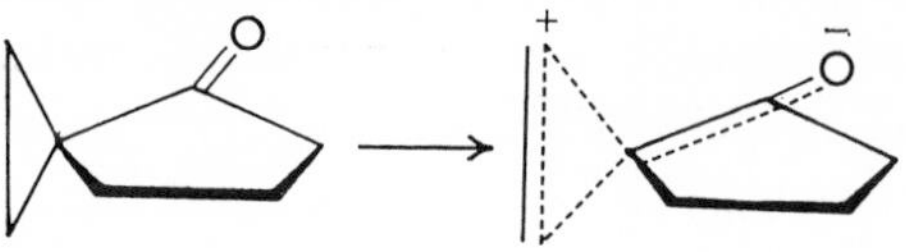

The cyclopropyl group exerts an influence over the rate of ionization of *t*-cumyl chlorides (Eq. 56) at a *para*-position of the phenyl group. Brown and Cleveland (*481*) found that the increase in rate due to the cyclopropyl group

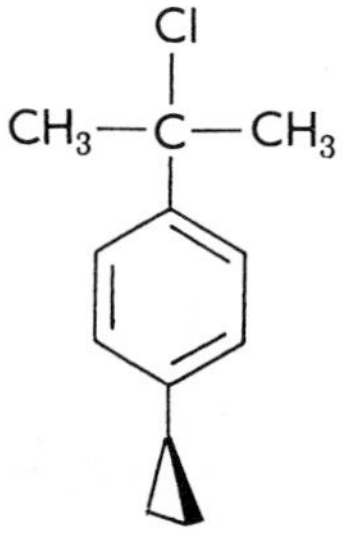

| 123 | 124 | 125 |

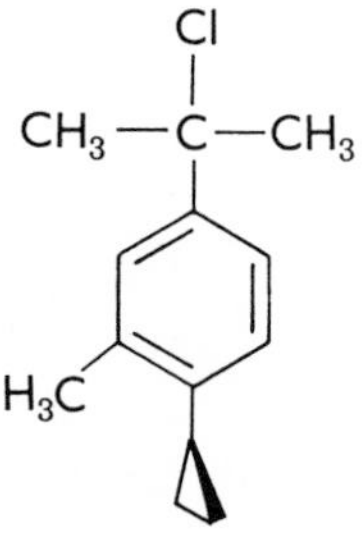

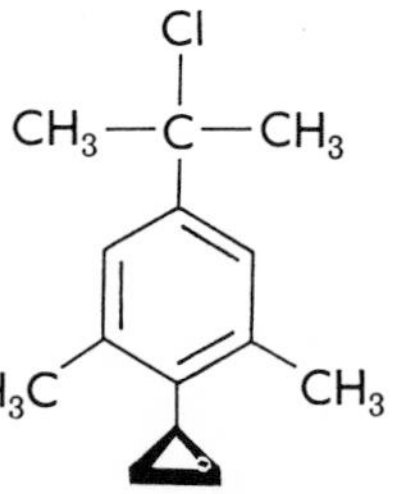

could almost be abolished by the introduction of methyl groups into the 3- and 5-positions of the ring. These additional groups effect a steric inhibition of the interaction of the cyclopropyl group with the developing cationic

TABLE 1.35 *Rates of Solvolysis of t-Cumyl Chlorides*[a,b]

t-Cumyl Chloride	$10^5 k$, sec.$^{-1}$	Rel k
4-H	12.4	1.00
4-Isopropyl	221	17.8
3-Methyl	24.8	2.00
4-Cyclopropyl	1947	157
3-Methyl-4-Cyclopropyl	2133	172
3,5-Dimethyl	47.3	3.9
3,5-Dimethyl-4-Cyclopropyl	460	37.1

[a] Ref. 481.   [b] In 90% aqueous dioxane at 25°C.

center, as might have been expected from the formulation of the excited state **122**. Rate data for a variety of *t*-cumyl chlorides (for example, **123–125**) are listed in Table 1.35. The relative positions of the cyclopropyl rings in **123** and **124** allow maximal interaction between the ring and the phenyl group.

The results from steric inhibition of cyclopropyl interaction with the phenyl ring and from the ultraviolet spectrum of **120** suggest a symmetrical acquisition of charge by the cyclopropyl ring, in contrast to the unsymmetrical structure suggested for the homoallylic ion intermediate **105**. In spite of the suggestion that some more symmetrical distribution of charge in **105** is possible than that shown in **105**, on the basis of the transformation of **104** into **105** through the transition state **126**, the unsymmetrical structure **105** is preferred on the grounds that the products arise always from reaction at C_3 and C_5.

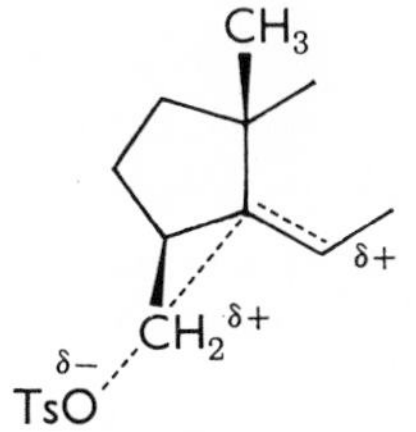

$$CH_3$$

$$\delta-\quad CH_2{}^{\delta+}$$

$$TsO$$

126

Good support for the idea of a symmetrical contribution from the cyclopropyl group to an adjacent cationic center comes from extensive studies of the effects of substitution in the cyclopropyl ring on the rate of solvolysis of cyclopropylmethyl 3,5-dinitrobenzoates carried out by Schleyer and Van Dine (*482*) and summarized in Fig. 1.25. The effect of the introduction of a single methyl group is indicated by the numbers next to the arrows near **127**, a cyclopropylmethyl derivative. There is almost no stereospecificity in the effect of charge stabilization by the extra methyl group, *cis*- and *trans*-methyl groups having about the same accelerative effect. An α-methyl is almost as effective at increasing the solvolysis rate as it is in other systems (see Table 1.27), but the ring methyls cause only a modest change in rate. The size of the increase is maintained for a second methyl group (**128** and **129**). The rate effects are shown next to the appropriate formulas in Fig. 1.25. These results favor the symmetrical intermediate (**130**), but it must be emphasized that the extent of charge distribution to the carbons, at which the methyl substituents are located in the transition state, must be quite small. A small positive charge at those positions would not have severe geometric requirements and would

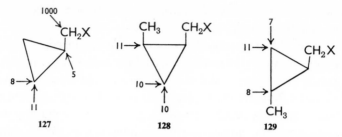

Figure 1.25 Relative rates of solvolysis of cyclopropylmethyl 3,5-dinitrobenzoates in 60% aqueous acetone at 100°C. The compound without added substituents reacts with a rate constant of 4.30×10^{-7} sec.$^{-1}$ (Ref. 482). The arrows point to numbers which signify the factor by which the rate is increased by a methyl introduced at that position.

not be easily saturated by the addition of more methyl groups as electron-supplying substituents.

A symmetrical intermediate is favored by the findings of Vogel and Roberts (*483*) that deamination of optically active 1-cyclopropylethylamine and solvolysis of 1-methyl-4(-1-cyclopropylethoxy)-pyridinium iodide (**131**) led to 1-cyclopropylethanol with almost no optical activity. The intermediate is shown as **130** in two forms. Richey and Richey (*494*) support the postulate of a symmetrical intermediate with the finding that optically active 1-cyclo-

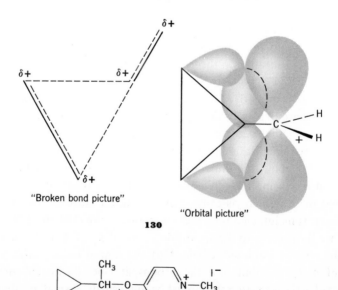

propylethanol racemizes at the same rate as it exchanges, using H_2O^{18} as tracer, in an aqueous perchloric acid medium.

The apparent contradiction between the large acceleration in rate of ionization, arising from the presence of a cyclopropyl ring next to a potential cationic center and the small extent of charge delocalization into the ring at the transition state, can be resolved if we accept the conclusion of Winstein and Kosower (*106*) that relief of ring strain is responsible for a major part of the effect of a cyclopropyl substituent. Although there is a very large difference between the reactivities of the isomeric chlorides, cholesteryl chloride (**132**) and 3,5-cyclocholestan-6β-yl chloride (**133**), it is possible to measure the rates of solvolysis of both halides and extrapolate the results to a set of comparable conditions. The *cyclo* chloride **133** reacts at a rate $10^{7.4}$ times as great as that of cholesteryl chloride **132**. The preparation of the *cyclo* chloride **133** from the alcohol and thionyl chloride in ether (see the discussion in Section 2.10) (*102*, *103*, *105*) always produces about 15% cholesteryl chloride **132**. Knowledge of the mechanism permits the conclusion that the two chlorides were formed by collapse of an intermediate ion-pair (or set of readily interconvertible ion-pairs). These data allow an estimate of the difference in the ground-state free energies of **132** and **133**, according to the relationships shown in Eqs. 128, 129, and 130.

(128)

(Only portions of the A and B rings are shown. See Fig. 1.24.)

(129)
$$K = \frac{6\beta\ (\mathbf{133})}{3\beta\ (\mathbf{132})} = \left(\frac{k_3}{k_6}\right)\left(\frac{k_{-6}}{k_{-3}}\right) = R \cdot P$$

R = reactivity ratio; P = partition factor

The reactivity ratio is simply the ratio of solvolysis rates which could be corrected for ion-pair return. The partition factor is the ratio of yields of 6β and 3β products and is presumed to represent at least a minimum value for the ratio of the rates of reaction of the intermediate to form these two products. The free-energy difference between the ground states is given by

(130)
$$\Delta F = RT \ln K$$

and is estimated to be about 9 kcal./mole. Apparently the overlap suggested by **130** can relieve a portion of the ring strain without much transfer of charge occurring in the transition state. We may conclude that *both* relief of strain and charge delocalization play a part in the rate effects produced by an α-cyclopropyl group.

From the careful examination of data for a few reactions, it is possible to obtain an idea of the interaction energy arising from participation of a π-bond and a notion of how this compares with solvent participation at the transition state in an S_DN reaction. The rate of reaction of 4-methyl-3-pentenyl tosylate (**134**) in acetic acid is 1200 times greater than that for ethyl tosylate in the same solvent (*94*). The products of reaction of **134** are those predicted for participation of the double bond (Eq. 131). Anchimeric assistance in this case is so effective that it is difficult to judge how much better the double bond is for stabilizing the transition state than the solvent.

(131)   **134**

The rate of solvolysis of 3-butenyl tosylate (**135**) in formic acid is only 3.7 times the rate of reaction of 1-butyl tosylate (**136**). Two facts may be brought forward to suggest that the reaction of butyl tosylate with formic acid involves a considerable degree of nucleophilic solvent attack at the transition state: (1) the effect of solvent change (acetic acid to formic acid) on the rate of solvolysis of 1-butyl *p*-bromobenzenesulfonate(brosylate) is less ($m = 0.38$, see Part 2, Section 2.6) than would be expected for ionization of a primary system ($m = 0.77$ for neopentyl tosylate, *474*) and (2) the effect of α-methyl substitution (comparing isopropyl tosylate with ethyl tosylate in formic acid, *60*) is far less than the 10^4–10^6 which might be expected for the comparison of two S_IN reactions, the rate factor being about 200. The products of solvolysis of 3-butenyl tosylate (**135**) in formic acid are cyclopropylmethyl formate, cyclobutyl formate, and 3-butenyl formate (**141**) (Eq. 132). Although some uncertainty exists about the precise product composition because the cyclic compounds were not completely stable under the conditions of the reaction, the products from **135** almost correspond to the products from cyclobutyl tosylate under the same conditions (*114*) (Eq. 133). The latter set of products is about what might have been predicted for solvolysis through the set of carbonium ions typified by **130**. The discrepancy in the proportion of 3-butenyl formate formed by the reaction of Eq. 132 and the reaction of Eq. 133 must be due to direct displacement by the solvent in an S_DN mechanism. The preferred transition state for the reaction of **135** must be **137** with a small proportion of the product formed via **140**. The transition state for the reaction of 1-butyl tosylate with the solvent must be **138**, assuming that the conformational arrangement shown allows more effective approach of the solvent to the backside of the carbon bearing the leaving group than the most probable initial-state conformation. The initial states and transition states for the reaction of 3-butenyl tosylate and 1-butyl tosylate are collected in Fig. 1.26.

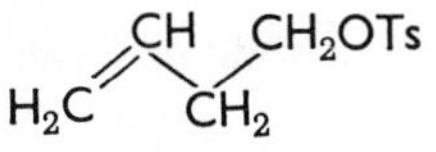

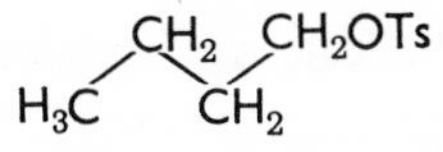

S_IN-*Transition states*$-S_DN$

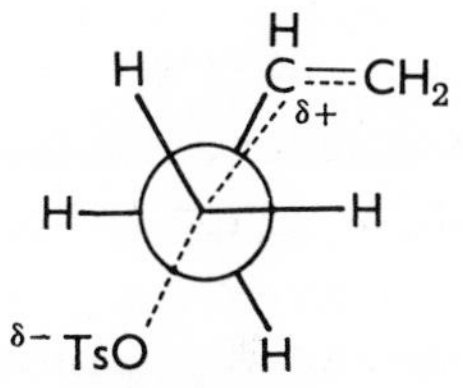

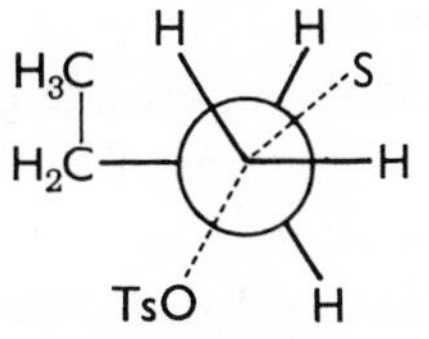

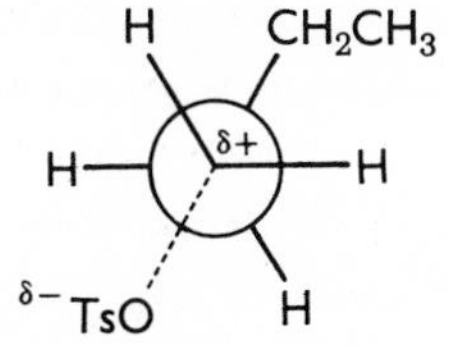

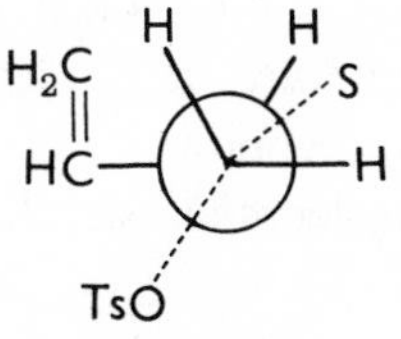

Figure 1.26 Initial states and transition states for the solvolysis of 3-butenyl tosylate and 1-butyl tosylate.

$$H_2C = \underset{CH_2}{\overset{CH}{\diagdown\diagup}} CH_2OTs \xrightarrow[\text{HCOOH}]{50°}$$

(132)

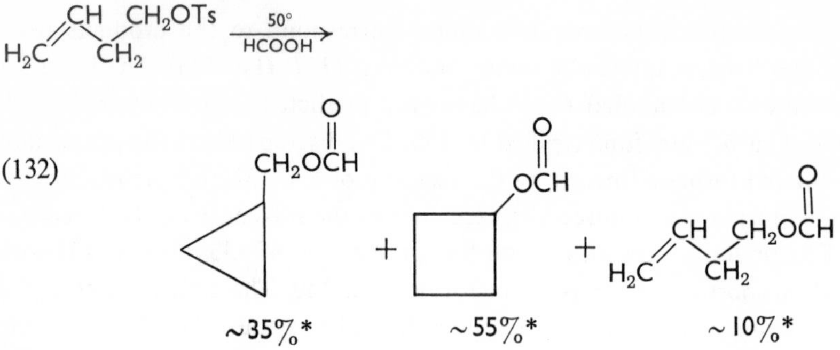

$\sim 35\%*$ $\qquad$ $\sim 55\%*$ $\qquad$ $\sim 10\%*$

141

(133)

$\xrightarrow[\text{HCOOH}]{50°}$ $43\%*$ $\qquad$ $52\%*$ $\qquad$ $5\%*$

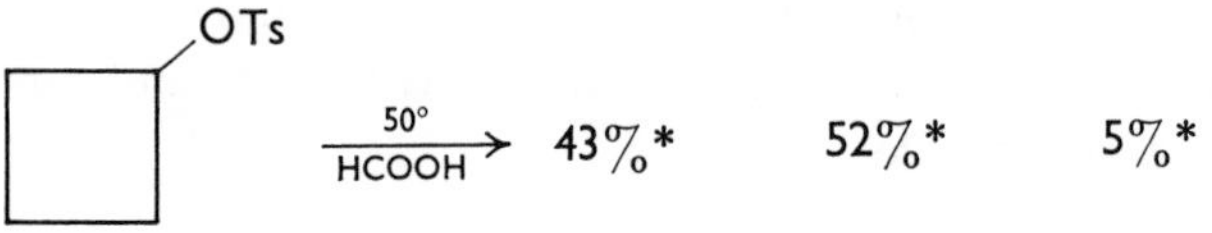

The asterisk indicates an estimate for zero sodium formate concentration.

To illustrate the relative positions of the transition-state free energies, we have assumed in the construction of Fig. 1.27 that all of the initial states have equal energy. The level for isopropyl tosylate was drawn on the basis of the rate difference between ethyl and isopropyl tosylates. The hypothetical transition state for ionization of butyl tosylate (**139**) was placed at a level above that of isopropyl tosylate by allowing for a rate difference of 10^4 to 10^6 between $S_I N$ reactions of a secondary and primary tosylate. The transition-state stabilization in the solvolysis of 3-butenyl tosylate should be the difference between the hypothetical 1-butyl tosylate $S_I N$ transition state and that actually observed. This stabilization due to the interaction of the π-electrons of the double bond with the developing cationic center on the 1-carbon amounts to 3.4–6.4 kcal./mole, *which represents a substantial degree of anchimeric assistance.* The difference between the $S_I N$ and the $S_D N$ transition states for the reaction of 1-butyl tosylate suggests that 2.5–5.5 kcal./mole represents the nucleophilic stabilization by the solvent in the $S_D N$ reaction state.

We might also ask whether the degree of stabilization at the transition state in the $S_I N$ reaction of 3-butenyl tosylate is small because of the weakness of bonds in electron deficient molecules. No sign of such weakness appears in the bond dissociation energies listed in Table 1.36.

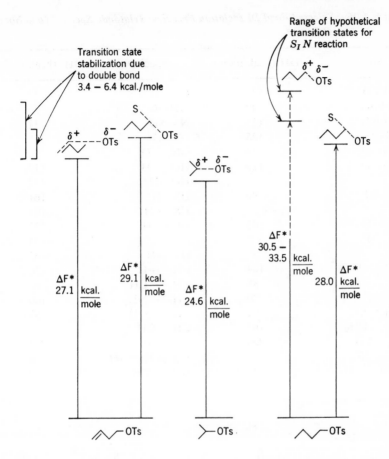

Figure 1.27 Free energies of activation for 3-butenyl tosylate, isopropyl tosylate and 1-butyl tosylate in formic acid at 50°C from Eq. 19 and the rate constants (k for 3-butenyl tosylate 3.1×10^{-6} sec.$^{-1}$).

The formation of strained rings through neighboring group participation by the π-electrons of a double bond is not limited to the formation of cyclopropane rings. LeNy (*115*) found that 4-cycloheptenylmethyl tosylate (**142**) solvolyzed in acetic acid about 30 times as rapidly as the corresponding saturated tosylate (**143**) to yield a single acetate, a derivative of bicyclo-[3.2.1] octanol (**144**) (Eq. 134). Lawton (*126*) discovered that 2-(3-cyclopentenyl)ethyl *p*-nitrobenzenesulfonate (nosylate) (**145**) reacted 95 times as rapidly with acetic acid as the saturated analog (**146**) and yielded *exo*-norbornyl acetate (**147**) (Eq. 135).

TABLE 1.36   *Selected Bond Dissociation Energies: Triatomic Species*[a] *(and Some Others)*

Species	DH°(kcal./mole)	Species	DH° (kcal./mole)
CO---O	127	CO---O$^+$	123
NN---O	40	NN---O$^+$	56
N---NO	115	N---NO$^+$	31
OS---O	125	OS---O$^+$	155
ON---O	73	ON$^+$---O	56
HO---H	119	HO$^+$---H	119
		HO---H$^+$	142
HS---H	90	HS---H$^+$	161
		HS$^+$---H	104
HC---H	106	HC$^+$---H	127
H$_2$---H	<0	H$_2$---H$^+$	>104
		H$_2$$^+$---H	>62
CH$_3$---H	104	CH$_3$$^+$---H	30
CH$_3$---CH$_3$	88	CH$_3$$^+$---CH$_3$	46
CH$_3$---NH$_2$	79	CH$_3$$^+$---NH$_2$	100
CH$_3$---OH	92	CH$_3$$^+$---OH	67
CH$_2$=CH$_2$	163	CH$_2$=CH$_2$$^+$	162
HC≡CH	230	HC≡CH$^+$	223
·CH$_2$CH$_2$---H	39	·CH$_2$CH$_2$$^+$---H	79
·CH$_2$---CH$_3$	96	·CH$_2$---CH$_3$$^+$	119

[a] From Ref. 82.

(134)

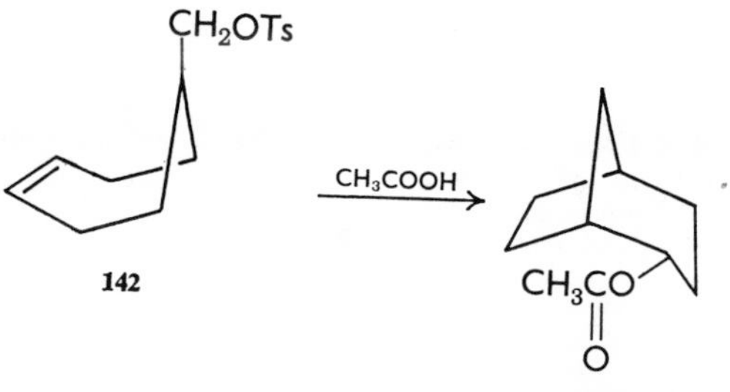

142   144

(135)

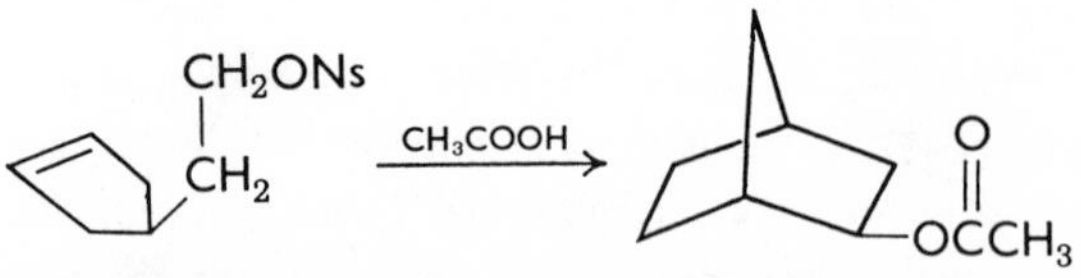

145   147

Bartlett and co-workers (*122*) measured the rate of **145** in formic acid as 640 times greater than the saturated compound. Bartlett and Sargent (*125*) noted that methyl groups substituted on the double bond had a marked effect on the rate as indicated below the formulas **145**, **146**, **148**, and **149**.

CH$_2$OTs

143

We shall postpone detailed consideration of the transition states for these ring closures briefly to the discussion of σ-participation except to note that the cumulative effect of the methyl groups is appreciable but small in comparison to the factor of 100–1000, which might have been expected for a methyl group α- to half of a positive charge. We should also note that a symmetrical participation of the double bond in the transition state for ring closure is suggested by the equivalence of the first and second methyl group on the rate, and that the transition-state stabilization resulting from the participation of the double bond may be estimated by the approach used to construct Fig. 1.27 as 8.2–11.2 kcal./mole for **148**.

The π-electrons of the unsubstituted benzene ring of 3-phenyl-2-butyl tosylate appear to be equivalent to those of an isolated double bond in the anchimeric assistance provided for the ionization of a tosylate group. The solvolysis rate of 2-phenylethyl tosylate is 2.1 times as great as that for ethyl tosylate in formic acid (*124*). (Compare the factor of 2.1 with the 3.7 found for k_{135}/k_{136}.) The stereochemical results of the reaction of 3-phenyl-2-butyl tosylate in acetic acid or formic acid (Fig. 1.28; compare with Figs. 2.48 and 2.49 for the additional complications introduced by the intermediacy of ion-pairs) suggest an important role for the phenyl group in the intermediate (or intermediates) even though the participation of the phenyl group at the transition state for ionization is so small that it is difficult to evaluate. The rate of solvolysis of *threo*-3-phenyl-2-butyl tosylate (**150**) is 2.38×10^{-6} sec.$^{-1}$ in acetic acid at 50°, about 0.6 the rate for 2-butyl tosylate (**151**) under the same conditions. However, it is difficult to make a proper comparison between these two figures since, on the one hand, decreased solvent access to the potential carbonium ion center of **150** as well as the negative inductive effect of the phenyl group (due to the sp^3–sp^2 bond dipole at the carbon α- to the leaving group) should decrease the rate observed for **150** and nucleophilic participation of the solvent in the ionization of **151** raises the rate over what one might find for a "pure" ionization process.

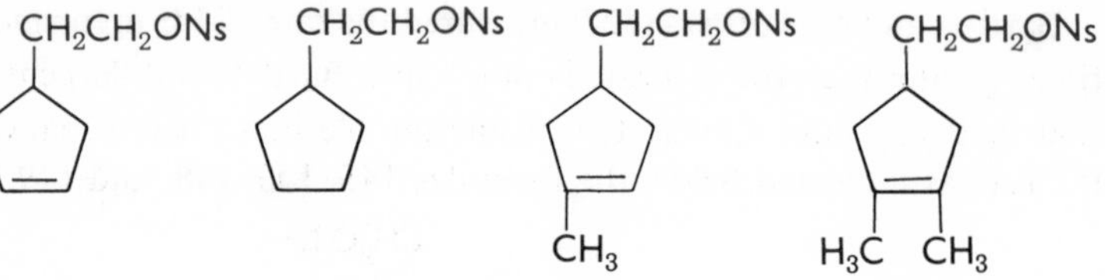

	145	146	148	149
$10^4 k$, sec.$^{-1}$ at 60°	1.10	0.0116	7.69	42.3

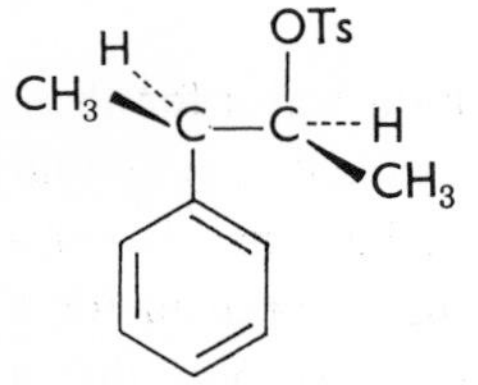

150 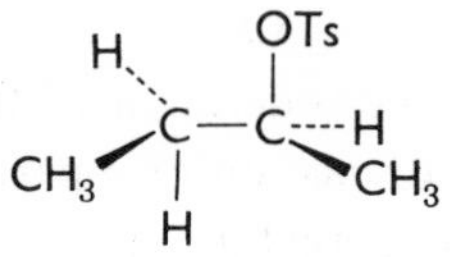   151

Cram (*124*) has estimated that the anchimeric assistance provided by the phenyl group at the transition state for the solvolysis of **150** corresponds to a rate factor of 24, or 2.2 kcal./mole. To appreciate what anchimeric assistance of this magnitude implies about the *nature of the intermediate derived from this transition state*, let us examine a case in which anchimeric assistance is large.

Baird and Winstein (*133*) analyzed the kinetics and products of reaction of 2-(*p*-hydroxyphenyl)ethyl bromide and concluded that the rate of reaction of the anion (**152**) was about 10^6 faster than the rate expected for unassisted solvolysis of the bromide. Under special conditions, a highly reactive intermediate, spiro 2.5 octa-1,4-dien-3-one (**153**) can be isolated. We may estimate the extra stabilization of the transition state (**154**) by first estimating what the rate of ionization of the bromide **152** would be without any interaction with the benzene ring. The estimated rate factor is 10^8–10^{10}, corresponding to a stabilization of 11–14 kcal./mole at 25°C.

If we assume that the stabilization available at the transition state is one

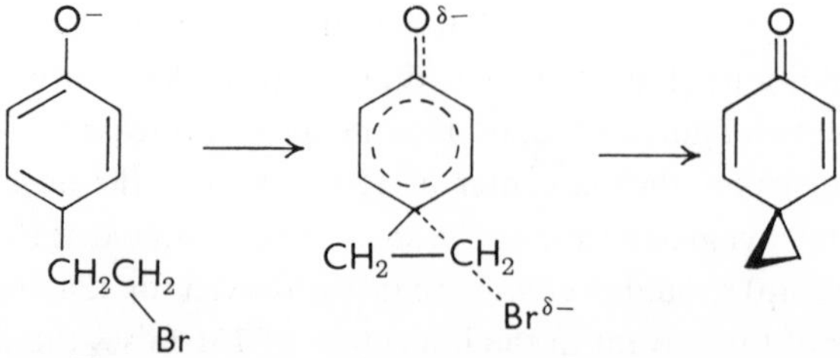

152   154   153

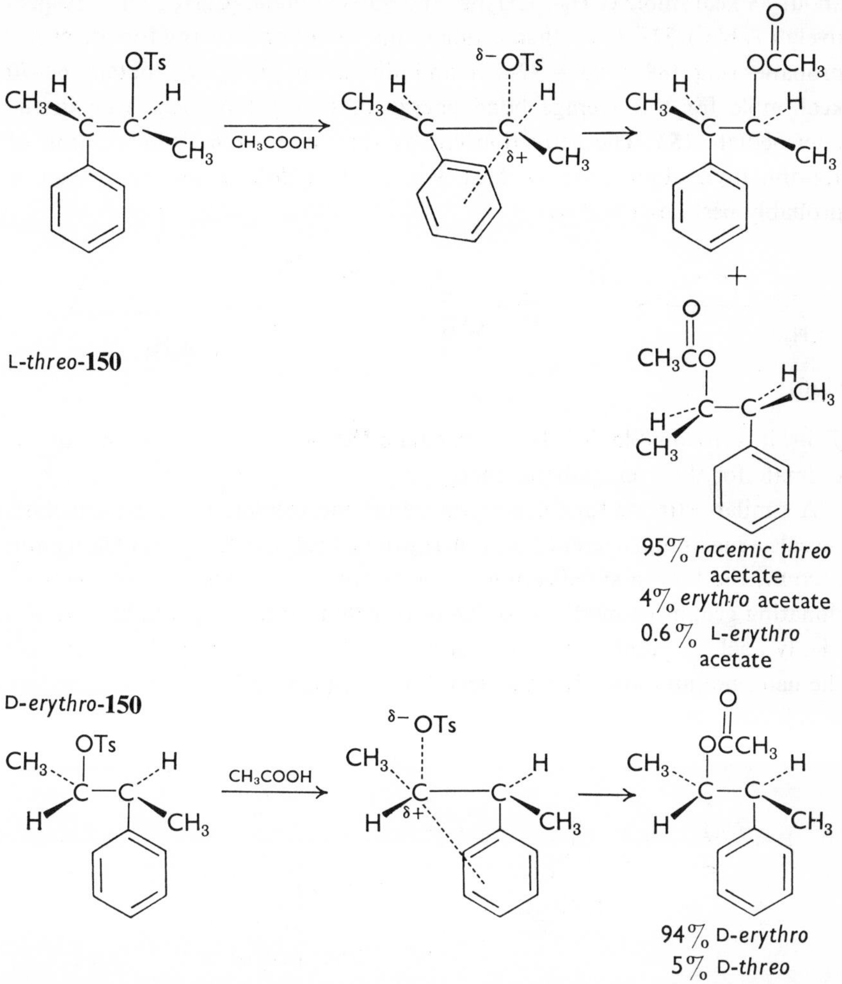

Figure 1.28 Products of solvolysis of two diastereomers of 3-phenyl-2-butyl tosylate in acetic acid, illustrating the high stereospecificity of product formation. (See the text for a discussion of the intermediates.)

half of the total stabilization produced by the interaction of the benzene ring and the carbon which released the bromide ion, the new bond would be "worth" 22–28 kcal./mole. (Actually, the intermediate is unstable so that the fraction of the final stabilization utilized at the transition state might be higher, cf. *12.*) The remainder of the bond energy required to construct a cyclopropane ring comes from the bond energies of the other bonds. Before ring closure, the bond dissociation energies for these bonds should have been about 88 kcal./mole (CH_2---CH_2Br) and 93 kcal./mole (C_6H_5---CH_2) respectively (Table 1.32). If we then estimate the total bond energy for the cyclopropane ring (88 + 93 + 22–28) and divide by three, we obtain 68–70 kcal./mole for the average bond energy of the cyclopropane ring in the intermediate **153**. The activation energy for the *cis-trans* isomerization of 1,2-dimethylcyclopropane is 59.4 kcal./mole (*116*), a process which is probably best described by:

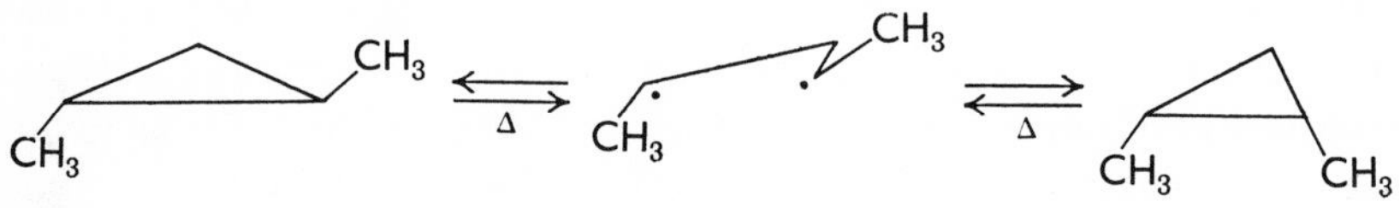

(136)

Thus, it is reasonable that the intermediate **153** can be isolated, in view of our estimate for the average bond energy.

A similar estimate for the corresponding intermediate from the solvolysis reveals a maximum average bond energy of 62 kcal./mole, without taking into account the loss in stabilization of the benzene ring. Addition of electron-donating groups (*p*-methoxy- or 2,4,6-trimethyl) to the ring and the use of a highly acidic solvent (see Part 3, Section 3.1) makes it possible to generate the benzenonium ions, **155** and **156** (Eq. 137) (*123, 135*).

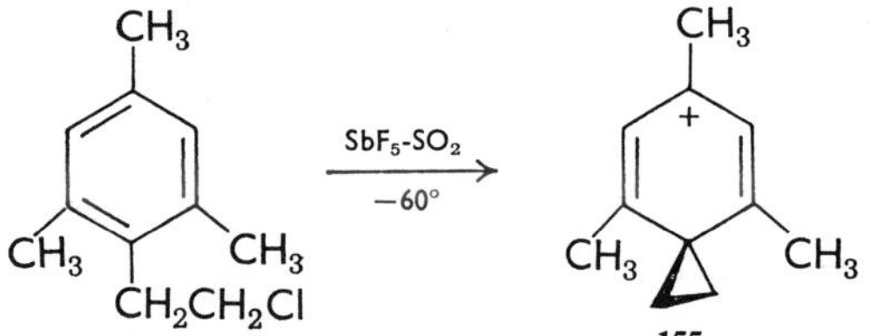

(Other resonance
forms can be written)

(Usually, **155** and **156** are called phenonium ions.) Even in a highly acidic solvent, it has not been possible to generate the phenonium ion **157** (*484*).

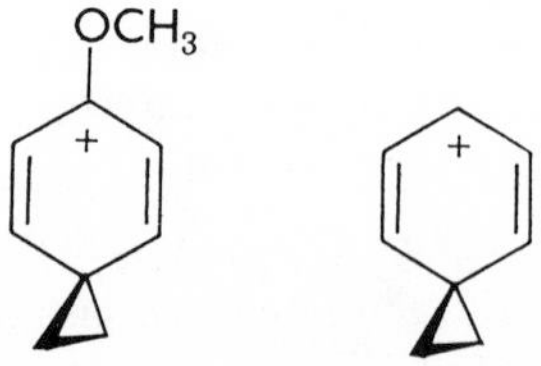

Given these reservations about the ease of formation of the symmetrical phenonium ion **157**, it might be better to account for the small amount of anchimeric assistance and the stereochemistry of the S_lN reaction for *threo*-**150** and *erythro*-**150** with unsymmetrical ions having a weak bond between C_1 of the aromatic ring and the carbon from which the leaving group departed. The *threo*-ion is shown as **158a** and **158b**, and the *erythro*-ion as **159a** and **159b**. The free energy versus reaction coordinate diagram for the reaction of **150** through the unsymmetrical ions is given in Fig. 1.29, and it is there emphasized through the small barrier separating the two unsymmetrical ions that a relatively small change in the degree of stabilization of the transition state or intermediate by a change in substituent or solvent can favor a single intermediate at the expense of two. Nevertheless, for compounds which

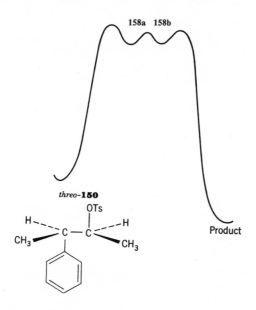

Figure 1.29 Free energy versus reaction coordinate diagram for the solvolysis of *threo*-3-phenyl-2-butyl tosylate.

solvolyze through transition states with very small degrees of stabilization (with respect to the appropriate reference compound), unsymmetrical transition states must certainly be written and unsymmetrical intermediates that can equilibrate with one another must be considered.

The questions of interpretation which we have raised concerning the operation of anchimeric assistance by π-electrons come up even more sharply

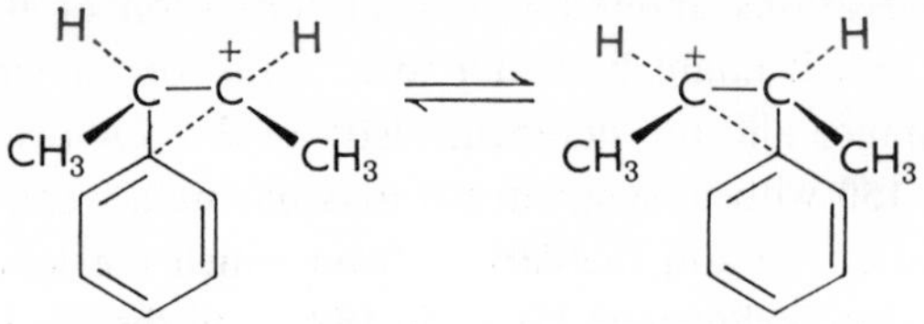

158a   158b

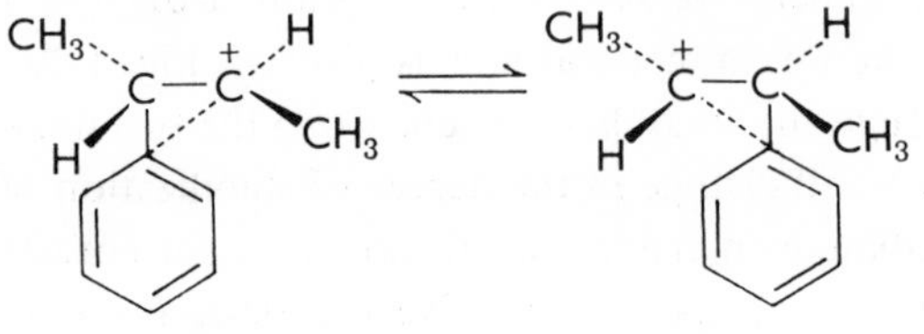

159a   159b

in the consideration of σ-participation. In fact, the most heated controversy in physical organic chemistry in recent years has revolved around the very existence of the intermediates postulated to arise from σ-bond participation and the evaluation of rates of solvolyses for many compounds in terms of the degree of anchimeric assistance at the transition state.

The stereospecific isomerization of camphene hydrochloride **(160)** to isobornyl chloride **(161)** has been known for many years and was

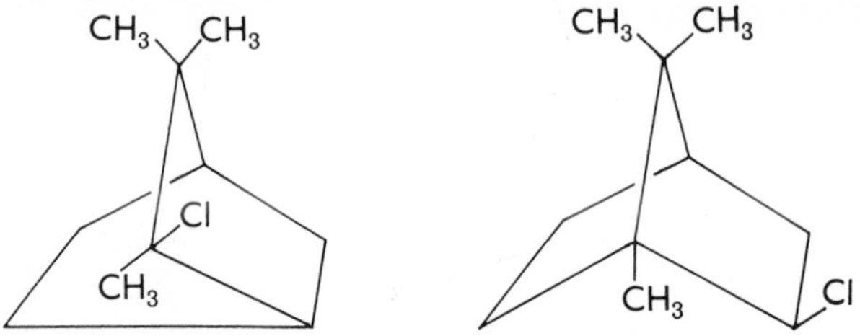

(138)

160   161

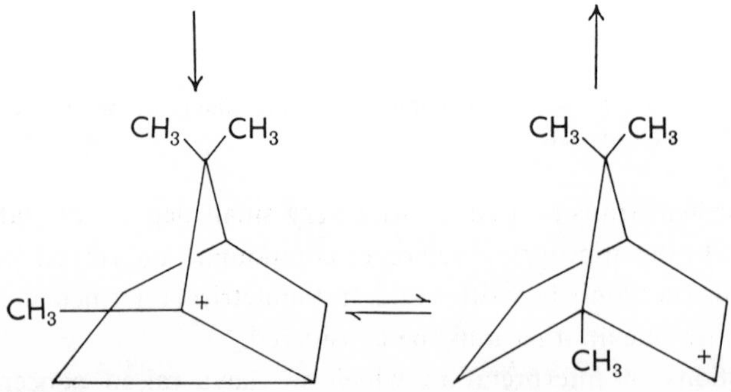

160a   161a

first ascribed to an ionization reaction by Meerwein and van Emster (*107*).

Neville, de Salas, and Wilson (*108*) suggested that the single "mesomeric" intermediate (**162**) could account for the highly stereospecific course of the rearrangement. The high reactivity of camphene hydrochloride (**160**) in solvolysis reactions compared with *t*-butyl chloride caused Hughes, Ingold, and co-workers to propose that the intermediate **162** could also account for the high rate. Part of the stabilization of the intermediate **162** would be effective at the transition state to ionization (*127*).

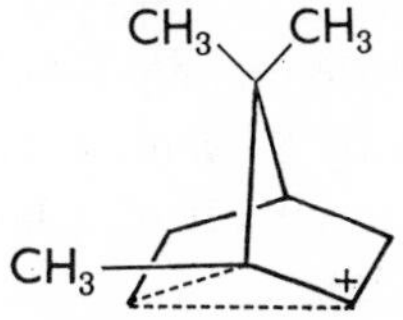

162

Winstein and Trifan (*110*) showed that the unsubstituted bicyclo[2.2.1]-heptane derivative, *exo*-2-norbornyl brosylate (**163**), solvolyzed in acetic acid about 350 times faster than the *endo*-isomer (**164**) (Eqs. 139, 140). Products are summarized in the equations, indicating that *exo*-ester is formed with essentially complete stereospecificity (*485*).

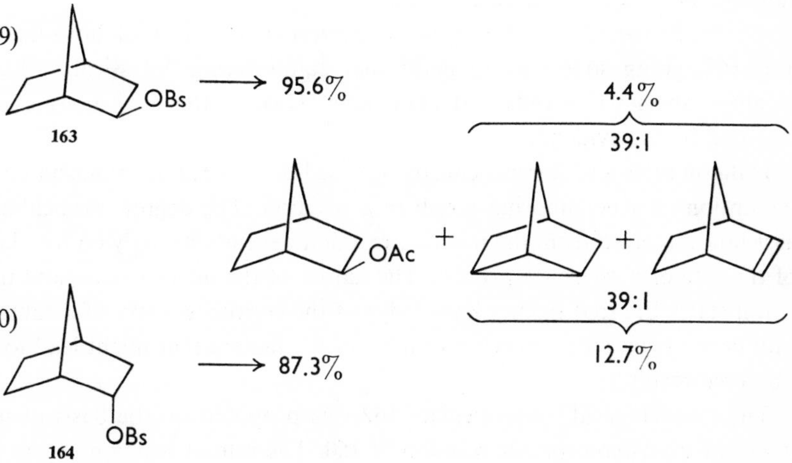

The solvolysis of optically active *exo*-2-norbornyl brosylate (**163**) is accompanied by racemization of the brosylate itself, due to ion-pair intermediates (see Section 2.10, Part 2). The intermediate **165** is postulated to account for these results.

This intermediate is representative of a large class of proposed intermediates in which a single carbon is bonded to more than the normal complement of other atoms. These species are commonly referred to as "nonclassical" or "bridged" (see the discussion by Sargent, *486*), and their role in physical organic chemistry has been the subject of a large and useful reprint-commentary volume by Bartlett (*155*).

In view of our examination of participation by π-electrons and, in particular, taking cognizance of the small interaction energies estimated for stabilization of the transition state (and by inference, for intermediates arising from the transition state), together with the expectation that σ-bonding electrons should be poorer donors than π-bonding electrons (a comparison that is certainly valid for the criteria of charge-transfer complex formation and charge-transfer band position; see Section 1.7), we must examine carefully the evidence for the role of "nonclassical" ions in solvolysis and other reactions. Brown (*111, 112, 487*) is the severest critic of formulations like **162** and **165**, going so far as to insist that equilibrating "classical" (that is localized species like **160a** and **161a**) ions (*113*) are the only intermediates required by the evidence.

Data on rates and stereochemistry are used to arrive at decisions on the intervention of a neighboring group in a reaction. The degree of anchimeric assistance inferred from the rate of a reaction depends strongly on the choice of the rate of a reference process. The nature of the intermediates and transition states inferred from a knowledge of the stereochemistry of a substitution depends on an appreciation for all of the factors that might lead to the observed result.

The "nonclassical" intermediate **162** was proposed on the basis of both high rate and stereospecific reaction of **160**. The rate of reaction of **160** was compared to that of *t*-butyl chloride. The intermediate **165** was proposed on the basis of the high rate of the *exo*-isomer **163** compared with that of the *endo*-isomer **164**.

Are the solvolysis rates of bicyclo[2.2.1]heptyl derivatives unusually high? Brown and Chloupek (*117*) have shown that the introduction of methyl substituents into the cyclopentyl ring markedly increases the solvolysis rate of derivatives and that such substitution can account for almost all of the rate increase from *t*-butyl chloride to camphene hydrochloride (**160**). Their data are summarized in Table 1.37. Brown (*487*) has also reported that the

TABLE 1.37 *Rate Comparisons Between Bicyclic and Cyclopentyl Chlorides*[a]

Compound		$10^6 k$, sec.$^{-1}$ [b]	Relative Rates
t-Butyl chloride		0.085	1.00
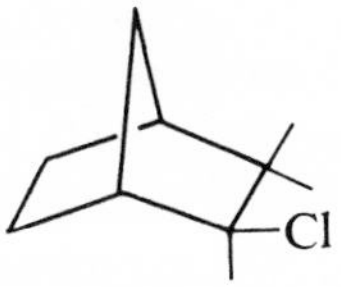	(**160**)	1160	13,600
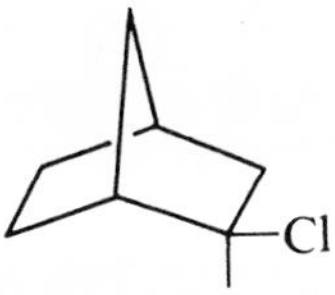	(**166**)	30.2	355
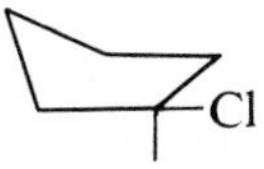	(**167**)	5.62	66
	(**168**)	14.5[c]	171
		10.6[d]	125
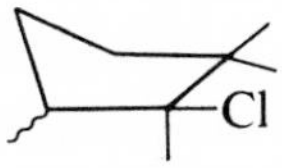	(**169**)[e]	202	2380
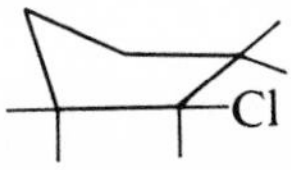	(**170**)	458	5390

[a] From Ref. 117. [b] In EtOH at 25°. [c] Chloride from *cis*-1,2-dimethylcyclopentanol. [d] Chloride from *trans*-1,2-dimethylcyclopentanol. [e] Formula is that recorded in the reference.

TABLE 1.38   *Rate Comparisons of the Methylated Cyclopentyl Tosylates*[a]

Tosylate		k (65°, sec.$^{-1}$ × 10^4)	Rel. Rate
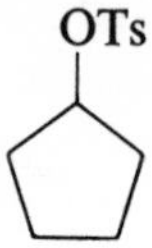 OTs (cyclopentyl)	**(172)**	2.07[b]	1.0
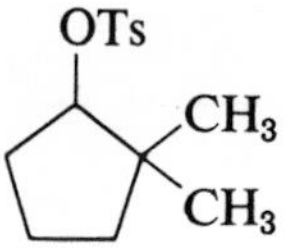 OTs, gem-dimethyl adjacent	**(173)**	1.78	0.86
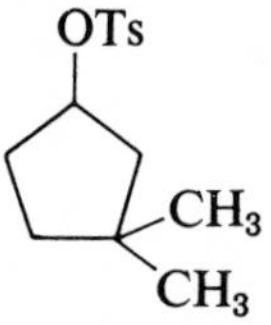 OTs, gem-dimethyl at 3-position	**(174)**	1.68	0.81
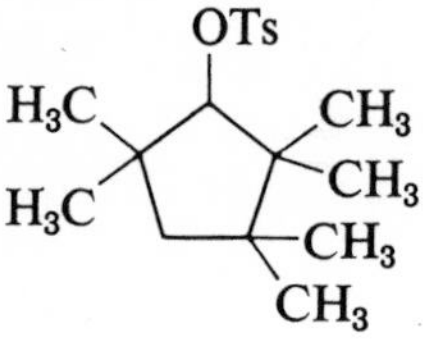 OTs with H₃C, H₃C and CH₃, CH₃, CH₃, CH₃	**(175)**	0.41	0.20
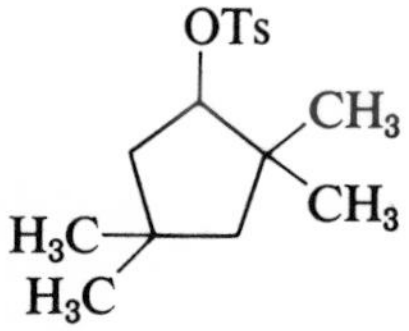 OTs with CH₃, CH₃ and H₃C, H₃C	**(176)**	0.32	0.15
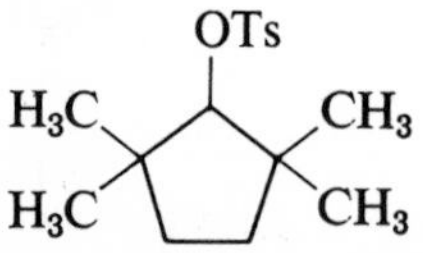 OTs with H₃C, H₃C and CH₃, CH₃	**(177)**	0.14	0.07

[a] From Ref. 488.   [b] This experimentally obtained value agrees well with the calculated value of 1.95×10^{-4} sec.$^{-1}$ from the data of H. C. Brown and G. Ham, *J. Amer. Chem. Soc.*, **78**, 2735 (1956).

solvolysis of *exo*-2-norbornyl brosylate **(163)** in acetic acid is only 12.4 times faster than the solvolysis of cyclopentyl brosylate **(171)**. However, the interpretation of the latter rate comparison is not easy, and it is certain from the rate studies of Krapcho and Horn (*488*) that nucleophilic participation by solvent is important in the transition state for solvolysis of secondary cyclopentyl tosylates as shown by the *decrease* in rate observed for increased methyl substitution (Table 1.38).

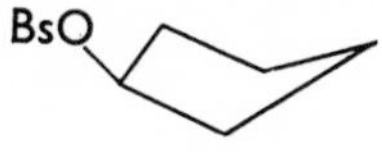

171

The contrast between the introduction of a methyl substituent into *exo*-2-norbornyl tosylate at the 1-position (**178**) and into the 2-position of cyclo-pentyl tosylate (**173**) is particularly striking and strongly suggests that the methyl group contributes to charge delocalization at the 1-position. The rate increase for **178**, k_{178}/k_{163}, is 50. (Schleyer and Kleinfelter, cited by Brown, *487*). The transition state for the reaction is shown as **179** in Eq. 141 with the products indicated as arising from the rearranged carbonium ion as shown by Brown and Bell (*489*).

(141)

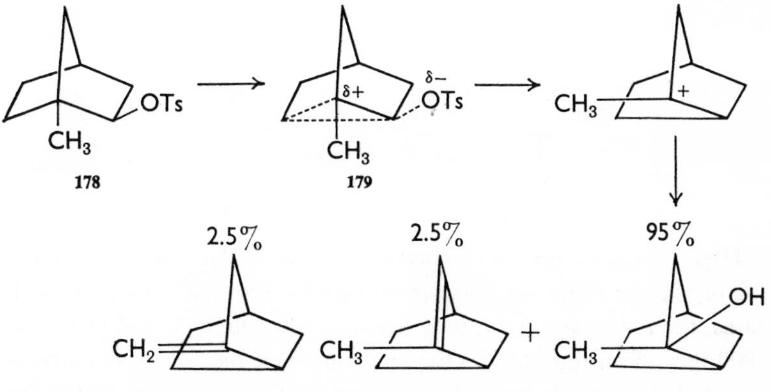

On the other hand, Brown has found that conversion of the 2-norbornyl derivatives from secondary systems into tertiary systems does not affect very much the ratio of norbornyl and cyclopentyl solvolysis rates. For example, solvolysis of 2-methyl-2-*exo*-norbornyl *p*-nitrobenzoate (**180**) in 60% aqueous dioxane is only 4 times faster than solvolysis of 1-methylcyclopentyl *p*-nitro-benzoate (**181**) in the same solvent. It is usual to suppose that the electron demand on a neighboring group decreases with an increase in the local ability to satisfy a developing cationic center, as in the change from a secondary system to a tertiary system.

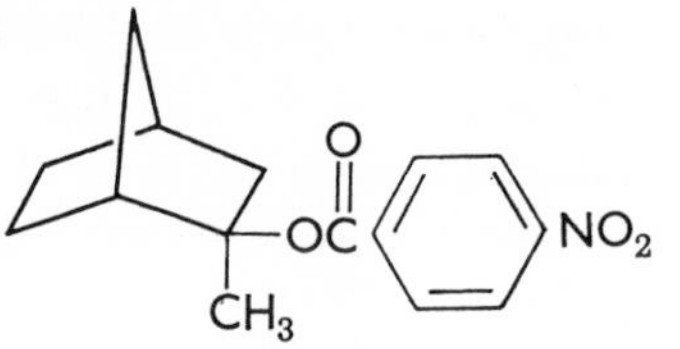

Charge delocalization to the 6-position, expected formally on the basis of the contributing forms to the intermediate **165, 165a, 165b,** and **165c** (see Eq. 135), is apparently unimportant, judging from the fact that 6,6-dimethyl-*exo*-2-norbornyl tosylate (**182**) solvolyses more slowly than *exo*-2-norbornyl tosylate (**183**) (*119*).

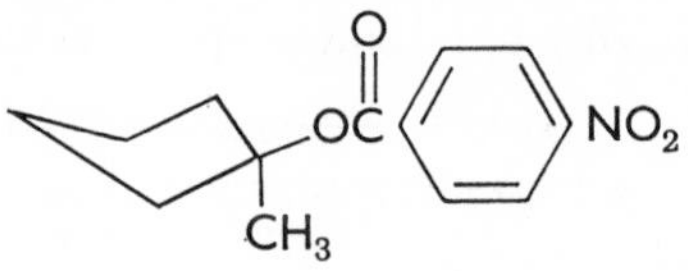

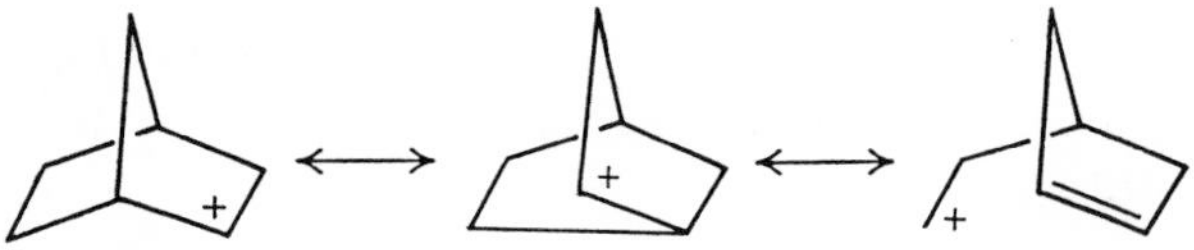

High reactivity for 2-*exo* derivatives is also claimed on the basis of the solvolysis rate ratios for corresponding *exo*- and *endo*- compounds. In many cases, the *exo/endo* rate ratio is between 100 and 1000 and ratios as high as 7000 have been found (*487*) for the isomers of the *tertiary*-2 derivative, **180**. We shall exclude the ratio for the *exo*- and *endo*-isomers of **180** from consideration because it is a certainty that the *endo*-isomer is unusually slow, given the fact that the rate ratio k_{180}/k_{181} is 4. In several cases, notably that of 7-ketonorbornyl tosylates (**185** and **186**) and the *exo*- and *endo*-methoxyl groups of camphor dimethyl ketal (**187** and **188**), the *exo-/endo*-ratio is *below unity.* Exo-/endo- ratios are listed in Table 1.39.

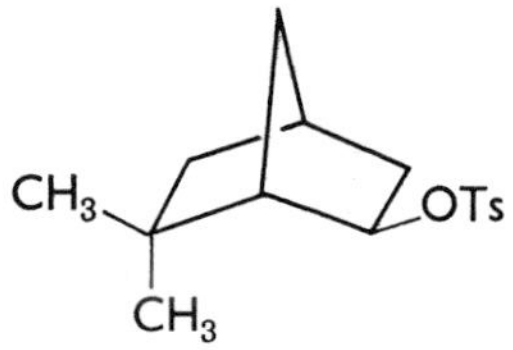

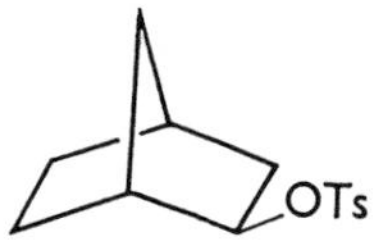

We should like to propose that the fact that *exo*-2-norbornyl brosylate (**163**) solvolyzes more rapidly than cyclopentyl brosylate (**171**) is evidence that an intramolecular mechanism for stabilizing the transition state of the bicyclic compound exists. The value of the rate factor k_{163}/k_{171} (12.4) suggests that the effect is small, in agreement with the small rate increase recorded for a 1-methyl substituent, and the rate decrease found for the 6,6-dimethyl compound. It seems reasonable to suppose that, as in the case of the α-cyclopropyl substituent, we can reconcile the apparent contradiction between some delocalization at the transition state and the ineffectiveness of groups which stabilize positive charge, by the proposal that much of the (small) driving force comes from the relief of strain. Thus, we believe that, for the least favorable case, the unsubstituted *exo*-2-norbornyl derivatives, σ-participation is very small and leads to a pair of readily interconvertible ions, **195** and **196**. In any case, it is hard to escape from the probability that a cationic center near a source of electrons (*n*-nonbonding pair, π-electrons, σ-bonding pair) will interact to some extent. Rather than argue about the precise limits for the commonly used labels for these ionic intermediates, we have tried to pursue the idea that we must define interactions quantitatively and recognize that the magnitude of the interactions depend on both intramolecular and extramolecular (solvent and gegenion) factors. Destabilizing the positive charge to be localized on the 2-carbon, as with 7-ketonorbornyl tosylates (**185**, **186**), or using a system which accommodates most of the charge on an atom removed from the norbornyl system, as in camphor dimethyl ketal (**187**) (studied by methoxyl exchange in methanol-d_4 by Traylor and Perrin, *121*), erases the special character of the norbornyl system. Schleyer (*297*) has developed a convincing case for attributing at least a portion of the *exo/endo* differential to C_1—H—C_2H repulsions (which can be called torsional strain). The student should work these out by considering initial state-transition state differences.

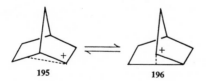

195   196

The n.m.r. spectrum of the norbornyl cation has been measured a highly acidic solvent composed of antimony pentafluoride-sulfur dioxide-sulfuryl chloride (*542*) (Fig. 3.4). (See Part 3, Section 3.1 for a discussion of stable carbonium ions.) At $-120°C$ the spectrum consists of three peaks with relative areas 4:1:6. The lines are reasonably sharp and show no sign of the broadening that might have been expected if one of the rearrangement processes

TABLE 1.39 *Exo/Endo Rate Ratios for Bicyclic Compounds*

Isomer Pair	10^6k, sec.$^{-1}$ [a] (*exo*)	Exo/Endo Ratio	Ref.
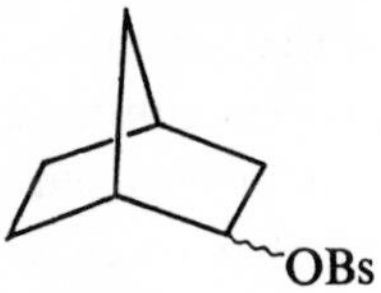 Norbornyl OBs [b]	88.2	350(1600) [c]	118
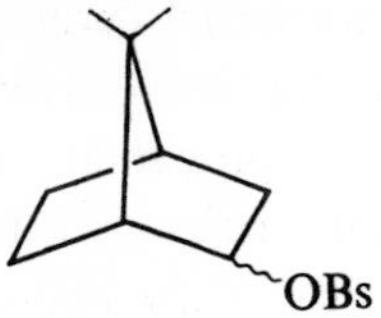 Apobornyl OBs	770	4100	118
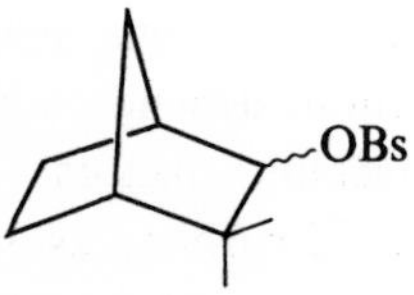 Camphenilyl OBs	32.9	1240	118
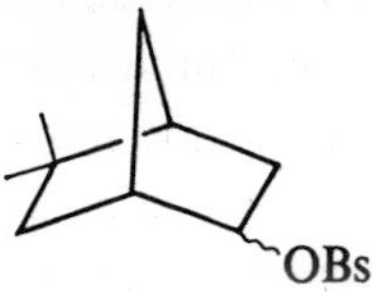 β-Fenchocamphoryl OBs	26.1	145	118
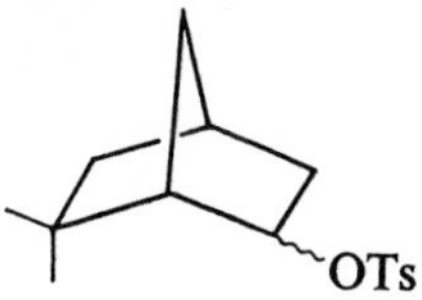 6.6-Dimethylnorbornyl OTs [d]	0.92	206	119
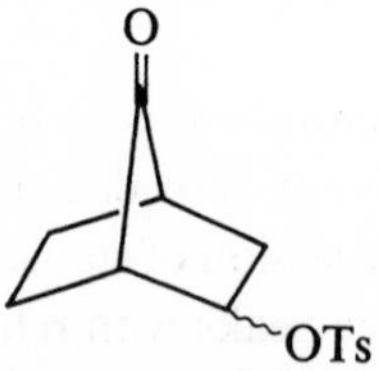 7-Ketonorbornyl OTs	0.0144	0.166	120

138

TABLE 1.39 (*Continued*)

Isomer Pair	$10^6 k$, sec.$^{-a}$ (*exo*)	*Exo/Endo* Ratio	Ref.
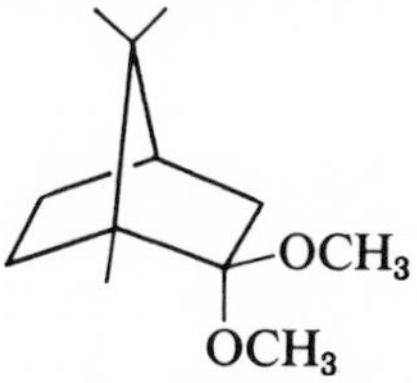 Camphor dimethyl ketal	66 [e]	0.10	121

[a] Titrimetric rate constants for AcOH at 25° except for **187/188**.   [b] *p*-Bromo-benzenesulfonates.   [c] Polarimetric *exo/endo* rate ratio.   [d] *p*-Toluenesulfonate.   [e] Observed rate (by n.m.r.) in CD_3OD containing 3% acetic acid.

leading to equivalence (Fig. 1.30) had a rate comparable to the chemical shift difference between the exchanging sites. Saunders, Schleyer, and Olah (*542*) have estimated that a rate of 3×10^5 sec.$^{-1}$ would have been detected as line broadening at $-120°$ for either 6,2-hydride shift or C_6—$C_1 \rightarrow C_6$—C_2 rearrangement. Assuming that the 6,2-shift has the same activation energy as the 3,2-shift (*490*), the rate of the 6,2-shift at room temperature may be calculated as 6×10^8 sec.$^{-1}$ in the solvent used for the n.m.r. measurements. However, antimony pentafluoride is a highly associated (5–10 units per *n*-mer) solvent (*545*), and even when diluted should be peculiarly adapted to transferring a fluoride ion from one "location" in a carbonium ion to another. We illustrate with **197 → 198**. The transfer of fluoride is analogous to the transfer of protons in hydrogen bonded systems like water, ice, sulfuric acid, and phosphoric acid by the "Grotthus mechanism." (See Part 2 of this book.)

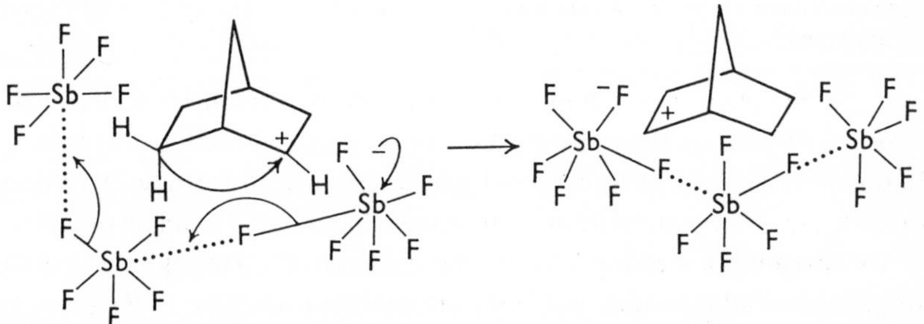

197   **198**

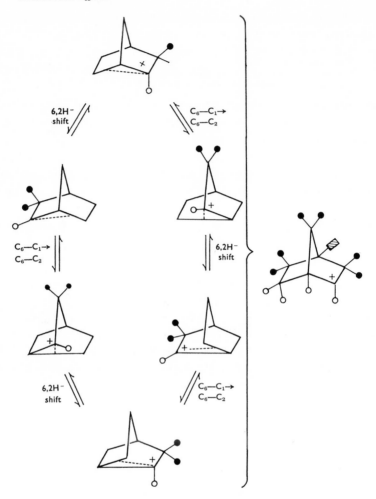

Figure 1.30 Formulas indicating the hydrogens which become equivalent in the n.m.r. spectrum at −120°C. The single hydrogen is indicated only at the right. All hydrogens become equivalent via a 3,2-hydride shift at room temperature and only a single n.m.r. line is observed.

It is likely, therefore, that the rate of 6,2-hydride shift is much smaller in the solvent acetic acid, perhaps by a factor of as much as 1000, but at least by a factor of 100. (This guess is based on the change in the rate of proton-hydroxide ion combination from ice to water, that is, from a highly organized to a less organized medium.) Thus, the criticism of Winstein that equilibrating ions would require too high an equilibration rate (*491*) must be moderated, and the rate of equilibration (assuming that **195** ⇌ **196** is appropriate) is then of a magnitude which might account for the 99.95% racemization observed in the solvolysis of **163**.

(142) $k_{195 \to 196} = 2 \times 10^3 \times 10^{-2} \times 6 \times 10^8 = 12 \times 10^9$ sec.$^{-1}$

   Internal   Solvent   Estimated
   return   effect   rate at 25°C

The great stereospecificity of the reactions of norbornyl compounds, the *exo*-isomer being the preferred product in the solvolysis of either *exo*- or *endo*-derivatives, has been illustrated directly by Goering and Schewene (*492*) who equilibrated *exo*- and *endo*-2-norbornyl acetates with perchloric acid in acetic acid and measured the rate of ionization of the *exo*-acetate by measuring the rate of racemization. They applied the treatment suggested in Eq. 129 to the data and concluded that *exo*-attack on the intermediate ion was favored over *endo*-attack by 4.4 kcal./mole. We suggest that about half of the relative stabilization of the transition state which favors *exo*-attack arises from weak σ-participation (cf. the rate factor k_{163}/k_{171} of 12.4) and about half arises from steric hindrance to *endo*-attack. (See also Schleyer, *297*.)

Brown and Takeuchi (*493*) have found that the reaction constant (ρ^+, for correlations with σ^+) correlating the solvolysis of the tertiary chlorides, **199**, **200**, and **201** (see Eq. 39, and Section 1.3) falls somewhat as the intramolecular electron supply (**199** $\to$ **201**) or nucleophilic participation by solvent (**199** $\to$ **200**) increases (cf. Winstein, *785*). The rates for the unsubstituted compounds are indicated below the formulas.

X = CH$_3$O, H, NO$_2$

199   200   201

$10^5 \, k$, sec.$^{-1}$
in ethanol

at 25°	36.9	1880	20,500
ρ^+	-4.9	-4.5	-4.3

To recapitulate our conclusions on σ-participation in norbornyl systems, there appears to be a small amount of anchimeric assistance from a σ-bond at the transition state, due partially to relief of ring strain, and amounting to about 1.5 kcal./mole. The intermediate derived from this transition state is stabilized by less than 3 kcal./mole in comparison with a localized carbonium ion (for example, a 2-norbornyl cation). The stabilization seems far too little to allow for the major reorganization of the bonds demanded for the symmetrical intermediate **165**, and we prefer two unsymmetrical intermediates in place of one (for example, **195** ⇌ **196**). Symmetrical intermediates (for instance, **153**) can be detected from the solvolysis of alkyl halides involving large anchimeric assistance. The occurrence of symmetrical transition states is less likely, for reasons which the student will be able to appreciate at this time. In spite of the vast effort that has already been devoted to π- and σ-participation in solvolyses, much remains to be done, especially in evaluating the rates of reaction of the intermediates and ion-pairs thought to be on the reaction pathway.

A rational approach to identification of systems which exhibit unusual reactivity has been made by Schleyer (*129, 131*) (see also Foote, *130*) by selecting the rates of reaction of a few simple systems and evaluating the rate changes expected from changes in bond angle strain, torsional strain and nonbonded interactions.

We might surmise from the rate constant estimated for the interconversion of **195** and **196** that the reactions of ion-pairs generated in most solvolysis reactions must be extremely rapid. The ion-pair, in many cases, preserves a "memory" of its origin, as shown by the variation in the ratio of cyclohexene to cyclohexyl acetate from three different solvolysis reactions (*132*).

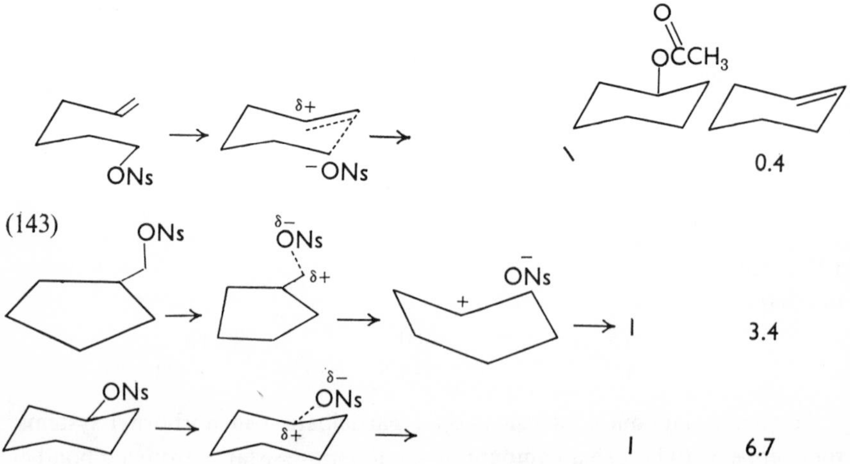

Other "memory effects" have been elucidated by Berson and co-workers (*495*).

In connection with the intramolecular stabilization of carbonium ions, it is worth noting that the molecular ion $C_7H_{11}Br\cdot^+$ in the mass spectrum of *exo*-2-norbornyl bromide is much less intense (factor of 10!) relative to the ion $C_7H_{11}^+$ than the same peak derived from *endo*-2-norbornyl bromide relative to the peak for $C_7H_{11}^+$ (*496*). The relative intensities can be interpreted in terms of two kinetic processes as shown in Eqs. 144 and 145:

(144) $\qquad exo\text{-}C_7H_{11}Br\cdot^+ \longrightarrow C_7H_{11}^+ + Br\cdot$

(145) $\qquad endo\text{-}C_7H_{11}Br\cdot^+ \longrightarrow C_7H_{11}^+ + Br\cdot$

Although we cannot be certain that the product ions are identical, the agreement of the relative reactivity in the gas phase with that judged from solvolysis studies as due to intramolecular stabilization of the transition state is interesting.

Problems

1. Draw a free energy versus reaction coordinate diagram for an S_IN mechanism involving: (a) one intermediate (b) two intermediates (c) three intermediates. Label the intermediates.
2. Illustrate with examples the following mechanisms for stabilizing a transition state. Define the reference reaction for each case.
   (a) Delocalization.
   (b) Hybridization.
   (c) Anchimeric assistance (*n*).
   (d) Anchimeric assistance (*π*).
   (e) Anchimeric assistance (*σ*).
   (f) Solvation.
   (g) Gegenion (counterion) interaction.
3. Assuming that the methyl contribution to radical stabilization is a constant fraction of the methyl contribution to carbonium ion stabilization, prepare a table comparing the carbonium ion and radical stabilizations of ethyl, isopropyl, and *t*-butyl species relative to methyl.
4. Estimate the rates of the gas-phase elimination reaction for isopropyl bromide and *t*-butyl bromide at 373°K (see footnote a, Table 1.24). Compare the probable transition states for the reaction in the gas phase with that in acetonitrile, and explain why there is such a large difference in the two rates.

5. Write a detailed mechanism for the formation of bicyclobutane from cyclo-propylcarbinylamine. What relation does this result have to our understanding of the acid-catalyzed ring-opening of cyclopropane? (See Eq. 108.)

6. Write the products of aprotic diazotization of 2-methyl-1-aminopropane-3-d_3 (see Eq. 109, Part 1).

7. Write a synthesis for 1-bromotryptycene. Predict the rate of solvolysis of this bromide in comparison to 1-bromobicyclo[2.2.2]octane.

8. Try to estimate from data in Section 1.5 the relative stabilities of the homo-adamantyl and adamantylcarbinyl carbonium ions.

9. Give the products and mechanisms for the following reactions:

(a)

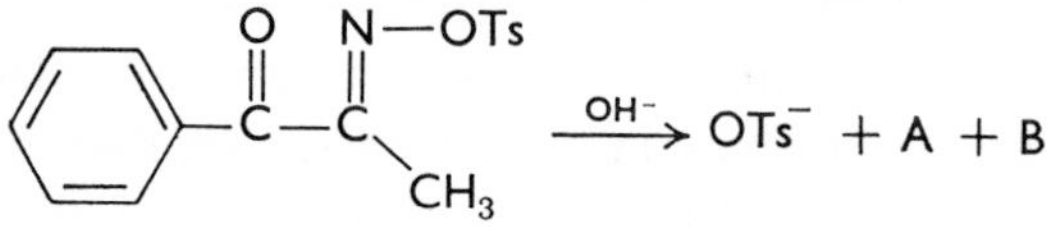

(b)

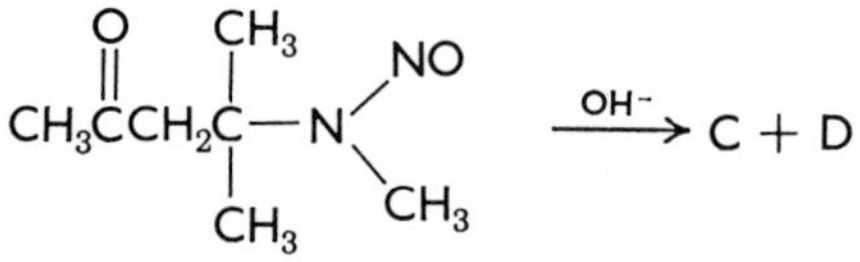

(c)

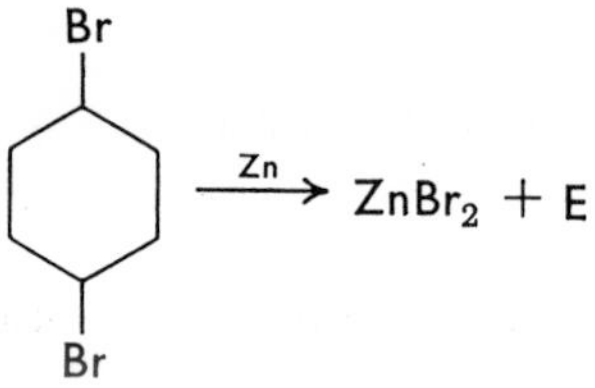

(d)

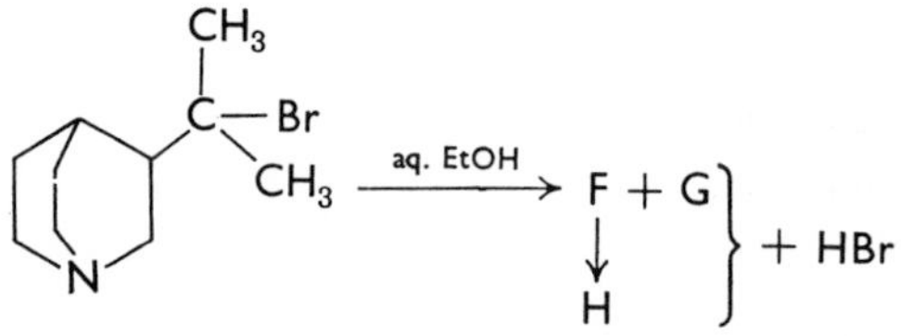

10. Explain Eq. 118 (Part 1).

11. Estimate the rate of ionization for the compounds produced by introducing one, two, and three dimethylamino groups into triphenylmethyl chloride. Name the reference compound and reference conditions and outline the procedure for the estimation.

12. Through a comparison of the initial and transition states, illustrate why a four-membered ring is more difficult to form than a five-membered ring.

13. Write the products of reaction of *erythro*-3-bromo-2-butanol and *threo*-3-bromo-2-butanol with concentrated hydrochloric acid.

14. Write the product and detailed mechanism of formation for the reaction of iodine, silver acetate, and cyclohexene in wet acetic acid (Ref. 497).

15. The trichloroacetate of 3,5-*cyclo*chloestan-6β -ol (**102**) rearranges on heating to an isomeric ester, which on hydrolysis with base yields a single alcohol. Write a mechanism for the rearrangement and a formula for the isomeric ester. Why is only one alcohol formed on hydrolysis?

16. Describe the possible effect of 3-methyl and 3,5-dimethyl substitution on the solvolysis of 4-vinyl-*t*-cumyl chloride.

17. Dehydronorbornyl brosylate is two to three times as reactive as the isomeric nortricyclyl brosylate in hydrolysis in aqueous acetone. The products of hydrolysis are nortricyclyl alcohol and dehydronorbornyl alcohol in a ratio of about six to one. Derive a ΔF for the equilibrium between the two brosylates and draw conclusions about the source of reactivity in these systems from the result.

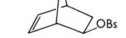   

Dehydronorbornyl brosylate   Nortricyclyl brosylate

18. Construct a figure like Fig. 1.27 for the 2-(3-cyclopentenyl)ethyl tosylates.

19. Explain the fact that polymethylation of a secondary cyclopentyl tosylate decreases the rate of solvolysis while polymethylation of a tertiary cyclopentyl system increases markedly the rate of solvolysis.

20. Show by means of a diagram like that in Fig. 1.30 how all of the hydrogens become equivalent in the 2-norbornyl cation through a 3,2-hydride shift in addition to the rearrangements shown in that figure.

21. Explain why the three nosylates—5-hexenyl, cyclopentylmethyl, and cyclohexyl—differ so markedly in the ratio of cyclohexene to cyclohexyl acetate on solvolysis in acetic acid.

22. What would the advantage of urea over sodium acetate be in solvolyses carried out in acetic acid? (Ref. 498.)

23. A crystallographic investigation of triphenylmethyl perchlorate (an ionic solid) shows that the phenyl groups are at an angle of about 54° to one another, so that the ion as a whole looks like a propeller. What implications does this finding have for the description of the transition state for reactions of triphenylmethyl derivatives or for other tertiary halides? (Ref. 528.)

24. Explain the formation of 2-methylcyclobutanone from the reaction of 3-pentynyl tosylate with formic acid (Ref. 499).

25. The reaction of 2,2-dimethyl-3-butenyl brosylate with acetic acid is sixty times faster than that of the saturated compound and yields a mixture of 2-methyl-pentadienes, 2-methyl-4-penten-2-yl acetate, and 4-methyl-3-pentenyl acetate. In view of some of the rate data cited in Section 1.5, explain the anchimeric acceleration in this case and outline a mechanism for the products (Ref. 712; see also Ref. 790).

26. Compound **A**, on heating in 1-methylpyrrolidone with tetrabutylammonium benzoate, yields compound **B**. Explain this result (Ref. 713).

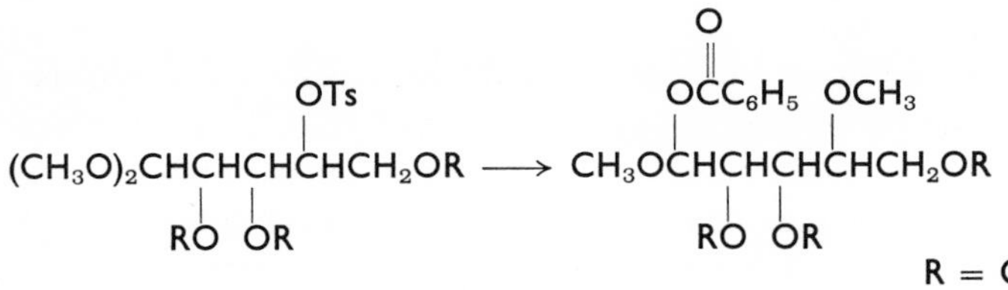

$$
\begin{array}{c}
\text{OTs} \\
|
\end{array}
$$

$$(CH_3O)_2CHCHCHCHCH_2OR \longrightarrow$$
$$
\begin{array}{cc}
| & | \\
RO & OR
\end{array}
$$
A

$$
\begin{array}{c}
\quad\quad\quad O \\
\quad\quad\quad \| \\
OCC_6H_5 \; OCH_3 \\
| \quad\quad\;\; |
\end{array}
$$
$$CH_3OCHCHCHCH_2OR$$
$$
\begin{array}{cc}
| & | \\
RO & OR
\end{array}
$$
B

$$R = C_6H_5CH_2$$

27. Explain the data in Table P27, especially the formation of cyclopentylmethyl derivatives rather than cyclohexyl derivatives, and the contrast between the relative rates and the relative proportions of products formed (Ref. 714).

TABLE P27

Compound	10^5k, sec.$^{-1}$ in CH_3COOH at 80°
6-Phenylhexyl brosylate (**A**)	0.392
trans-6-Phenyl-5-hexenyl brosylate (**B**)	1.27
6-Phenyl-5-hexynyl brosylate (**C**)	0.37

$$
\begin{array}{cccc}
& 64\% & & 36\% \\
(P27.1) & C \rightarrow C_6H_5C\equiv CCH_2CH_2CH_2OCOCH_3 & + &
\end{array}
$$

(with cyclopentene ring structure labeled $C_6H_5C=$ bearing $OCOCH_3$)

$$
\begin{array}{cc}
& 30.4\% \\
(P27.2) & B \rightarrow \textit{trans}\text{-}C_6H_5CH{=}CHCH_2CH_2CH_2OCOCH_3 \; + \\
& + \; 7.8\% \; \text{alkenes}
\end{array}
$$

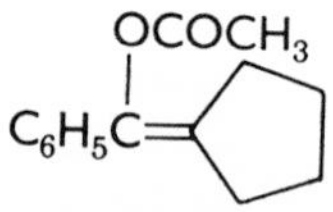

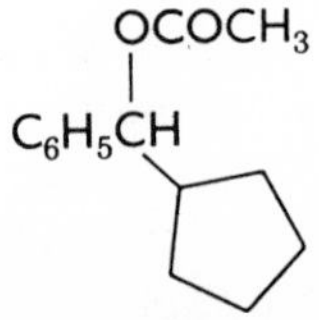

(with cyclopentane ring structure labeled C_6H_5CH bearing $OCOCH_3$)

28. Explain the fact that 1-aminoapocamphane (**A**) is readily converted into the alcohol with nitrous acid.

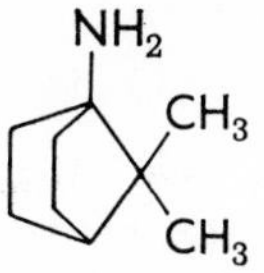

A

RADICAL TRANSITION STATES

1.6 Free Radical Reactions

A free radical is any species in which there is one unpaired electron. The unpaired electron confers a positive contribution to the magnetic suscepti-bility (*paramagnetic susceptibility*) and the possibility for undergoing transi-tions in a magnetic field under the influence of radiation in the microwave region. (Electron paramagnetic resonance = e.p.r., and electron spin reso-nance = e.s.r.) In most cases, a species with an unpaired electron is reactive and free radicals engage in a variety of chemically interesting and tech-nologically important reactions.

We shall cover only selected aspects of free radical chemistry. A clear exposition of the chemistry of free radicals has been published by Pryor (*422*), complementing the extensive survey by Walling (*173*).

Free radicals may be generated by *homolytic* cleavage of one or more covalent bonds or by oxidation or reduction. (Homolytic means equal division of the electrons of a bond between the two product species.) Azoiso-butyronitrile (**42**) dissociates to form 2-cyano-2-propyl radicals (**203**) and nitrogen at a convenient rate between 60 and 80°C.

$$(146) \quad (CH_3)_2C-N=N-C(CH_3)_2 \xrightarrow[\Delta]{\text{various solvents}} (CH_3)_2C\cdot + N_2$$

$$\underset{\underset{42}{CN}}{\overset{}{|}} \qquad \underset{CN}{\overset{}{|}} \qquad\qquad \underset{\underset{203}{CN}}{\overset{}{|}}$$

Azomethane (**204**) decomposes at an appreciable rate only near 300°C, but it may be readily decomposed by irradiation with ultraviolet light near 3500 A (the position of the weak $n \to \pi^*$ transition of the unconjugated azo group).

$$(147) \qquad\qquad CH_3N=NCH_3 \xrightarrow{h\nu} 2\,CH_3\cdot + N_2$$
$$ \underset{204}{}$$

The mechanism of the photodecomposition of azo compounds is not known in detail but the observation by Bartlett and McBride (*715*) that a triplet radical pair is formed by the photolysis of the azoalkane **205** at low tem-peratures suggests that the radicals arise from a triplet-excited state, according to the equations 148–150. Azo compounds can undergo photosensitized decomposition, which probably proceeds by transfer of excitation from the excited triplet state of the sensitizer to the azo compound, to form the ground state of the sensitizer molecule and the triplet state of the azo compound

148

(Eq. 151). We cannot be certain whether n,π^* or π,π^*-triplet states are the immediate precursors of the radical species. (For discussion of these topics, see Turro, *423*, and Calvert and Pitts, *716*.)

(148) $$CH_3\ddot{N}{=}\ddot{N}CH_3 \xrightarrow{h\nu} CH_3\ddot{N}\overset{\uparrow\ \downarrow}{=}\dot{N}CH_3\ (n,\pi^*\ S)$$

S = singlet (Paired spins)

(149) $$CH_3\ddot{N}\overset{\uparrow\ \downarrow}{=}\dot{N}CH_3\ (n,\pi^*\ S) \longrightarrow CH_3\ddot{N}\overset{\downarrow\ \downarrow}{=}\dot{N}CH_3\ (n,\pi^*\ T)$$

T = triplet (Parallel spins)

(150) $$CH_3\ddot{N}\overset{\downarrow\ \downarrow}{=}\dot{N}CH_3\ (n,\pi^*\ T) \longrightarrow CH_3\overset{\downarrow}{\cdot}\quad N{\equiv}N\quad \overset{\downarrow}{\cdot}CH_3$$

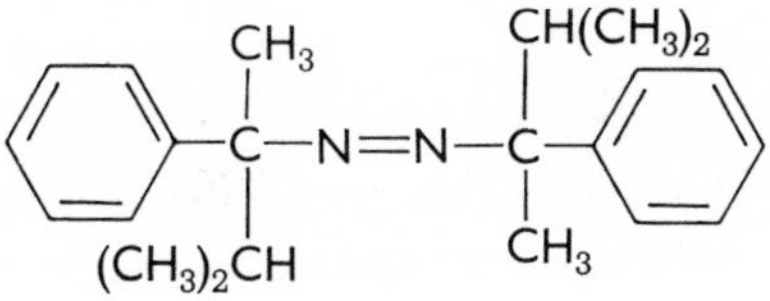

205

(151) $$\text{Sensitizer}^*(T) + RN{=}NR \longrightarrow RN{=}NR^*(T) + \text{Sensitizer}$$

Benzoyl peroxide (**206**) decomposes thermally to yield benzoyloxy (**207**) and phenyl (**208**) radicals. Apparently all of the reaction proceeds via **207** since the course of the reaction may be diverted in wet carbon tetrachloride with iodine (Eqs. 152–154).

(152) $$\underset{\mathbf{206}}{C_6H_5\overset{O}{\overset{\|}{C}}O{-}O\overset{O}{\overset{\|}{C}}C_6H_5} \longrightarrow 2\ \underset{\mathbf{207}}{C_6H_5\overset{O}{\overset{\|}{C}}O\cdot}$$

(153) $$\underset{\mathbf{207}}{C_6H_5\overset{O}{\overset{\|}{C}}O\cdot} \longrightarrow \underset{\mathbf{208}}{C_6H_5\cdot} + CO_2$$

(154) $$\underset{\mathbf{207}}{C_6H_5\overset{O}{\overset{\|}{C}}O\cdot} + I_2 \longrightarrow C_6H_5\overset{O}{\overset{\|}{C}}OI \xrightarrow{H_2O} C_6H_5\overset{O}{\overset{\|}{C}}OH + HOI$$

Oxy radicals may be generated by the thermal decomposition of hyponitrites (di-*t*-butyl hyponitrite, **209** (*717*), Eq. 155), peroxalates (di-*t*-butyl peroxalate, **210** (*718*), Eq. 156) and peroxides (di-*t*-butyl peroxide, **211**, Eq.

157). The relative rates of these reactions are compared below, and indicate that the formation of a stable molecule is reflected by an increased accessibility of the transition state to the initial state. The products of decomposition of **209** and **210** are very similar in isooctane, with *t*-butyl alcohol as the major component of the mixture (90%) along with di-*t*-butyl peroxide (10%) and a trace of acetone. The peroxide **211** arises from cage recombination of *t*-butoxy radicals. *Cage recombination* results from reaction of radical species with one another before they have had the opportunity to escape from the region of the solution within which they were formed (Eq. 158). We refer to cage recombination often and treat the subject somewhat more comprehensively under the general heading of *reaction partners* (Part 2, Section 2.10).

(155) $(CH_3)_3CO-N=N-OC(CH_3)_3 \xrightarrow{\Delta} 2 (CH_3)_3CO\cdot + N_2$

209

(156) $(CH_3)_3CO\overset{O}{\underset{\diagdown}{C}}O\overset{O}{\underset{\diagup}{C}}OC(CH_3)_3 \longrightarrow 2 (CH_3)_3CO\cdot + 2 CO_2$

210

(157) $(CH_3)_3COOC(CH_3)_3 \longrightarrow 2 (CH_3)_3CO\cdot$

211

$k_{156} > k_{155} \gg k_{157}$ $k_{155} = 1.07 \times 10^{-4}$ sec.$^{-1}$ at 55°C

10^7 10^6 1 in benzene

(158) $10\,\overline{(CH_3)_3CO\cdot\ N_2\ \cdot OC(CH_3)_3} \longrightarrow (CH_3)_3COOC(CH_3)_3$
$+ 18\,(CH_3)_3CO\cdot + 10\,N_2$

(Numbers reflect observed stoichiometry in formation of **211**, a consequence of cage behavior under certain conditions. The bar over the species at the left represents the cage.)

Free radicals may be generated by reduction of neutral species, as in the reaction of sodium with naphthalene (**212**) to yield the naphthalene radical anion (**213**) (Eq. 159), or by reduction of positively charged species, illustrated by the reaction of 1-ethyl-4-carbomethoxypyridinium iodide (**214**) with zinc in acetonitrile to form the neutral free radical, 1-ethyl-4-carbomethoxypyridinyl (**215**) (Eq. 160) (*136, 140*). Oxidation of 2,4,6-tri-*t*-butylphenol (**216**) with potassium ferricyanide produces the free radical, 2,4,6-tri-*t*-butylphenoxyl (**217**) (*138, 139*) (Eq. 161).

We may classify radical reactions into two broad classes: *E* (electron-transfer reactions) and *S* (substitution reactions). The former class can be

(159)

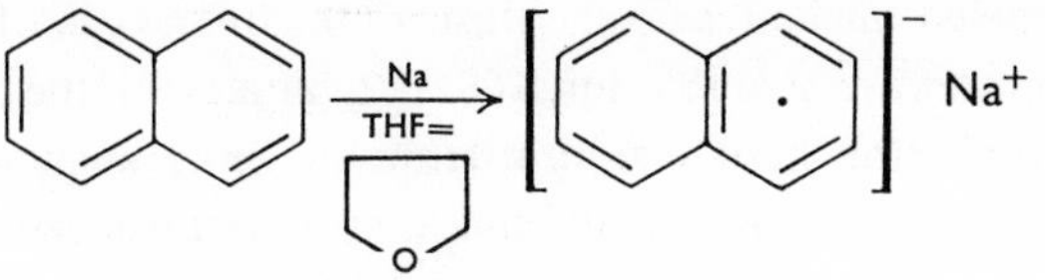

212   213

(160)

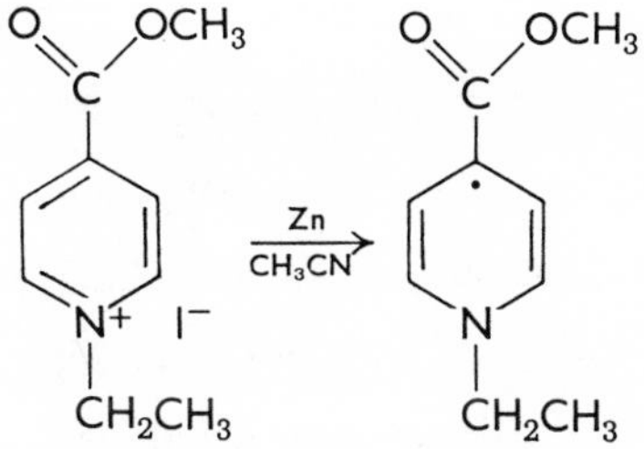

214   215

(161)

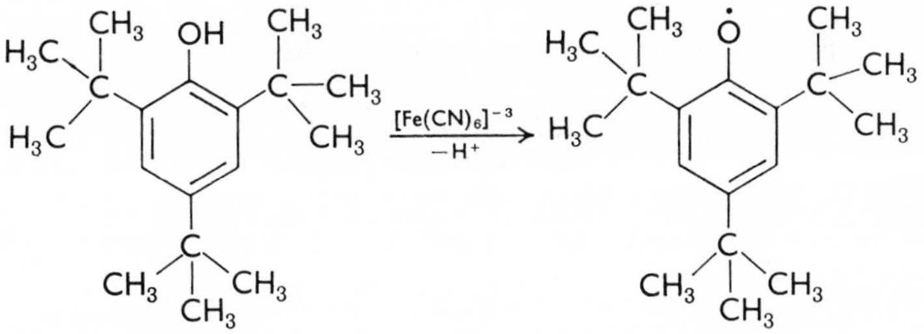

216   217

subdivided into two groups: E_+—reactions that add an electron to the substrate (Eqs. 162–164) and E_-—reactions that remove an electron from the substrate (Eqs. 165–167).

(162) $E_+ R\cdot$ $R\cdot + e^- \longrightarrow R^-$

(163) $E_+ RH$ $RH + e^- \longrightarrow RH\cdot^-$ (cf. Eq. 159)

(164) $E_+ R^+$ $R^+ + e^- \longrightarrow R\cdot$ (cf. Eq. 160)

(165) $E_- R\cdot$ $R\cdot \longrightarrow R^+ + e^-$

(166) $E_- RH$ $RH \longrightarrow RH\cdot^+ + e^-$ (cf. Eq. 161)

(Note that the free electron shown in $RH\cdot^+$ indicates that an unpaired electron is present in the molecule and should not be so construed as to unbalance the equation.)

(167) $E_- R^-$ $R^- \longrightarrow R\cdot + e^-$

The substitution reactions of radicals fall into the same categories as we utilized in Section 1.4 but care must be taken to properly identify the roles of the species involved in the reaction. Illustrations of the use of the categories for radical reactions are given in Eqs. 168–172, along with the terms that have been used elsewhere for these reactions. It should be appreciated that some of the common terms are still useful, but that the categorization offers the opportunity for making comparisons which might not have been apparent otherwise.

(168) $S_I R$ $AB \cdot \longrightarrow A \cdot + B$

   Example: radical "*unzipping*" of polymer (cf. also Eqs. 144, 145)

            $RCF_2CF_2CF_2CF_2 \cdot \longrightarrow R \cdot + 2 CF_2{=}CF_2$

(169) $S_D R$ (on X) $R \cdot + XY \longrightarrow RX + Y \cdot$

            Atom-transfer reactions

(170) $S_D R$ (on $RCH_2CH_2 \cdot$) $R \cdot + RCH_2CH_2 \cdot \longrightarrow RH + RCH{=}CH_2$

      Disproportionation, and a special case of $S_D R$ (on H)

(171) $S_A R$ (on X in X$=$Y) $R \cdot + X{=}Y \longrightarrow RXY \cdot$

            Radical addition (reverse of Eq. 168)

   In terms of the classification of Eq. 171, a polymerization by radical addition could be written $S_A R/XY_n$, in which n indicated the number of monomer units. A polymerization by cation addition would be written as $S_A E/XY_n$ and a polymerization by nucleophilic addition (carbanion addition) as $S_A N/XY_n$.

(172) $S_A R$ (on R$\cdot$) $R \cdot + R \cdot \longrightarrow RR$

            Radical dimerization

   Radical reactions may be studied in the gas phase, in matrices, and in solution. Radicals may be generated in solid phases by irradiation (ultraviolet, visible light, γ-rays, nuclear particles), and, thus, must be important in the processes responsible for radiation damage, cross-linking within solid polymers, and other solid-state reactions. Radicals generated within crystals are usually oriented with respect to the undamaged crystal lattice, and e.p.r. spectra of oriented radicals offer much useful information about the nature of the hyperfine splitting of the e.p.r. spectrum.

   Most studies of radical reactions are carried out by generating the desired species from a precursor and examining either the products of the overall reactions of the system, or the kinetics of the overall reaction, or both. Since most radicals are too reactive to be isolated and examined by themselves, the slow step in the reaction is the formation of the radical. The rates of other steps are deduced by examining the results of the competition of the radical of interest with a standard radical for a given substrate. The absolute rates for the steps in several polymerization reactions have been determined by the *rotating-sector technique* (for a description of the method and other aspects of polymerization kinetics, see *422*).

Reactive radicals can be studied by generating them within an inert medium at low temperatures. The methyl radical has been prepared by the photolysis of methyl iodide in a methane matrix at 77°K. (A matrix around a species is formed by codeposition of a substrate for example, methyl iodide, with a carrier gas like methane or argon on a cold surface. A reactive species like a radical may also be formed in the vapor phase and deposited with argon.) The e.p.r. spectrum of the methyl radical was measured with methyl radical made in this way (*134*). Analysis of the e.p.r. spectrum of $C^{13}H_3 \cdot$ led to the conclusion that the methyl radical is planar or almost planar (see Section 2.10). The degree of control which the experimenter can exercise over matrix conditions is limited and problems arise with respect to homogeneity, presence of species other than those desired, and diffusibility under the conditions used. The formation of the methyl radical, for example, probably depends upon local melting of the matrix around the thermally excited radical pair produced by irradiation, so that the iodine atom can diffuse away from the methyl radical before recombination occurs (Eqs. 173–175). (The transition is $n \rightarrow \sigma^*$, *386*.)

$$(173) \qquad CH_3I \longrightarrow CH_3I^* \ (n,\sigma^* \ S)$$

$$(174) \qquad CH_3I^* \ (n,\sigma^* \ S) \longrightarrow \overline{CH_3 \cdot \ I \cdot}$$

$$(175) \qquad \overline{CH_3 \cdot \ I \cdot} \longrightarrow CH_3 \cdot_{matrix} + I \cdot_{matrix}$$

Two techniques often used to produce unstable radicals in a form suitable for direct observation of their behavior are flash photolysis and rapid mixing. *Flash photolysis* involves the irradiation of a small amount of substrate with a large number of photons, converting a substantial proportion of the absorbing species to the excited state, from which radicals may be produced. *Rapid mixing* depends upon bringing together two reactants in solution within a reaction chamber (very effective: a four-jet mixer; very convenient and reasonably good: an ordinary three-way stopcock). *Cyclic voltammetry*, electrochemical reduction, or oxidation in which the potential is first increased to a particular limit and then decreased to the starting potential, is often valuable for the study of fairly unstable radicals. The degree to which the reaction is not completely reversible is a measure of the reactivity of the radicals towards the components of the medium but the interpretations are sometimes complicated by the fact that the region around the electrode is different from the bulk solution in composition.

From the point of view of detailed studies on the mechanism of reactions of radicals, reactive radicals are inconvenient in that they may be examined only under these conditions suitable for their production or storage. Since the discovery by Gomberg of the stability of the triphenylmethyl radical (*719*), many free radicals stable enough to be isolated or retained in solution have been prepared. The explicit advantage of "stable" free radicals for the study of mechanisms and other properties of radicals is that their stability allows reactions to be carried out under a variety of conditions of temperature, solvent, etc., including those which are drastically different from the conditions necessary for the preparation of the free radical. In addition to the pyridinyl radical **215**, and the phenoxyl radical **217**, we might mention di-*t*-butyl nitroxyl **218** (*137*), diphenylpicrylhydrazyl **219**, perchlorotriphenyl-methyl **220** (*720*), perfluorotriphenylmethyl **221** (*721*), and the *violene* radicals similar to the radical cation from tetraphenylhydrazine, the tetraphenylhy-drazinylium ion **222** (*722*) and dimethylviologen radical cation 223 (*623*).

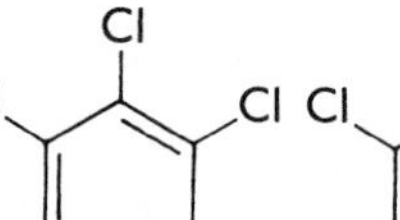

218 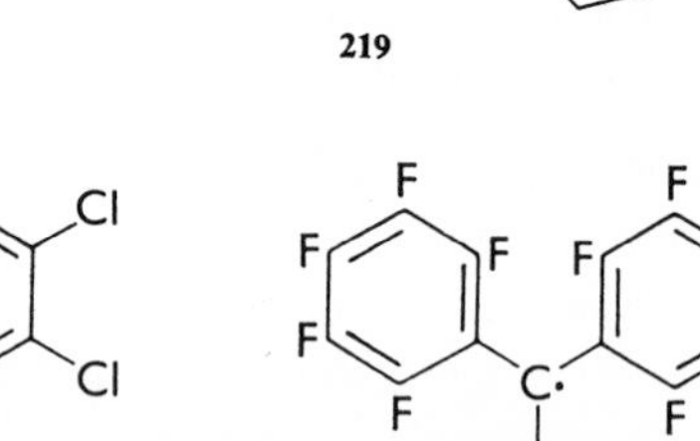   219

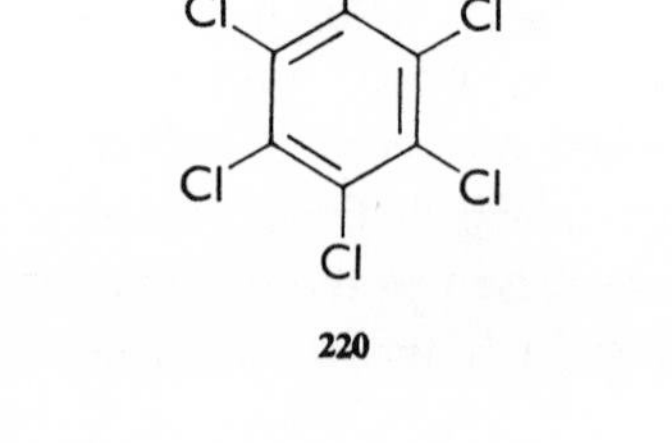

220 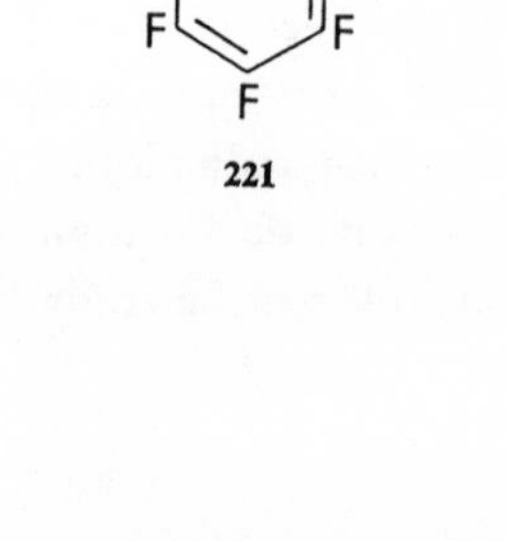   221

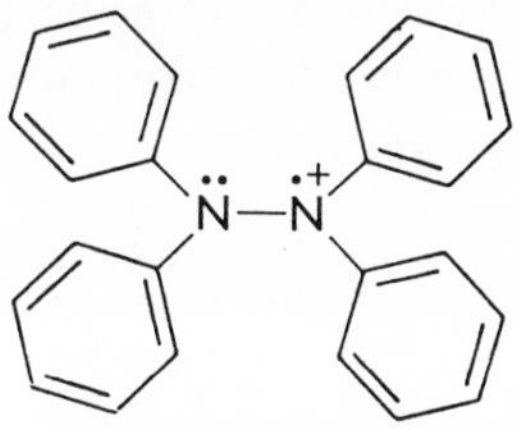

222

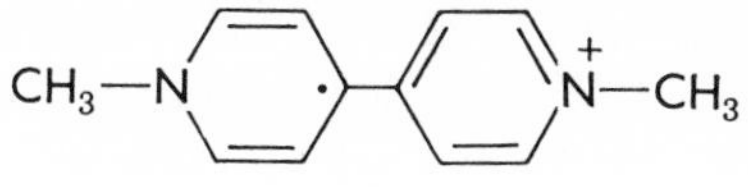

223

Stable radicals which have been used for trapping radicals that escape from cages are galvinoxyl **224** (*595, 723*) and its "aza" analog, 2,3′,5′,6-tetra-*t*-butylindophenoxyl **41** (BIP) (*286, 287*) (see Eq. 83).

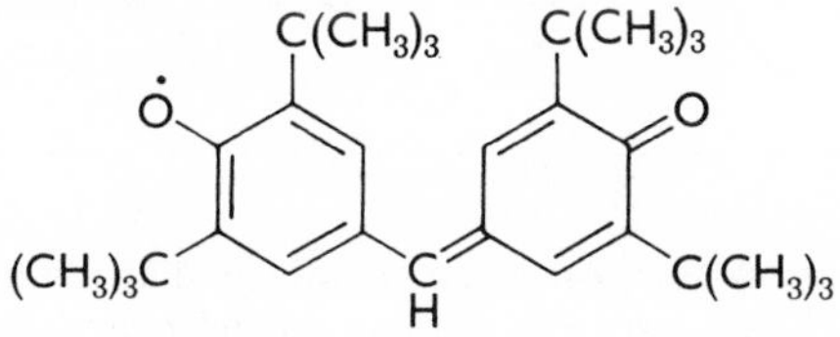

224

The position of the equilibrium between free radicals and their covalent dimers is very much dependent on the structure of the species participating in the equilibrium. Steric repulsion and electrostatic repulsion are factors which tend to destabilize the dimer. Delocalization and the presence of electronegative atoms (atoms which have a high affinity for electrons, that is, a high effective nuclear charge) stabilize the radicals. A free energy versus reaction coordinate diagram, which illustrates the behavior of the hexaphenylethane-triphenylmethyl and ethane-methyl systems, is shown in Fig. 1.31. The activation energy for the dissociation of hexaphenylethane has been reported as 19 kcal./mole (*142*), a figure that is strikingly lower than the 84 kcal./mole estimated by Benson (*143*) for ethane (Eqs. 176, 177). Bent and Cuthbertson (*144*) have shown with a study of the heats of hydrogenation of ethane and hexaphenylethane that steric effects are responsible for a destabilization of about 17 kcal./mole.

(176) $(C_6H_5)_3CC(C_6H_5)_3 \longrightarrow 2 (C_6H_5)_3C\cdot$

(177) $CH_3CH_3 \longrightarrow 2 CH_3\cdot$

The increasing ease of dissociation along the series of the dimers, CH_3CH_3, NH_2NH_2, HOOH, F_2, is explicable in terms of lone-pair repulsion (electrostatic destabilization) in the dimer and electronegativity as the stabilizing influence in the radicals.

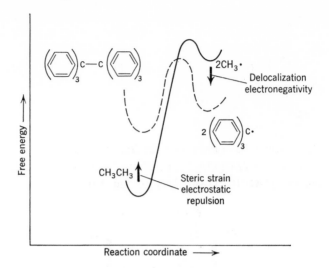

Figure 1.31 A free energy versus reaction coordinate diagram illustrating the relative positions of the equilibria between ethane and methyl radicals and hexaphenylethane and triphenylmethyl radicals. The positions of the curves are to be interpreted in a qualitative sense only.

The rate of radical recombination is usually close to diffusion-controlled and, in cases for which estimates might be made, has a very small activation energy. The rate of radical formation varies widely with structure, as we have already seen in the comparison of the rate constants for the reactions described by Eqs. 155–157.

The structural change most often made to favor the formation of radicals is to include within the molecule a grouping that gives rise to a stable molecule as product. The stabilization of molecules like nitrogen (from the azo group) and carbon dioxide (from peroxyesters) is in part reflected in a stabilization of the transition state, the reference for the stabilization being the transition state that forms the same radical products without the stable molecule (note Eqs. 155–157 and the associated data) (Fig. 1.32).

The dimerization of peroxy radicals formed during oxidation of hydrocarbons or hydrogen abstraction from hydroperoxides leads to very unstable tetroxides (Eqs. 178–181).

(178) $RH + B \cdot \text{ (initiator)} \longrightarrow R \cdot + BH$

(179) $R \cdot + O_2 \longrightarrow ROO \cdot$

(180) $ROOH + B \cdot \text{ (initiator)} \longrightarrow ROO \cdot + BH$

(181) $ROO \cdot + ROO \cdot \longrightarrow ROOOOR (RO_4R)$

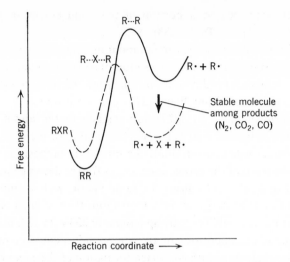

Figure 1.32 Free energy versus reaction coordinate diagram for two reactions which produce the same product plus or minus a stable molecule (X).

The tetroxide decomposes to give either peroxide or oxy radicals, possibly through a common cage intermediate (Eq. 182) (*146–149*). Bartlett and Günther (*724*) have found that the peroxy radicals can react with oxyradicals to form trioxides, which ultimately lead to the products derived from the oxy radicals (Eq. 183).

(182)

$$RO-OO-OR \longrightarrow [RO\text{---}O\!=\!O\text{---}OR] \longrightarrow \overline{RO\cdot \ O_2 \ \cdot OR}$$

$$\text{Transition state}$$

$$2\,ROO\cdot \qquad\qquad\qquad ROOR \qquad 2RO\cdot + O_2$$

(183) $\qquad RO\cdot + ROO\cdot \rightleftharpoons ROOOR \quad$ (to right $< -30°C$)

$\qquad\qquad RO\cdot + ROOH \longrightarrow ROH + ROO\cdot$

A combination of extreme destabilization of the dimers (RO_4R and RO_3R) by lone-pair repulsion and low O—O bond energies (51 kcal./mole for HOOH, Table 1.33) and stabilization of the monomeric radicals ($RO\cdot$, $ROO\cdot$) by the high nuclear charge on oxygen is responsible for the instability of the tetroxide and trioxide. The *fragmentation reaction* (see Section 1.5 for an examination of the role of fragmentation reactions in the chemistry of carbonium ions) shown in Eq. 182 is driven in part by the stabilization of the transition state imparted by a portion of the bond energy of the oxygen molecule (119 kcal./mole, Table 1.33).

A comparison of three simple azo compounds is instructive on the nature of the transition states for the decomposition of azo compounds into radicals and nitrogen. Azobenzene (**225**) does not undergo thermal decomposition to radicals, phenylazotriphenylmethane (**226**) has a half-life of 51 minutes at 50°C, and azotriphenylmethane (**227**) is so unstable that it cannot be isolated at temperatures as low as -40°C (*161*). The stability of the product radical plays an important role in determining the rate of decomposition for an azo compound. The trend of the activation energies for the decomposition of azo-alkanes listed in Table 1.40 reflects the same factor, with symmetrical sub-stitution lowering the energy of activation more than a single substitution of a particular radical stabilizing group (compare **233** with **234**, for example). The mechanism of decomposition of azo compounds might then be viewed as proceeding via single step, with concerted formation of the cage combination of a radical pair and nitrogen (Eq. 184), or as a two-step reaction, in which the bonds to the substituents on the azo group are severed one by one (Eqs. 185, 186) (*158, 159*).

225 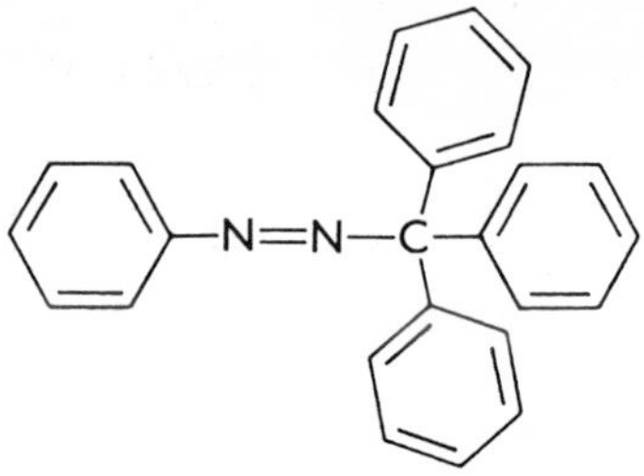   226

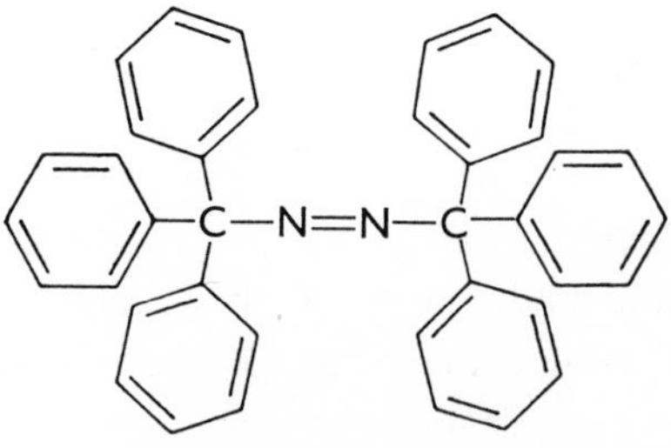

227

(184) $R-N{=}N-R \longrightarrow [R{\cdots}N{\equiv}N{\cdots}R] \longrightarrow \overline{R{\cdot}\ N_2\ {\cdot}R}$

Transition state

(185) $R—N{=}N—R \longrightarrow [R{\cdot}{\cdots\cdot}{\cdot}N{=}N—R] \longrightarrow \overline{R{\cdot}\ {\cdot}N{=}N—R}$

Transition state

(186) $\overline{R{\cdot}\ {\cdot}N{=}NR} \longrightarrow [R{\cdot}\ {\cdot}N{\equiv}N{\cdots\cdot}R] \longrightarrow \overline{R{\cdot}\ N_2\ {\cdot}R}$

Transition state

TABLE 1.40 *Energies of Activation: Decomposition of Azo Compounds*

Compound	Medium	E_a, kcal./mole	ΔS, e.u.	Ref.
$CH_3N{=}NCH_3$ (204)	Vapor	52.7[a]	12.2	*161*
$CH_3CH_2N{=}NCH_2CH_3$ (228)	Vapor	49.9	12.2	*161*
$(CH_3)_3CN{=}NC(CH_3)_3$ (229)	Vapor	44.4[a]	16–17	*161*
$C_6H_5CH_2N{=}NCH_2C_6H_5$ (230)	Vapor	36.4	5	*161*
$C_6H_5CH(CH_3)N{=}N(CH_3)CHC_6H_5$ (231)	Dodecane	32.6	7.0	*160*
$C_6H_5CH(CH_3)N{=}NCH(CH_3)_2$ (232)		36.5	9.3	*159*
$C_6H_5CH(CH_3)N{=}NCH_3$ (233)	Hexadecane	38.6	14.0	*160*
$C_6H_5C(CH_3)_2N{=}N(CH_3)_2CC_6H_5$ (234)	Toluene	29.4	11.0	*161*

[a] The activation energy for decomposition of dimethyl peroxide is 36.1 kcal./mole (Ref. 145) and for di-*t*-butyl peroxide, 34 kcal./mole (Ref. 143).

The substitution of deuterium for the α-hydrogen in **233** has an effect on the rate through a *secondary hydrogen isotope effect* as illustrated in the results of Seltzer (*160*) summarized in Table 1.41. The rate decrease for a single

TABLE 1.41 *Isotope Effects on Rates of Decomposition of Azo Compounds*[a,b]

Compound	$10^4 k$, sec.$^{-1}$
$C_6H_5CH(CH_3)N{=}NCH_3$ (232)[c]	1.16
$C_6H_5CD(CH_3)N{=}NCH_3$ (235)	1.04
$C_6H_5CH(CH_3)N{=}NCD_3$ (236)[d]	1.19

[a] Ref. 160. [b] In diphenyl ether-benzoquinone at 161.0°.
[c] $k_{232}/k_{235} = 1.12 \pm 0.01$. [d] $k_{232}/k_{236} = 0.97 \pm 0.01$.

deuterium-for-hydrogen substitution on the side of the azo group which leads to the most stable radical (and which ought to be the farthest along the pathway to cleavage at the transition state) is about 12%. In contrast, substitution of *three* deuteriums for hydrogens on the methyl side of **232 (236)** leads to a small rate *increase* (about 3%). We conclude that the bond to the α-phenylethyl group is considerably more stretched at the transition state than the bond to the methyl group. The unsymmetrical radical product, **237**, has actually been claimed from the low temperature photolysis of the azo-isobutyronitrile **42** in a glass (*218*) but the interpretation of the e.p.r. spectrum may require reexamination in view of the results of Bartlett and McBride (*715*) already alluded to. Photolysis of **205** in a glass at 77°K gives a triplet diradical and the D value of the e.p.r. spectrum (the zero-field splitting) [see Part 3 for further discussion of D values] indicated that the radicals were separated by 6 to 7 A, or roughly the distance expected for a pair of radicals separated by a nitrogen molecule. An indication of the correctness of this view of the e.p.r. results lies in the fact that photolysis of the *meso*-isomer of **205** in methylcyclohexane glass at 77°K yields *pure meso*-hydrocarbon (radical dimer) **238** (Eq. 187). Similarly photolysis of *dl*-**205** under the same conditions forms *dl*-**238**. Only radicals that maintained stereochemical integrity with respect to one another when trapped in a glassy matrix could yield such specific results.

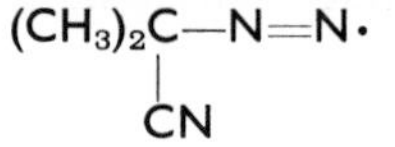

$$(CH_3)_2C-N=N\cdot$$
$$|$$
$$CN$$

237

(187)

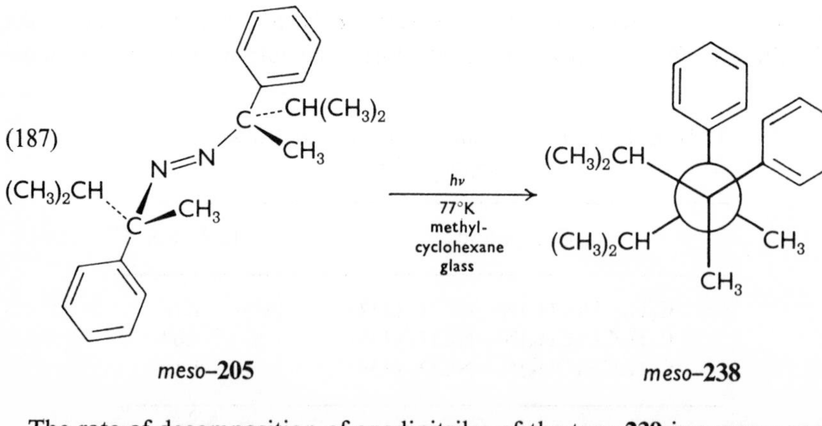

meso–**205**   meso–**238**

The rate of decomposition of azodinitriles of the type **239** is a measure of (a) the tendency of compounds of medium rings to relieve strain by forming an intermediate with one less bond to the ring and (b) the stability of radicals derived from rings of different sizes. Rate data for **239** are listed in Table 1.42 for the reaction shown in Eq. 188. The parallel between the trends shown in Table 1.42 and that of the rates of solvolysis of tertiary alkyl chlorides of the type **240** (Eq. 189) is easy to see from the data given in Table 1.43.

TABLE 1.42   *Rates of Azocompound Decomposition*[a]

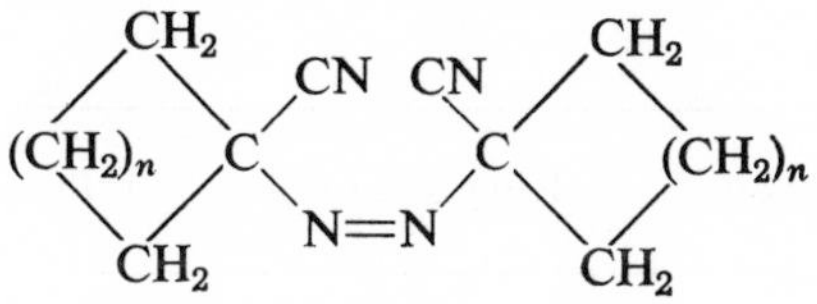

239

Compound 239	(Ring Size)	$10^4 k$, sec.$^{-1}$ 80°C	$\Delta E_a{}^b$ kcal./mole	ΔS^* e.u.
$n = 1$	C_4	0.00173	32.1	1.3
$n = 2$	C_5	0.726	33.8	18.9
$n = 3$	C_6	0.063	35.4	17.8
$n = 4$	C_7	12.2	27.5	6.1
$n = 5$	C_8	83.5	25.9	5.9
$n = 7$	C_{10}	18.1	28.0	8.5

[a] Ref. 725.   [b] Activation energy.

The effect of adding phenyl substituents to the alkyl group R in the perester, RCO_3—$C(CH_3)_3$, is illustrated in Table 1.44. The augmentation of rate decreases for each successive phenyl group probably because steric hindrance does not permit the maximum stabilization to be attained at the transition state. The rate of decomposition of a series of phenylperacetates (Eq. 190) is affected by substituents in the phenyl ring, but the ρ is only -1.2 (*150–152*), and it is possible that initial state effects contribute to the observed total effect of the substituents. [Substituents might alter the intrinsic stability of the initial state to some extent, and this factor must not be excluded from our considerations even if we are confident that the major portion of the effect of a substituent is usually expressed at that stage where the call upon substituent properties (electron-supply or withdrawal) is greatest, that is, at the transition state insofar as substituent effects on rates are concerned.]

TABLE 1.43   *Rates of Solvolysis of 1-Chloro-1-Methyl-cycloalkanes* [a]

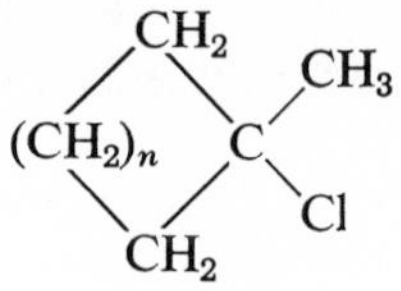

240

Compound 240	(Ring Size)	$10^6 k$, sec.$^{-1}$ [b]
$n = 1$	C_4	0.62
$n = 2$	C_5	367
$n = 3$	C_6	2.94
$n = 4$	C_7	320
$n = 5$	C_8	842
$n = 6$	C_9	129
$n = 7$	C_{10}	52.3
$n = 8$	C_{11}	35.3
$n = 10$	C_{13}	8.4
$n = 12$	C_{15}	5.3
$n = 14$	C_{17}	5.6
t-butyl		8.9

[a] Refs. 726, 727.   [b] In 80% ethanol at 25°C.

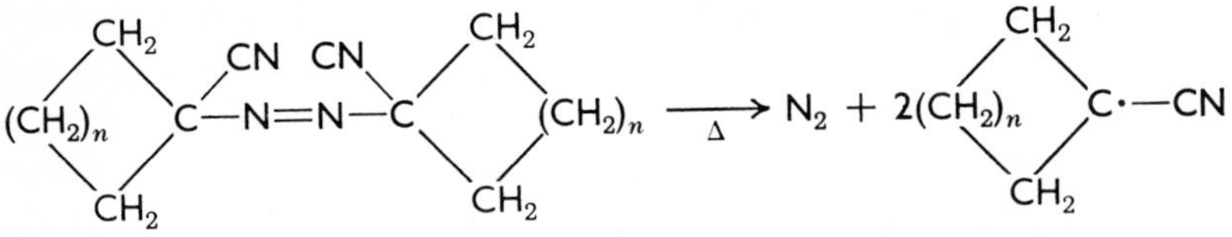

239

(188)

(189)

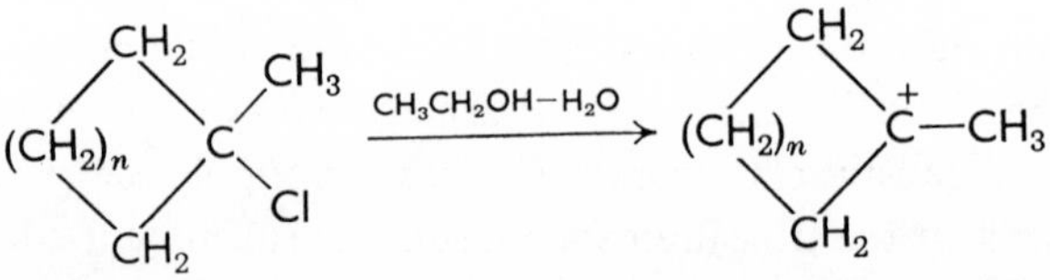

240

TABLE 1.44 *Decompositions of Peresters*[a]

Compound	k, sec.$^{-1}$ [b]	Relative k	ΔH^* kcal./mole	ΔS^* e.u.
$CH_3\overset{O}{\overset{\|}{C}}OOC(CH_3)_3$	2.1×10^{-11}	1.0	39	20
$C_6H_5CH_2\overset{O}{\overset{\|}{C}}OOC(CH_3)_3$	6.3×10^{-8}	3000	27.9	2.0
$(C_6H_5)_2CH\overset{O}{\overset{\|}{C}}OOC(CH_3)_3$	3.7×10^{-6}	180000	25.0	0.5
$(C_6H_5)_3C\overset{O}{\overset{\|}{C}}OOC(CH_3)_3$	1.7×10^{-4}	8100000	24.1	4.9

[a] From Ref. 728. [b] Extrapolated to 25°C except for triphenyl derivative.

$$\text{(190)} \quad XC_6H_4CH_2\overset{O}{\overset{\|}{C}}OOC(CH_3)_3 \xrightarrow{\Delta} XC_6H_4CH_2\cdot + CO_2 + \cdot OC(CH_3)_3$$

The reactions we have reviewed thus far for the generation of radicals from singlet molecules (that is, molecules with no unpaired electrons) are all homolytic fragmentations. Another very general method for the production of free radicals from singlet molecules is that of charge transfer (Eq. 191). The characteristics of charge-transfer processes and the absorption spectra associated with charge transfer are treated in the next section (Section 1.7) of the book.

$$\text{(191)} \quad A + B \longrightarrow A\cdot^+ + B\cdot^-$$

Electron-transfer reactions (the *E*-class, see Eqs. 162–167) are often, but *not always*, rapid. Broadening of the e.p.r. spectrum of a free radical in the presence of another molecule with which the radical can react by transferring or accepting an electron in a reversible fashion is a good method for determining rates of electron-transfer reaction with constants between 10^6–10^8 l. mole^{-1} sec.$^{-1}$. Stopped-flow reactors may be used for the study of electron-transfer reactions covering a wide range of rates, provided that detection methods are available for the low concentrations required to study fast bimolecular reactions.

The act of electron transfer must conform to the Franck–Condon principle, as Libby pointed out (*163*), for the relatively slow exchange reaction observed between hexaquoferric and hexaquoferrous ions in water.

(192) $Fe(H_2O)_6{}^{++} + Fe^*(H_2O)_6{}^{+++} \longrightarrow Fe(H_2O)_6{}^{+++} + Fe^*(H_2O)_6{}^{++}$

The water in the coordination shell around ferric ion is, on the average, closer to the iron than that around the ferrous ion because of the greater attraction exerted by the higher nuclear charge. Transfer of an electron between the initial states would create a ferrous ion with an extremely tight, unstable coordination shell and a ferric ion with a very loose, unstable coordination shell. Distortion of the solvent shells around the two ions is part of the activation process and permits electron transfer between the two ions.

Comprehensive accounts of electron-transfer processes in organic chemistry are not available but it is likely that the wisdom accumulated in the study of inorganic ions will soon be applied to organic reactions (see *729*, for example).

The remainder of this section will be devoted to S_DR reactions on halogen and hydrogen. An example which is quite typical of the kind of atom transfer reactions which occur between inorganic ions is presented to show the clear relationship between reactions in inorganic and organic systems.

Chromium(II) (chromous ion) (the valence state is indicated by the Roman numeral; the charge is shown in the usual way) has a *labile coordination shell*. A labile shell is one with which exchange or other replacement reactions take place rapidly, as in the example shown:

(193) $(H_2O)_6Cr(II) + H_2O^{18} \longrightarrow (H_2O)_5(H_2O^{18})Cr(II) + H_2O$

In contrast, chromium(III) has an inert coordination shell, one with which exchange or replacement reactions occur slowly. The half-life for the exchange of water with the water of the coordination shell of chromium(III) is about 30 hours at 25°.

(194) $(H_2O)_6Cr(III) + H_2O^{18} \longrightarrow (H_2O)_5(H_2O^{18})Cr(III) + H_2O$

Cobalt(III) ions have inert coordination shells, and cobalt(II) has a labile coordination shell. Taube (*164*) utilized the large rate difference in reactivity of the coordination shells of ions to elucidate the mechanism of an important group of inorganic oxidation-reduction reactions, those which fall into the class of S_DR reactions. The overall reaction of chromium(II) with cobalt(III) is shown as:

(195)   Cr(II) (*labile*) + Co(III) (*inert*) $\longrightarrow$ Cr(III) (*inert*) + Co(II) (*labile*)

* Indicates label, that is, radioactive iron.

The reaction of chromous ion with pentamino-chlorocobaltic ion produces cobaltous ion and chlorochromic ion (Eq. 196). Chloride ion added to the reaction mixture does *not* appear in the product.

(196) $(H_2O)_6Cr(II)^{++} + (NH_3)_5Co(III)Cl^{++} \longrightarrow (H_2O)_5Cr(III)Cl^{++}$
$$+ (H_2O)_6Co(II)^{++} + 5NH_3$$

Only direct attack of the chromous ion on the chlorine attached to the cobaltic ion could lead to the observed result, requiring a *bridged* transition state **241**. Further consideration of these interesting reactions between purely inorganic systems is beyond the scope of this book (consult *164–168, 283*), but a number of important studies have been carried out with inorganic ions and organic halides.

$$[(H_2O)_5Cr(II)\cdots Cl\cdots Co(III)(NH_3)_5]^{++++}$$
241

Polyanyi and his co-workers (*169, 170*) discovered long ago that the reaction of sodium vapor with alkyl halides could be followed with relatively simple means and had a rate range which was moderately sensitive to the structure of the organic halide (Eq. 197). The reaction of alkali metals with simple organic halides has been adopted by those interested in examining the precise details of chemical mechanism by utilizing crossed molecular beams (*171*). Bernstein and his students (*730*) and Brooks (*731*) have carried through the elegant experiment in which it was shown that potassium atoms react much more readily with the iodide end of the methyl iodide molecule than with the methyl end (Eq. 198).

(197) $\qquad\qquad Na + RX \longrightarrow Na^+X^- + R\cdot$

(198) $\qquad\qquad K + ICH_3 \longrightarrow K^+I^- + CH_3\cdot$

Halogen atom abstraction studies in organic chemistry can be carried out by generating reactive radicals in the presence of organic halides and analyzing the ratio of products formed from the halides to obtain relative rates (*172*). For example, phenyl radical might be produced through the decomposition of phenylazotriphenylmethane (**226**) in the presence of 1-butyl bromide and 1-butyl chloride. The ratio of bromobenzene to chlorobenzene in the product (readily analyzed by v.p.c., vapor-phase chromatography) would give the relative rate of reaction of phenyl radical with the two halides. Chain transfer constants, measured by examining the lowering of molecular weight of the polymeric product by a halide in a polymerization, yield *rough relative rates* of reaction of radicals (the ends of the growing radical chain) with halides (see *173, 422*). As we shall see, it is now possible to measure halogen abstraction reactions directly, to yield results which are much more informative about the relationship of reactivity and structure than the older, more qualitative methods.

Halpern and Maher (*174*) found that the pentacyanocobaltate ion [cobalt(II)] reacts with organic halides to form an organopentacyano-cobaltate ion [cobalt(III)] and a halopentacyanocobaltate ion [cobalt(III)], as shown in Eqs. 199 and 200.

(199) $Co(II)(CN)_5^{3-} + XR \longrightarrow XCo(III)(CN)_5^{3-} + \cdot R$

(200) $R \cdot + Co(II)(CN)_5^{3-} \longrightarrow RCo(III)(CN)_5^{3-}$

Certain intrinsic limitations prevent the reaction in Eq. 199 from being applied to a broad range of organic halides. The pentacyanocobaltate(II) ion is unstable to hydrolysis and is normally generated immediately before use. Its instability makes it unsuitable for reactions with half-lives over 30 minutes. The reactions must be carried out in aqueous solution at a pH greater than 12, limiting the substrates to water-soluble organic halides in which the halogen is resistant to elimination, displacement, and hydrolysis. Haloacids represent one of the classes of substrates which may be studied with pentacyanocobaltate(II) ion, and a summary of reaction rates is given in Table 1.45. An interesting variety of organocobalt compounds is accessible through the reaction shown as Eq. 200, for example, the pyridine derivative **242** formed from 2-iodopyridine.

Another reaction of inorganic reducing agents with alkyl halides is that of chromium(II) as studied by Castro and Kray (*177, 178*). The course of the reaction is quite similar to that of the pentacyanocobaltate(II) ion, except that the alkylchromous ion is susceptible to further reaction (Eqs. 201, 202). The formation of propene from allyl chloride through a reaction subsequent to the formation of the allylchromous ion is illustrated in a proposed scheme due to Castro and co-workers (*178*) (Eqs. 203 and 204). A different sort of reaction is possible, in principle, since Anet and LeBlanc have reported the existence of relatively stable alkylchromic ions like benzylchromic ion **243** (*179*).

242   243

Some rate data for the reaction of chromous ion with alkyl halides has been added to Table 1.45.

TABLE 1.45   *Rates of Reaction of Organic Halides with Penta-cobaltate (II)* [a,b] *and Chromium(II)* [c,d]

Halide	k_2, l. mole^{-1} sec.$^{-1}$
Co(II) Reactions	
ICH_2COO^-	890[e]
ICH_2COOCH_3	88000
ICH_2CONH_2	29500
$ICH_2SO_3^-$	17.6
$ICH_2CH_2COO^-$	0.54
$ICH_2CH_2COOCH_3$	~3

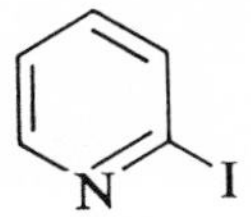	
$BrCH_2COO^-$	0.28
$BrCH_2COOCH_3$	~34

meso-$^-OOCCH(Br)CH(Br)COO^-$	78
dl-$^-OOCCH(Br)CH(Br)COO^-$	~6.5
$ClCH_2COO^-$	~0.0002
$ClCH_2CONH_2$	~0.0006
$ClCH_2COOCH_3$	~0.001
Cl_2CHCOO^-	0.019
Cl_3CCOO^-	0.44
Cr(II) Reactions	
$CH_2{=}CHCH_2Cl$	0.02
meso-$CH_3CH(Br)CH(Br)CH_3$	0.3
$C_6H_5CH(Cl)CH_3$	0.04
$C_6H_5CH(Cl)CH_2Cl$	0.77
$C_6H_5CH(Cl)CH_2Br$	1.59

[a] Ref. 174.   [b] In H_2O at 25°.   [c] Refs. 177, 178.   [d] In 1:1 dimethyl-formamide-H_2O using $HClO_4$ ($\mu = 1.0$) and $CrSO_4$ at 29.7°.   [e] Fast reactions were measured using a stopped-flow device.

The free radical formed from the alkyl halide may be isolated if it is sufficiently stable (that is, sufficiently unreactive towards the reactants present in the solution and towards itself). The sterically hindered and resonance-stabilized free radical **244** has been prepared from the corresponding chloride by reduction with chromous chloride in acetic acid (*180*).

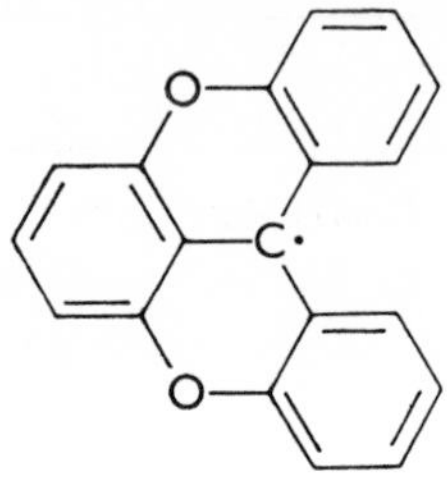

244

(201) $CH_2{=}CHCH_2Cl + Cr(II)^{++} \longrightarrow CH_2{=}CHCH_2\cdot + ClCr(III)^{++}$

(202) $CH_2{=}CHCH_2\cdot + Cr(II)^{++} \longrightarrow CH_2{=}CHCH_2Cr(II)^{++}$

(203) $CH_2{=}CHCH_2Cr(II)^{++} \equiv [CH_2{=}CH\bar{C}H_2Cr(III)]^{++} + Cr(II)^{++}$
$\longrightarrow [CH_2{=}CHCH_2{}^-Cr(II)]^+ + Cr(III)^{+++}$

(204) $[CH_2{=}CH\bar{C}H_2Cr(II)]^+ + H_3O^+ \longrightarrow CH_2{=}CHCH_3 + Cr(II)^{++}$

Stable organic free radicals have been used for halogen abstraction reactions and demonstrate conclusively the advantages, which accrue to studies of the mechanisms of radical reactions, from using a radical stable enough to be transferred from one environment to another. Westheimer, Kurz, and

TABLE 1.46   *Rates of Reaction of 1-Ethyl-4-carbo-methoxypyridinyl with Polychloromethanes in Acetonitrile*[a]

Halocarbon	k_2, l. mole^{-1} sec.$^{-1}$ [b,c]
CH_2Cl_2	2.6×10^{-8} [d]
$CHCl_3$	2.08×10^{-5}
$CDCl_3$	1.71×10^{-5}
CCl_4	3.3

[a] Ref. 175.   [b] Measurements at 25°.   [c] Rate constants per halogen atom.   [d] Extrapolated from measurements at higher temperature.

Hutton (*176*) discovered a photochemical and/or thermal reaction of dihydro-pyridines with carbon tetrachloride and bromotrichloromethane and pro-posed that a chain reaction occurred, in which one of the key steps was the abstraction of a halogen by a pyridinyl radical. (The complete mechanism for this reaction is given in the next section, Section 1.7.) Kosower and Poziomek confirmed this hypothesis with the finding that stable pyridinyl radicals like **215** were extremely reactive towards carbon tetrachloride (*175*). Kosower and Schwager (*136*) investigated the rates of reaction of the pyridinyl radical **215** with a whole range of organic halides as shown in Tables 1.46 and 1.47.

The mechanism of reaction of **215** with a halide resembles that of the inorganic ions described above. The first, rate-determining step is a transfer

TABLE 1.47 *Rates of Reaction of Halocarbons with 1-Ethyl-4-carbomethoxypyridinyl in Acetonitrile*[a,b]

Halocarbon	k_2, l. mole^{-1} sec.$^{-1}$ [c,d]
$ClCH_2Cl$	2.6×10^{-8} [e]
	5.0×10^{-6} [f]
$BrCH_2Cl$	5.0×10^{-5}
ICH_2Cl	1.4×10^{-1}
ICH_3	4.7×10^{-6}
I_2	ca. 10^7–10^8 [g]
O_2	ca. 10^6–10^7 [g]

[a] Ref. 175, except as noted. [b] Measured at 25°. [c] Rate constants per halogen atom, except as noted. [d] Rate constants based on flash photolysis studies are very approximate (I_2 and O_2) and are not corrected for the fact that the reactants are symmetrical. [e] Extrapolated from measurements at elevated temperatures. [f] At 80°; at 75°, approximate k for disappearance of radical alone in acetonitrile is 6.7×10^{-7} sec.$^{-1}$. [g] Ref. 182.

of the halogen to the radical, and a second molecule of radical is consumed in a rapid reaction with the reactive radical produced in the first step from the halocarbon (Eqs. 205 and 206). Dibromomethane is used as the halide in the illustration.

(205)

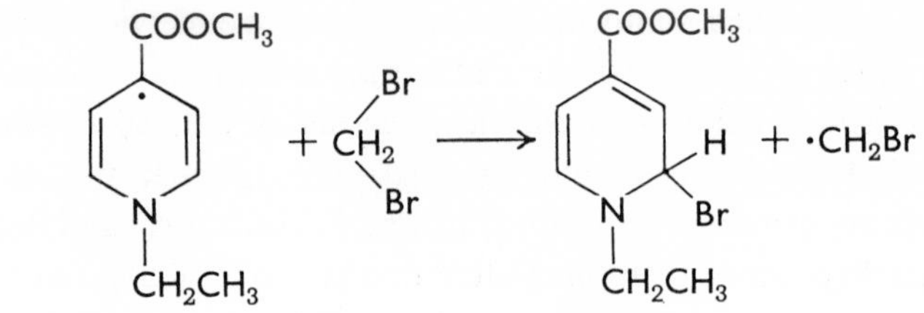

(206)

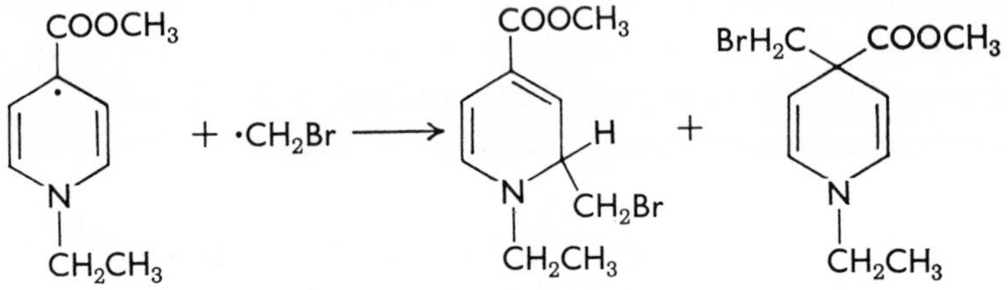

The product of combination of the bromomethyl radical with the pyridinyl radical is a mixture of two isomers, **246** and **247**, as shown by n.m.r. studies on the product (*620*). The ultimate product (the one isolated from the first step of the reaction) is not the dihydropyridine derivative **245**, but the pyridinium bromide **248**, which arises from the ionization of the highly reactive halide **245** (Eq. 207). How can one be so certain that the intermediate **245** actually occurred on the reaction pathway from **215** to **248**?

(207)

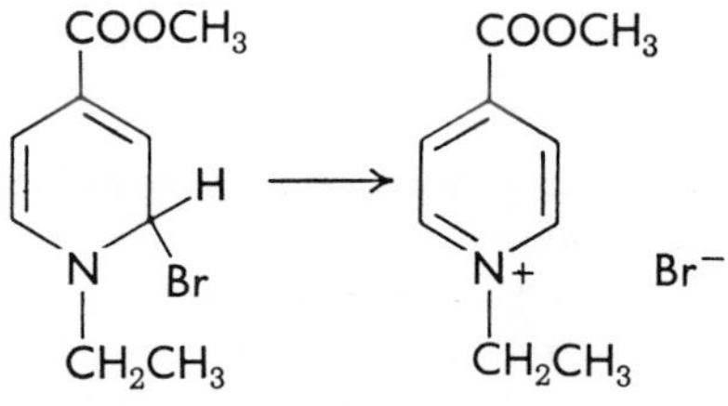

It was commonly believed (see *173*) before the studies of the pyridinyl radical halogen abstraction reaction that "carbonium ion character" contributed to the stabilization of the transition state for halogen abstraction reactions, as shown with the formulas **249** and **249a**.

$$R\cdots\cdot X\cdots B \longleftrightarrow \overset{+}{R}\cdots X\cdots\overset{-}{B}$$

249   249a

Since the pyridinyl radical should, according to this view, derive considerable stabilization from the corresponding carbonium ion (a stable "carbonium ion," the pyridinium ion), the importance of contributions like **249a** to the transition state for halogen atom abstraction should be emphasized in the reactions of the pyridinyl radical. A suitable mechanistic criterion for reactions which proceed from relatively nonpolar initial state through relatively polar transition states is the effect of solvent (see Part 2). The charge separation implied by **249a** should be accentuated in the transition state by polar solvents and the rate of the abstraction reaction should therefore be highly sensitive to the solvent polarity.

The reaction of the pyridinyl radical **215** with dibromomethane was examined in a series of solvents of increasing polarity. (Polarity was measured by the criterion of **Z**-value, which is explained in detail in Section 2.6.) The rate constants are summarized in Table 1.48. The insensitivity of the rate to solvent

TABLE 1.48   *Solvent Effect on the Rate of Reaction of 1-Ethyl-4-Carbomethoxypyridinyl with Dibromomethane*[a]

Solvent (**Z**-value)[b]	$10^4 k_2$, l. mole^{-1} sec.$^{-1}$ [c,d]
$CH_3CN(71.3)$	0.98
$CH_2Cl_2(64.2)$	0.48[e]
$(CH_3)_2CHOH(75.8)$	0.28
$CH_3CH_2OH(79.6)$	0.33

[a] Ref. 175.   [b] See Part 2 of this book.   [c] Measurements at 25°.
[d] Rate constants per halogen atom.   [e] Extrapolated from measurements at higher temperature.

polarity change demonstrates that the transition state has about the same degree of charge separation as the initial state. The solubility of both the initial reactants in solvents like heptane suggests that both dibromomethane and the pyridinyl radical **215** are not very polar molecules. We must conclude that the transition state does not have an appreciable degree of charge separation. The product from a neutral transition state must be itself neutral, forcing us to write the bromodihydropyridine **245** as the initial product.

Some hydrogen abstraction reactions exhibit a measurable solvent effect, apparently related to hydrogen bonding of the solvent to the oxy radicals used for the investigations (see Bacha and Kochi, *732*, and Walling and Wagner, *733*).

The secondary hydrogen isotope effect was measured, using the two compounds, chloroform and deuterochloroform. The decrease in rate as a result of deuteration was 20%, slightly larger than the 14% reported by Zavitsas and Seltzer (*181*) for the formation of methyl or trideuteromethyl radicals by decomposition of methyl trideuteromethyl phenylcarbinyl hypochlorite **250**. (Rates are listed in Table 1.46.)

$$CH_3-\underset{\underset{C_6H_5}{|}}{\overset{\overset{CD_3}{|}}{C}}-OCl$$

250

The selectivity of the pyridinyl radical **215** towards halogen is impressive and far greater than the selectivity of polystyryl radical (*173*) which, in turn, is more selective than the sodium atom (*169, 170*). The rate of the reaction of **215** increases as the strength of the carbon–halogen bond decreases, and the rate differences reflect bond energy differences as long as the rates of reactions which produce the same product radical (*the same leaving group*) are compared. For the reaction shown in Eq. 208, the rate constant rises by a factor of 10^3 for the change from chlorine to bromine, and a further 10^4 for the change from bromine to iodine.

$$(208) \qquad Py \cdot + XCH_2Cl \longrightarrow PyX + \cdot CH_2Cl$$

215

Kosower and Lindqvist (*182*) were able to estimate rate constants for the reaction of the pyridinyl radical **215** with the iodine molecule by studying the kinetics of recovery of pyridinium iodide **214** after flash photolysis (see Section 1.7) (Table 1.47).

The trend in rate constants for the reaction of the pyridinyl radical with the series of chlorocarbons listed in Table 1.49 suggested that the activation free energy differences might be a convenient measure of the bond energy differences. A free energy versus reaction coordinate diagram for the reaction of the pyridinyl radicals with halocarbons is shown in Fig. 1.33. A set of curves comparing the first part of that diagram for different halocarbons is given in Fig. 1.34. An arbitrary division of the differences between initial product stability and product radical stabilities has been made. The estimated bond energies based on the rate data are presented in Table 1.50. The comparison of the estimates with those from the literature and the simplicity of the method for obtaining the bond energy differences suggest that this method of obtaining comparative bond energies is worth further exploration.

Comparatively little work has been done on the S_DR reactions of radicals

TABLE 1.49 *Rate and Activation Free Energy Comparison of Chloro-methanes*[a]

Halocarbon	k_2, l. mole^{-1} sec.$^{-1}$ [b]	ΔF^*, kcal./mole	$\Delta\Delta F^*$, kcal./mole
CH_3Cl	1.1×10^{-12}	31.4	
			5.9
CH_2Cl_2	2.6×10^{-8}	25.5	
			3.9
$CHCl_3$	2.1×10^{-5}	21.6	
			7.1
CCl_4	3.3	14.5	

[a] Ref. 175. [b] Rate constant per chlorine atom at 25°.

on hydrogen. Ayscough and Russell (*185*) have looked at the reaction of diphenylpicrylhydrazyl (**219**) with 2,4,6-tri-*t*-butylphenol (**216**). The forward reaction

(209) $\qquad$ **219(DPPH·) + 216 $\rightleftharpoons$ 219H(DPPH$_2$) + 217**

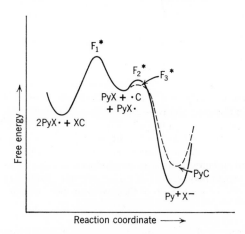

Figure 1.33 A free energy versus reaction coordinate diagram for the reaction of pyridinyl radicals with halocarbons. Py· is the pyridinyl radical (in this case, 1-ethyl-4-carbomethoxypyridinyl), XC is the halocarbon, PyX is the covalently bonded adduct of halide ion to the pyridinium ring, C· is the radical produced by abstraction of the halogen X from the halocarbon, Py$^+$X$^-$ is the ionic pyridinium halide, and PyC is the dihydro-pyridine (or dihydropyridines) formed by combination of the pyridinyl radical with the halocarbon radical (Ref. 175). (Reprinted with the permission of the *Journal of the American Chemical Society*.)

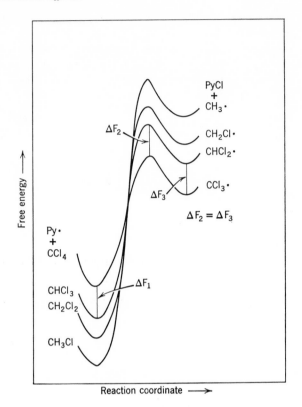

Figure 1.34 A free energy versus reaction coordinate diagram for the reaction of pyridinyl radical (in this case, 1-ethyl-4-carbomethoxypyridinyl) with the chloromethane series: CH_3Cl, CH_2Cl_2, $CHCl_3$, and CCl_4. The product PyCl represents the covalently bonded adduct of chloride ion to the pyridinium ring. The curves are drawn so as to divide the measured rate differences about equally between initial halocarbon stability and product radical stability. It must be emphasized that this division is arbitrary and that all of the differences may well reside in, for example, product radical stability (Ref. 175). (Reprinted with the permission of the *Journal of the American Chemical Society*.)

has a rate constant of 0.12 l. mole^{-1} sec.$^{-1}$ and the reverse reaction a rate constant of approximately 2 l. mole^{-1} sec.$^{-1}$ at 20°C. A large isotope effect was found for the forward reaction with k_H/k_D of about 12. Gas phase proton or hydrogen-atom transfers do not show large isotope effects (*186*) in contrast to the isotope effect for proton transfer to sterically hindered bases, with the large k_H/k_D of 24 ascribed to tunneling by Funderburk and Lewis (*187*).

The rate constant for the reaction of the phenoxyl radical **217** with its precursor **216** has been estimated by Kreilick and Weissmann (*734*) from the

TABLE 1.50 *Carbon–Halogen Bond Energies*

Halocarbon	DH, kcal./mole
CH_3---Cl	80(83.5)[a]
CH_2Cl---Cl	74.1, 77.6[b]
$CHCl_2$---Cl	70.2, 73.7[b](72)[c]
CCl_3---Cl	63.1, 66.6[b](68 ± 3)[d](68.4)[e]

[a] First figure listed in Ref. 183, second figure in Ref. 184. [b] Derived from figures for CH_3Cl by subtraction of $\Delta\Delta F^*$, with first figure based on Ref. 183 and second figure on Ref. 184. [c] Given in Ref. 183 as doubtful. [d] Ref. 183. [e] Ref. 184.

broadening of the e.p.r. spectrum of **217** as 660 l. mole^{-1} sec.$^{-1}$, almost 1000 times faster than the reaction of DPPH· with the same phenol **216**.

DaRooge and Mahoney (*51*) have carefully examined the rates of the reaction of the phenoxyl radical **217** with simple phenols and, with some reservations about anomalously fast 4-substituted compounds, found that the rates could be correlated with a reaction constant (ρ) of -2.42. (The total rate is correlated by a reaction constant of -2.72, but half of the radical is consumed in an extremely fast second step by the reactive radical produced from the simple phenol in the first step.) The rates of hydrogen abstraction from simple phenols by DPPH· have been reported to be correlated by a reaction constant of -4.54, but this may be high as a result of the anomalous reactivity of the 4-substituted phenols which were used (*49*). The two steps of the reaction are shown for 4-methoxyphenol in Eqs. 210 and 211.

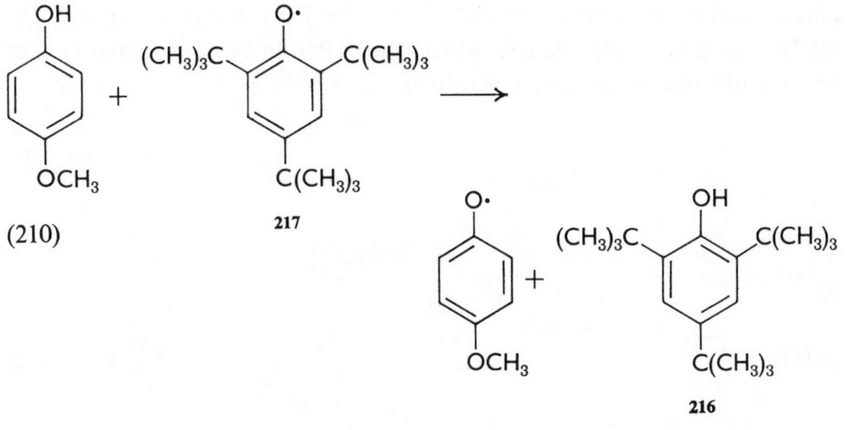

(210)

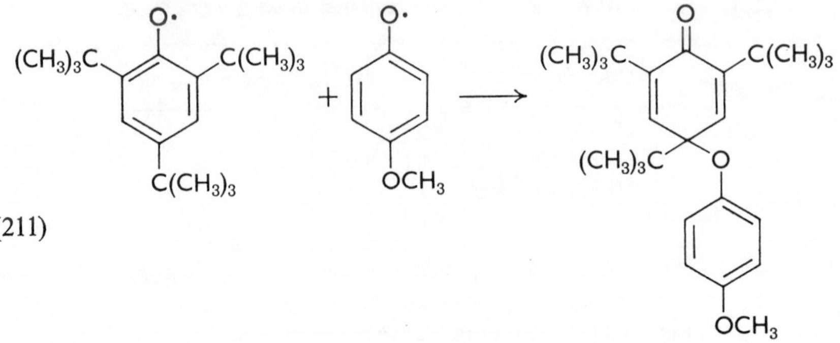

(211)

The isotope effect (k_H/k_D) for the reaction of the phenoxyl radical **217** with 4-phenylphenol is about 7.5, suggesting that a substantial degree of bond-breaking has occurred in the transition state. Nevertheless, the magnitude of the reaction constant (ρ) gives some occasion for suspicion that the mechanism may not be as simple as "hydrogen atom transfer." We can illustrate this by showing:

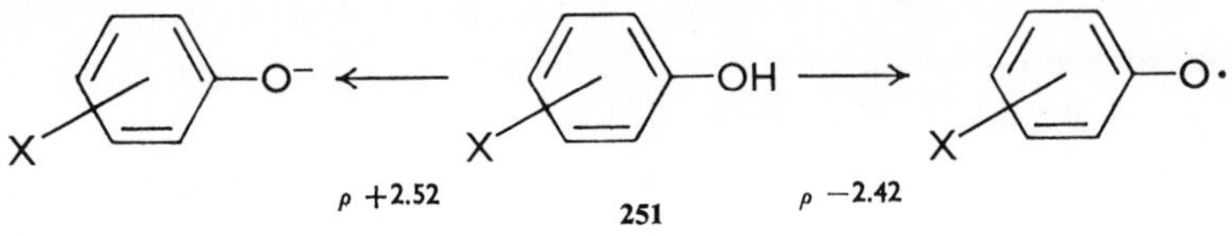

ρ +2.52   **251** ρ −2.42

in which it is clear that the ρ for the ionization of phenols (Table 1.15) is about the same in absolute magnitude as ρ for the reaction of Eq. 210. We might imagine a charge-transfer process as shown in Eq. 212 to account for the resemblance in substituent sensitivity.

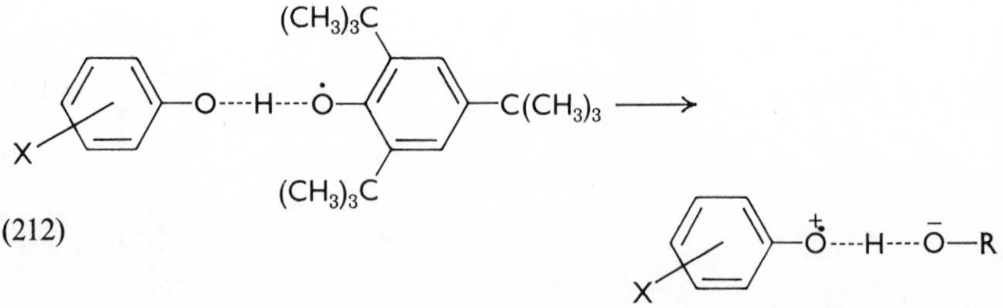

(212)

Further work on the reaction of stable free radicals promises much in the way of detailed understanding of radical reaction mechanisms.

Problems

1. Write out the scheme for the formation of ethyl radicals from azoethane, $CH_3CH_2N{=}NCH_2CH_3$, via (a) thermal decomposition (b) photolysis.
2. Identify the reaction pathway necessary to account for the products from azoethane which does not occur in the decomposition of azomethane.
3. The compound, 2,3-diazabicyclo[2.2.2]octene-2 (**A**), gives a moderately high quantum yield of fluorescence (Ref. 735). What implications does this finding have for the photochemistry of **A**?

A

4. Using actual examples, write an illustration for each of the following mechanisms of radical formation or reaction:
   (a) $E_+R{\cdot}$.
   (b) E_+RH
   (c) E_+R^+
   (d) $E_-R{\cdot}$
   (e) E_-RH
   (f) E_-R^-
   (g) S_IR
   (h) S_DR
   (i) S_AR
5. Explain the stability of the following radicals:
   (a) $(CF_3)_2NO{\cdot}$
   (b) Perchlorobenzhydryl radical.
   (c) Galvinoxyl.
   (d) 1-Ethyl-4-carbomethoxypyridinyl.
   (e) Triphenylmethyl.
6. Explain the instability of the following radicals:
   (a) Phenyl.
   (b) Methyl.
   (c) Benzyl.

(d) Phenoxyl.

(e) Hydroxyl.

7. After answering this question, reexamine your discussion for Problems 5 and 6. Define stability and instability.

8. Illustrate with formulas the formation of *dl*-238 from *dl*-205 at 77°K.

9. Invent at least two new fragmentation reactions for the production of free radicals.

10. How would the Franck–Condon principle apply to electron-transfers between organic molecules, for example, naphthalene and naphthalene radical anion in tetrahydrofuran?

11. Explain the rate difference between the reaction of pentacyanocobaltate(II) with iodoacetate ion and methyl iodoacetate (Table 1.45).

12. Write out the reaction scheme for 1-isopropyl-4-carbomethoxypyridinyl and iodochloromethane.

13. Write the transition states for the fragmentation of the hypochlorite **250** in solvents of different polarity. Should there be a solvent effect on the isotope effect, as measured by k_H/k_D?

14. Write out the reaction scheme for 2,4,6-tri-*t*-butylphenoxyl radical and 4-cyanophenol. Is the reaction faster or slower than the reaction of the radical with 4-methoxyphenol? Estimate the relative rate for the reaction with the two phenols.

15. Explain the observation that *t*-butyl 2-phenylthio-perbenzoate decomposes 65,000 times faster than *t*-butyl perbenzoate (Ref. 736).

16. The radical anion derived from sodium and biphenyl in 1,2-dimethoxyethane reacts with cholesteryl chloride (**132**) to yield only 5-cholestene (**B**) after the reaction mixture was treated with water. The same reagent gave a mixture of 5-cholestene (**B**) and 3,5-cyclocholestane (**C**) by reaction with 3,5-cyclo-cholestan-6β-yl chloride (**133**). The ratio of **B** to **C** varied with temperature, rising from 2:3 at −70°C to 8:1 at 25°C. Explain these results in terms of probable intermediates and their structure (Ref. 737).

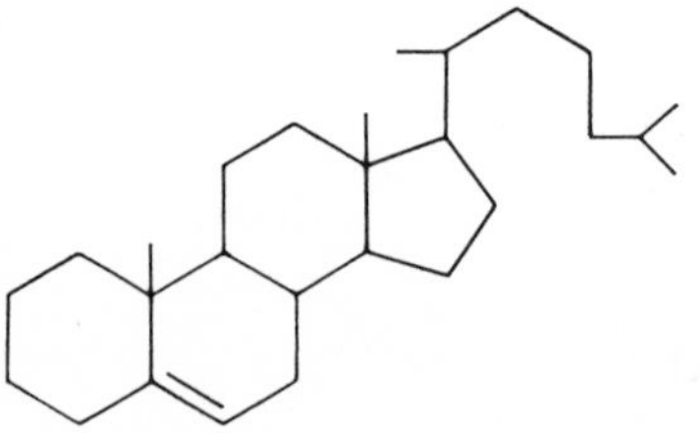

B 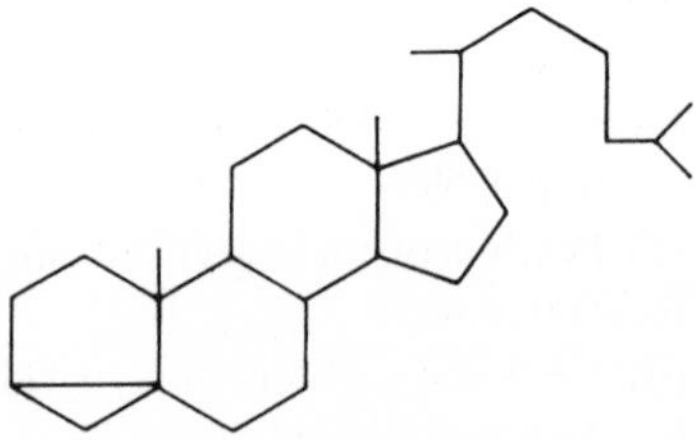   C

1.7 Charge-Transfer Complexes and Reactions

The fact that iodine dissolved in carbon tetrachloride to give a violet solution (a color that resembled that of iodine vapor) and in benzene to yield a brown solution was known since the latter part of the nineteenth century. The explanation for these colors eluded chemists until Mulliken (*189, 190*) put forward a comprehensive theory of charge-transfer spectra, and indicated how weak ground-state interactions could lead to striking spectroscopic phenomena, arising from a new type of electronic transition called a charge-transfer transition. Brackman (*188*) proposed a more qualitative theory embodying the same basic principle at about the same time.

An understanding of weak interactions between molecules, as well as insight into weak intramolecular interactions, is vital to understanding chemical reactions, especially for perceiving how two apparently similar transition states might actually differ in energy. Charge-transfer interactions are small and, in the ground state, are fairly difficult to distinguish from other types of electrical interaction like mutual polarization. Kosower (*50*) has reviewed the role of charge-transfer complexes in chemical reactions, and more complete surveys of charge-transfer complexes and their spectra may be found in the books by Briegleb (*191*) and Andrews and Keefer (*192*). We shall review the nature of charge-transfer complexes, cite a few charge-transfer maxima, summarize the principles that appear to govern the reactions of charge-transfer complexes, and give several examples of charge-transfer reactions. One of the important applications of charge-transfer complexes, the measurement of solvent polarities by means of the solvent dependent transition of a charge-transfer complex, is discussed fully in Section 2.6. *A charge-transfer complex is a combination of a donor and acceptor which exhibits a special light absorption called a charge-transfer transition.*

A donor (D) may be defined as any molecule capable of losing an electron, with donor ability conveniently measured (or rather reflected in) the ionization potential I_p. An acceptor (A) is any molecule capable of acquiring an electron, but acceptor ability is not so easy to measure, since it is relatively difficult to obtain the relevant *electron affinity*. The electron affinity does bear some relation to the one-electron reduction potential.

Donors and acceptors interact, according to charge-transfer complex theory, to form a complex which, in the simplest case, may be expressed as:

(213)
$$D + A \overset{K_c}{\rightleftharpoons} D,A$$

The charge-transfer complex, (D, A), absorbs light in a way different from either the donor or acceptor alone, in that a new absorption band is present in addition to the original or slightly modified bands of the components of the complex. In its simplest form, the light absorption process may be written:

$$(214) \qquad\qquad D,A \longrightarrow D\cdot^{+},A\cdot^{-}$$

Theory suggests that the ground state is stabilized by a small contribution from the excited state. A corresponding contribution to the excited state then leads to a modified Eq. 214:

$$(215) \qquad\qquad (D,A)(\leftrightarrow D\cdot^{+},A\cdot^{-}) \longrightarrow (D\cdot^{+},A\cdot^{-})(\leftrightarrow D,A)$$

The question of the magnitude of the contribution of the charge-transferred form to the ground state is thus raised and, because such charge-separations should be reflected in ground-state properties, can be investigated experimentally. Such estimates as are available have placed reliance largely on the dipole moment, but it is not easy to translate experimental measurements of dipole moments, especially those of modest magnitude, into estimates of the extent of charge transfer because of uncertainty about the extent of mutual polarization. Polarization, of course, leads to charge asymmetry without an electron formally being transferred to the molecule causing the polarization. The pyridine–iodine complex (**252**) has a dipole-moment of 4.90 D in *n*-heptane, and at least a portion of the difference between this moment and the dipole moment of pyridine itself (**253**), 2.28 D, is probably due to a charge-transfer contribution to the ground state of this moderately stable complex (see *193*) (K_c ca. 100).

252   **253**

A search for abnormal distances within charge-transfer complex crystals has thus far been fruitless using X-ray crystallography, and nuclear quadrupole resonance and infrared spectroscopy have provided little support for the notion that there is appreciable charge-transfer in the ground state of most complexes. (The dipole moment (12.4 D) measured for the "complex" of triethylamine and iodine in dioxane indicates that the properties of the solution are actually due to a salt, perhaps triethylamine hydriodide, formed as a result of a sequence of reactions beginning with a one-electron transfer from triethylamine to iodine) (*193, 50*).

The remarkable difference between the spectrum of benzene and iodine separately and that of the benzene–iodine complex is illustrated in Fig. 1.35. A list of charge-transfer maxima for a variety of complexes is given in Table 1.51. Donors may be grouped according to whether the source of the electron that is transferred lies in a nonbonding orbital (*n*), a multiple bond (*π*), or a single bond (*σ*). This is the same classification used to list neighboring groups. Acceptors may be *v* (vacant orbital), *π*, or *σ*.

For some reason, the notion of charge transfer (like that of nonclassical carbonium ions and, a long time ago, resonance) was eagerly adopted to explain all sorts of phenomena, not excluding the effect of inhibitors on the process by which a T2H bacteriophage inserts DNA into an *E. coli* cell. We must emphasize that it is not a trivial matter to prove that a particular absorption band is due to a charge-transfer transition. One method is generally applicable for those cases in which the compounds required are available. Since the charge-transfer absorption arises from the change in the

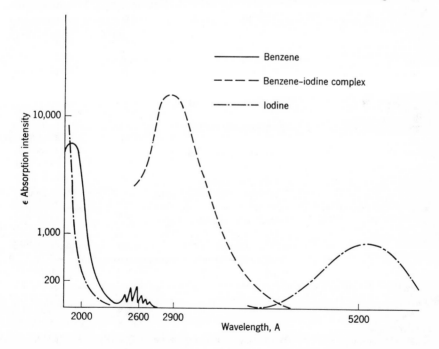

Figure 1.35 A comparison of the spectrum of benzene and iodine with that of benzene–iodine complex in a nonpolar solvent.

TABLE 1.51 *Selected Charge-Transfer Maxima for Donor–Acceptor Complexes (50)*

Donor	Acceptor	Solvent	$\lambda_{max}(\varepsilon_{max})$
Pentacarbomethoxycyclo-	1-Methylpyridinium	CH_2Cl_2	3500(768)
pentadienide	Tropylium	CH_2Cl_2	4700(1870)
	2,4,6-Trimethylpyrylium	CH_2Cl_2	4180(758)
	Pentaphenylpyrylium	CH_2Cl_2	4200(17,000)
	1-Methylquinolinium	CH_2Cl_2	4020(1020)
Pyrene	1-Methylquinolium	$CHCl_3$	4200(—)[a]
Iodide	1-Methylpyridinium	$CHCl_3$	3738(1200)[b]
	Hexamethylpyridinium	$CHCl_3$	3253(560)
	1-Ethyl-4-carbomethoxy-pyridinium	$CHCl_3$	4489(1230)[b]
	2,4,6-Trimethylpyrylium	$CHCl_3$	4400(—)[a]
	Tropylium	CH_2Cl_2	5715(—)[a]
Toluene	Tropylium	$ClCH_2CH_2Cl$	3250(—)[a]
Mesitylene		CH_3CN	3650(—)[a]
Benzene	Tetracyanoethylene	CH_2Cl_2	3840(3570)
Toluene		CH_2Cl_2	4060(3330)
o-Xylene		CH_2Cl_2	4300(3860)
m-Xylene		CH_2Cl_2	4400(3300)
p-Xylene		CH_2Cl_2	4600(2650)[b]
Mesitylene		CH_2Cl_2	4610(3120)
Hexamethylbenzene		CH_2Cl_2	5450(4390)
Pyridine		CH_2Cl_2	4125(10,500)[b]
[2.2]-Paracyclophane		CH_2Cl_2	5210(—)[a]
[6.6]-Paracyclophane		CH_2Cl_2	4900(—)[a]
[3.3]-Paracyclophane		CH_2Cl_2	5990(—)[a]
Pyrene		CH_2Cl_2	7240(1137)
Benzene	Hexacyanobutadiene	CH_2Cl_2	4400(4400)[c]
Pyrene		CH_2Cl_2	8700(2630)[b]
Pyrene	1,2,4,5-Tetracyanobenzene	$CHCl_3$	4950(—)[a]
	Hexacyanobenzene	CH_2Cl_2	6370(—)[a]
	2,3-Dicyano-p-benzoquinone	CH_2Cl_2	7180(—)[a]
	Tetracyano-p-benzoquinone	CH_2Cl_2	11290(—)[a,b]
Hexamethylbenzene	Tetrabromo-p-benzoquinone	CCl_4	5270(2000)
	Tetrachloro-p-benzoquinone	CCl_4	5180(2500)
	Tetraiodo-p-benzoquinone	CCl_4	5110(1400)
	p-Benzoquinone	CCl_4	4180(2000)
	Tetramethyl-p-benzoquinone	CCl_4	3930(1200)
Benzene	Iodine	CCl_4	2920(16,400)
o-Xylene		CCl_4	3160(12,500)
m-Xylene		CCl_4	3180(12,500)
p-Xylene		CCl_4	3040(10,100)
Mesitylene		CCl_4	3320(8850)
N,N-Dimethylaniline	Tetrachloro-p-benzoquinone	CH_2Cl_2	6540(—)[a]
N,N,N′,N′-Tetramethyl-p-phenylene-diamine		CH_2Cl_2	9530(—)[a]

TABLE 1.51 (*Continued*)

Donor	Acceptor	Solvent	$\lambda_{max}(\varepsilon_{max})$
1,4-Dimethoxybenzene		CH_2Cl_2	5440(—)[a]
1,2,4,5-Tetramethoxybenzene		CH_2Cl_2	6590(—)[a]
Tetrakis-(Dimethylamino)-ethylene	1,3,5-Trinitrobenzene[d]	CH_3CN	5450(210)[b]
Hexamethylborazine	Tetracyanoethylene	$CHCl_3$	4610(2000)
B-Triphenylborazine		$CHCl_3$	4100(1100)
N-Triphenylborazine		$CHCl_3$	4950(—)[a]
Fluorobenzene	Iodine	CCl_4	2880(14,600)
Ferrocene	Tetracyanoethylene	cyclohexane	10,750(465)
1,1'-Dimethylferrocene		cyclohexane	12,250(—)[a]
Amino[2,2]paracyclophane		CH_2Cl_2	6970(—)[a]
Benzene	Iodine atom	C_6H_6	4950(—)[a]
N,N,N',N'-Tetramethyl-p-phenylenediamine	7,7,8,8-Tetracyanoquino-dimethane	$CHCl_3$	11,630(—)[a]

[a] Not measured. [b] Only longest wavelength maximum given. [c] *Sic.* [d] Isolated complex has composition D-2A.

location of an electron, substituents that cause a change in the electron-donating ability of the donor or in the electron-accepting ability of the acceptor will affect the ease with which the electron moves. *The position of a charge-transfer absorption band must vary with the ionization potential of the donor and with the electron affinity of the acceptor.* The comparison of the position of absorption bands with the ionization potential of the donor was found by McConnell, Ham, and Platt (*194*) to be facilitated by a relationship (Eq. 216) that was linear for ionization potentials between 7 and 12 e.v. (1 electron-volt = 23.06 kcal./mole) (*195*).

The charge-transfer transition for pyridinium iodides shows an absorption maximum that is very sensitive to the nature of the substitution on the acceptor, the pyridinium ring. Data for this transition as shown are recorded in Table 1.13 (Eq. 217).

$$(216) \qquad E_T = h\nu_{CT} = I_p^v - C_1 + \frac{C_2}{I_p^v - C_1}$$

E_T = transition energy

$h\nu_{CT}$ = transition energy for charge-transfer band

C_1, C_2 = adjustable constants

I_p^v = *vertical* ionization potential

(217)

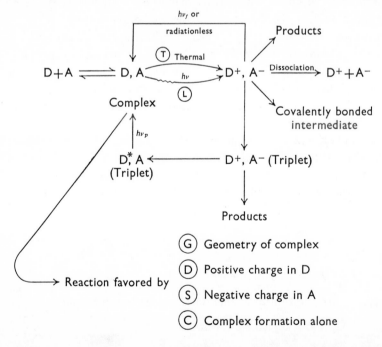

Charge-transfer transitions of the type shown in Eq. 217 for the pyridinium iodides, in which the ground state is an ion-pair and the net charge of the complex is destroyed upon excitation, should exhibit a high solvent sensitivity. *A second criterion for the identification of charge-transfer transitions in which absorption occurs in a charged ground state is sensitivity of the position of the absorption band to the polarity of the solvent.* The explanation of this phenomenon is given in detail in Part 2, Section 2.6, in connection with the use of the solvent sensitivity of a charge-transfer transition as an empirical measure of solvent polarity.

A third criterion may be applied in special cases, for which some unique property of either the donor or the acceptor allows a further test of the nature of the transition. For electronic transitions of iodides, two bands are

Figure 1.36 A general scheme for the reactions of charge-transfer complexes (Ref. 50).

expected, since the iodine atom produced by removal of an electron from the iodide ion

(218) $\qquad \text{I}^- \xrightarrow{h\nu} \text{I} \cdot + e^-$

may be in either the $^2P_{3/2}$ or the $^2P_{1/2}$ state. These states are separated by 21.8 kcal./mole. Two charge-transfer bands are observed for most pyridinium iodides in nonpolar solvents, and for 1-methyl-pyridinium iodide itself, the bands are separated by 21.8 kcal./mole. For other pyridinium iodides, the band separation is often greater, but occasionally less than 21.8 kcal./mole. (The separation of the bands is obtained by calculating the transition energies for each band and taking the difference.)

Relatively little research has been directed towards elucidating the reactions of charge-transfer complexes, but there is enough information available to make possible the construction of a general scheme for possible reactions involving charge-transfer complexes (Fig. 1.36), and a list of categories for these reactions is given in Table 1.52 (*50*).

TABLE 1.52 *Categories of Reactions of Charge-Transfer Complexes*[a]

C Processes mediated through the formation of a complex (as chaperon, for example).

G Reactions that lead to products with an orientation or structure other than that which might have been expected on the basis of random collision of reaction partners (Diels–Alder reaction) or a knowledge of similar reactions in related molecules (1,4-dihydropyridine formation in dithionite reduction of pyridinium rings rather than 1,2-dihydropyridine formation).

S Reactions favored by the acquisition of charge in the acceptor portion of the complex but which are reactions of the acceptor portion alone (solvolysis of 2,4,7-trinitrofluorenyl *p*-toluenesulfonate).

D Reactions favored by the loss of charge from the donor portion of the complex but which are reactions of the donor portion alone (perhaps racemization of hydrocarbons).

T Thermal electron transfer (as in the formation of ferricinium tetracyanoethylene anion radical ion-pair from ferrocene:tetracyanoethylene complex).

L Reactions that follow charge-transfer light absorption (the actual "reaction") are those studied in connection with the photochemistry of charge-transfer complexes. It is not known whether the fact that D^+A^- is formed in an excited vibrational state has any chemical consequences.

[a] Ref. 50.

We shall consider only photochemical and thermal electron transfer. A set of potential energy versus distance curves are presented in Fig. 1.37 for the approach of a donor and an acceptor in the absence of solvent. The same curves are shown again in Fig. 1.38 with an additional curve to indicate how solvation of the charged species would affect the course of the interaction. The curves are drawn so that the intermolecular distance in the ion-pair is about 0.6 A greater than that in the uncharged complexes (π–π complexes).

There are a number of interesting points to be discerned by an examination of the curves. First, photochemical and thermal electron transfer bear no

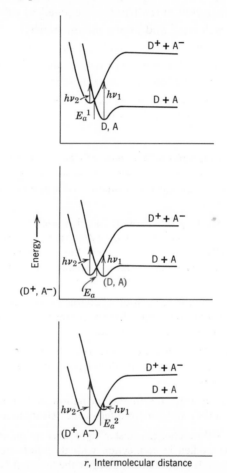

Figure 1.37 Potential energy curves for the interaction of a donor and acceptor in a nonpolar solvent. See caption, Fig. 1.38, for an explanation of the symbols. (From Ref. 50 and used with permission of John Wiley and Sons, Inc.)

well-defined relationship to one another. Photochemical electron transfer is the process described by an arrow from one of the lower curves (D,A) to the upper curve (D$^+$,A$^-$). Thermal electron transfer is described by passage over the energy barrier labeled E_a. Second, solvent has a pronounced effect upon the thermal electron transfer, but on photochemical transfer only if the ground state is charged. Photochemical electron transfer from a neutral ground state forms a charged excited state with the same solvent arrangement

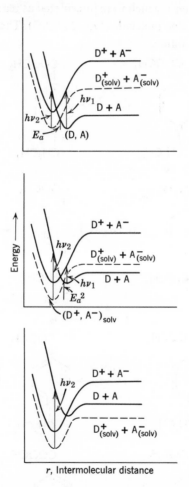

r, Intermolecular distance

Figure 1.38 Potential energy curves for the interaction of a donor and acceptor with the effect of solvent indicated. The symbols are to be understood as follows: E, transition energy; superscript 1 refers to D + A, superscript 2 to D$^+$ + A$^-$; subscript T to thermal reaction, subscript L to photochemical reaction (see Table 1.52). (From Ref. 50 and used with the permission of John Wiley and Sons, Inc.)

that obtained for the ground state. Third, the rate of thermal electron transfer may be so great that the species observed may not be those initially added to the solution. Presumably, the formation of a salt from triethylamine and iodine is the result of several reactions.

Kosower and Lindqvist (*182*) found that the solution which resulted from the flash photolysis of 1-ethyl-4-carbomethoxypyridinium iodide (**214**) contained the 1-ethyl-4-carbomethoxypyridinyl radical (**215**). The radical disappeared in two steps, which were interpreted as reaction with iodine atom and reaction with iodine molecule (Eqs. 219–223). The final product was the original pyridinium iodide.

(219)

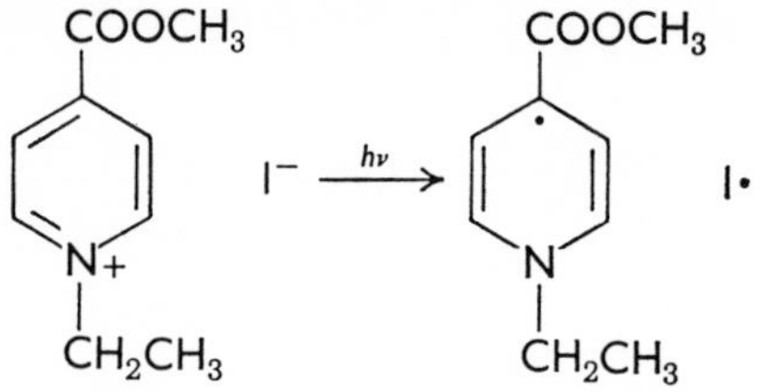

(220)

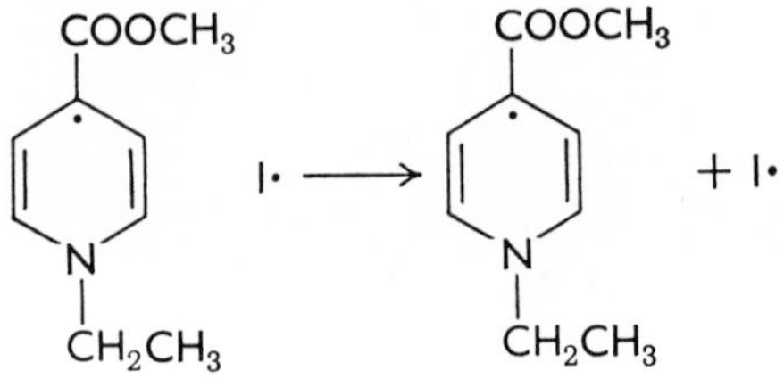

(221) $I\cdot + I\cdot \longrightarrow I_2$

(222)

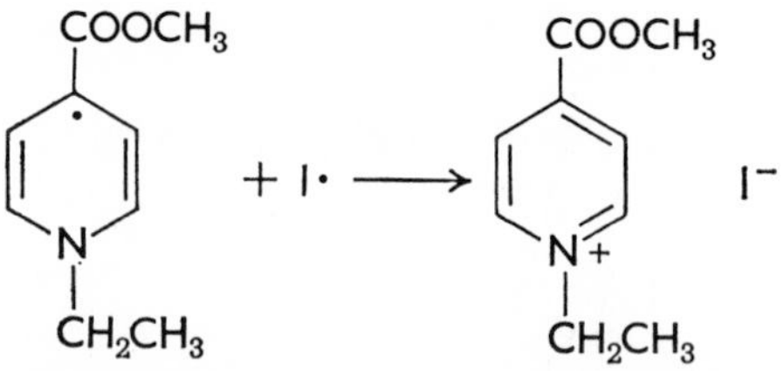

(223)*

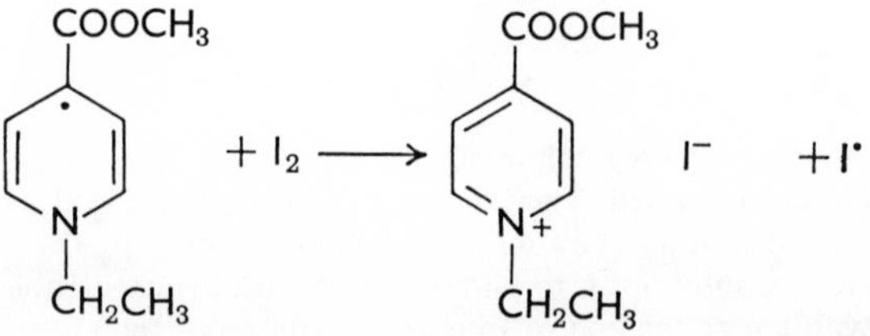

* See Problem 1, this section.

A good illustration of the effect of solvent on the rate of a thermal electron transfer is in the reaction of tetramethyl-*p*-phenylenediamine (**254**) and tetrachloro-*p*-benzoquinone (**255**). The two reagents interact in chloroform solution to yield a complex which exhibits a charge-transfer absorption band on the basis of comparison with the spectra of combinations of related compounds. If the solvent were made more polar by the addition of acetonitrile or ethanol, dissociated radical ions arising from electron transfer are the species present in solution (Eqs. 224–225).

(224)

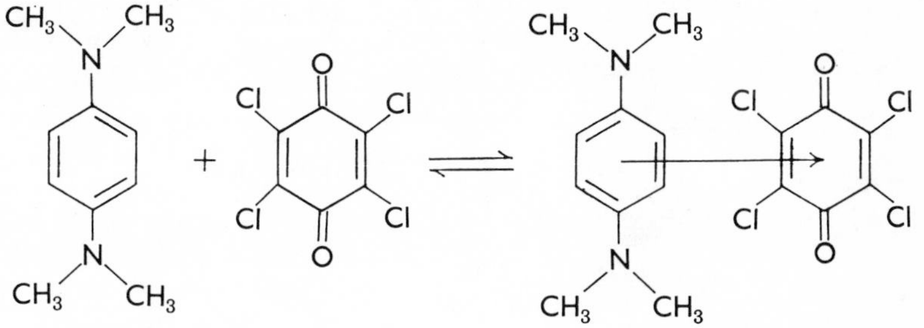

254 255 (D, A)

(225)

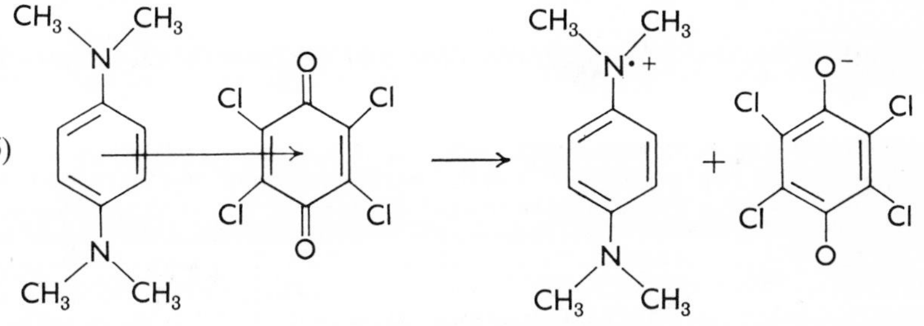

A number of cycloaddition reactions appear to proceed by thermal electron transfer within a charge-transfer complex followed by collapse of the resulting diradical ion-pair to a cyclobutane derivative. The reaction of vinyl methyl ether (**256**), 2,3-dihydropyran (**257**), and *p*-methoxystyrene (**258**) with tetracyanoethylene in tetrahydrofuran was studied by Williams, Wiley, and McCusick (*196*) (Eqs. 226–228). In all three cases, a colored complex was obtained which, although not definitely established as a charge-transfer complex, is probably such a complex, to judge from the behavior of tetracyanoethylene with many other donors (see Table 1.51). The solvent effect on the reaction of **258** with tetracyanoethylene was extremely large, with 12 seconds required for the disappearance of the intermediate complex (color) in formic acid and 2,600,000 seconds required in cyclohexane. It is assumed

(226) 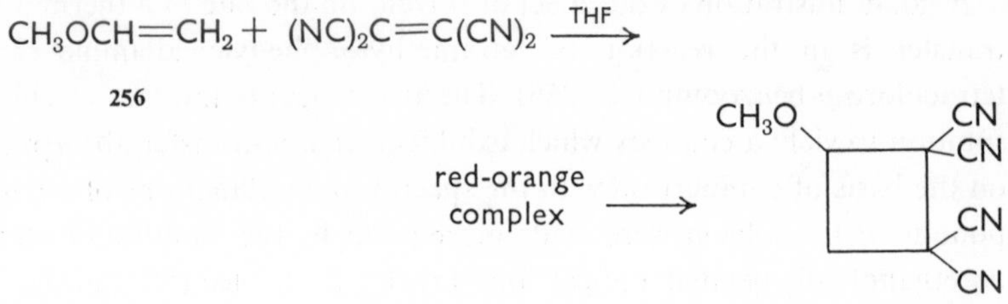 $CH_3OCH{=}CH_2 + (NC)_2C{=}C(CN)_2 \xrightarrow{THF}$

256

red-orange
complex $\longrightarrow$

(227) 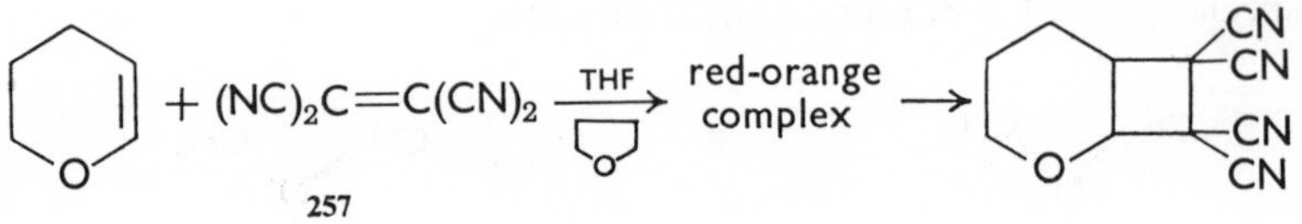 $+ (NC)_2C{=}C(CN)_2 \xrightarrow{THF}$ red-orange complex $\rightarrow$

257

(228) 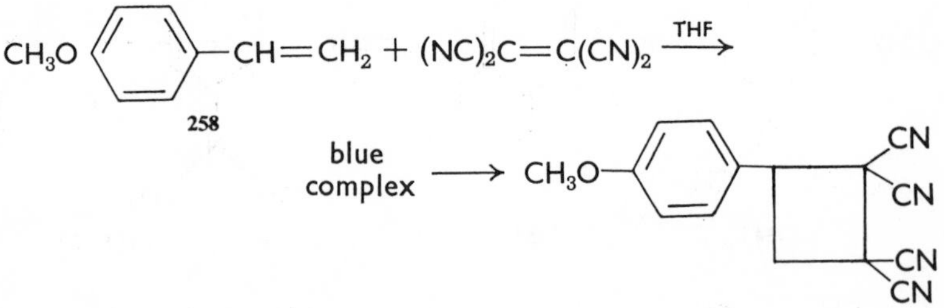 CH_3O $-CH{=}CH_2 + (NC)_2C{=}C(CN)_2 \xrightarrow{THF}$

258

blue complex $\longrightarrow CH_3O-$

that the time for the disappearance of the color reflects the rate of the overall reaction.

Photochemical charge transfer is observed for the pyridinium iodides. Thermal electron transfer is found for the reactions of ethers with tetra-

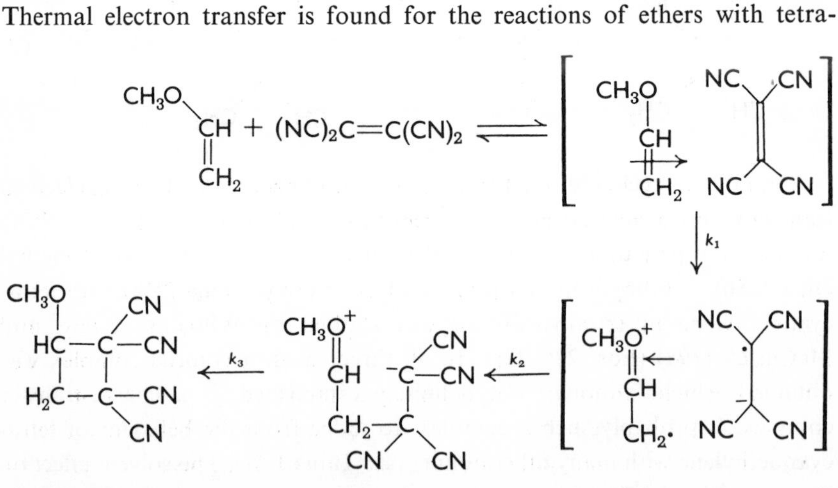

Figure 1.39 Proposed mechanism for 1,2-cycloaddition of donor alkenes to acceptor alkenes (Ref. 50).

cyanoethylene shown in Eqs. 226–228. A detailed mechanism for the reaction in Eq. 226 is given in Fig. 1.39. The 1,4-dihydropyridines can undergo either thermal or photochemical electron transfer with bromotrichloromethane or carbon tetrachloride, to initiate a series of reactions culminating in the formation of chloroform and a pyridinium salt. The mechanism for the overall reaction (Fig. 1.40) gives an indication of the possible complexity in

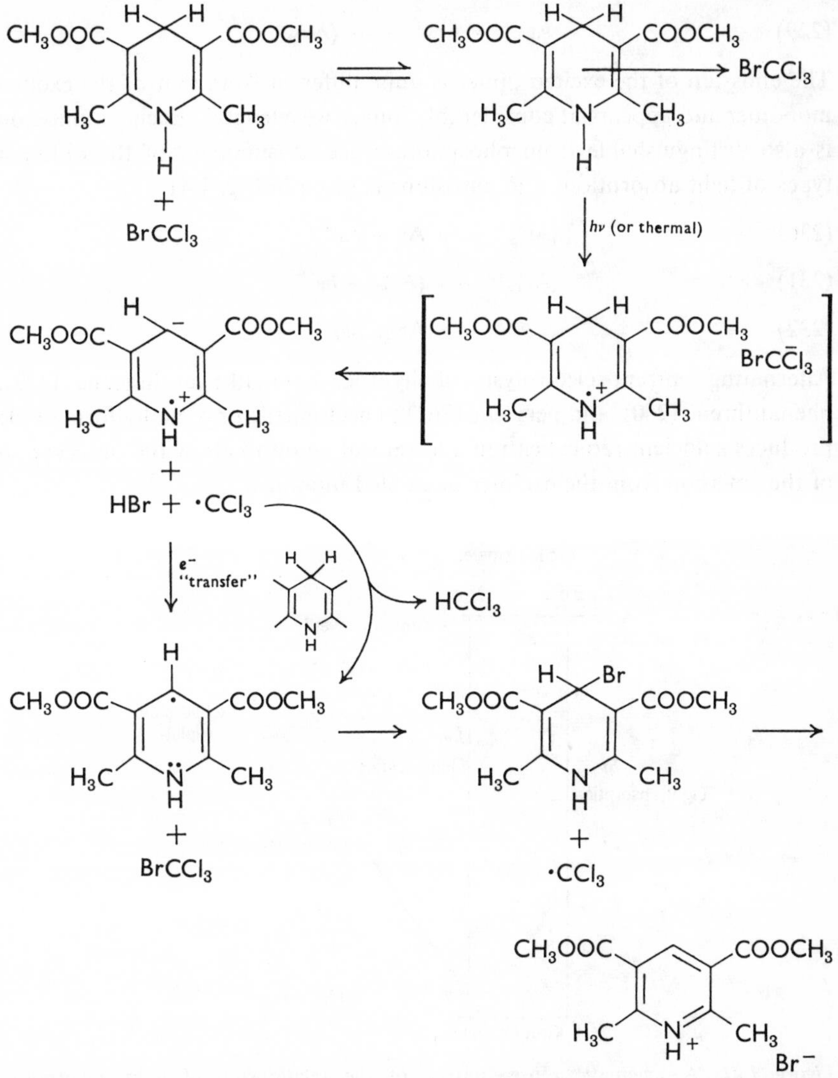

Figure 1.40 Reaction of 1,4-dihydropyridines with bromotrichloromethane (Ref. 50).

charge-transfer reactions, as a result of the formation of radicals that can carry on radical chain reactions (*176*).

The reaction of the cation radicals and anion radicals, derived from an aromatic hydrocarbon, results in *chemiluminescence* (light produced via a chemical reaction) (*738–740*) as the result of the formation of an *excimer* (in this case, an excited dimer) which may emit light, or dissociate to produce ground-state hydrocarbon and excited monomer, or both:

(229) $Ar\cdot^+ + Ar\cdot^- \longrightarrow (Ar)_2^*$

The emission of the excited dimer is quite different from that of the excited monomer and appears at considerably longer wavelengths. Excimer emission is also distinguishable from phosphorescence. A summary of the different types of light absorptions and emissions is given in Fig. 1.41.

(230) $(Ar)_2^* \longrightarrow Ar + Ar^*$

(231) $(Ar)_2^* \longrightarrow (Ar)_2 + h\nu$

(232) $Ar^* \longrightarrow Ar + h\nu_f$

Alternating current electrolysis of hydrocarbons like anthracene (**259**), phenanthrene (**260**), and perylene (**261**) in acetonitrile or dimethylformamide produces sufficient radical cation and radical anion to allow the observation of the emission from the excimer or excited monomer.

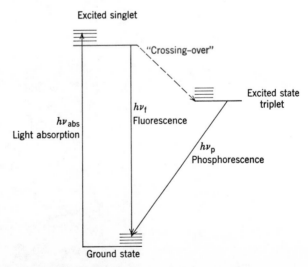

Figure 1.41 A schematic representation of the relationship of light absorption, fluorescence, and phosphorescence.

A polymerization reaction found by Yang and Gaoni (*197*) apparently results from initiation through the formation of reactive radical ions by charge transfer between a donor alkene and an acceptor alkene, as illustrated with the example of the reaction of 4-vinylpyridine and 2,4,6-trinitrostyrene (Fig. 1.42).

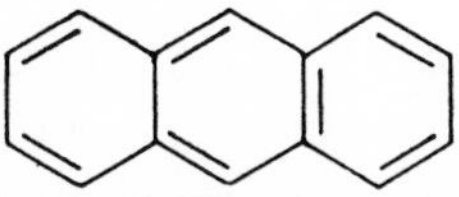

259

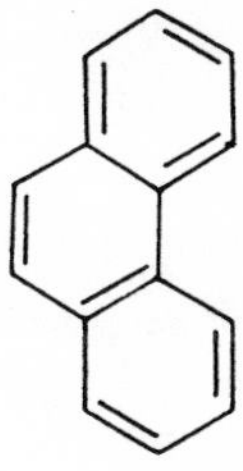

260 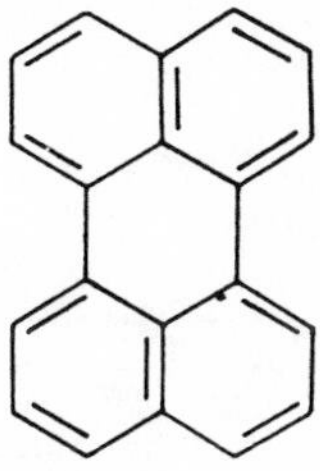　　　　**261**

Many qualitative examples illustrating the role of charge-transfer reactions in organic chemistry may be found in the work of Russell (*742*).

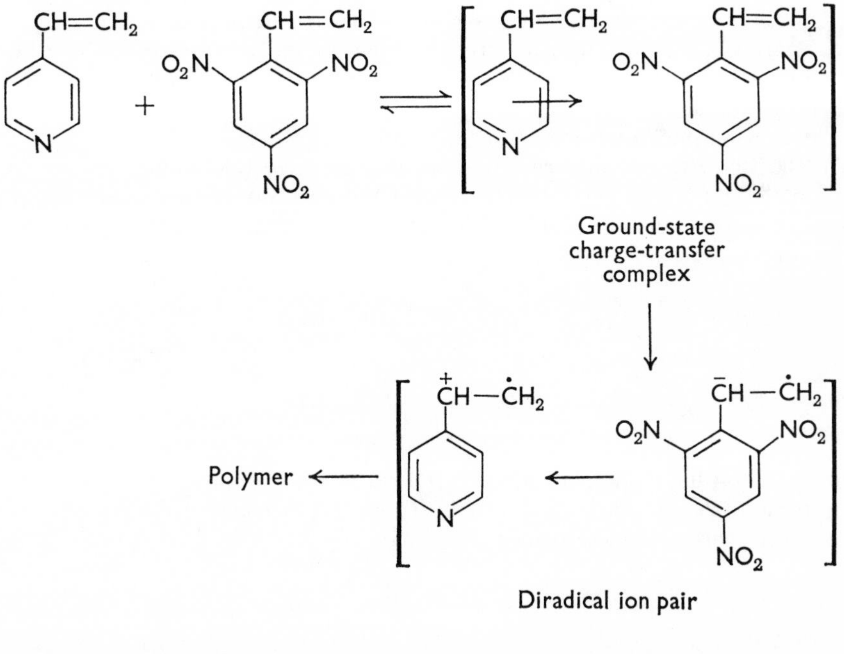

Ground-state
charge-transfer
complex

Diradical ion pair

Figure 1.42 Copolymerization of 2,4,6-trinitrostyrene and 4-vinylpyridine (Ref. 50).

The occurrence of charge-transfer transitions is sufficiently common so that one must be alert to the possibility in interpreting any absorption spectrum in the visible or ultraviolet region. Charge-transfer reactions (either thermal or photochemical) are clearly important for many reactants and should be further investigated in a quantitative way even though the complications introduced by radical intermediates make the research difficult.

Problems

1. Write two detailed mechanisms for the overall reaction shown in Eq. 233 (Part 1).
2. Write a mechanism for the formation of triethylamine hydriodide from triethylamine and iodine.
3. Define the following terms: (a) donor (b) acceptor (c) charge-transfer complex (d) charge-transfer transition.
4. Select from Table 1.51 a series of data that illustrate the following: (a) Variation in position of charge-transfer band with donor ability. (b) Variation in position of charge-transfer band with acceptor ability.
5. Write an example (different from that in the text, if possible) for each of the reaction categories of charge-transfer complex reactions.
6. Bearing in mind that the equilibrium constant for the formation of the benzene-iodine charge-transfer complex is small, what would you expect as the result of flash photolysis of a solution of iodine in benzene? What transient absorption bands might result from the irradiation? (Ref. 743.)
7. The isomeric *cis*- and *trans*-1,2-bis(trifluoromethyl)-1,2-dicyanoethylenes (**A** and **B**) react with vinyl *t*-butyl sulfide (**C**) to give two different isomeric products. Write the mechanism of formation and formulas for these two compounds (Refs. 744, 746).

$$NC \diagdown C = C \diagup CN \qquad NC \diagdown C = C \diagup CF_3 \qquad CH_2 = CHSC(CH_3)_3$$
$$F_3C \diagup \qquad \diagdown CF_3 \qquad F_3C \diagup \qquad \diagdown CN$$

$$\qquad A \qquad\qquad\qquad B \qquad\qquad\qquad C$$

8. Tetrakis-(dimethylamino)-ethylene (**D**) reacts with tetracyanoethylene (**E**) to form a salt with the composition D.2E. Write a formula for the product and a mechanism for its formation (Ref. 745).

ISOPOLAR TRANSITION STATES

1.8 Cycloadditions

A cycloaddition can be defined as the combination of at least two (it might be more) molecular groupings with, respectively, m and n atoms to form a ring system of $[m + n]$ members. The addition of alkenes (dienophiles) to 1,3-dienes, as shown in the example of butadiene and maleic anhydride,

(233)

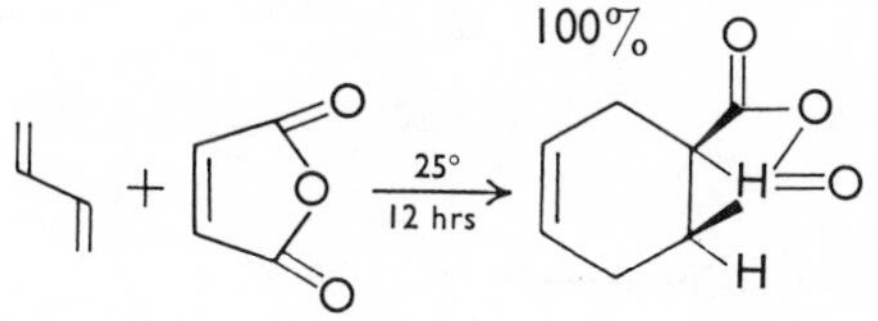

is a $[2 + 4]$ cycloaddition (Diels and Alder, *128*, reviewed in *141*). Change of either substituent and medium has little effect on the rates of cycloadditions leading Doering to facetiously label cycloadditions as "no mechanism" reactions (*198*).

Through a judicious combination of molecular orbital theory and symmetry principles, Woodward and Hoffmann (*199–203*) achieved a notable advance in our understanding of cycloadditions and closely related rearrangements (Section 1.9). We shall call both classes of reactions *isopolar* because the transition states differ little in charge distribution from the initial states. In this section, we shall consider $[2 + 2]$ cycloadditions (via diradicals), $[2 + 3]$ cycloadditions ("1,3-dipolar additions"), $[2 + 4]$ cycloadditions, and some of the theory which relates these reactions.

[2 + 2] Cycloadditions

Many polyfluoroalkenes and other alkenes substituted by electron-withdrawing groups react with themselves or similar molecules to form cyclobutane derivatives, usually upon heating. Three typical examples are the dimerization of tetrafluoroethylene (**262**) to octafluorocyclobutane (**263**) (Eq. 234), the dimerization of allene (**264**) to a mixture of 1,2-*bis*-methylene- (**265**), and 1,3-*bis*-methylenecyclobutanes (**266**) (Eq. 235), and the dimerization of acrylonitrile (**267**) to a mixture of *cis*- (**268**) and *trans*-1,2-dicyanocyclobutanes (**269**) (Eq. 236).

(234) 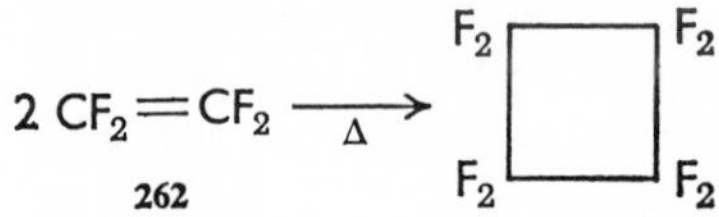 $2\, CF_2{=}CF_2 \xrightarrow{\Delta}$

262

263

(235) 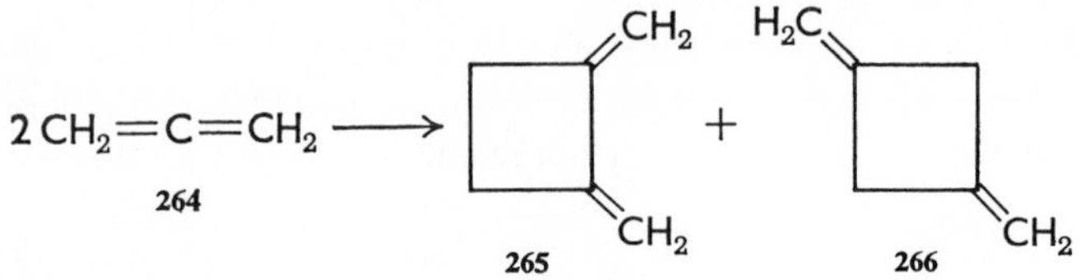 $2\, CH_2{=}C{=}CH_2 \longrightarrow$

264

+

265   **266**

(236) 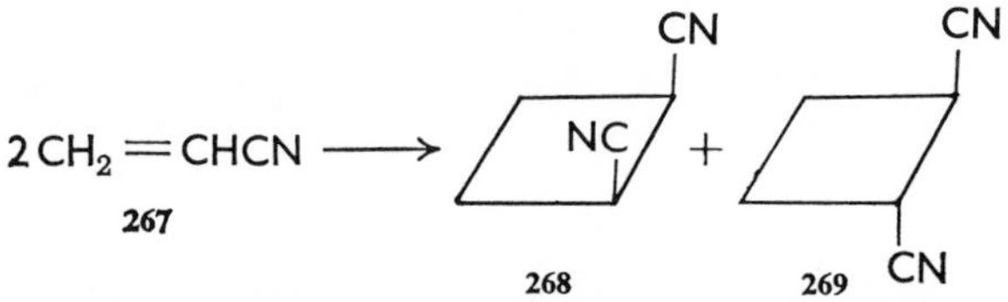 $2\, CH_2{=}CHCN \longrightarrow$

267

+

268   **269**

A reaction of special interest is that of **262** with 1,3-butadiene to yield 3-vinyl-1,1,2,2-tetrafluorocyclobutane (**270**) (Eq. 237), a compound derived by [2 + 2] cycloaddition rather than [2 + 4] cycloaddition and formed in preference to **263**.

(237) 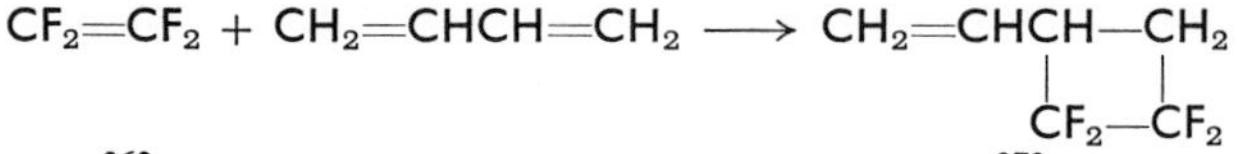 $CF_2{=}CF_2 + CH_2{=}CHCH{=}CH_2 \longrightarrow CH_2{=}CHCH{-}CH_2$
                                                                    $\overset{|}{C}F_2{-}\overset{|}{C}F_2$

262   **270**

Roberts and Sharts (*205*) pointed out that the formation of cyclobutane derivatives and the substituent arrangement in the cyclobutanes could be explained by postulating an intermediate diradical. In the reaction of styrene and 1,1-dichloro-2,2-difluoroethylene (**271**) (Eq. 238), the observed product (**272**) is produced via the diradical **273**, not **274**.

Isoprene (**275**) and chloroprene (**276**) react with **271** to yield as major products those cyclobutanes derived from the most substituted diradicals (**277** and **278**), indicating that charge separation is not significant in determining the nature of the diradicals formed (Eqs. 239, 240) (*206, 208*). The chlorine and methyl substituents on the diene increase the rate of reaction with **271** only very slightly over that found for 1,3-butadiene.

A careful examination of the reaction of **271** with the three isomers of 2,4-hexadiene (*trans,trans-* , *cis,trans-* and *cis,cis-*) by Montgomery, Schueller, and Bartlett (*207*) revealed that ring closure from the diradical competed

(238)

$$\text{C}_6\text{H}_5-\text{CH}=\text{CH}_2 + \text{CF}_2=\text{CCl}_2 \longrightarrow \left[\begin{array}{c} \text{C}_6\text{H}_5-\text{HC}-\text{CH}_2 \\ | \quad\quad | \\ \text{Cl}_2\dot{\text{C}}-\dot{\text{C}}\text{F}_2 \end{array} \right]$$

271

273

$$\begin{array}{c} \text{C}_6\text{H}_5-\text{HC}-\text{CH}_2 \\ | \quad\quad | \\ \text{Cl}_2\text{C}-\text{CF}_2 \end{array}$$

272

not

$$\left(\begin{array}{c} \text{C}_6\text{H}_5-\text{HC}-\text{CH}_2 \\ | \quad\quad | \\ \text{F}_2\text{C}-\text{CCl}_2 \end{array} \right)$$

274

(239)

$$\begin{array}{c} \text{CH}_2=\text{C} \overset{\text{CH}_3}{\underset{\text{CH}=\text{CH}_2}{|}} \end{array} + \text{Cl}_2\text{C}=\text{CF}_2 \longrightarrow \left[\begin{array}{c} \text{CH}_3 \\ | \quad \text{CH} \\ \text{H}_2\text{C}-\text{C}\overset{\cdot}{\diagup}\diagdown\text{CH}_2 \\ | \quad\quad | \\ \text{F}_2\text{C}-\dot{\text{C}}\text{Cl}_2 \end{array} \right]$$

275

271

277

$$\begin{array}{c} \text{CH}_3 \\ | \\ \text{H}_2\text{C}-\text{C}\diagdown \\ | \quad\quad | \quad \text{CH}=\text{CH}_2 \\ \text{F}_2\text{C}-\text{CCl}_2 \end{array}$$

(240)

$$\begin{array}{c} \text{CH}_2=\text{C} \overset{\text{Cl}}{\underset{\text{CH}=\text{CH}_2}{|}} \end{array} + \text{Cl}_2\text{C}=\text{CF}_2 \longrightarrow \left[\begin{array}{c} \text{Cl} \\ | \quad \text{CH} \\ \text{H}_2\text{C}-\text{C}\overset{\cdot}{\diagup}\diagdown\text{CH}_2 \\ | \quad\quad | \\ \text{F}_2\text{C}-\dot{\text{C}}\text{Cl}_2 \end{array} \right]$$

276

271

277

$$\begin{array}{c} \text{Cl} \\ | \\ \text{H}_2\text{C}-\text{C}\diagdown \\ | \quad\quad | \quad \text{CH}=\text{CH}_2 \\ \text{F}_2\text{C}-\text{CCl}_2 \end{array} \quad \textbf{278}$$

278

with rotation around one of the single bonds in the diradical. The course of the reaction is illustrated in Fig. 1.43, in which it is clear that the isomers of the cyclobutane product A and B can arise only from the *trans,trans-* and *cis,trans*-2,4-hexadienes. Isomers C and D form only from the *cis,trans-* and *cis,cis*-2,4-hexadienes. If the diradicals (*z* and *w*) formed from different

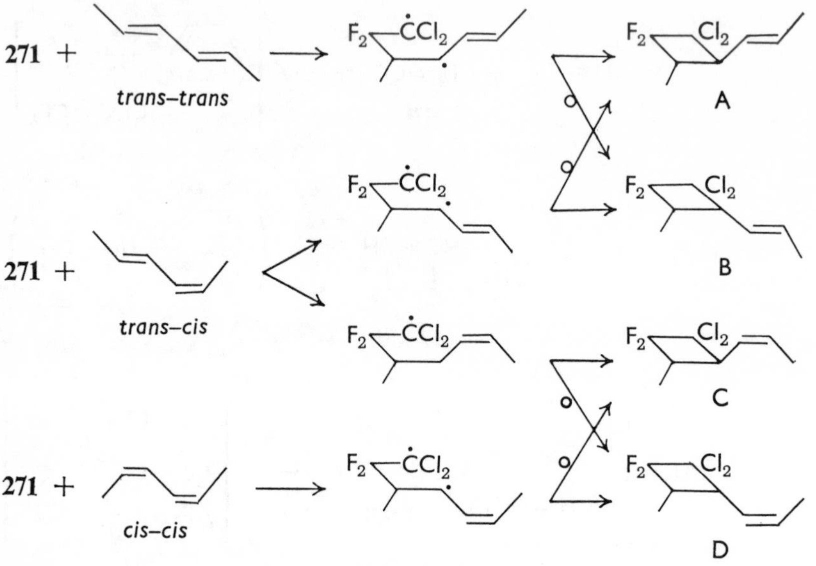

Figure 1.43 Products from the reaction of 1,1-dichloro-2,2-difluoroethylene (**271**) with three isomers of 2,4-hexadiene. The symbol "—∘—" on the arrows indicates rotation around a single bond (Ref. 207).

geometric isomers of the diene reached thermodynamic equilibrium before closing (or collapsing) to the cyclobutane product, the ratio of the cyclobutanes x and y (Fig. 1.44) would be the same regardless of the source of the diradical. The data on the A/B and C/D ratios listed in Table 1.53 demonstrate conclusively that rotational equilibrium is not attained in the inter-

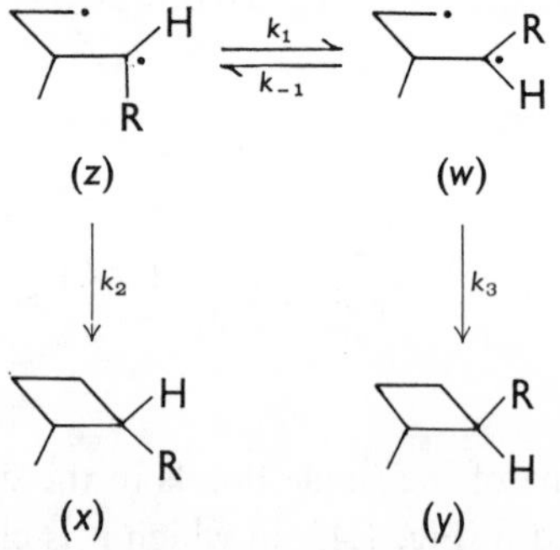

Figure 1.44 Rate processes which equilibriate the isomeric diradicals z and w (constants k_1 and k_{-1}) are compared with the processes which lead to the cyclobutane products (x and y) (constants k_2 and k_3) (Ref. 207).

TABLE 1.53 *Isomer Distribution in Cycloadducts from* $Cl_2C{=}CF_2$ *and 2,4-Hexadiene*[a]

Diene Isomer	T, °C	Product Isomers (Percent)			
		C	A	B	D
trans-trans	80.05	0	84.2	15.8	0
		0	83.2	16.8	0
trans-cis	80.05	34.2	44.2	13.7	7.9
		36.0	43.7	13.8	6.6
		35.5	43.7	14.1	6.7
cis-cis	80.05	75.9	0	0	24.1
		76.0	0	0	24.0
trans-trans	100.62	0	82.3	17.7	0
		0	82.1	17.9	0
trans-cis	100.62	33.2	44.9	14.5	7.4
		33.2	46.6	13.8	6.4
		37.3	44.8	12.1	5.8

[a] Ref. 207.

mediates, since the isomer ratios obtained from the *cis,trans*-2,4-hexadiene differ from those found for the products of reaction from the *trans,trans*- and *cis,cis*-2,4-hexadienes. From a consideration of the differences in product ratios derived from two sources, Bartlett and co-workers (*207*) estimated that the rate of rotation around the relevant carbon–carbon single bond is about ten times as great as the rate of ring closure. They further assume that only the normal rotational barrier (1 kcal./mole per bond opposition or 3 kcal./mole) holds and can thus estimate that the rate constant for rotation is about 1×10^{11} sec.$^{-1}$.

$$(241) \qquad k_1 = \frac{kT}{h} e^{-3000/RT}$$

The rate constant for ring closure is then 1×10^{10} sec.$^{-1}$. The assumption that only the normal rotational barrier opposes rotation in the diradical may be questioned on the basis of the growing body of evidence, indicating a weak but significant interaction between radicals in the ground state. This interaction leads to radical dimers (which may be singlet or triplet) in which no new covalent bond is formed. Since a survey of this evidence is given in Part

3, Section 3.2, we shall cite here only the result of Itoh and Nagakura (*209, 787*) that the association constant for the formation of diamagnetic dimer (**279**) from 1-methyl-4-carbomethoxypyridinyl (**280**) at 77°K in isopentane

(242)

is about 10^4 liters/mole. The association constant is much lower at 25°C, perhaps between 5 and 10 liters/mole (*212, 620*). Studies of diradicals by Itoh and Kosower (*778*) suggest that the K for intramolecular association of 1,3-diradicals would be about 100 and for 1,4-diradicals about 10. Unless the association of **280** is largely due to dipole-dipole interaction, or mutual polarization of π-systems, we should diminish the rate constant estimated for ring closure of the tetramethylene 1,4-diradical by a factor of about 10, to 1×10^9 sec.$^{-1}$, as a result of the possible added stability of the diradical from radical-radical interaction. An estimate of the rate constant for ring closure of the trimethylene 1,3-diradical based on the data of Benson (*210*) gives 8×10^7 sec.$^{-1}$ at 80°, the same temperature for which the rate constant for the 1,4-diradical was estimated (*207*). It seems likely that the high rate for the ring closure reaction is responsible for 1,2-addition being favored by a considerable margin over 1,4-addition in many of the [2 + 2] cycloaddition reactions. Cyclopentadiene reacts less rapidly with **271** than butadiene (about 70% as fast) and, in spite of the favorable geometry, yields 1,4-adduct only twice as fast as 1,2-adduct.

A calculation of the energy required to generate the 1,4-diradical (Fig. 1.43) is presented in Table 1.54 for tetrafluoroethylene. The double bond in **271** is probably more stable than the double bond of tetrafluoroethylene, but the intermediate diradical is stabilized more by two chlorine substituents than two fluorines (see Fig. 1.34).

We shall briefly consider evidence which shows that a 1,3-diradical has sufficient lifetime to react in two ways and that, in some cases, bond rotation in 1,3-diradicals is faster than spin inversion.

Thermal decomposition of 4-methyl-1-pyrazoline (**281**) (Eq. 243) is faster than the decomposition of 4-methyl-1-pyrazoline $4\text{-}d_1$ (**282**) (Eq. 244), with

TABLE 1.54 *Heat of Formation of Diradical Intermediate in 1,2-Cycloaddition of Tetrafluoroethylene to Butadiene*[a,c]

Fluorinated C=C	131 kcal./mole[b]
C—C (no correction for substitution)	83 kcal./mole
Stabilization energy of allylic radical	25 kcal./mole
Stabilization energy of diene	3.5 kcal./mole

$$CF_2{=}CF_2 + CH_2{=}CH{-}CH{=}CH_2$$
$$\rightarrow \cdot CF_2CF_2CH_2\overset{\displaystyle\cdot}{C}H{\cdots}CH{\cdots}CH_2$$

$\Delta H = -3 \times 83 - 25 + 131 + 147 + 3.5 = +7.5$ kcal./mole

[a] Ref. 207. [b] From a comparison of the heats of some reactions of tetrafluoroethylene compared with those of ethylene, as, for example, the polymerization of $CF_2{=}CF_2$ to polymer at 660° has $\Delta H = -42$ kcal./mole while the corresponding figure for ethylene is -24.7 kcal./mole at 400°. [c] This calculation should be regarded only as permissive since none of the quantities used are known accurately with the possible exception of the figure for the fluorinated double bond.

k_H/k_D of 1.07 at 242° (*154*). The products, methylcyclopropane (**283**) and isobutene (**284**), differ in ratio from the two cases with an apparent k_H/k_D of 1.81 for hydrogen migration, implying strongly that there is an intermediate (presumably the 1,3-diradical) and that it can react by either ring closure or hydrogen migration, processes which differ in isotope effect.

(243)

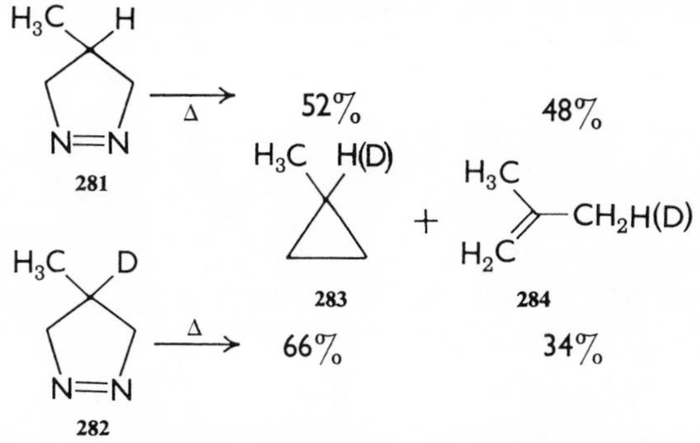

Photochemical decomposition of the triazoline **285** yields a mixture of *cis*- and *trans*-aziridines (**286** and **287**) and an imine (**288**) (Eq. 245). Irradiation of the triazoline by itself yields products which appear to arise from a singlet excited state and therefore from a singlet diradical. Sensitized irradiation (in

(245)

which the light is absorbed by benzophenone via an $n \to \pi^*$ transition, and the excited state rapidly "crosses over" to an excited triplet, which then reacts with the triazoline to generate a triplet triazoline and, eventually a triplet diradical—compare with Eqs. 148–150 and see *423, 716*) produces a mixture of isomers, which is very similar for both *cis-* and *trans-*isomers of the starting material **285**, in contrast to the rather different mixtures of products obtained from the same isomers of **285** via the singlet route. These facts are summarized in Table 1.55 (*162*). If we assume that spin inversion is required before the geometry of the product aziridine has been determined through 1,3-inter-action, these data indicate that this particular variety of 1,3-diradical under-goes bond rotation faster than spin inversion.

A reaction that may be related to the "ordinary" [2 + 2] cycloaddition reaction is the [2σ + 2] cycloaddition reaction discovered by Cairncross and Blanchard (*215*) and illustrated for the case of 3-methylbicyclo[1.1.0]butane-carbonitrile and ethylene as shown:

(246)

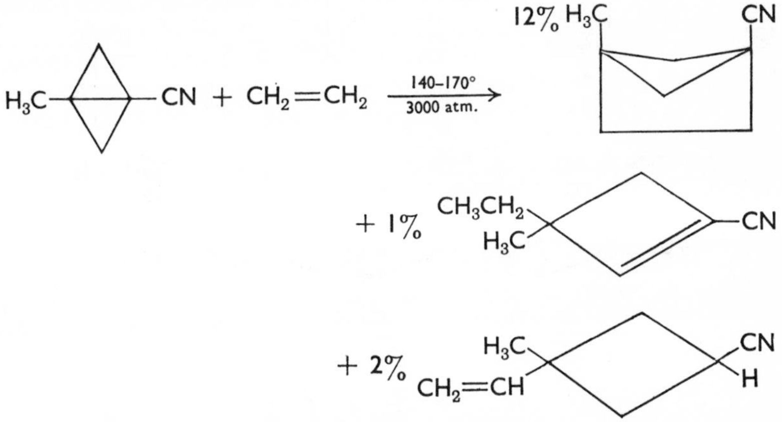

We should now try to understand why [2 + 2] cycloaddition is relatively slow (compared to, for example, [2 + 4] cycloaddition) and is a two-step process rather than a concerted reaction. (Another kind of [2 + 2] cyclo-addition via a diradical ion-pair has been discussed in Section 1.7.) A brief reminder of how one views bond formation in molecular orbital theory for two methyl radicals is shown in Fig. 1.45. The two methyl groups in ethane may be joined by a σ-bond or by a σ^*-bond. The latter is, of course, an antibond, and two methyl groups joined in this way would either dis-sociate or emit a quantum of light corresponding to the σ^*–σ bond-energy difference. The potential energy curves for the two bonding situations are

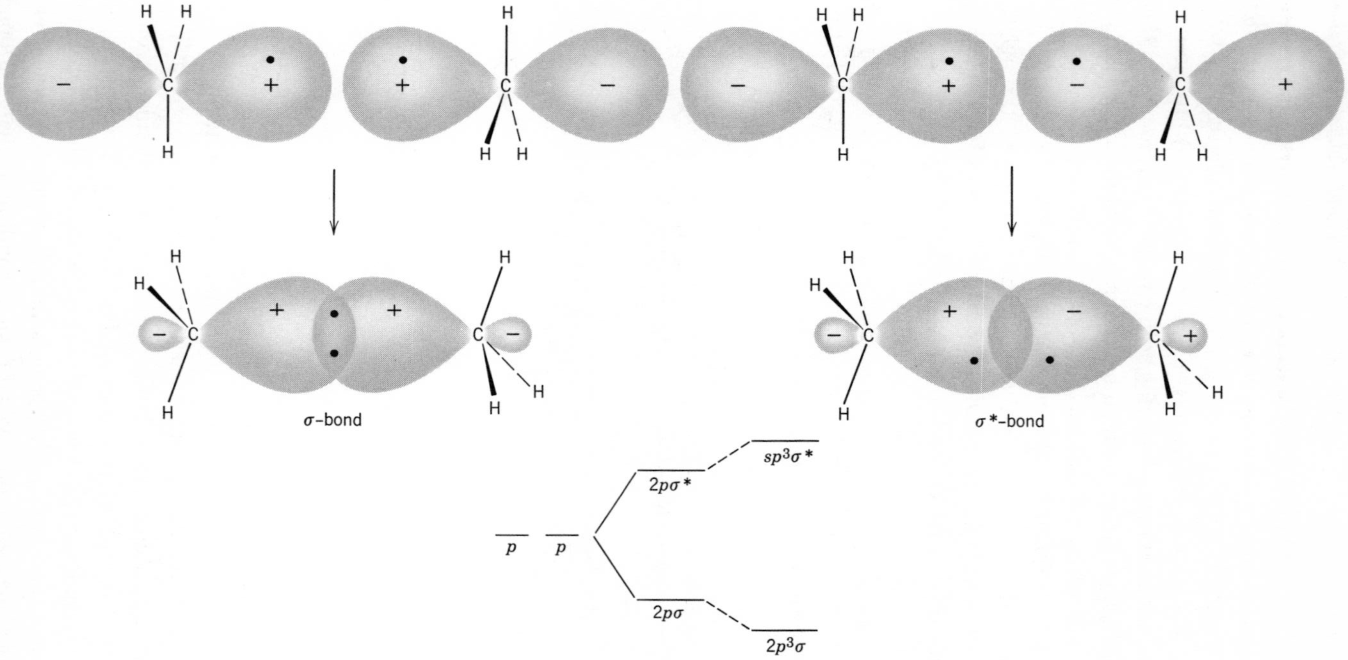

Figure 1.45 Molecular orbitals picture of the formation of σ- and σ*-bonds from methyl radicals.

204

TABLE 1.55 *Photodecomposition of Triazolines*[a]

		Product, Percent Yield		
285 Isomer	Excited State	*cis*	*trans*	Imine
cis	Singlet[b]	65	17	18
trans	Singlet[b]	22	66	12
cis	Triplet[c]	60	36	4
trans	Triplet[c]	54	42	4

[a] Ref. 162. [b] The yields of the products formed by irradiation were unaffected by piperylene or oxygen. [c] Irradiation in the presence of benzophenone.

shown in Fig. 1.46. The signs refer to signs of the wave functions for the electrons.

The molecular orbital picture for the π-bond in ethylene and for the π^*-bond produced by an antibonding combination of the p-orbitals is shown in Fig. 1.47. If we bring together two ethylene molecules and try to make a cyclobutane ring, we immediately find that one bond and one antibond should form (Fig. 1.48). Net bonding for this situation is zero, and on the basis of

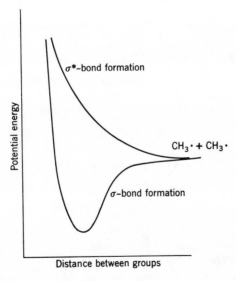

Figure 1.46 Potential energy curves for the formation of σ- and σ^*-bonds between two methyl radicals.

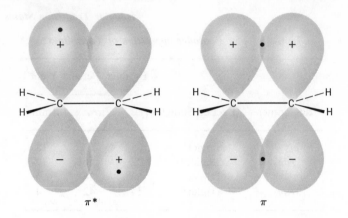

Figure 1.47 Molecular orbitals picture for the π- and π^*-bonds of ethylene.

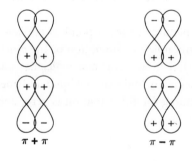

$\pi + \pi$ $\pi - \pi$

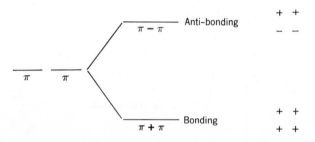

Figure 1.48 Bringing together two ground-state ethylenes to form two new bonds, one of which is bonding and the other, antibonding.

206

this simple molecular orbital picture, we should predict that cyclobutane formation from ethylene should not occur. The contribution of Woodward and Hoffmann to our understanding of cycloadditions was to recognize that an analysis of the symmetries of the orbitals involved in the change of bonding in the reactants and products (see also Longuet-Higgins and Abrahamson, *204*) could account qualitatively for the ease or difficulty with which a particular cycloaddition might occur. The bonding combinations possible for two ethylenes and the corresponding bonding combinations for the cyclobutane are shown in Fig. 1.49. The symbols refer to symmetric (S) or antisymmetric (A) arrangements with respect to the two symmetry planes (Fig. 1.50) σ_1 and σ_2. Identical signs of the wave function on either side of the symmetry plane is an S arrangement with respect to that plane and opposite signs result in an A arrangement.

A *correlation diagram* which allows us to readily examine the relationship of the energy levels of the reactants to those of the products can easily be derived from the combinations shown in Fig. 1.49. The difference between the levels of the π- and σ-bonds is based on the knowledge that the second bond of ethylene is weaker than the carbon–carbon bond of ethane, and this ordering holds for cyclobutane after allowing for ring strain. The upper orbital derived from the "combination" of two ethylenes (the SA orbital) goes over into an antibonding σ^*-orbital in the cyclobutane ring (Fig. 1.51). Absorption of light by one of the ethylenes would transfer an electron to the

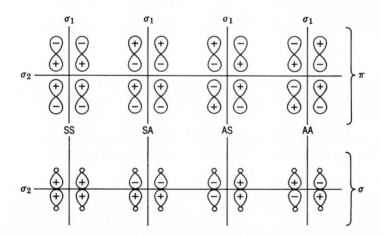

Figure 1.49 Orbitals combinations along with the symmetries for two ethylene molecules and for cyclobutane (adapted from Ref. 200).

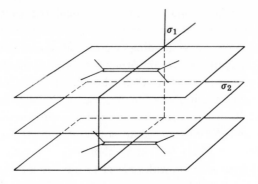

Figure 1.50   The symmetry planes used to label the combinations in Fig. 1.49 (adapted from Ref. 200).

AS orbital, and the reaction would then be thermoneutral, producing a singlet diradical as the initial product (Fig. 1.52).

Since ethylene does not readily produce cyclobutane, the reaction for the simple case must be too difficult to achieve under ordinary conditions. Weakening the double bond by electron-withdrawing substituents or by strain [as in allene (*211*)] has the effect of raising the SA level and lowering the AS level. We might anticipate that thermal electron transfer (SA → AS) would become possible as the ethylenes approached one another and the separation of the two levels decreased. We must also remember from our consideration of the potential energy versus distance diagrams for charge-

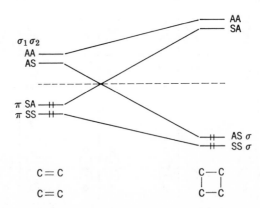

Figure 1.51   Molecular orbital correlation diagram for the combination of two ethylenes into a cyclobutane. The designations of the energy levels are made clear in Fig. 1.49, using the symmetry planes designated in Fig. 1.50 (adapted from Ref. 200).

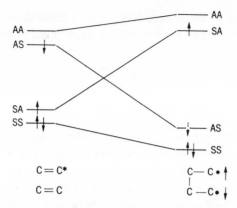

Figure 1.52 Molecular orbital correlation diagram for the combination of a ground state ethylene with an ethylene which has been transformed into an excited molecule through a $\pi \rightarrow \pi^*$ transition.

transfer complexes (Figs. 1.37 and 1.38) that thermal electron transfer can require far less energy than photochemical *vertical* electron transfer. Thus, the theory quite naturally leads us to the idea that a thermal [2 + 2] cyclo-addition via a singlet diradical should occur for a pair of alkenes.

It will be recognized that the correlation diagram is closely related to the type of diagrams used in the "united atom" treatment for the energy levels of diatomic molecules.

[2 + 3] Cycloadditions

Huisgen and his co-workers (*213, 214*) have explored a broad group of cycloaddition reactions which they have called "1,3-dipolar cycloadditions." Although the 1,3-dipole formulation is quite useful in predicting the results of a reaction, the evidence on the mechanism of many of the reactions suggests that these cycloadditions proceed via isopolar transition states. Of the three groups of "1,3-dipoles" which we will discuss, it is possible that one group does react with the development of considerable charge separation at the transition state, but unfortunately there is no information on the mechanism of reaction because all of the members of this group are unstable intermediates that are generated in the same medium in which they are consumed. For the other two groups, there is little to suggest that the separation of charge is augmented in the transition state. The solvent effect, for example, is usually quite small. We prefer, therefore, to label these reactions [2 + 3] cycloadditions, for which the general equation might be written:

(247)

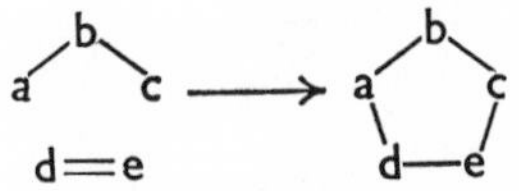

Three groups of "1,3-dipoles" comprise almost all those which have been studied. These are, in the terminology which classifies them by the 1,3-dipolar structure which can be written, 1,3-dipoles with a double bond and a non-bonding pair on the central atom (**286** ↔ **286a**), 1,3-dipoles with a non-bonding pair on the central atom (**287** ↔ **287a**) and 1,3-dipoles with a double bond (**288** ↔ **288a**). It is the last group which bears a somewhat dubious relationship to the other "1,3-dipoles," as we can see from Fig. 1.53, in which we perceive the necessity for rotating a *p*-orbital 90° in order to attain a "true" "1,3-dipole."

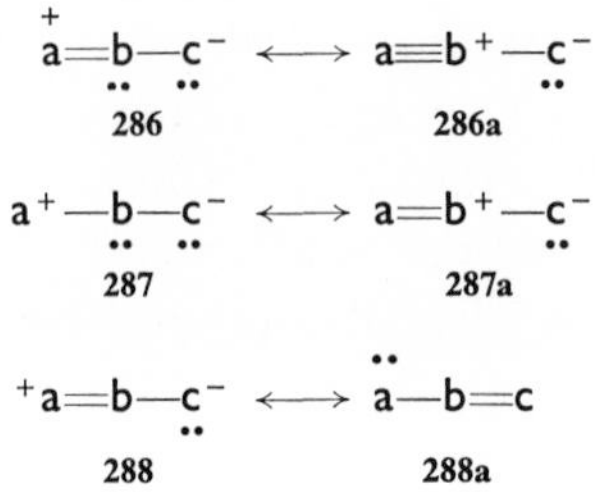

Examples of each of the groups of "1,3-dipoles" are given in Tables 1.56, 1.57, and 1.58.

An important clue to the nature of the [2 + 3] cycloaddition is found in the medium insensitivity of the rate of the reaction of a "1,3-dipole" of the type **286** ↔ **286a** with a strained alkene. The reaction of diphenyldiazo-

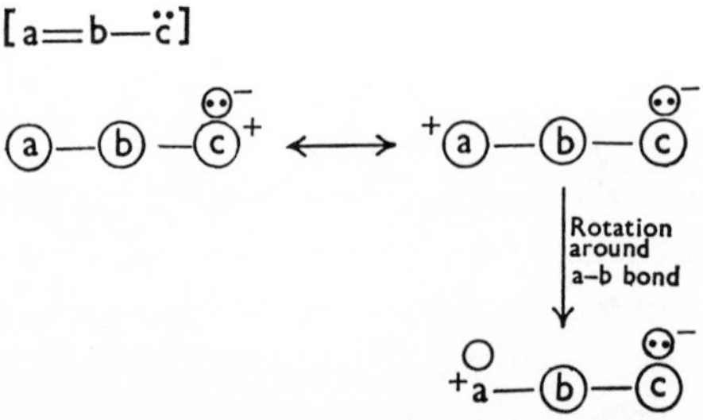

Figure 1.53   The creation of a 1,3-dipole from a methylene or nitrene.

TABLE 1.56 *[3] Substrate Systems for [2 + 3] Cycloadditions*[a,b]

Type: $\overset{+}{a}=b-\overset{-}{\underset{\cdot\cdot}{c}} \leftrightarrow a=\overset{+}{b}-\overset{-}{\underset{\cdot\cdot}{c}}$ (286 ↔ 286a)

Atom System	1,3-Dipolar Form	Alternate Form	Name
CNC	$-\overset{+}{C}=N-\overset{-}{\underset{\cdot\cdot}{C}}\big<$	$-C\equiv\overset{+}{N}-\overset{-}{\underset{\cdot\cdot}{C}}\big<$	Nitrile ylide
CNN	$-\overset{+}{C}=N-\overset{-}{\underset{\cdot\cdot}{N}}-$	$-C\equiv\overset{+}{N}-\overset{-}{\underset{\cdot\cdot}{N}}-$	Nitrile imine
CNO	$-\overset{+}{C}=N-\overset{-}{\underset{\cdot\cdot}{O}}:$	$-C\equiv\overset{+}{N}-\overset{-}{\underset{\cdot\cdot}{O}}:$	Nitrile oxide
NNC	$:\overset{+}{N}=N-\overset{-}{\underset{\cdot\cdot}{C}}\big<$	$:N\equiv\overset{+}{N}-\overset{-}{\underset{\cdot\cdot}{C}}\big<$	Diazoalkane
NNN	$:\overset{+}{N}=N-\overset{-}{\underset{\cdot\cdot}{N}}-$	$:N\equiv\overset{+}{N}-\overset{-}{\underset{\cdot\cdot}{N}}-$	Azide
NNO	$:\overset{+}{N}=N-\overset{-}{\underset{\cdot\cdot}{O}}:$	$N\equiv\overset{+}{N}-\overset{-}{\underset{\cdot\cdot}{O}}:$	Nitrous oxide

[a] Ref. 213. [b] The concerted nature of the reaction has not been established in all cases.

methane (289) with 5,6-dicarbethoxy-5,6-diaza-bicyclo[2.2.1]heptene-2 (290) may be written:

(248)

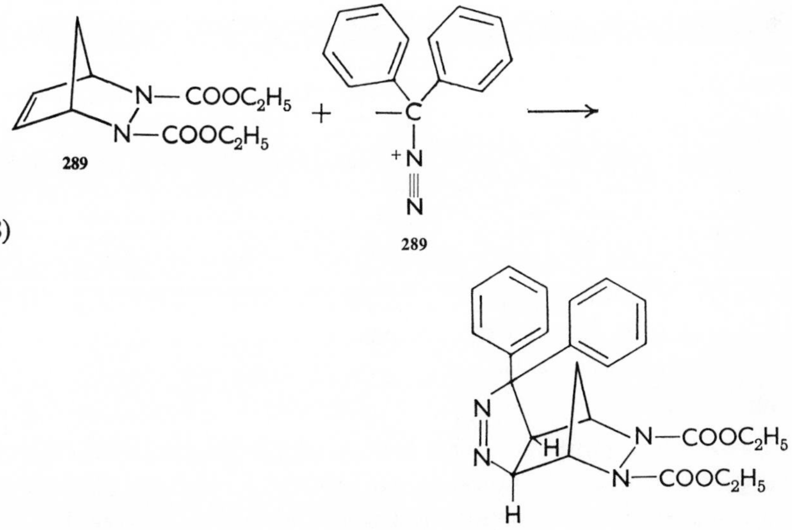

TABLE 1.57   *[3] Substrate Systems for [2 + 3] Cycloadditions*[a,b]

Type: $\overset{+}{a}$—b—$\overset{-}{\underset{\cdot\cdot}{c}}$ ↔ a=$\overset{+}{b}$—$\overset{-}{\underset{\cdot\cdot}{c}}$ (**287** ↔ **287a**)

Atom System	1,3-Dipolar Form	Alternate Form	Name
CNC	$>\overset{+}{C}$—$\overset{\mid}{N}$—$\overset{-}{\underset{\cdot\cdot}{C}}<$	$>C$=$\overset{\mid}{N}$—$\overset{+}{\underset{\cdot\cdot}{C}}<$	Azomethine ylide
CNN	$>\overset{+}{C}$—$\overset{\mid}{N}$—$\overset{-}{\underset{\cdot\cdot}{N}}$—	$>C$=$\overset{\mid}{N}$—$\overset{+}{\underset{\cdot\cdot}{N}}$—	Azomethine imine
CNO	$>\overset{+}{C}$—$\overset{\mid}{N}$—$\overset{-}{\underset{\cdot\cdot}{O}}$:	$>C$=$\overset{\mid}{N}$—$\overset{+}{\underset{\cdot\cdot}{O}}$:	Nitrone
NNN	—$\overset{+}{N}$—$\overset{\mid}{N}$—$\overset{-}{\underset{\cdot\cdot}{N}}$—	—N=$\overset{\mid}{N}$—$\overset{+}{\underset{\cdot\cdot}{N}}$—	Diazene ylide (*)
NNO	—$\overset{+}{N}$—$\overset{\mid}{N}$—$\overset{-}{\underset{\cdot\cdot}{O}}$:	—N=$\overset{\mid}{N}$—$\overset{+}{\underset{\cdot\cdot}{O}}$:	Azoxy
ONO	:$\overset{+}{O}$—$\overset{\mid}{N}$—$\overset{-}{\underset{\cdot\cdot}{O}}$:	O=$\overset{\mid}{N}$—$\overset{+}{\underset{\cdot\cdot}{O}}$:	Nitro
COC	$>\overset{+}{C}$—$\overset{\cdot\cdot}{O}$—$\overset{-}{\underset{\cdot\cdot}{C}}<$	$>C$=$\overset{+}{O}$—$\overset{-}{\underset{\cdot\cdot}{C}}<$	Carbonyl ylide
CON	$>\overset{+}{C}$—$\overset{\cdot\cdot}{O}$—$\overset{-}{\underset{\cdot\cdot}{N}}$—	$>C$=$\overset{+}{O}$—$\overset{-}{\underset{\cdot\cdot}{N}}$—	Carbonyl imine (*)
COO	$>\overset{+}{C}$—$\overset{\cdot\cdot}{O}$—$\overset{-}{\underset{\cdot\cdot}{O}}$:	$>C$=$\overset{+}{O}$—$\overset{-}{\underset{\cdot\cdot}{O}}$:	Carbonyl oxide
NON	—$\overset{+}{N}$—$\overset{\cdot\cdot}{O}$—$\overset{-}{\underset{\cdot\cdot}{N}}$—	—N=$\overset{+}{O}$—$\overset{-}{\underset{\cdot\cdot}{N}}$—	Nitrosimine (*)
NOO	—$\overset{+}{N}$—$\overset{\cdot\cdot}{O}$—$\overset{-}{\underset{\cdot\cdot}{O}}$:	—N=$\overset{+}{O}$—$\overset{-}{\underset{\cdot\cdot}{O}}$:	Nitroso oxide (*)
OOO	:$\overset{+}{O}$—$\overset{\cdot\cdot}{O}$—$\overset{-}{\underset{\cdot\cdot}{O}}$:	:O=$\overset{+}{O}$—$\overset{-}{\underset{\cdot\cdot}{O}}$:	Ozone

[a] Ref. 213.   [b] The concerted nature of the reaction has not been established in all cases. In fact, [2 + 3] cycloadditions have not been observed for the [3] substrates marked (*).

An intermediate with the structure of an ion-pair (for example, **291**) would have arisen from a transition state with much more separation of charge than the initial state, and a solvent effect would have been observed for the rate

TABLE 1.58 *[3] Substrate Systems for [2 + 3] Cycloadditions*[a,b]

Type: $\overset{+}{a}=b-\overset{-}{\underset{..}{c}} \leftrightarrow \overset{..}{a}-b=c$ (**288** $\leftrightarrow$ **288a**)

Atom System	1,3-Dipolar Form	Alternate Form	Name
CCC	$-\overset{+}{C}=\overset{\vert}{C}-\overset{..-}{C}<$	$-\overset{..}{C}-\overset{\vert}{C}=C<$	Vinylmethylene[c]
CCN	$-\overset{+}{C}=\overset{\vert}{C}-\overset{..-}{N}-$	$-\overset{..}{C}-C=N-$	Iminomethylene[c]
CCO	$-\overset{+}{C}=\overset{\vert}{C}-\overset{..-}{\underset{..}{O}}:$	$-\overset{..}{C}-\overset{\vert}{C}=O$	Ketomethylene[c]
NCC	$:\overset{+}{N}=\overset{\vert}{C}-\overset{..-}{C}<$	$:\overset{..}{N}-C=C<$	Vinylnitrene
NCN	$:N=\overset{\vert}{C}-\overset{..-}{\underset{..}{N}}-$	$:\overset{..}{N}-\overset{\vert}{C}=N-$	Iminonitrene
NCO	$:N=\overset{\vert}{C}-\overset{..-}{\underset{..}{O}}:$	$:\overset{..}{N}-\overset{\vert}{C}=O$	Ketonitrene

[a] Ref. 213. [b] The concerted nature of the reaction has not been established for these cases, which are particularly difficult to investigate since they are all unstable intermediates. [c] The use of the name methylene rather than carbene is discussed in Part 3 of the book.

constant. (The dipole moment of a diazoalkane is about 1.5 D, the local dipole for the strained double bond is small, and the dipole moment for an ion-pair is 11–12 D.) The data in Table 1.59 indicate that the reaction shown in Eq. 248 is insensitive to solvent over a Z-value range of 17. (See Part 2 for a discussion of the empirical solvent polarity measure, Z-value. A rate factor of over 10^4 might have been expected if the appropriate transition state were that which led to **291**).

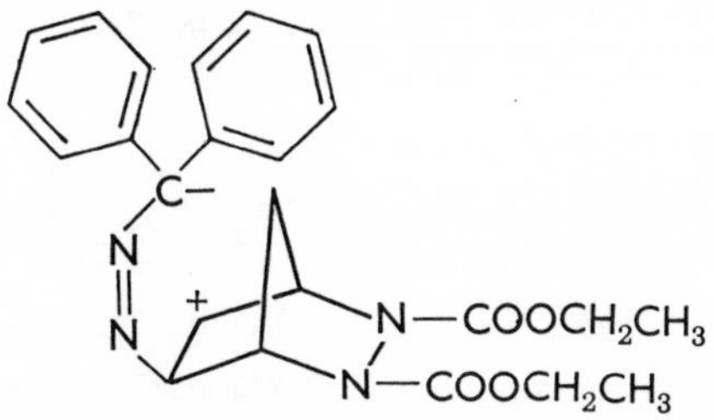

291

TABLE 1.59   *Effect of Solvent on a [2 + 3] Cycloaddition*[a]

[3] Substrate of Type **286** ↔ **286a**

Reaction of **289** with **290**

Solvent	Z-value[b]	$10^4 k$, l. mole^{-1} sec.$^{-1}$
Benzene	54	2.43
Dioxane	—	2.93
Ethyl acetate	—	2.27
1,2-Dimethoxyethane	—	3.64
Acetone	65.7	2.38
Acetonitrile	71.3	2.61
Dimethylformamide	68.5	2.90

[a] Ref. 214.   [b] Ref. 216, Table 2.3.

Another [2 + 3] cycloaddition, in which the change in the dipole moments of the reactants to that of the product is greater than the change for the reactants of Eq. 248, exhibits very little change in rate for a substantial change in solvent polarity. The reaction of the nitrone **292** (the *N*-oxide of benzaldehyde *N*-methylimine) with ethyl acrylate (**293**) is faster in ethanol than in toluene by a factor of five (*217*). The rate increase which might have been anticipated for this solvent change (ΔZ about 26) for the formation of an ion-pair intermediate would be about 10^6, and we must conclude that the transition state to product has about the same charge separation as the initial state.

A second significant aspect of the [2 + 3] cycloaddition is the stereo-

(249)

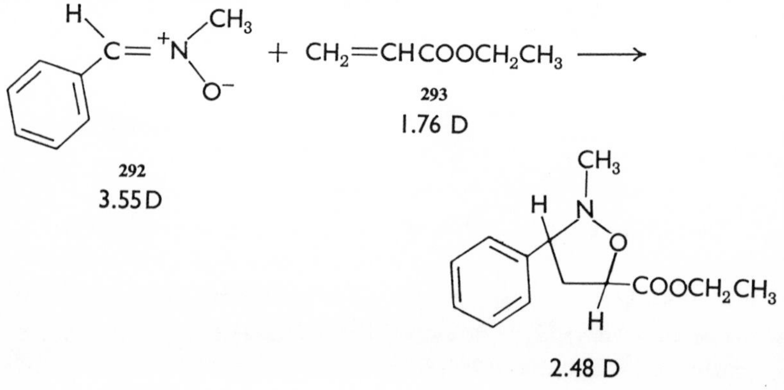

292
3.55 D

293
1.76 D

2.48 D

specificity of the reaction, as shown by the formation of different isomers from diphenylnitrile imine (294) and the isomeric stilbenes, the *cis*-(295) and the *trans*-(296). The isomeric products may be oxidized to the same tetraphenylpyrazole (297).

(250)

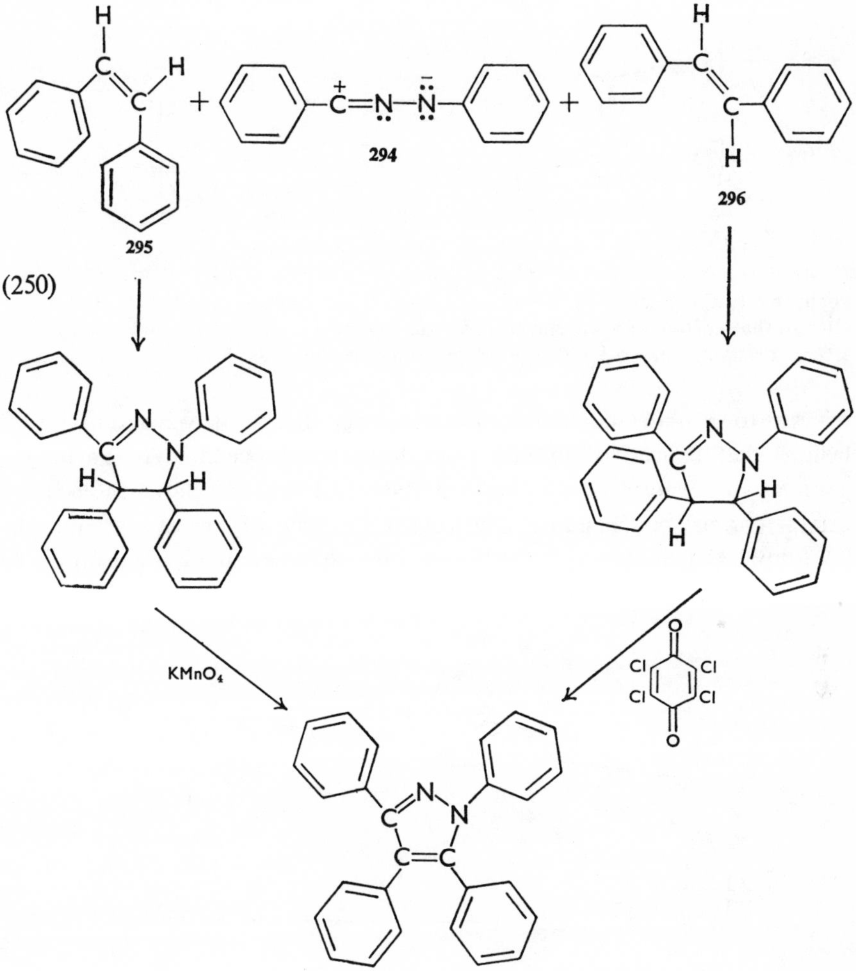

The stereospecificity of the [2 + 3] cycloaddition distinguishes it from the [2 + 2] cycloaddition which involves an intermediate diradical. The lack of a solvent effect on the rate of [2 + 3] cycloaddition excludes ion-pair intermediates which might preserve the stereochemical relationships of the reactants through the product-forming step. Insofar as we have information

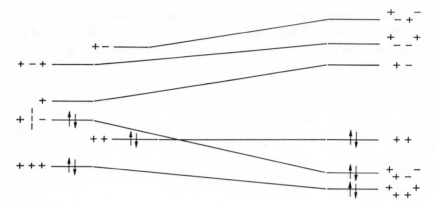

Figure 1.54 A molecular orbital correlation diagram for a [2 + 3] cycloaddition, applicable to the cases $a^+ = \ddot{b} - \ddot{c}^- \leftrightarrow a \equiv b^+ - \ddot{c}^-$ listed in Table 1.56. The signs refer to that portion of a wavefunction on the side of the molecular plane toward the second reactant. Thus, a bonding π-orbital would be shown as $++$.

relevant to an understanding of the mechanism of [2 + 3] cycloaddition, we believe that concerted formation of the product occurs. (An apparent anomaly in the form of a substituent effect is discussed below.) Molecular orbital correlation diagrams, constructed for each of the two groups of " 1,3-dipoles" in reaction with an alkene, show that the orbitals of the product are readily correlated with those of the reactants (Figs. 1.54 and 1.55). Rather

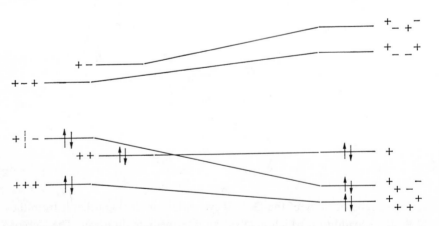

Figure 1.55 A molecular orbital correlation diagram for a [2 + 3] cycloaddition, applicable to the cases $\overset{+}{a} - \ddot{b} - \ddot{c}^- \leftrightarrow a = b^+ - \ddot{c}^-$ listed in Table 1.57. The signs refer to the wave function on one side of the molecule. A bonding π-orbital would be shown as $++$, and a nonbonding p-orbital as $+$.

than labeling the symmetries of the orbitals involved in the cycloaddition, we have indicated the signs of the wave functions on the side of the molecule that approaches the second reactant. A bonding π-orbital would thus be shown as ++. The identical symmetries of the initial and final orbitals are easily seen in these diagrams. A molecular orbital formulation for the course of the reaction in somewhat different terms has been advanced by Huisgen (*214*).

Alkenes vary in reactivity with the strain in the double bond, as would be expected. [The greater the strain, the more reactive the alkene, as one can see from the rate trend in Table 1.60 on changing from maleic anhydride (**298**) to norbornene (**299**).] Substituents in the [3] substrate usually have a small effect (except for steric effects which should be important for a concerted, highly organized transition state). The rates of some [2 + 3] cycloadditions are listed in Table 1.60 for several [3] substrates and a number of azides. The reaction constant for three of the series listed in the Table is close to unity, but in the case of pyrrolidinyl cyclohexene (**300**), the ρ is +2.6. The ρ-value for the reaction of **300** with azides is so much greater than that observed for other "1,3-dipoles" that we may immediately suspect a change in mechanism. The data in Table 1.60 reveal that the high ρ-value is a result of an anomalously high rate for the reaction of *p*-nitrophenyl azide and **300**. In view of the

TABLE 1.60 *Rates of Some [2 + 3] Cycloadditions*[a,b]

[3] Substrate Type (Azides): **286** ↔ **226a**

Azide, R—N̈—N̈≡N	$10^7\, k$, l. mole^{-1} sec.$^{-1}$			
R =	Maleic Anhydride (**298**)	*N*-Phenyl Maleimide	Norbornene (**299**)	Pyrrolidinyl Cyclohexene (**300**)
p-NO$_2$C$_6$H$_5$—	1.3	11	1530	1,480,000
C$_6$H$_5$—	7.2	28	254	9930
p-CH$_3$OC$_6$H$_5$—	21	67	187	3400
C$_6$H$_5$CH$_2$—	53	95	22	25
ρ[c]	−1.2	−0.7	+0.8	+2.6[d]

[a] Ref. 214. [b] In benzene at 25°. [c] Based on the relationship $\log k/k_0 = \rho\sigma$. [d] The extraordinary magnitude of this ρ-value is based largely on the rate constant found for the *p*-nitrophenyl azide and is discussed in the text.

donor properties expected for a vinylamine (**300**) and the acceptor properties expected for *p*-nitrophenyl azide (**301**), it seems most probable that this reaction proceeds via charge transfer [a thermal electron transfer (see Section 1.7)]:

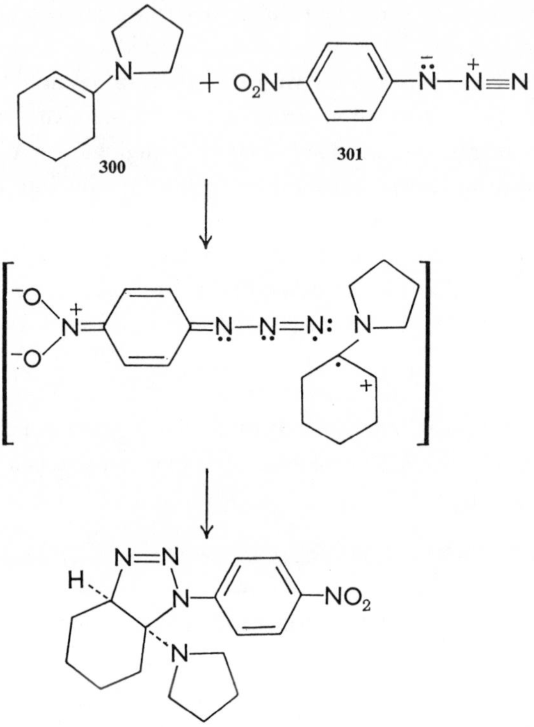

300   **301**

(251)

The variety of possible [2 + 3] cycloadditions forces us to be aware of the potential "1,3-dipolar character" in any suitable [3] substrate. The general view presented by Huisgen (*214*) is probably valid, but there is much scope for detailed mechanistic investigation in the field of [2 + 3] cycloadditions, as exemplified by the cautionary remarks in the literature (*750, 751*).

[2 + 4] Cycloadditions

By far the most important [2 + 4] cycloaddition is the Diels–Alder reaction, for which we have already presented an example in Eq. 233. As in the case of other isopolar reactions, medium change has very little effect on the rate of a [2 + 4] cycloaddition. The stereospecificity of the reaction is very high and suggests that the reaction is concerted. In some cases, like the reaction of anthracene (259) and tetracyanoethylene (TCNE, 302), formation of a charge-transfer complex may be observed. In spite of the striking color of many of the complexes (259 → 302 is green), the role of such complexes in the mechanism of the addition reaction is uncertain (see the discussion of Berson and Remanick, *219*).

(252)

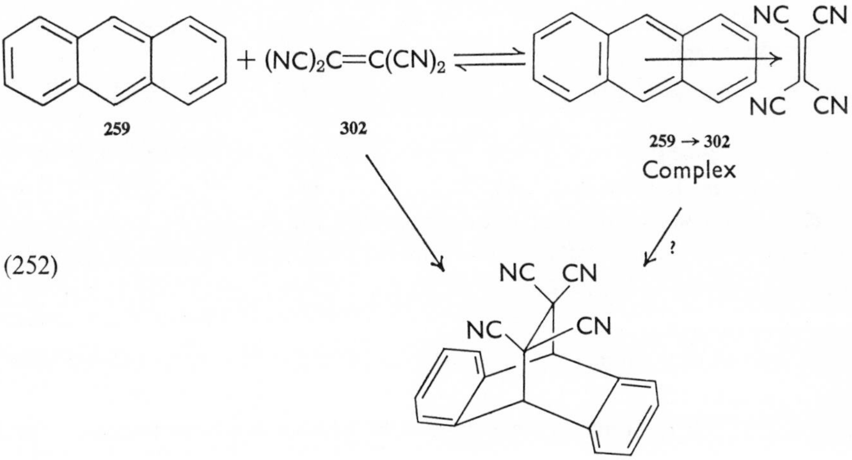

259   302

259 → 302
Complex

The lack of solvent effect on [2 + 4] cycloaddition shows conclusively that charge-transfer character is not accentuated in the transition state. The complex may play some role in determining the relative orientation of the reactants.

The [2 + 4] cycloaddition reaction can be reversed to form diene and alkene. A study of the decomposition of the adduct of 2-methylfuran and maleic anhydride by Seltzer (*220*) through the use of the secondary hydrogen isotope effect (see Halevi, *221*) revealed that the reaction was concerted.

(253)

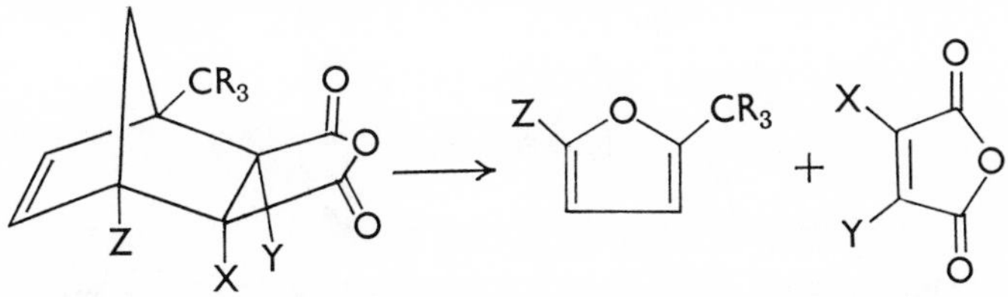

303

303a   X = Y = Y = R = H

303b   X = Y = D

Z = R = H $k_{303a}/k_{303b} = 1.16$

303c   X = Y = R = H

Z = D $k_{303a}/k_{303c} = 1.08$

303d   X = D

Y = Z = R = H $k_{303a}/k_{303d} = 1.03$

303e   Y = D

X = Z = R = H $k_{303d}/k_{303e} = 1.00$

The equivalence of X and Y with respect to the secondary hydrogen isotope effect implies that the bonds to the carbons carrying these hydrogens are equally stretched at the transition state. (See the rather different view of Woodward and Katz (*222*) for an isomerization reaction which is properly discussed in the next section.)

Molecular orbital correlation diagrams for [2 + 4] cycloadditions indicate that the reaction should be facile. The symmetry plane for butadiene plus ethylene is shown in Fig. 1.56, and the correlation diagram in Fig. 1.57. The orbitals of the reactants go over smoothly into those of the products. No barrier is expected and, indeed, the reaction is usually quite facile (see Eq. 233).

We shall close our discussion of [2 + 4] cycloadditions with an example involving an unusual diene. Cyclobutadiene (**304**) can be liberated from cyclo-butadiene iron tricarbonyl (**305**) by oxidation with ceric ion and reacts with

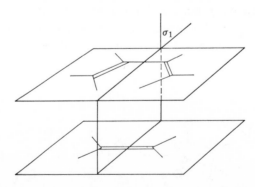

Figure 1.56   Symmetry plane used in making the assignments of the symmetries of the orbitals shown in Fig. 1.57 (adapted from Ref. 200).

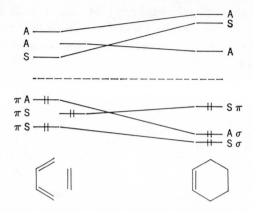

Figure 1.57 Molecular orbital correlation diagram for [2 + 4] cycloaddition of ethylene and 1,3-butadiene. (A, antisymmetric and S, symmetric with respect to the symmetry plane defined in Fig. 1.56) (adapted from Ref. 200).

dimethyl maleate (**306**) and dimethyl fumarate (**307**) in a stereospecific manner (*223, 224*). The *endo*-orientation of **308** is explicable on the basis of the maximum overlap of occupied and unoccupied orbitals (see *202*).

(254)

305   304

(255)

304   306   308

(256)

304   307

Cyclopentadiene (**6**) and cyclobutadiene (**304**) react rapidly to yield **309**, a single compound. In this reaction the cyclobutadiene (like strained alkenes) serves as the [2] reactant. The product has the *endo*-configuration according to the n.m.r. spectrum (*224*).

(257)

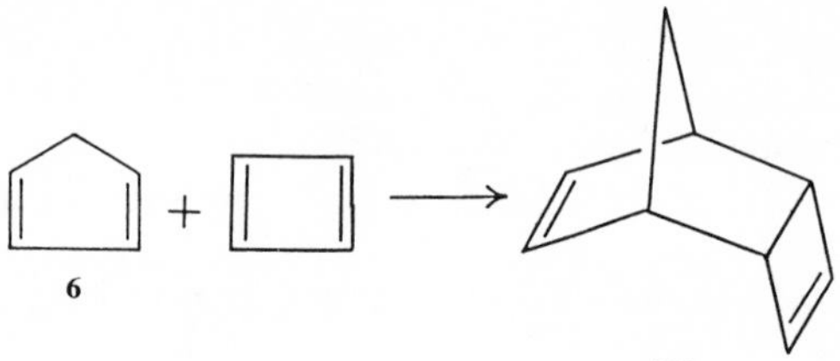

6

304   309

The behavior of cyclobutadiene in [2 + 4] cycloadditions suggests rather strongly that the ground state is singlet, rather than triplet, since the triplet (diradical) should have formed mixtures of products. Barring an unusually great radical-radical interaction in the postulated diradical intermediates (for example, **310**, see the discussion under [2 + 2] cycloaddition), it is probably safe to accept the singlet assignment for the ground state of cyclobutadiene.

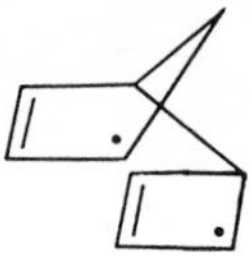

310

Our survey of cycloadditions shows that they may be understood on a common basis using molecular orbital correlation diagrams, even though the mechanisms for the several cycloadditions we have discussed are not the same.

Problems

1. Write examples of the following:
   (a) [2 + 2] cycloaddition.
   (b) [2 + 3] cycloaddition.
   (c) [2 + 4] cycloaddition.
2. What are the products of the reaction of *cis*- and *trans*-piperylene with **271**?

3. Explain why recombination of the radicals formed by photolysis of **205** at 77°K is stereospecific while the diradical formed by sensitized photolysis of **285** (Eq. 245, Part 1) leads to a mixture of isomers.

4. Write all the molecular orbitals for
   (a) Ethane
   (b) Ethylene
   (c) 1,3-Butadiene
   (d) 1,2-Butadiene
   (e) Cyclobutane
   and by choosing suitable planes, assign symmetries. Do not forget the excited state orbitals.

5. Draw a molecular orbital correlation diagram for bringing together two azomethane molecules to form a tetra-azacyclobutane. How readily would you expect the reaction to proceed?

6. Write an example of a [2 + 3] cycloaddition for the following [3] substrates:
   (a) Nitrile ylide.
   (b) Diazoalkane.
   (c) Phenyl azide.
   (d) Azoxybenzene.
   (e) An azomethine ylide.
   (f) Ozone.

7. Is the product of the reaction you have written for Problem 6f stable? How does it decompose? (Refs. 747–749.)

8. For the reactions you have written for Problems 6a and 6e, draw the molecular orbital diagrams.

9. Explain why thermal electron transfer (Eq. 251, Part 1) might lead to the same product as might be predicted on the basis of a concerted [2 + 3] cycloaddition.

10. Draw a molecular orbital correlation diagram for the reaction of cyclobutadiene with dimethyl maleate (Eq. 255, Part 1).

11. The reaction of tetracyanooxirane (**A**) with *trans*-stilbene is governed by the rate equation:

(P11a)
$$v = k_1(A) \frac{k_2(\text{stilbene})}{k_{-1} + k_2(\text{stilbene})}$$

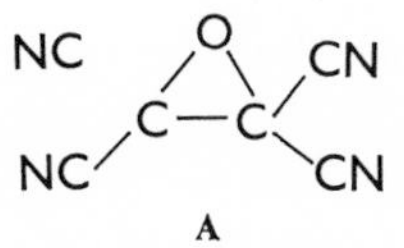

A

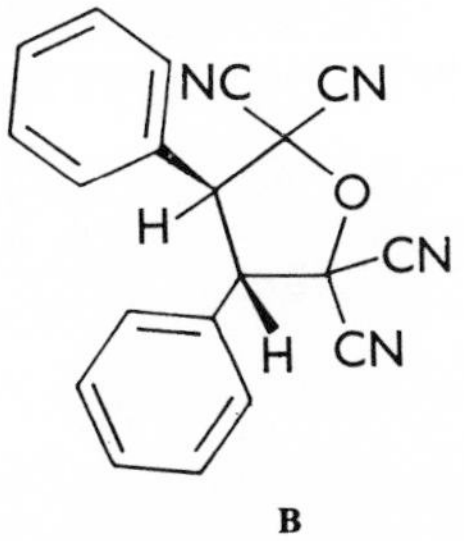

B

The mechanism which fits these kinetics is:

(P11b)
$$A \underset{k_{-1}}{\overset{k_1}{\rightleftharpoons}} A^*$$

(P11c)
$$A^* + \text{stilbene} \xrightarrow{k_2} \text{product (B)}$$

The product is formed stereospecifically. Formulate A^* and write a mechanism for its reaction with stilbene (Refs. 752, 753).

12. Show how the hydrogen iodide plus hydrogen iodide reaction fits the idea of a $[2\sigma + 2\sigma]$ cycloaddition (Ref. 754).

1.9   Rearrangements

Along with cycloaddition reactions, a number of other chemical transformations appear to proceed through isopolar transition states. The stereochemistry and facility (or lack of it) of many rearrangements, isomerizations, and fragmentations are nicely rationalized by molecular orbital correlation diagrams. The presentation adopted here is that of Woodward and Hoffmann (*200*) which should be compared with the essentially identical scheme of Longuet-Higgins and Abrahamson (*204*) (see also *230*).

The correlation diagram presents a relationship between the symmetries of the orbitals of the reactants and products. If the symmetries of the set of occupied orbitals of the reactants are smoothly related to the corresponding set of occupied orbitals in the products, we expect the reaction to be more facile than if this relation does not exist. By the word *corresponding*, we mean two ground states, two first excited states, etc. Only the symmetries of the electrons in the bonding orbitals (the *local* symmetries of the bonding electrons) need be considered so that substituents do not alter the conclusions drawn from a consideration of the correlation diagrams. We must also emphasize that a smooth correlation of the symmetries does not automatically mean that the process described by the correlation is fast, but only that it is faster than some other process which is not smoothly correlated. The actual barriers to reaction are still influenced by such factors as the bond strengths of the bonds undergoing change and steric effects. The existence of a smooth correlation does not preclude the operation of another (completely different) reaction pathway.

We have divided the section on rearrangements into discussions of electrocyclic reactions, fragmentations and atom transfers, and sigmatropic reactions.

Electrocyclic Reactions

An analysis of reaction stereochemistry, based on orbital symmetries, was first applied by Woodward and Hoffmann (*199*) (see also the suggestion of Oosterhoff cited in *225*). The initial formulation (*199*) was in terms of the orbitals of the reactants, but this was soon expanded to the type of diagram we use in this book (*200, 204*). An *electrocyclic reaction* is one in which a molecule with a system of n π-electrons is converted into (or formed from) a ring system with $n - 2$ π-electrons and one new σ-bond. A typical electrocyclic reaction is the conversion of cyclobutene to 1,3-butadiene:

(258)

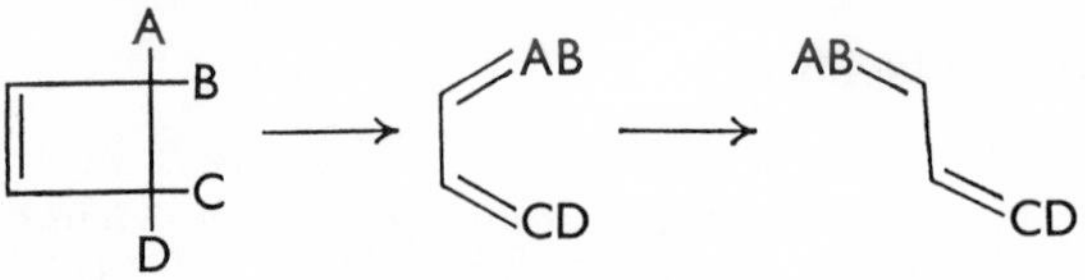

If the ring-opening is concerted, two possible pathways can be imagined for the process, leading to different butadiene isomers. If the groups rotate away from one another, the product will be A-*trans*,C-*trans* and the process by which this product is formed can be called *disrotatory*. If the groups rotate in the same direction, the product will be A-*cis*,C-*trans*, formed through a process called *conrotatory*. These possibilities are depicted in Fig. 1.58.

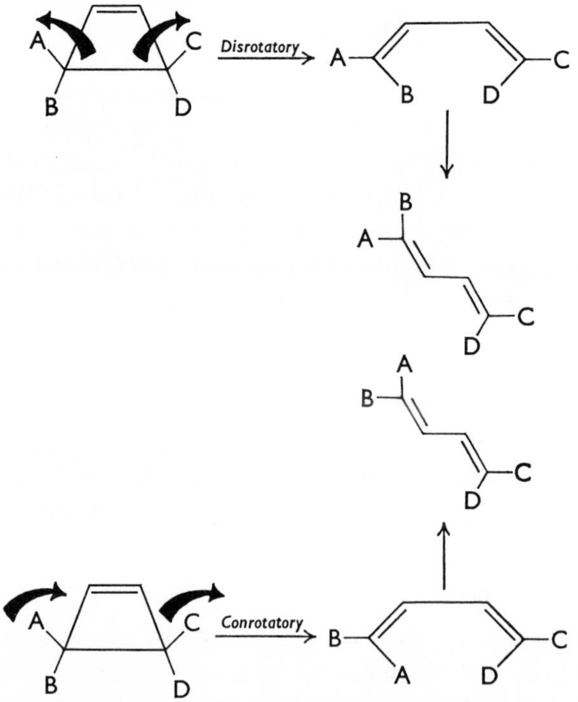

Figure 1.58 Two pathways for the ring-opening of cyclobutene to 1,3-butadiene. *Conrotatory* refers to the process in which the *A*–*C*–*B* and *C*–*C*–*D* groups rotate in the same directions. *Disrotatory* refers to the process in which the *A*–*C*–*B* and *C*–*C*–*D* groups rotate in opposite directions. Note that in cases for which the initial *cis*-1,3-diene has a barrier to free rotation around the central carbon–carbon single bond, the direction of the rotation can be important.

All known cases of cyclobutene ring opening are stereospecific. Thermal isomerization of *cis*-3,4-dicarbomethoxycyclobutene-1 (**311**) produces only *cis,trans*-1,4-dicarbomethoxy-1,3-butadiene (**312**) (Eq. 259) (*226*).

(259)

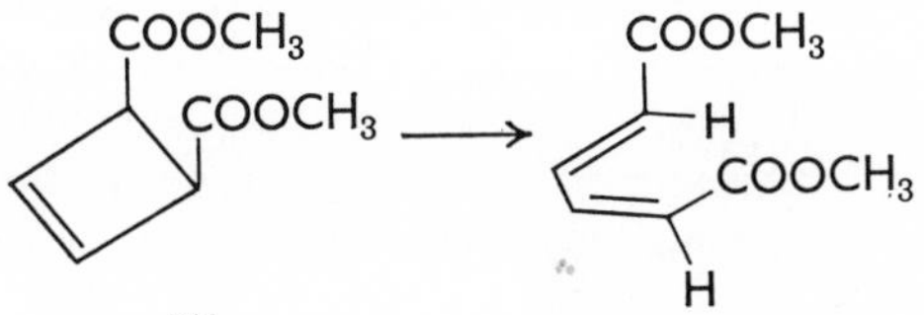

311

312

Criegee found that *cis*-3,4-dimethylcyclobutene-1 (**313**) rearranges to *cis,trans*-1,4-dimethyl-1,3-butadiene (**314**) (Eq. 260), and that *trans*-3,4-dimethyl-cyclobutene-1 (**315**) forms *trans,trans*-1,4-dimethyl-1,3-butadiene (**316**) (Eq. 260) (*227*).

(260)

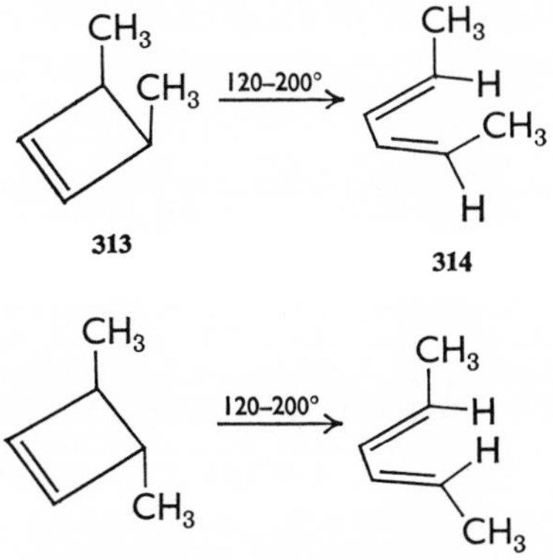

313

314

315

316

The examples given show that thermal isomerization of cyclobutenes to 1,3-dienes occurs in a *conrotatory* fashion. Molecular orbital correlation diagrams indicate that conrotatory opening should indeed be favored over disrotatory opening. To examine the relationships of the orbitals, we first define an axis of symmetry for the conrotatory mode of opening and a plane of symmetry for the disrotatory mode (Fig. 1.59). The symmetries of several of the orbitals with respect to the axis or plane of symmetry are shown in Fig. 1.60. The molecular orbital correlation diagrams shown in Fig. 1.61 follows from the symmetry relationships between the corresponding states.

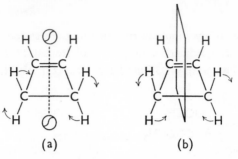

Figure 1.59 Symmetry elements for cyclobutene ring opening. A symmetry axis is designated for conrotatory ring opening (*a*) and a symmetry plane for disrotatory ring opening (*b*) (adapted from Ref. 204).

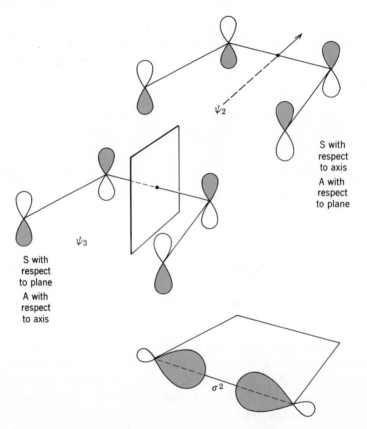

Figure 1.60 Symmetry relationships among orbitals in cyclobutene and butadiene. The σ-orbital is symmetric (S) for both the axis and the plane. The shading indicates (+) wave function, unmarked (−) wave function.

228

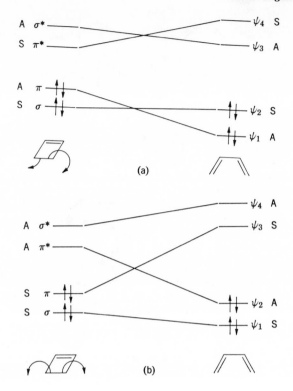

Figure 1.61 (*a*) Conrotatory ring opening–molecular orbital correlation diagram. (*b*) Disrotatory ring opening–molecular orbital correlation diagram.

It is relatively easy to see that excitation of an electron into the π^* orbital from the π-orbital should change the mode of ring opening from conrotatory to disrotatory.

An extremely interesting example of cyclobutene-1,3-diene ring inter-conversion is that of the 1,3-cyclooctadiene(*cis,cis*- and *cis,trans*-)bicyclo-[4.2.0]octene-2 system illustrated in Fig. 1.62 (*755, 756*). The *cis,cis*-diene ring closes only after photochemical excitation because the constraint imposed by the four-carbon bridge does not permit a thermal and conrotatory ring closure. The constraint is removed in the *cis,trans*-diene which does undergo thermal ring closure. The *cis,trans*-diene is generated through the excited diene triplet as shown in Fig. 1.63. The reactions shown in Fig. 1.62 are understandable without special difficulty in terms of molecular orbital correlation diagrams like those of Figs. 1.61*a* and 1.61*b*.

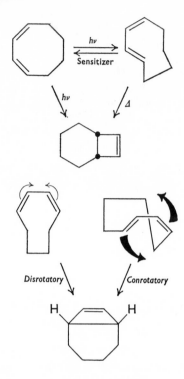

Figure 1.62 Photochemical disrotatory conversion of *cis,cis*-1,3-cyclooctadiene into bicyclo[4.2.0]octene-2. Thermal conrotatory conversion of *cis,trans*-1,3-cyclooctadiene into bicyclo[4.2.0]octene-2.

An electrocyclic reaction for 1,3,5-trienes would be disrotatory for the ground state and conrotatory for the first excited state. The thermal isomerization of 2,4,6-octatriene produces 5,6-dimethyl-1,3-cyclohexadiene.

(261)

317   318

(262)

319   320

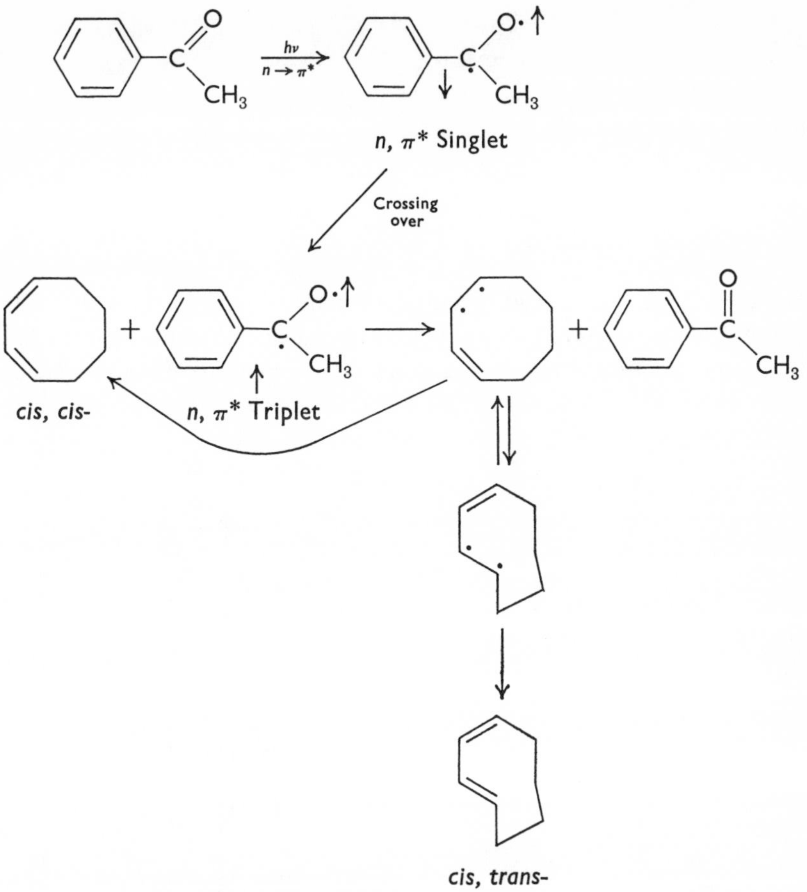

Figure 1.63 Conversion of *cis,cis*-1,3-cyclooctadiene into *cis,trans*-1,3-cyclooctadiene via the excited diene triplet produced by means of a reaction of the ground-state diene with the excited triplet of acetophenone.

The *trans,cis,trans*-2,4,6-octatriene (**317**) yields *cis*-5,6-dimethyl-1,3 cyclohexadiene (**318**) (Eq. 261), and *trans,cis,cis*-2,4,6-octatriene (**319**) forms *trans*-5,6-dimethyl-1,3-cyclohexadiene (**320**) (Eq. 262) (*228*).

The interconversion of *cis,cis,cis*-1,3,5-cyclooctatriene (**321**) and bicyclo-[4.2.0]octadiene-2,4 (**322**) is rapid between 80 and 100°, but slow enough at 30° so that the isomers may be isolated in pure form. The disrotatory ring opening requires consideration of the symmetry relationships of the orbitals with the symmetry element, a plane σ_1, as is the case for the cyclobutenes. (Consider Fig. 1.60.) The disrotatory ring opening is, of course, not constrained by the two-carbon bridge joining the ends of the conjugated system. The molecular orbital correlation diagram for disrotatory ring opening and ring closure is given in Fig. 1.64.

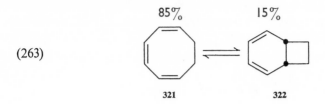

(263)

321   322

The diene, **322**, reacts readily with maleic anhydride in a [2 + 4] cyclo-addition. The triene, **321**, does not react with maleic anhydride to form **323**, until the temperature is raised to a point high enough to effect conversion

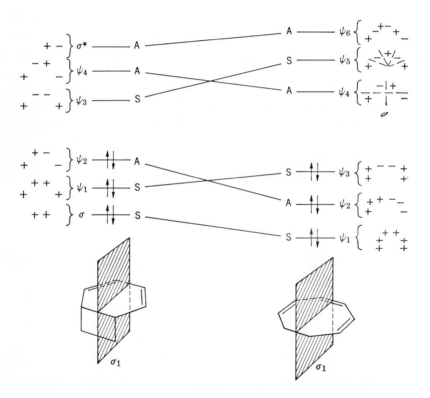

Figure 1.64 Molecular orbital correlation diagram for disrotatory ring closure of *cis, cis,cis*-1,3,5-cyclooctatriene (**321**). The signs indicate the sign of the wave function for the orbitals at specific atoms above the plane of the conjugated system in the order in which the atoms appear in the formulas below, except for ψ_4 and ψ_5, in which the location of the nodes made it difficult to show the signs at the atoms.

into the diene **322**. Thus, [2 + 6] cycloaddition, which is predicted to be slow on the basis of a molecular orbital correlation diagram, is much slower than the electrocyclic reaction **321** → **322**.

323

One of the most interesting predictions made on the basis of the molecular orbital correlation diagrams concerns the direction of ring opening of cyclopropyl cations (*199, 204*). Disrotatory ring opening of a cyclopropyl cation is shown in Fig. 1.65*a*. Conrotatory ring opening to an allyl carbanion is illustrated in Fig. 1.65*b*. A comparison of these correlation diagrams suggests that cations will open in a disrotatory manner and that carbanions will open in a conrotatory way. The opening of cyclopropyl radicals will probably occur in a conrotatory mode, but the mode might well be altered by other factors of molecular structure.

The solvolysis of cyclopropyl derivatives produces allyl compounds. If ring opening were concerted with the ionization of the leaving group, the rate of the S_1N reaction (see Section 1.5) would depend upon acceleration from developing π–π interaction and deceleration resulting from the steric interaction of groups pushed closer together in the transition state. It is reasonable to assume that the backside of the carbon bearing the leaving group would provide the opportunity for π-interaction. Disrotatory ring opening, with π–π interaction developing on the backside of the carbon bearing the leaving group for 2,3-dimethylcyclopropyl derivatives, leads to the expectation that *cis*-2,3-dimethylcyclopropyl compounds with the methyl groups *cis* to the leaving group will solvolyze much more slowly than *cis*-2,3-dimethyl-cyclopropyl compounds with the methyl groups *trans* to the leaving group. In the former case, the ring opening process forces the methyl groups closer together in the transition state, and in the latter case, the small strain that exists because of the *cis*-relationship of the methyl groups in the reactant is relieved in the transition state (Fig. 1.66). Schleyer and co-workers (*229*) have found that the tosylate **324** in which the methyl groups are *trans* to the leaving group solvolyzes in acetic acid 4500 times faster than the all *cis*-tosylate **325**.

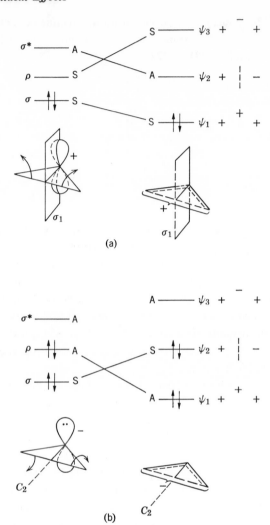

Figure 1.65 (*a*) Molecular orbital correlation diagram for disrotatory ring opening of the cyclopropyl cation. (*b*) Molecular orbital correlation diagram for the conrotatory ring opening of the cyclopropyl anion.

$$h_{326}^{150°} \ 7.76 \times 10^{-6} \ \text{sec.}^{-1} \ (248)$$

Apparently, the steric strain developed in the transition state for the solvolysis of **325** is approximately equal to the acceleration expected for methyl substitution on an allylic position (*ca.* 70 per methyl group) since **325** solvolyzes in acetic acid only 4 times faster than the unsubstituted cyclopropyl tosylate **326**. If the substituents are incorporated into a ring, the opposite relationship between isomers should be expected since opening to a *trans*-allylic ion (**330**, Fig. 1.66) would produce far too much ring strain (for a six-membered ring).

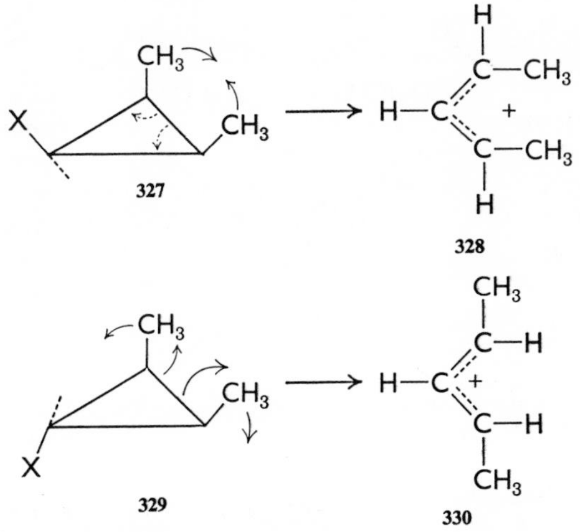

Figure 1.66 The influence of the position of the leaving group relative to substituents on the cyclopropyl ring on the nature of the products.

The bicyclic compound, *endo*-7-norcaryl tosylate (**331**), solvolyzes in acetic acid about 5500 times as rapidly as the *exo*-7-norcaryl tosylate (**332**), a cyclopropyl derivative which has the same reactivity in acetic acid at 150° as cyclopropyl tosylate (**326**).

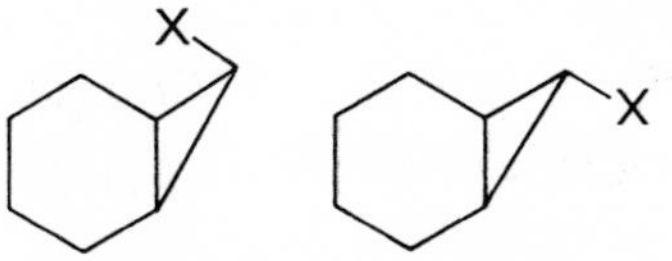

The conrotatory ring opening suggested by the correlation diagram (Fig. 1.65*b*) for cyclopropyl anions has been confirmed for the isoelectronic aziridines by Huisgen and co-workers (*788*). The interconversions illustrated below were investigated and photochemical ring-opening was shown to follow a steric course opposite to that of thermal ring-opening. Highly reactive trapping agents (in [2 + 3] cycloadditions) like dialkyl azodicar-

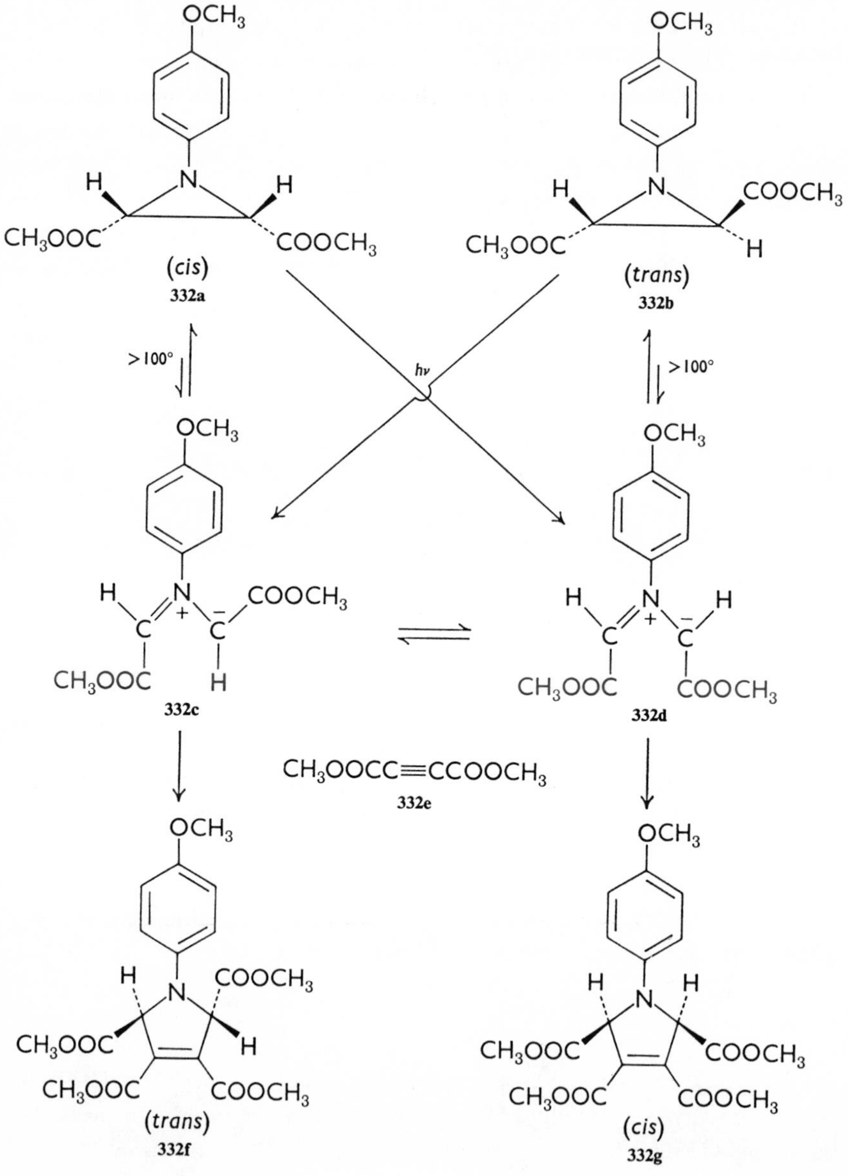

boxylates and tetracyanoethylene can be used in place of dimethyl acetylene dicarboxylate (**332e**) to trap the immediate azomethine ylides (**332c** and **332d**).

The examples presented in this section make it clear that valuable qualitative understanding of electrocyclic reactions is attained by use of molecular orbital correlation diagrams.

Fragmentation and Atom Transfers

One case of the reversal of [2 + 4] cycloaddition was discussed in Section 1.8. We might have called that case a [6 → 4 + 2] fragmentation, so that it would have been clear that isopolar fragmentations, like radical and ionic fragmentations, exist. However, in the fragmentations [5 → 4 + 1] that we shall now consider, the question of disrotatory or conrotatory ring opening comes up and for that reason, it is more convenient to include them in Section 1.9.

The treatment of 3-pyrroline with the disodium salt of nitrohydroxylamine and dilute hydrochloric acid produces butadiene and nitrogen.

(264)

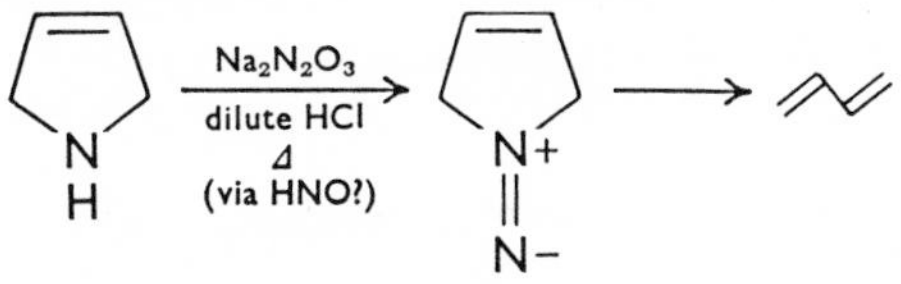

Lemal and McGregor (*757*) have discovered that ring-openings of this type are stereospecific and can be rationalized by the use of molecular orbital correlation diagrams. *Trans*-2,5-dimethyl-3-pyrroline (**333**) is deaminated in

(265)

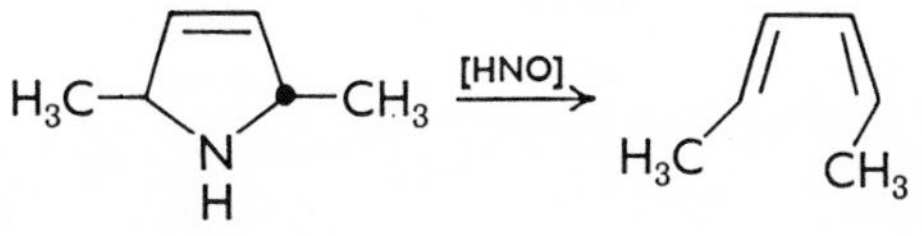

333   334

(266)

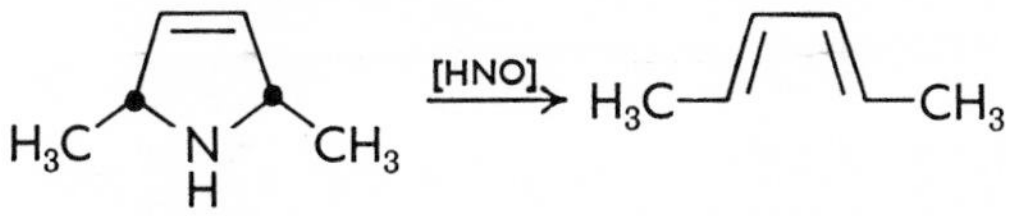

335   336

the manner of Eq. 264 to pure *cis,trans*-2,4-hexadiene (**334**) (Eq. 265) and *cis*-2,5-dimethyl-3-pyrroline (**335**) is converted into pure *trans,trans*-2,4-hexadiene (**336**).

A comparison of the molecular orbital correlation diagrams for conrotatory and disrotatory ring fragmentations is given in Fig. 1.67. It is well to remember that the two σ-bonds from the ring carbons to the ring nitrogen of the diazenium group are formed from two molecular orbitals, one of which is bonding (**337**) and the other, antibonding (**338**), across the nitrogen.

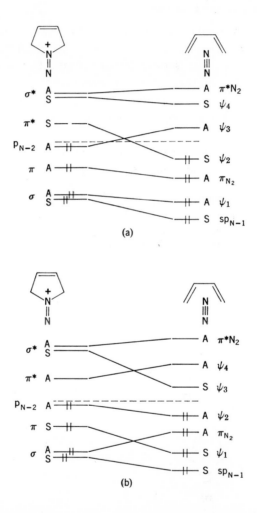

(a)

(b)

Figure 1.67 (*a*) Conrotatory [5 → 4 + 1] fragmentation–molecular orbital correlation diagram for the formation of diene and nitrogen from a diazene (adapted from Ref. 757). (*b*) Disrotatory [5 → 4 + 1] fragmentation–molecular orbital correlation diagram for the formation of diene and nitrogen from a diazene (adapted from Ref. 757).

337   338

McGregor and Lemal (*758*) and Mock (*759*) have demonstrated that the fragmentation of the isomeric sulfolenes **339** and **340** occurs in a disrotatory fashion. In addition, they found that the [1 + 4] cycloaddition of sulfur dioxide and the dienes is stereospecific as expected on the basis of molecular orbital correlation diagrams.

(267)

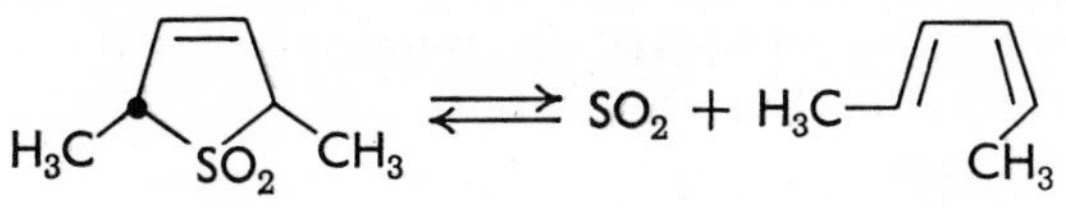

339   334

(268)

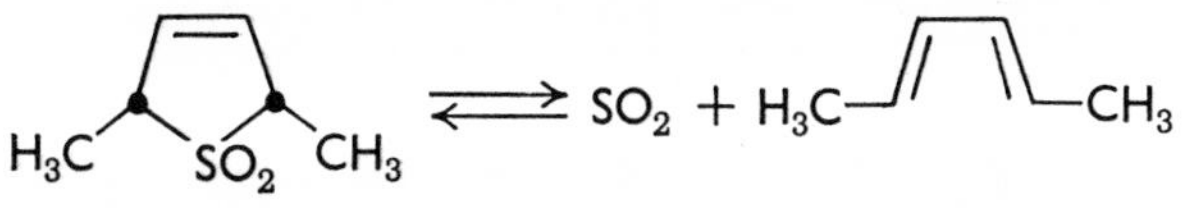

340   336

We can only mention here the possible application of molecular orbital correlation diagrams to atom transfer reactions. For example, if diimide reacts with alkenes as *cis*-diimide, Hoffmann and Woodward (*760*) have concluded that such a reaction would be thermally allowed. Hoffmann (*761*) has extended the use of correlation diagrams to many other types of reactions, and his papers should be consulted for further details.

(269)

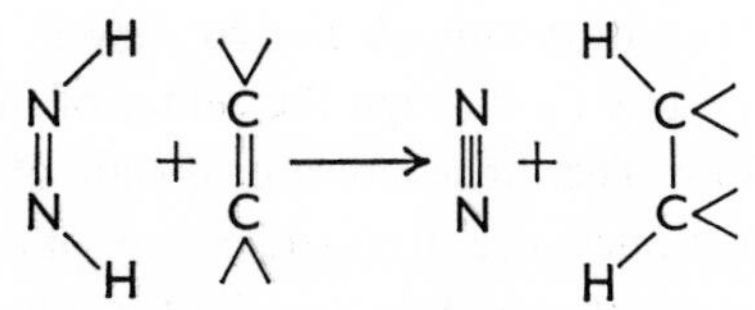

Sigmatropic Changes of Order

Another broad class of reactions, for which interpretation is very much facilitated by an understanding of the symmetry relationships of the orbitals of the molecules, includes hydrogen migrations, certain "valence isomerizations," the Cope and Claisen rearrangements, and "thermal reorganizations." These reaction descriptions, which are not mutually exclusive, belong to the class called *sigmatropic changes of order* by Woodward and Hoffmann (*201*). An [*i, j*] sigmatropic change of order involves the migration of a σ-bond, flanked by one or more π-electron systems, to a new position whose termini are $i - 1$ and $j - 1$ atoms removed from the original locations. In general, these reactions are influenced very slightly by the environment and do not respond in the same way to substituent changes as reactions through polar and radical transition states. Sigmatropic reactions probably proceed through *isopolar transition states.*

Let us consider the case of hydrogen transfer within a system in which the hydrogen is bonded to atom *j* (**341**). The transition state for the transfer of

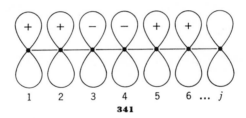

341

the hydrogen can be viewed as a combination of a hydrogen atom and a π-radical with *j* *p*-orbitals. If the hydrogen atom is transferred to the first carbon on the same face of the π-system from which it departed, the process is said to occur in a *suprafacial* manner. If the transfer takes the hydrogen to the first carbon on the face of the π-system opposite to that from which it departed, the process is *antarafacial.*

The suprafacial transition state has a plane of symmetry, σ, perpendicular to the plane of the molecule and the plane passing through the π-orbitals (taking the latter as being in a straight line, for the moment). The symmetry of the antarafacial transition state is not so easy to describe, and we shall designate a symmetry axis C_2 through the center of the *j* atom system of the π-radical portion alone. The highest occupied state of the π-radical is clearly the state with the most relevance to consideration of the transition state. The radical has $2k + 3$ electrons (in **341**, $k = 2$); for odd values of k, migration of hydrogen from atom j to C_1 takes place by the suprafacial route, and for even or zero values of k, migration occurs by the antarafacial route. Migrations of hydrogen within the excited state immediately above the highest occupied state follow exactly the opposite rules. The rules are summarized in Table 1.61. A graphic description of hydrogen atom migration in propene, and 1,3-pentadiene is shown in Fig. 1.68. It is immediately obvious that thermal [1,3]-isomerization in propene is not likely on steric grounds. (If the π-system twisted to the extent necessary to overcome the long bonds required for the transition state in Fig. 1.68, the species would no longer be an allyl

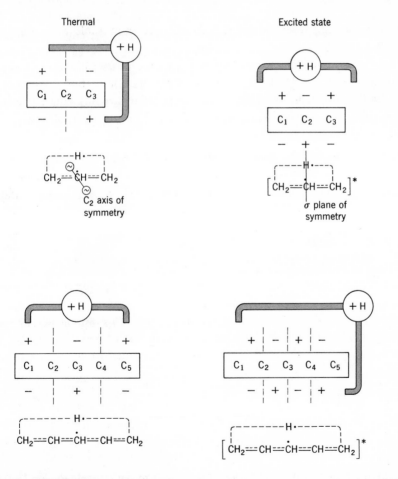

Figure 1.68 A comparison of the transition states for hydrogen atom migration within propene and 1,3-pentadiene. Both thermal and photochemical (first excited state) pathways are shown for each system.

TABLE 1.61   *Transition States for [1, j] Sigmatropic Changes*[a,b]

[1, j]	Thermal	Excited State
[1, 3]	Antarafacial (C_2)	Suprafacial (σ)
[1, 5]	Suprafacial (σ)	Antarafacial (C_2)
[1, 7]	Antarafacial (C_2)	Suprafacial (σ)

[a] Ref. 201.   [b] Cf. Ref. 789.

radical plus a hydrogen atom, and the rules given in Table 1.61 would not apply.)

The only thermal isomerizations which should be possible within rings of moderate size are [1,5]sigmatropic changes. The migration of hydrogen within the cycloheptatriene ring occurs as [1,5]sigmatropic change, as shown by the following examples, for which rate data are listed in Table 1.62.

TABLE 1.62   *Rate Constants for [1, 5]Hydrogen Migrations*[a]

Compound	k, sec.$^{-1}$[b]	E_a, kcal./mole	Ref.
7-Phenylcycloheptatriene	3.6×10^{-5}	27.6	233
7-Deuteriocycloheptatriene	6.0×10^{-7}	31	234
7-Methoxycycloheptatriene	2.48×10^{-5}	26.4	235
1,4-*bis*-(7-cycloheptatrienyl)-benzene (**342**)	3.33×10^{-5}	30.6	232

[a] At 121° from Ref. 232.   [b] Rate of the change from a 7-substituted cycloheptatriene to a 3-substituted cycloheptatriene.

(270)

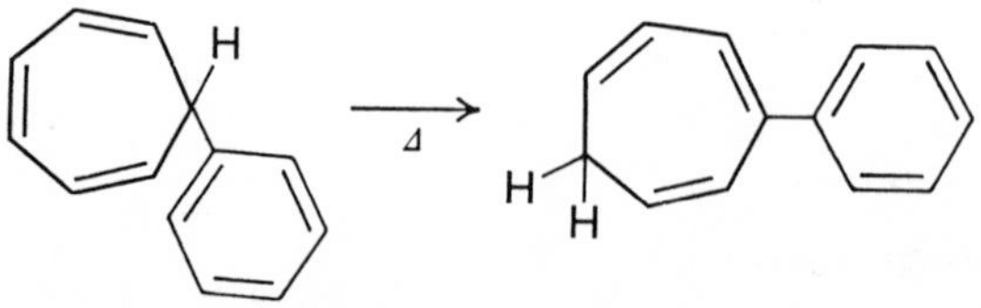

Changing the solvent from tetrachloroethylene to deuterochloroform had no effect on the rate of rearrangement of 1,4-*bis*(7-cycloheptatrienyl)-benzene (**342**) as expected for a reaction through an isopolar transition state. However,

(271)

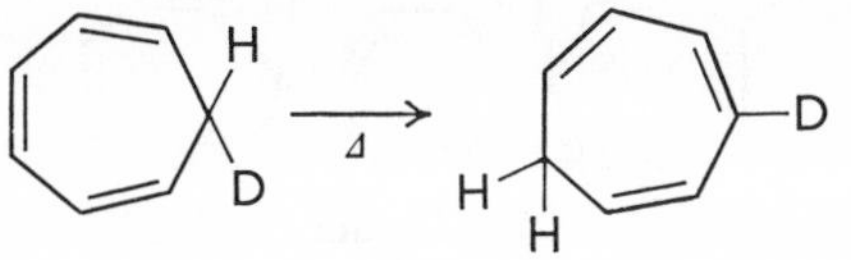

(272)

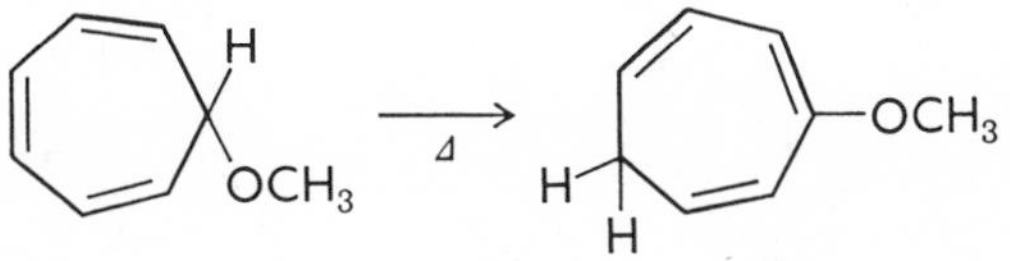

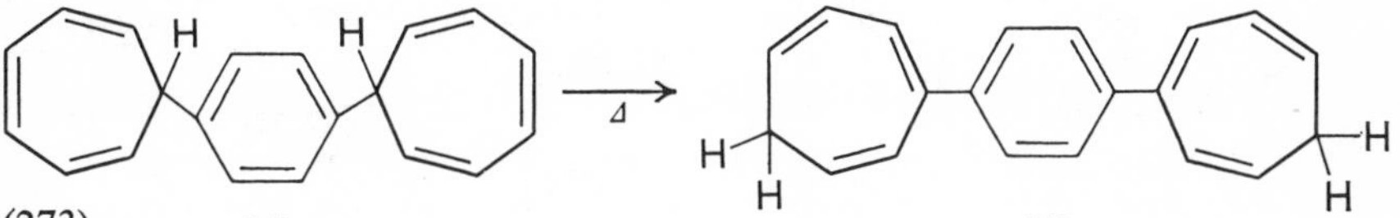

(273)   342   343

it is difficult to predict what might have been expected for a reaction through a transition state with some change in charge separation from that of the ground state because the Z-value [solvent polarity parameter (see Part 2, Section 2.6)] of tetrachloroethylene is not known. The effect of substitution on the rate of the [1,5]hydrogen migration is in accord with viewing the transition state as being more stabilized by π-overlap than the initial state, as would certainly be true in the model we have adopted for discussion of the sigmatropic changes (transition state = radical + radical). Further heating of 1,4-*bis*(3-cycloheptatrienyl)-benzene (343) results in additional [1,5]hydrogen migrations. The photochemical reaction proceeds by apparently specific [1,7]hydrogen migration. These transformations permit the preparation of all of the pure isomers of 342, as outlined in Fig. 1.69. Although 1,3-hydrogen migration is symmetry allowed via the excited state, Woodward and Hoffmann suggest that the [1,7]sigmatropic change is preferred as a result of the higher degree of stabilization of the transition state through conjugation for the latter pathway as compared with the former. The rate data in Table 1.62 indicate that the role of conjugation in the transition state may indeed be significant.

In considering the sigmatropic changes of order, we utilize a model for the transition state and apply some simple consideration of symmetry to rationalize the results observed in actual reactions. The use of radical species to construct the transition states is predicated on: (a) a need to see how the molecular orbitals of the fragments will interact, and (b) the isopolar character

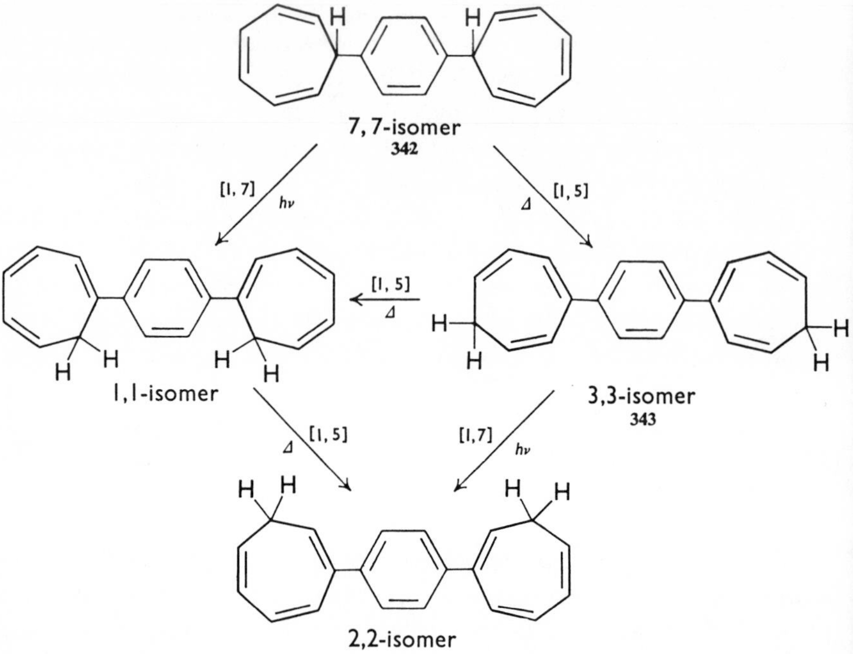

Figure 1.69 Thermal and photochemical rearrangements of 1,4-*bis*-(7-cyclohepta-trienyl)-benzene (from Ref. 232).

of the transition state. In spite of the somewhat artificial character of this model, the use of radical fragments to construct the transition state immediately permits us to understand the vast differences in the rates of the

(274)

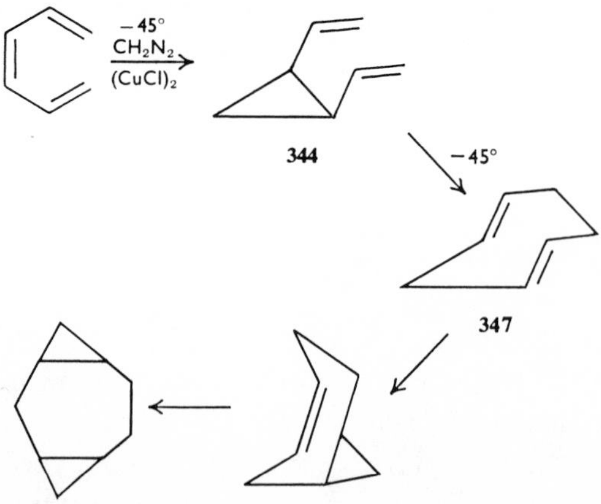

[3,3]sigmatropic changes of order ("Cope rearrangements") for *cis*-1,2-divinylcyclopropane (**344**), *cis*-1,2-divinylcyclobutane (**345**), and *cis*-1,2-divinylcyclopentane (**346**). The *cis*-1,2-divinylcyclopropane is so unstable that when it is generated at $-45°$, it rearranges rapidly to 1,4-cycloheptadiene (**347**) which may be detected, along with other products unavoidably formed by the reagents used (*242*) (see also *240*).

The formation of the transition state may be formulated as in Eq. 275 for all three divinylcyclic compounds. The stabilization of the allylic radical fragments should be approximately the same for the transition states from **344**, **345**, and **346**. The cyclobutane compound **345** rearranges rapidly only on heating to 120° ($k^{96.8°}$ 5×10^{-4} sec.$^{-1}$, $\Delta H*23.1$ kcal./mole, $\Delta S* - 11.7$ e.u.), forming 1,5-cyclooctadiene (**348**) (*241*), and the divinylcyclopentane (**346**) gives rise to an equilibrium mixture of **346** and 1,5-cyclononadiene at 220°, the latter (**349**) constituting only 5% of the reaction mixture (*243*) (Eqs. 276, 277).

(275)

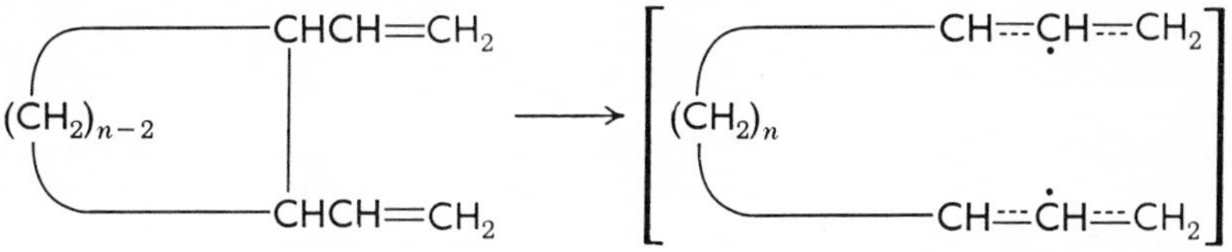

(276)

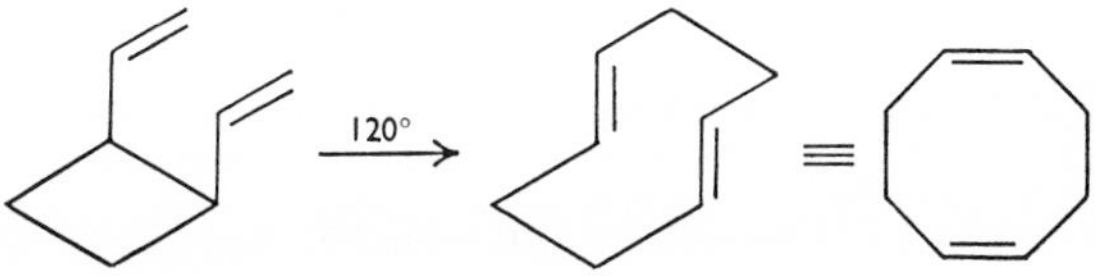

345   348

(277)

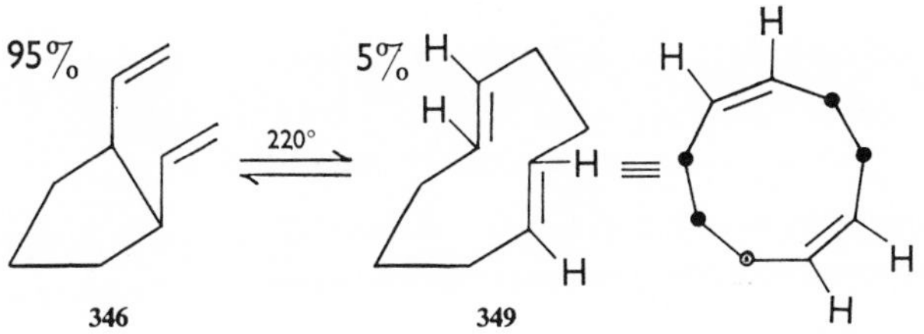

346   349

The difference in rates is related to the difference in carbon–carbon bond energies for the different rings, and it is thus convenient to consider the bond dissociation energies as a measure of this difference.

(278) $R - R \longrightarrow R\cdot + \cdot R$

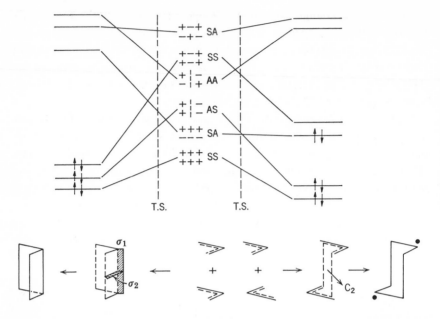

Figure 1.70 A molecular orbital correlation diagram to the two possible products of condensation of two allylic radicals. On the left is the diagram for the formation of a book-like, six-center transition state and on the right is the diagram for the formation of a chair-like four-center transition state. Note the difference in the behavior of the lower SA level at the two possible transition states. C_2 is a twofold axis of symmetry and σ_1 and σ_2 are planes of symmetry. The signs of the wave functions for the molecular orbitals are shown for only one side of the molecular plane (adapted from Ref. 203).

We shall return to the *cis*-polyvinylcyclopropane structural type after briefly reviewing the conclusions of Hoffmann and Woodward (*203*) as to the geometry of the transition state for the condensation of two allylic radicals. The lower of the two possible transition states to products is a four-center (chair-like) transition state, not a six-center (book-like) transition state (Fig. 1.70). The work of White and his co-workers (*236–239*) on the [3,3]sigmatropic change of order typified by the rearrangement of allyl phenyl ether (the "Claisen rearrangement") is in agreement with the conclusions derived from the molecular orbital correlation diagram:

Doering and Roth (*246*) examined the products of the [3,3]sigmatropic change of order for both *meso-* and *racemic*-3,4-dimethyl-1,5-hexadiene (**350**).

(280)

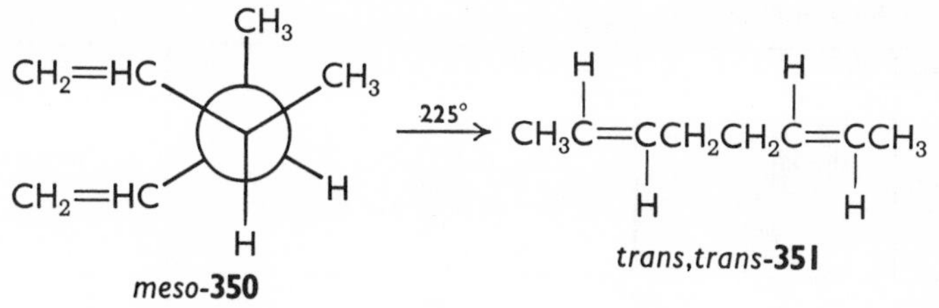

$$CH_2{=}HC \quad \overset{CH_3}{\underset{H}{\bigcirc}} \quad \overset{CH_3}{\underset{H}{}} \quad \xrightarrow{225°} \quad CH_3\overset{H}{\underset{H}{C}}{=}CCH_2CH_2\overset{H}{\underset{H}{C}}{=}CCH_3$$

meso-**350**

trans,trans-**351**

(281)

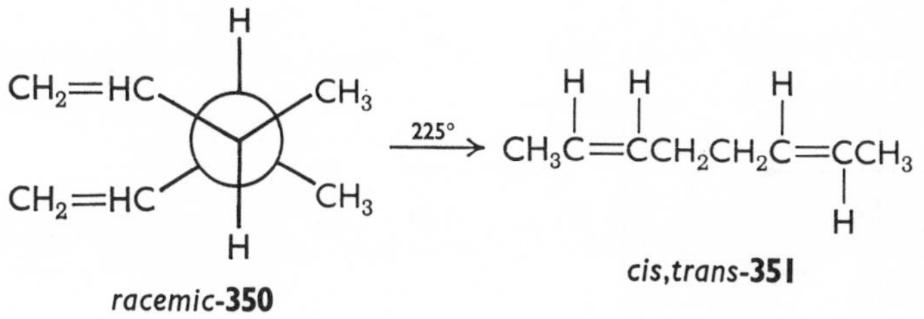

$$CH_2{=}HC \quad \overset{H}{\underset{H}{\bigcirc}} \quad \overset{CH_3}{\underset{CH_3}{}} \quad \xrightarrow{225°} \quad CH_3\overset{H}{C}{=}\overset{H}{C}CH_2CH_2\overset{H}{\underset{H}{C}}{=}CCH_3$$

racemic-**350**

cis,trans-**351**

The possible conformational arrangements in the transition states leading to the product, 2,6-octadiene (**351**), were carefully considered as shown in Fig. 1.71, leading to the conclusion that the products could be rationalized on the basis of reaction through the least sterically strained transition states (Table 1.63).

TABLE 1.63   *Products of [3, 3]Sigmatropic Change for 3,4-Dimethyl-1,5-Hexadienes* [a]

	Geometry of 2,6-Octadiene (**351**)		
Isomer	*cis-trans*	*cis-cis*	*trans-trans*
racemic[b]	< 1%	9%	90%
meso[c]	99.7%	—	0.3%

[a] From Ref. 246.   [b] At 180°.   [c] At 225°

The fact that both steric and molecular orbital treatments predict the same result for this example of a [3,3]sigmatropic change of order suggests that both factors must be considered for all such reactions.

CH₂=CH—CH(CH₃)CH(CH₃)—CH=CH₂ ⟶

$$CH_2{=}CH{-}CH(CH_3)CH(CH_3){-}CH{=}CH_2 \longrightarrow$$
350
$$CH_3{-}CH{=}CH{-}CH_2CH_2{-}CH{=}CH{-}CH_3$$
351

350 Isomer	Transition-state conformation	Orientation*	Double-bond geometry **351**
rac	*quasi*-boat	(a) 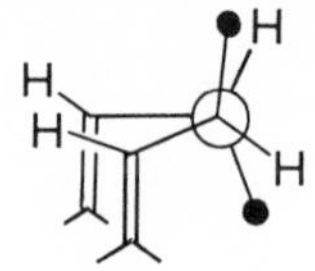	*cis-trans*
rac	*quasi*-chair ("aa")	(b) 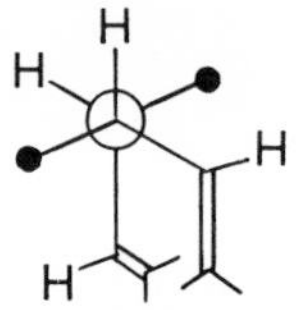	*cis-cis*
rac	*quasi*-chair ("ee")	(c) 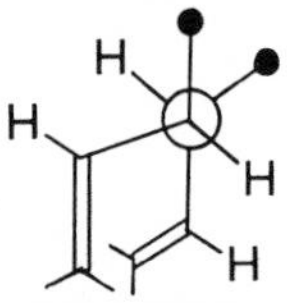	*trans-trans*
meso	*quasi*-boat	(d) 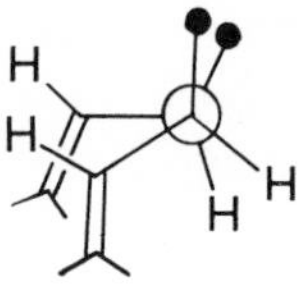	*trans-trans*
meso	*quasi*-boat	(e) 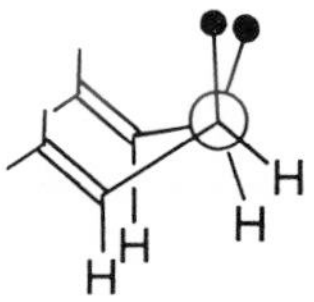	*cis-cis*
meso	*quasi*-chair ("ea")	(f) 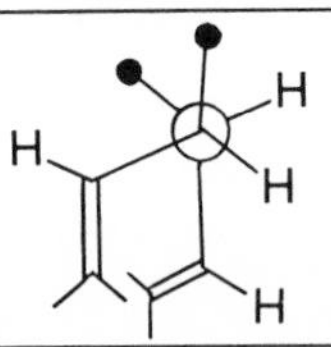	*cis-trans*

Figure 1.71 Transition-state arrangement and product geometry in the [3,3]sigmatropic change for *meso*- and *racemic*-3,4-dimethyl-1,5-hexadiene (adapted from Ref. 230).

* In the Newman formulas †, the solid circles represent the methyl groups (Ref. 247).

† Newman formulas refer to that portion of the drawing in which the central two carbons in the chain are represented by a circle (rear carbon) and a point (front carbon).

248

The stereospecific rearrangements of the 1-hydroxydicyclopentadienes investigated by Woodward and Katz are examples of [3,3]sigmatropic changes of order (*222*).

(282)

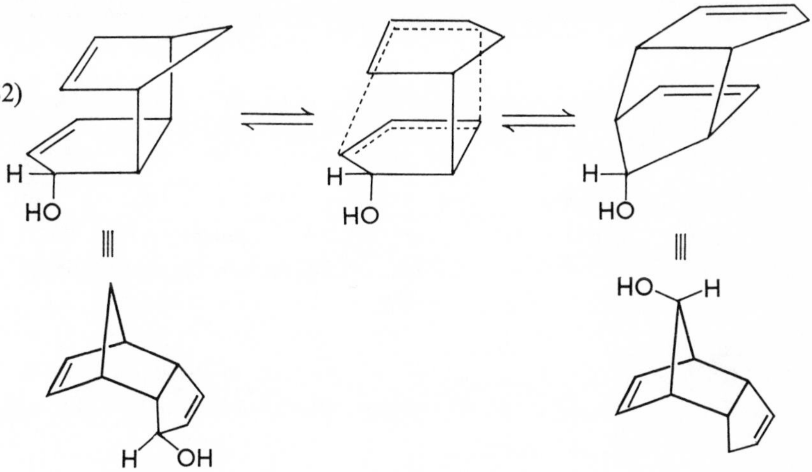

The great tendency of the *cis*-1,2-divinylcyclopropane system to rearrange has suggested a variety of interesting syntheses, like that of 1-ethyl-4,5-dihydroazepine (**352**) from *cis*-2,3-divinyl-1-ethylaziridine (**353**) (*763*) and 3,6-dihydroazepin-2(3H)-one (**354**) from *cis*-2-vinylcyclopropylisocyanate (**355**) (*764*).

(283)

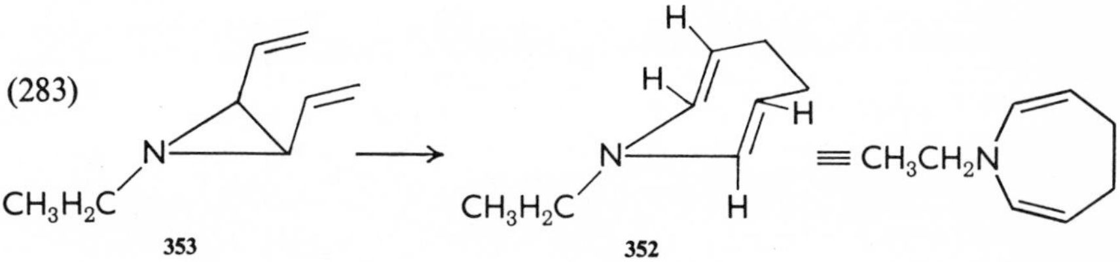

(284)

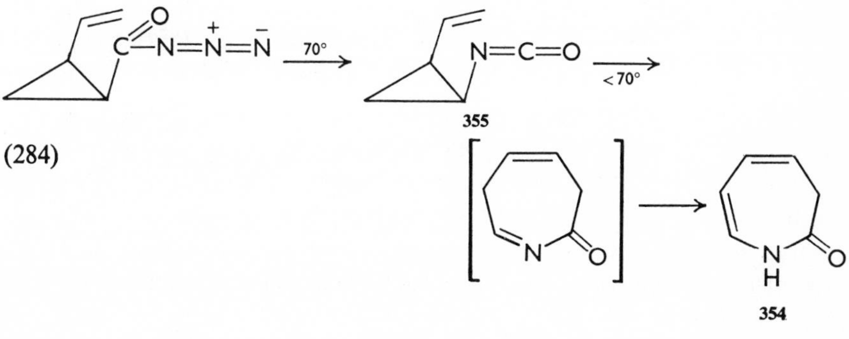

Incorporation of one of the vinyl groups into a cyclopentane ring reduces the rate of rearrangement by a large factor and the divinylcyclopropane **356** has a half-life of one day at 25° (*765*).

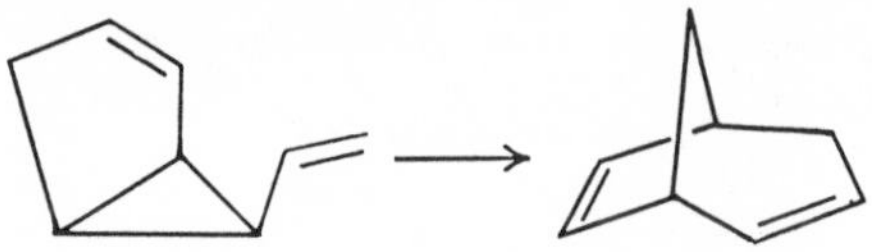

356

Certain [*i,j*]sigmatropic changes of order (in which $i = j$) may be called degenerate if the product of isomerization is chemically the same as the starting material. Doering and Roth (*242*) foresaw the generality of the phenomenon typified by the isomerization of "homotropilidene," bicyclo-[5.1.0]octa-2,5-diene (**357**), and their prediction of the properties of tricyclo-[3.3.2.0^{4,6}]deca-2,7,9-triene ("bullvalene") was almost immediately confirmed by Schröder (*766*), who isolated the compound from the mixture obtained by photolysis of cyclooctatetraene.

(286)

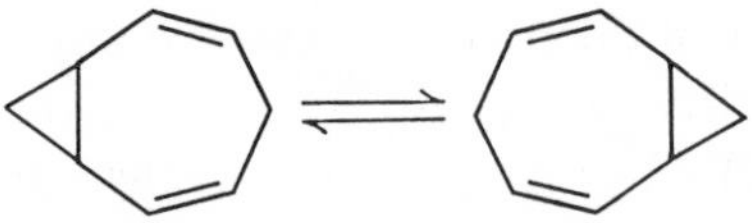

357   **357**

Irradiation of 9,10-dihydronaphthalene also produces bullvalene (**358**) (*767*).

(287)

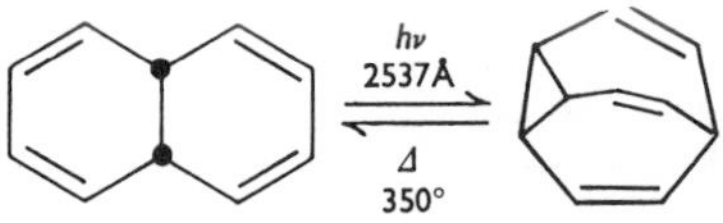

358

As indicated by the isomerizations shown in Fig. 1.72, any atom of the molecule can occupy any position, with the number of valence isomers given by 10!/3 or 1.2×10^6. The molecular environment for a particular hydrogen atom is completely averaged in an n.m.r. measurement above 100°C. As the temperature is lowered the n.m.r. spectrum broadens, indicating that the rate of exchange between the different environments for the hydrogen is similar to the separation of the resonance absorptions in c.p.s., that is, 200 c.p.s. corresponding to rate constants of about 2×10^2 sec.$^{-1}$. Saunders (*244*) has reported the rate of isomerization as 5.40×10^2 sec.$^{-1}$ at 0° on the basis of

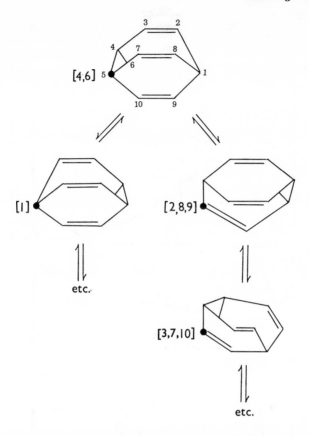

Figure 1.72 Isomerization of bullvalene, a degenerate [3,3]sigmatropic change of order. The square brackets next to atom 5 in the top formula show the new position of the atom in the isomers.

n.m.r. data like that shown in Fig. 1.73. Allerhand and Gutowsky (*768*) obtained a similar rate constant by a spin-echo technique and, in addition, found that silver ion, which complexes with alkenes, slows the rate of isomerization by a factor of about 10 at 50°. [Isomerization of bullvalene in the presence of silver ion requires a higher activation energy (15.1 ± 0.8 kcal./mole) than isomerization of bullvalene (12.8 ± 0.1 kcal./mole).]

The ketone, barbaralone (**359**) (tricyclo[3.3.1.0^{4,6}]nona-2,7-dien-9-one), undergoes a degenerate [3,3]sigmatropic change of order even faster than that of bullvalene and the n.m.r. spectrum at −91° is still slightly broadened (*245*).

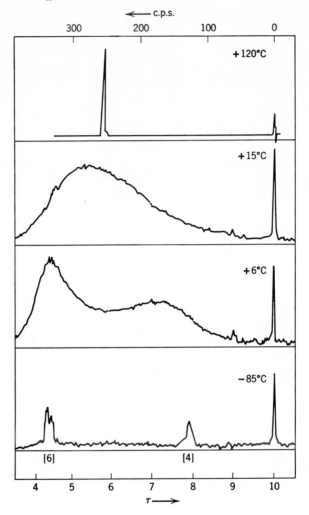

Figure 1.73 The n.m.r. spectrum of bullvalene (*358*) (c = 0.4 M) in carbon disulfide at different temperatures. The peak at 10 is due to the internal reference, tetramethylsilane (adapted from Ref. 769 and used with the permission of the authors and *Angewandte Chemie*).

(228)

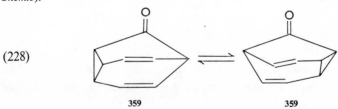

Degenerate sigmatropic changes of order have been reviewed by Schröder, Oth, and Merenyi (*769*).

Problems

1. Define the following terms:
   (a) Electrocyclic.
   (b) Conrotatory.
   (c) Disrotatory.
   (d) [*i*, *j*] sigmatropic change of order.
   (e) Thermal reorganization.
   (f) Isopolar fragmentation.
   (g) Suprafacial.
   (h) Antarafacial.
   (i) Degenerate sigmatropic changes of order.
   (j) "Claisen rearrangement."
   (k) "Cope rearrangement."
2. Give the products of the following reactions:
   (a) *cis*-3,4-Dimethylcyclobutene-1 $\xrightarrow{\Delta}$
   (b) *trans*-3,4-Dimethylcyclobutene-1 $\xrightarrow{\Delta}$
   (c) *cis*-3,4-Dimethylcyclobutene-1 $\xrightarrow{hv}$
   (d) *trans*-3,4-Dimethylcyclobutene-1 $\xrightarrow{hv}$
3. Draw molecular orbital correlation diagrams to explain the transformations in Problems 2a and 2c.
4. Write the product of the thermal rearrangement of *trans,cis,trans*-2,4,6-octatriene. Draw a molecular orbital correlation diagram to explain the result.
5. The compounds 3-methylene-1-methylcyclobutene and 2-methyl-1,3,4-pentatriene interconvert at 350° in pentane. Explain this reaction, using molecular orbital diagrams if necessary, and comment upon the temperature required (Ref. 770).
6. Hexamethylprismane (**A**) (hexamethyltetracyclo[2.2.0.0^{2,6}.0^{3,5}]hexane) is isomerized readily to hexamethylbicyclo[2.2.0]hexa-2,5-diene(hexamethyl-"Dewar benzene") (**B**). Various catalysts (including powdered glass and palladium, Lindlar catalyst) accelerate the reaction which has a half-life of somewhat less than an hour at 129° without catalysts. Explain why the reaction is slow and suggest a role for the catalysts (Ref. 771).

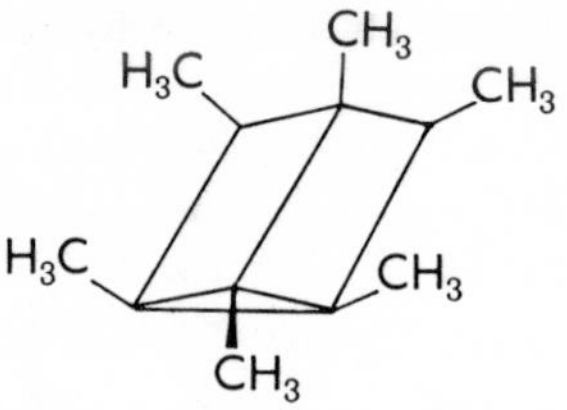

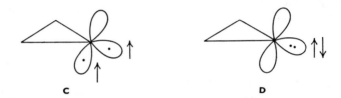

A 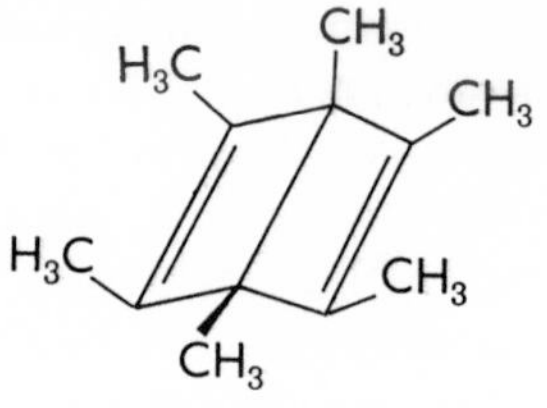   B

7. With the aid of molecular orbital correlation diagrams, predict the course of ring opening for the following:
   (a) Cyclopropylidene (**C**) triplet.
   (b) Cyclopropylidene (**D**) singlet.

C   D

   (c) *cis*-2,3 Dimethyl cyclopropanone hydrate (**E**) plus acid.
   (d) Bicyclo[4.2.0]octadiene-2,4 (*cis*).
   (e) Bicyclo[4.2.0]octadiene-2,4 (*trans*)(**F**).

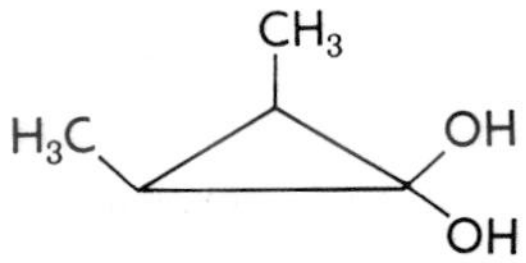

E    F

8. Describe the complete course of the reaction from *cis*-2,5-dimethyl-3-pyrroline to products upon treatment with the disodium salt of nitrohydroxylamine and dilute hydrochloric acid. Rationalize the nature of the product with a molecular orbital correlation diagram. Would the course of the reaction be similar if the starting material were the pyrroline **G**?

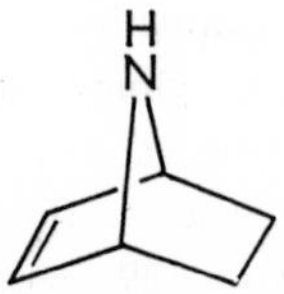

G

9. Show the expected products for (a) thermal isomerization and (b) photochemical rearrangement of 7-cycloheptatrienyl benzene. Indicate by means of a molecular orbital diagram how to account for the difference between the thermal and photochemical reactions. (Note that it is necessary to carefully describe only the transition state).

10. Suggest a synthesis for *cis*-1,2-divinylcyclopropane. (The only clue given in this section is an indication of its stability. You must therefore choose a means which should work in principle.)

11. Write ten isomers for a methylbullvalene.

PART TWO

Medium Effects

The sublimation of the self-transcending emotions
has transformed "magic" into "science"; but there
is no hard-and-fast boundary between the two.
Unconscious, pre-rational, "magical" thinking
enters both into the creative act and into the
beliefs or superstitions of the scientist. As
Dubos said, "the alchemist never entirely ceased
to live and function within the academician."

The Act of Creation, Arthur Koestler

2.0 Introduction

Chemical transformations may be studied in an amazing variety of environments, including gas phases, liquid phases, solid phases, phase interfaces (macroscopic and microscopic), defects in solids, liquid crystalline phases, and polymer phases. Microscopic phase interfaces are those between one phase and another for which the first phase is so well dispersed in the second phase that one can no longer discuss the "bulk" (that is, macroscopic) properties of the first phase without consideration of the effect of the second phase on those properties. Micelles in liquids are examples of such well-dispersed phases. Defects in solids are places in which a regular lattice is interrupted. An atom or molecule located next to a defect would experience an interaction with the lattice much more asymmetric than an atom or molecule located within a regular lattice.

Liquid solutions offer both practical and theoretical advantages for the study of chemical reactions. It is easy to obtain *macroscopically homogeneous* solutions of many reactants, to vary the nature of liquid, to add other reagents, to control physical conditions with great uniformity, to study the reaction rate, and to isolate products. Most of the physical organic chemical theory is based on the study of reactions carried out in liquid solution.

Interest in other phases (liquid crystalline, crystalline) has been shown and should develop further in the near future. The special problems posed by micelles are of interest and importance for the theory of reactions in homogeneous liquid solutions and are crucial to an understanding of reactions in biological systems.

Most of the following discussion will be confined to liquid solutions and will include the areas of solvent effects, salt effects, and "cage effects" (reaction partners). Acidity functions (cf. discussion of Bell, *468*) for the evaluation of the difference in behavior of concentrated acids from the expected by extrapolation from dilute acids are being critically reexamined (for example, Arnett and Mach, *469*) and will not be treated in this text.

2.1 Some Aspects of Solvent Structure

It is common for the student to forget that the liquid in which reactants are dispersed (the *solvent*) is composed of molecules. Solvents are usually discussed in elementary courses, if they are mentioned at all, as if they were continuous media characterized by a parameter called the *dielectric constant, D*. Several of the more recent texts recognize the importance of specific effects like hydrogen bonding and the difference in the solvation of cations and anions (*300, 301*). A whole variety of problems in physical and organic chemistry (and physical organic chemistry) requires a detailed understanding of the role of the solvent in chemical reactions.

Consider a molecule S surrounded by solvent molecules (Fig. 2.1). The free energy of the molecule S is determined by its free energy of formation plus

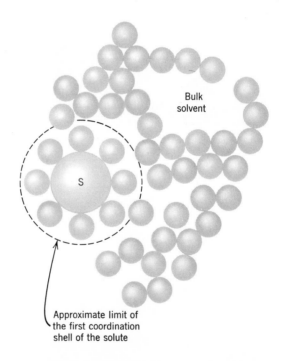

Bulk
solvent

S

Approximate limit of
the first coordination
shell of the solute

Figure 2.1 A solute molecule within a group of solvent molecules. The first coordination shell is that group of solvent molecules in immediate contact with the solute molecule and does not represent the limit of influence of the solute on the structural arrangements in the solvent.

260

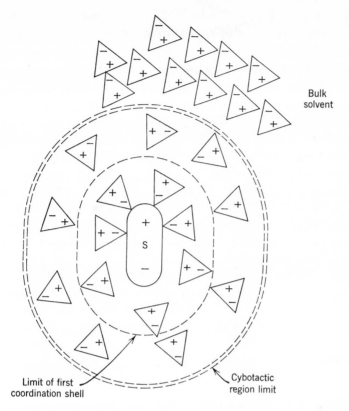

Figure 2.2 A dipolar solute molecule within a group of solvent molecules. Note that the arrangements in the cybotactic region are quite different from those in the bulk solvent. The solvent within the first coordination shell is more highly organized than the solvent in other regions.

the free energy of transfer to the solution. The latter term includes the heat of interaction of the solute molecule S with the solvent molecules, the work required to produce a cavity in the solvent and an entropy term. It is obvious that the solvent molecules immediately around the solute molecule are no longer described by the same parameters as those used for the bulk solvent. The more polar the solute, the greater the divergence between the properties of the solvent molecules near the solute and those in the bulk solvent (Fig. 2.2). Normally, the interactions between the solvent molecules near the solute will be different from those in the bulk solvent and this will lead to a structural arrangement of the solvent molecules near the solute which is different from the solute in the bulk solvent. (The lifetime of solvent structural arrangements is a question which we shall consider in a subsequent section.) In between the solvent arrangement induced by the solute and that of the bulk solvent must be a transition region in which the solvent has neither arrangement and may even, in some cases, have no particular arrangement, or *order*, at all. We define the group of solvent molecules in immediate contact with the solute as the first coordination shell. We further define the whole volume in which the order of the solvent molecules has been affected by the solute as the *cybotactic region (303)*. The latter region includes both the first coordination shell and the transition region. Gurney (*302*) refers to the cybotactic region as the solvent *cosphere* of the solute.

Let us now compare two situations, one in which two dipolar molecules are close enough to one another, so that they share a cybotactic region and a second, in which many molecules of pure solvent (= bulk solvent) are placed between charged parallel plates (Figs. 2.3*a* and 2.3*b*). The solvent in the cybotactic region between the two dipolar molecules will be arranged differently from the solvent between the charged plates. Although the figures are exaggerations in the sense that the solvent molecules are shown as completely oriented in both cases, the arrangements illustrated are sufficiently different, so that even if they make a modest contribution to the average structure of the solvent, the parameters measured for one situation cannot be simply related to those measured for the second situation.

Dielectric constants are determined by evaluating how solvent between two plates affects the strength of the field that can be built up (Fig. 2.3*b*). The usual measurement is made with a *macroscopic* (that is, many times molecular size) distance between the plates. The dielectric constant therefore reflects an average of solvent arrangements over macroscopic distances. The dielectric constant parameter is appropriate for solvent between charged species, separated by distances appreciably greater than the sum of the cybotactic region limits, but is inappropriate at the *microscopic* level for the solvent between the dipolar molecules of Fig. 2.3*a*. For many chemical reactions, it is the microscopic level that determines the result, that is, the *local environment*, created by the solvent molecules around the initial states and transition states (or final states, depending on whether we are dealing with kinetics or equilibrium), determines the course of the chemical reaction. The more different the cybotactic region is from the bulk solvent, the less reliable will be our predictions made on the basis of properties of bulk solvent.

Posing the solvent problem in this way suggests that it will be important to understand solvent structure, and the effect of solutes on solvent structure. We might ask what progress theoretical chemistry (and theoretical chemists,

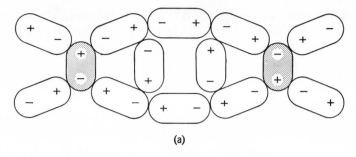

(a)

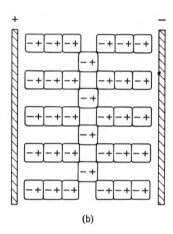

(b)

Figure 2.3 (*a*) Solvent molecule arrangement between two dipolar molecules within the cybotactic region limit. (*b*) Solvent molecule arrangement in strong electric field.

since all science is created by people) has achieved in understanding the behavior of matter in the liquid state. Two general approaches have been used: one treats liquids as dense gases, and the other deals with them as imperfect solids. As a review by Henderson indicates (*304*), only the very simplest model systems are susceptible to calculation, and even these simple model systems (for example, hard spheres) cannot be treated very exactly for three-dimensional cases.

In the absence of well-defined theoretical approaches to the structure and properties of liquids, empirical treatments of solvent behavior are necessary and desirable. We shall illustrate later the use of a chemical reaction (solvolysis of *t*-butyl chloride) and an electronic transition (the charge-transfer band of 1-ethyl-4-carbomethoxypyridinium iodide) as probes at the microscopic level to help us to understand solvent-solute interaction.

In order to make the comparisons between the microscopic and macroscopic levels clear, we shall first consider in more detail what a dielectric constant is.

Problems

1. List possible environments for chemical reactions and draw approximate diagrams indicating the place of the following molecules within these environments on a molecular scale:
   (a) *t*-Butyl chloride.
   (b) Water.
   (c) Methanol.
   (d) Ethanol.
   (e) Glycylglycine.
   (f) Cyclohexane.
   (g) Tetra-*n*-butylammonium bromide.
   (h) Benzene.
   (i) Dimethylsulfoxide.
2. Define the following terms:
   (a) Cybotactic region.
   (b) First coordination shell.
   (c) Dielectric constant.

2.2   Dielectric Constant

By imposing surface charges, $+q$ and $-q$, on two parallel plates (Fig. 2.4a), a charge density (charge per unit area), σ, is produced which leads to the electric displacement, $\mathbf{D}$, for the field acting on a unit charge between the plates:

$$(1) \qquad\qquad \mathbf{D} = 4\pi\sigma$$

Inserting a polarizable medium between the plates reduces the field strength by a factor called the *dielectric constant*, D:

$$(2) \qquad\qquad \mathbf{E} = 4\pi\sigma/D = \mathbf{D}/D$$

The displacement of charge within the medium produces a field in a direction opposite to that arising from the charge on the plates. *This* displacement of charge, the polarization, $\mathbf{P}$, may be obtained from the difference between $\mathbf{D}$ and $\mathbf{E}$ (Eq. 3). $\mathbf{P}$ is the charge density per unit area created by the field within the medium.

$$(3) \qquad\qquad \mathbf{D} = \mathbf{E} + 4\pi\mathbf{P} = D\cdot\mathbf{E}$$

In a medium made of molecules without permanent dipoles, the polarization is due to the distortion of electronic structure (electronic polarization) and small changes in atomic positions (atomic polarization). Together these are called *distortion polarization* ($\mathbf{P}_d$). Molecular polarizability, α, is defined as the time-average dipole moment induced in a molecule by a field of unit intensity. The distortion polarization for N_0 molecules per cm.^{3} with an actual field $\mathbf{F}$ at the molecule is given by Eq. 4. The field $\mathbf{F}$ at the molecule is due to the field $\mathbf{E}$ plus the polarization of the cavity in which the molecule is located (Fig. 2.4b). (See the derivation of Debye, *305*) (Eq. 5). Since $\mathbf{P} = \mathbf{P}_d$ for non-polar molecules, and expression for the polarizability, α, in terms of the dielectric constant, D, may be obtained by eliminating $\mathbf{P}$ from Eqs. 3, 4, and 5 (Eq. 6).

$$(4) \qquad\qquad \mathbf{P}_d = N_0\alpha\mathbf{F}$$

$$(5) \qquad\qquad \mathbf{F} = \mathbf{E} + 4\pi\mathbf{P}/3$$

$$(6) \qquad\qquad \frac{D-1}{D+2} = \frac{4\pi}{3}N_0\alpha$$

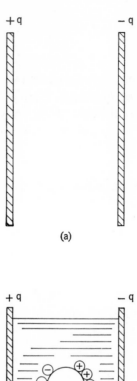

(a)

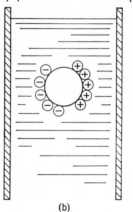

(b)

Figure 2.4   (*a*) Parallel plates bearing a charge (no medium). (*b*) Parallel plates with a medium between the plates within which a polarized cavity is present.

The expression shown in Eq. 6 is not valid for molecules with permanent dipole moments since these will line up with the field and add to the degree of polarization. Debye (*305*) derived an expression for the average moment of a molecule with a dipole moment, μ, in an electric field by taking a Boltzmann distribution and averaging over all directions (Eq. 7) ($\bar{m}_F$ is the average moment in the direction of the field F, $d\Omega$ is a solid angle).

(7)
$$\overline{m}_F = \frac{\int A e^{(\mu F \cos \theta)/kT} \mu \cos \theta \, d\Omega}{\int A e^{(\mu F \cos \theta)/kT} d\Omega}$$

The approximate value of $\overline{m}_F$ is given by Eq. 8. A correction for the *orientation polarization* may be thus added to Eq. 6, yielding the usual Debye–Clausius–Mosotti expression, used for the evaluation of many dipole moments through measurement of the temperature-dependent part of the polarization.

(8)
$$\overline{m}_F = \frac{\mu^2}{3kT} F$$

(9)
$$\frac{D - 1}{D + 2} = \frac{4\pi}{3} N_0 \alpha + \frac{4\pi}{3} N_0 \frac{\mu^2}{3kT}$$

Onsager (*306*) pointed out that a portion of the field (the "reaction field," induced by the dipole in the polar (polarizable) liquid surrounding the dipole) would follow the dipole. Using a model based on this idea, an attempt was made to account for the dielectric constant of polar liquids in terms of the dipole moment measured in dilute solution in nonpolar liquids. Cole (*307*) has discussed this approach and many of the attempts to apply correction terms and has commented, "Somewhere in such proliferation of correction terms, one may well begin to question whether the treatments are warranted for a model in which even the immediate neighbors of a molecule are represented by a macroscopic continuum." Kirkwood (*308*) extended the Onsager theory by trying to take into account the short-range, local interactions which affect the reorientation of the dipoles. Harris and Alder (*309*) used a somewhat different approach and obtained the formula (Eq. 10), which is applicable to all liquids, including polar, associated liquids like water. The factor *g* (which resembles a factor with the same symbol in Kirkwood's formula but is obtained in a different way) varies from 1.0 for unassociated liquids to 3.6 for the highly associated liquid, hydrogen cyanide, and falls to 0.7 for the contra-associated liquid, pyridine. (Contra-association is head-to-tail interaction between molecular dipoles.) A more extensive discussion of these formulae may be found in Robinson and Stokes (*310*) and in the review by Brown (*311*).

(10)
$$\frac{D - 1}{D + 2} = \frac{4\pi}{3} N_0 \alpha + \frac{4\pi}{3} N_0 \cdot \frac{\mu^2}{3kT} \cdot \frac{9D}{(2D + 1)(D + 2)} \cdot g$$

The dipole moment is a molecular property but its evaluation is based on an idealized situation for measurements in liquid solution. It is difficult to relate the dielectric constant, D, to the dipole moment of an isolated molecule, μ, for any liquid in which there is appreciable association between the molecules. We are sure that there is some relationship between the dielectric constant and the molecular dipole but we must realize that this relationship is not simple, *even for a pure liquid*. If we then add the further complications produced by the presence of solutes (Figs. 2.2 and 2.3*a*), it is clear that we must be extremely cautious in utilizing the dielectric constant as a reference parameter on the *microscopic level*. The effective dielectric constant (as used, for example, by Kirkwood and Westheimer in their correlation of the acidities of dicarboxylic acids (*312, 313*)) is really a disposable parameter, which is adjusted to obtain good agreement between calculated and experimental results.

A summary of macroscopic solvent properties including the melting point, boiling point, dielectric constant, density, and viscosity is given in Table 2.1.

TABLE 2.1 *Macroscopic Solvent Parameters*

Solvent	M.P. °C	B.P. °C	Density d g ml^{-1}	Dielectric Constant D	Viscosity η Centipoises g cm.$^{-1}$ sec.$^{-1}$ $\times 10^{-2}$	Refractive Index $n_D^{t°C}$
H_2O	0	100	1.000 (4°)	78.4 (25°)	1.002 (20°)	1.3325^{25}
D_2O	3.8	101.4	1.106 (10°)	77.9 (25°)	1.243 (20°)	1.3384^{20}
NH_3	−78	−33	0.681 (−33°)	23 (−33°)	0.254 (−33°)	1.325^{16}_{5899}
HF	−89.4	19.5	1.002 (0°)	83.6 (0°)	0.256 (0°)	1.1574^{25}
H_2S	−86	−60	1.539 (0°)	175 (−73°)	—	—
HCN	−14	26	0.690 (18°)	118.3 (25°)	0.206 (18°)	1.2675^{10}
H_2SO_4	10.4	290–317	1.827 (25°)	100 (25°)	24.5 (25°)	1.429
NH_2NH_2	1.4	113.5	1.011 (15°)	53 (20°)	—	1.470^{22}
NH_2CHO	2.6	105 (11 mm.)	1.129 (25°)	109.5 (25°)	3.302 (25°)	1.4453
NH_2COCH_3	82.3	221	0.999 (85°)	59 (83°)	—	—
$(CH_3)_2NCHO$	−61	153	0.945 (25°)	37 (25°)	—	1.4269^{25}
$(CH_3)_2NCOCH_3$	20	165	0.937 (25°)	37.8 (25°)	0.919 (25°)	1.4351^{25}
$CH_3NHCOCH_3$	29.5	206	0.942 (40°)	165.5 (40°)	3.019 (40°)	1.4301^{20}
$(CH_3)_2SO$	18.4	189	1.096 (25°)	46.6 (25°)	1.96 (25°)	1.4787^{21}
CH_3NO_2	−28.5	101.3	1.131 (25°)	35.9 (30°)	0.595 (25°)	1.3935^{20}
$C_6H_5NO_2$	5.8	210.8	1.193 (25°)	34.8 (30°)	1.634 (30°)	1.5562^{20}
CH_3COCH_3	−95.4	56.2	0.785 (25°)	20.7 (25°)	0.295 (30°)	1.3588^{20}
$[(CH_3)_2N]_3PO$	—	98–100 (6 mm.)	1.024 (25°)	30 (20°)	—	1.4570^{25}
CH_3OH	−97.5	64.5	0.787 (25°)	32.6 (25°)	0.545 (25°)	1.3288^{20}
CH_3CH_2OH	−114.5	78.3	0.785 (25°)	24.3 (25°)	1.078 (25°)	1.3576^{25}

Table 2.1 (Continued) *Macroscopic Solvent Parameters*

Solvent	M.P. °C	B.P. °C	Density d g ml^{-1}	Dielectric Constant D	Viscosity η centipoises g cm.$^{-1}$ sec.$^{-1}$ $\times 10^{-2}$	Refractive Index $n_D^{t°C}$
 (pyridine)	−41.8	115.6	0.973 (30°)	12.3 (25°)	0.829 (30°)	1.5095[20]
CH$_3$CN	−45.7	81.6	0.777 (25°)	36.2 (25°)	0.325 (30°)	1.3441[20]
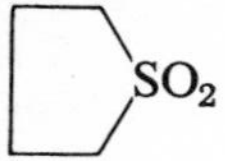 (sulfolane, SO$_2$)	28.9	283	1.262 (30°)	44 (30°)	9.87 (30°)	—
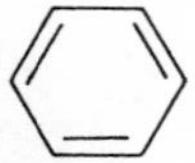 (benzene)	5.5	80.1	0.871 (25°)	2.27 (25°)	0.603 (25°)	1.5011[20]
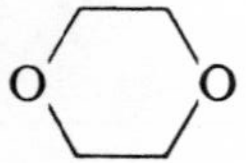 (dioxane, O)	11.8	101	1.027 (25°)	2.21 (25°)	1.196 (25°)	1.4224[20]
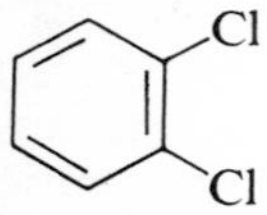 (o-dichlorobenzene, Cl Cl)	−16.7	180.3	1.300 (25°)	9.93 (25°)	1.96 (25°)	1.5486[25]
CH$_3$CHCl$_2$	−96.6	51.3	1.168 (25°)	10.4 (25°)	0.787 (25°)	1.4164[20]

Compound						
$ClCH_2CH_2Cl$ OH	−35.3	84.1	1.246 (25°)	10.0 (25°)	0.466 (25°)	1.4430^{25}
$HOCH_2CHCH_2OH$	18.6	290 (dec.)	1.258 (25°)	42.5 (25°)	945 (25°)	1.4746^{20}
HOOH	−89	151.2	1.449 (25°)	74 (25°)	1.24 (25°)	1.414^{22}
$CH_3CH_2CH_2OH$	−127	97.1	0.780 (25°)	20.1 (25°)	2.004 (25°)	1.3850^{20}
SO_2	−75.5	−10.1	1.46 (−10.1°)	15.4 (0°)	4.03 (0°)	1.410
$n\text{-}C_6H_{14}$	−95	68	0.659 (20°)	1.88 (28°)	0.474 (20°)	1.3749^{20}
$CHCl_3$	−63	62.0	1.480 (25°)	4.64 (25°)	0.568 (20°)	$1.4430^{25.4}$
CCl_4	−22	76.9	1.585 (25°)	2.22 (25°)	0.845 (30°)	1.4593^{25}
CH_3COOH	16.6	118.5	1.049 (20°)	6.17 (20°)	1.040 (30°)	1.3721^{20}
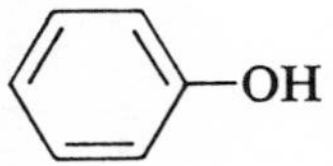 (benzene ring)–OH	43	182	1.08 (58°)	9.90 (58°)	4.076 (45°)	1.5403^{45}
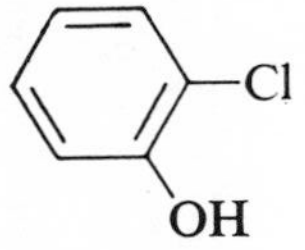 (benzene ring with Cl and OH)	8.7	175.4	1.22 (58°)	5.41 (58°)	—	1.5573^{25}
 (benzene ring with Cl and OH)	52.9	173.7	1.25 (58°)	2.62 (58°)	—	$1.5267^{69.1}$
(benzene ring with two Cl, 1,4-)	−96.7	41.4	1.318 (25°)	7.07 (25°)	0.387 (20°)	$1.4220^{24.8}$
ClCH=CHCl (trans)	−53	48.8	1.249 (25°)	2.15 (25°)	0.404 (20°)	1.4397^{25}
ClCH=CHCl (cis)	−82	60.3	1.274 (25°)	9.31 (25°)	0.467 (20°)	1.4428^{25}

General references: 302, 322, 323.

2.3 Dynamic Dielectric Constant

The dielectric constant, which we have discussed thus far, was determined at low frequencies or with a static field and is, therefore, the *static dielectric constant*. If the electric field varies with time, molecules with a permanent dipole will change orientation in order to follow the field. The faster the field is varied, the more rapid is the motion required from the dipole. (Molecular dipoles change orientation through motion of the bond set composing the dipole.) In a certain range of frequencies, the dipoles will no longer be able to follow the field and a decrease in dielectric constant corresponding to the loss of the orientation polarization will be observed. Note that the polarization is not constant through the frequency region for molecular vibrations, due to an appreciable change in the polarizability of a molecule, probably because the electrons are somewhat less tightly bound in higher vibrational states. At very high frequencies (visible light), only a contribution from electronic polarization is observed, and the dielectric constant is given by the square of the refractive index:

$$(11) \qquad\qquad D_0 = n^2$$

A few attempts have been made to use the refractive index as a characteristic solvent property with respect to the ability of a solvent to interact with

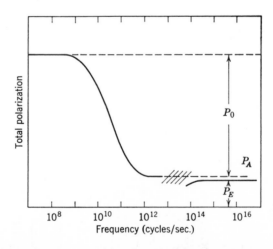

Figure 2.5a Contributions to total polarization with constant field and changing frequency. The region around 10^{13} cycles/sec. is explained by anomalous polarizability at vibrational frequencies.

solutes. It is clear from the nature of the refractive index or the *dynamic dielectric constant*, D_0, that only a minor portion of solute-solvent interactions will be measured by D_0 except for nonpolar solutes in nonpolar solvents. The changing contributions to the total polarization with frequency are illustrated in Fig. 2.5*a*.

Problems

1. Derive Eq. 6 from Eqs. 3, 4, and 5 (Part 2).
2. Draw a diagram to explain what is meant by the average moment $\bar{m}_F$.
3. Write down the separate terms for distortion polarization and orientation polarization. Draw diagrams to show how these two terms would be reflected in the interaction of benzene ($\mu = 0$), furan ($\mu = 0.7$ D) and nitrobenzene ($\mu = 3.97$ D) with the molecules neopentane, naphthalene, methyl iodide, and dimethylsulfoxide. (A separate diagram for each contribution would help in devising the sum.) Is this approach satisfactory for dimethylsulfoxide?
4. Consider the Kirkwood–Westheimer treatment of the strengths of dicarboxylic acids (Refs. 312, 313), and interpret in molecular terms the significance of the *effective dielectric constant*.
5. From Table 2.1, select five compounds that fit the following distribution of parameters: the lowest, the highest, the "average," and one each in between the lowest and the "average" and between the highest and the "average." Consider each of the six parameters listed in the table.
6. Why is the dielectric constant lower at higher temperatures?
7. Compare the static and dynamic dielectric constants for the group listed in Problem 5 for static dielectric constant.
8. Define static and dynamic dielectric constants.
9. Explain in detail why the dynamic dielectric constant is not constant in the frequency range corresponding to vibrational transitions.

2.4   Relaxation Times

If we take an ensemble of molecules in the average state, E_i (Fig. 2.5b), and perturb the state so that a new average state, E', is attained, the ensemble will return to its original state, $E_f(= E_i)$ (or to another state, E_f, the difference depending on whether a heat sink is available to remove the added energy) in a first-order decay process. If the concentration of molecules in the state E' is called M, the loss of M is described by an ordinary first-order rate equation:

$$(12) \qquad\qquad -\frac{d\mathrm{M}}{dt} = k\mathrm{M}$$

The concentration of M at time t is given by:

$$(13) \qquad\qquad \mathrm{M} = \mathrm{M}_0 e^{-kt}$$

We can describe the return of the ensemble to E_f as a *relaxation*, characterized by the time for the average energy (or the population of E') to fall to $1/e$ (*e* is the base of natural logarithms $= 2.718...$) of its original value. The *relaxation time*, τ, $= 1/k$, so that we can write:

$$(14) \qquad\qquad \mathrm{M} = \mathrm{M}_0 e^{-t/\tau}$$

At the time that $t = \tau$, M has the value which is $1/e$ of the original value.

$$(15) \qquad\qquad \mathrm{M} = \mathrm{M}_0 e^{-1}$$

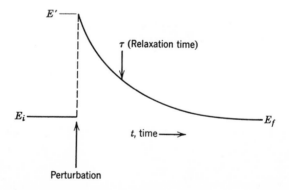

Figure 2.5b A schematic showing perturbation of an ensemble of molecules in the average state E_i to produce an ensemble in the average state E'. The excited ensemble relaxes (returns) to the final state in a first-order process characterized by the relaxation time, τ.

The perturbation of a system in chemical equilibrium (using temperature-jump, pressure-jump, etc.) produces an unstable system in which the concentrations of the participants in the equilibrium differ from the equilibrium values by an amount ΔC_i. The unstable system returns to equilibrium (that is, relaxes) via processes characterized by a set of relaxation constants. These constants, except for the simple cases, are related to both the equilibrium and rate constants for all of the processes which contribute to the relaxation and thus have a complex relationship to ordinary chemical rate constants. For the simple case:

$$(16) \qquad A + B \underset{k_{21}}{\overset{k_{12}}{\rightleftharpoons}} Z$$

$$(17) \qquad \frac{dZ}{dt} = k_{12}(A)(B) - k_{21}(Z)$$

We utilize the subscript e to refer to the concentrations to which the system will return after relaxation and ΔC for the deviations from equilibrium concentration.

$$(18) \qquad \Delta C = \Delta Z = -\Delta A = -\Delta B$$

$$(19) \qquad -\frac{d\Delta C}{dt} = k_{12}(A_e + \Delta C)(B_e + \Delta C) - k_{12}(Z_e + \Delta C)$$
$$= k_{12}(A_e B_e + A_e \Delta C + B_e \Delta C + \Delta C^2) - k_{21} Z_e + k_{21} \Delta C$$

The deviations in concentration are quite small so that ΔC^2 can be disregarded as negligible. From the expression for equilibrium

$$(20) \qquad \frac{k_{12}}{k_{21}} = \frac{Z_e}{A_e B_e}$$

we may simplify Eq. 19:

$$(21) \qquad -\frac{d\Delta C}{dt} = \{k_{12}(A_e + B_e) + k_{21}\}\Delta C = \frac{\Delta C}{\tau}$$

The expression within the brackets in Eq. 21 is the reciprocal of τ, the relaxation time characteristic of the process which returns the system to equilibrium. The individual rate constants might be obtained by measuring the relaxation times at different concentrations of A and B and extrapolating to zero A + B concentrations. The deviation of concentration can be expressed by an equation with the same form as Eq. 14.

$$(22) \qquad \Delta C = \Delta C_0 e^{-t/\tau}$$

Further information on the treatment of more complex equilibria can be found in the text of Amdur and Hammes (*421*).

Dipolar molecules are oriented in an electric field, with the average moment given by:

(23)
$$\bar{m}_F = \frac{\mu^2 F_0}{3kT}$$

If the field is turned off, or changes rapidly to a smaller field, the ensemble of oriented dipoles will relax, according to the relation:

(24)
$$\bar{m}_F = \frac{\mu^2 F_0}{3kT} e^{-t/\tau}$$

Debye (*305*) has estimated the relaxation time on the basis of a model of a sphere of radius a rotating in a liquid with viscosity ("friction constant") η as

(25)
$$\tau = \frac{8\pi\eta a^3}{2kT}$$

η = macroscopic viscosity in poise

k = Boltzmann constant

a = radius of the spherical molecule

T = temperature in °K

For water, a can be taken as 2×10^{-3} cm., η is 0.01 poises, and τ is then 25 picoseconds (1 picosecond = 1 psec. = 1×10^{-12} seconds).

If the electric field is alternated from one direction to the opposite direction at a frequency comparable to the time for the relaxation of the dipoles in a system, the dielectric constant measured for that system will become frequency dependent in a way which is usually expressed:

(26)
$$D^* = D' - iD'' = D_0 + \frac{(D - D_0)}{1 + i\omega T}$$

D_0 = dynamic dielectric constant (Eq. 11)

D = static dielectric constant

ω = frequency of the alternation expressed in radians/second

T = relaxation time related to τ by Eq. 27

D^* = dielectric constant at frequency ω

$i = \sqrt{-1}$

(27)
$$T = \frac{3D}{2D + D_0} \tau$$

After our discussion on the importance of not using the dielectric constant D (a macroscopic constant) on the microscopic level for the local environment, the student might well wonder why the macroscopic viscosity can apparently be used with equanimity on the microscopic level. The averaging of intermolecular interactions, which results in the macroscopic viscosity, must also take place on the microscopic level *for the time scale of dielectric relaxation*. Unusually low relaxation times for molecules like *t*-butyl chloride (2 psec. in *n*-heptane as compared with 9 psec. for ethyl bromide) indicates that rotational relaxation can be extremely fast. For *t*-butyl chloride in a nonpolar solvent, dielectric relaxation and rotational relaxation might be closely related, not involving appreciable motion in any part of any solvent molecule in the cybotactic region. Gordon (*321*) has interpreted the band shapes of the infrared absorptions of methane as suggesting extremely short rotational relaxation times for methane in methane.

Many liquids and solutions exhibit more than one dielectric relaxation time, reflecting the presence of more than one type of dipolar species. The relaxation associated with a local dipole within a larger molecule can be distinguished from the relaxation of the molecule as a whole. Especially long relaxation times in associated liquids are ascribed to the presence of molecular clusters, with relaxation times as great as 2200 psec. reported for the straight chain alcohols. Some selected relaxation times are listed in Table 2.2.

The interpretation of dielectric relaxation times, reviewed by Smyth (*314, 315*), in terms of specific processes involving molecules is not simple, and the view that a rotational process is the primary factor in relaxation is hard to reconcile with the evidence that rotational relaxations can be much faster (τ as little as 0.02 psec.) than dielectric relaxations. Kirkwood and Shumaker (*316*) have pointed out that proton fluctuation among basic sites on a large protein can lead to relaxation without actual motion of the dipoles involved. Presumably the proton transfer responsible for the fluctuation in proton site occurs through organized groups of water molecules (see Section 2.5). The relaxation time for this process might be between 0.2 psec. (k for $H^+ + OH^-$ in ice 1×10^{-14} l. mole^{-1} sec.$^{-1}$) and 20 psec.

The spins of nuclear magnets provide another type of ensemble which can be perturbed, a relaxation time T_1 then characterizing one type of return of the ensemble to equilibrium. The *spin-lattice relaxation time* T_1 is related to the interaction of the nuclear magnets with the rapidly fluctuating magnetic field produced by the nuclear magnets of the environment. The fluctuation arises from the motion of the molecules carrying the nuclear magnets and the interaction produces transitions between the energy levels of the nuclear magnet. The net effect of the interaction with the environment or *lattice* is to relax the excited state of the ensemble of nuclear magnets, the excess energy being converted to heat.

TABLE 2.2   *Dielectric Relaxation Times*[a]

Molecule	Solvent	Temperature °C	psec.[b]
t-Butyl chloride	Pure	20	4.8
	CCl$_4$	20	3.5
	n-Heptane	20	2.0
Ethyl bromide	Pure	25	9.0
Toluene	Pure	20	6.3
Benzyl chloride	Benzene	20	21 est.
CH$_2$Cl group			2.6
Anisole	Pure	20	14.7
CH$_3$O group			3.2
Chlorobenzene	Benzene	20	7.5
2,4,6-Tribromophenol	Benzene	20	22
2,4,6-Tri-*t*-butylphenol	*trans*-Decalin	20	500
HO group			3.7
1-Naphthol	Benzene	20	15
HO group			3.4

[a] Refs. 314, 315.   [b] 1 psec. $= 1 \times 10^{-12}$ seconds.

It would not be possible to present in a limited space an adequate notion of the vast field of nuclear magnetic resonance. The student who has not previously encountered these ideas should consult any one of a number of excellent texts and references (*318, 442, 509*). For present purposes, it is sufficient to understand that some nuclei like that of hydrogen have magnetic moments, that these moments can be oriented by the application of an external (or laboratory) magnetic field, that nuclei with spin 1/2 are divided into two classes by the external magnetic field (class of higher energy-spin antiparallel to external field; class of lower energy-spin parallel) and that transitions can be induced between the energy levels corresponding to the two classes of nuclei, these transitions constituting the nuclear magnetic resonance (n.m.r.) phenomenon when detected by appropriate means.

From the relation

$$(28) \qquad N_2 = N_1 e^{-(\mu H_0 / kT)}$$

N_2 = number of nuclei with spins antiparallel to net field at nucleus (upper state)

N_1 = number of nuclei with spins parallel to net field at nucleus (lower state)
(state = energy level)

μ = nuclear magnetic moment

H_0 = net field at nucleus (external magnetic field as modified by shielding or other intramolecular magnetic effects)

k = Boltzmann constant

T = temperature in °K

we may calculate the distribution of nuclei of spin 1/2 between two energy levels. If we now perturb the ensemble of spins by providing quanta of an energy equal to the separation of the two levels, we can displace the equilibrium and increase N_2. The rate of decrease in the excess N_2 is then given by

$$(29) \qquad -\frac{d(\Delta N_2)}{dt} = \frac{(\Delta N_2)}{T_1}$$

with the integrated expression as

$$(30) \qquad (\Delta N_2) = (\Delta N_2)_0 e^{-t/T_1}$$

The inter- and intramolecular contributions to T_1 have been estimated theoretically as functions of quantities called the correlation times (*318, 442*). The intramolecular correlation time τ_c is approximately the time required for the molecule to turn through one radian and is one-third the relaxation time estimated by Debye (Eq. 24) for a spherical molecule (see Eq. 24 for explanation of symbols).

$$(31) \qquad \tau_c = \frac{\tau}{3} = \frac{4\pi\eta a^3}{3kT}$$

For molecules like water, the correlation time is very small (for water, τ_c is 2.7 psec. at 20°) and the relationship between the intramolecular relaxation time for the spin ensemble (T_1) and the correlation time is

$$(32) \qquad \left(\frac{1}{T_1}\right)_{\text{intra}} = \frac{3\gamma^4\hbar^2}{10r_0^6} \cdot 3\tau_c$$

> γ = magnetogyric ratio for the hydrogen nucleus $(2.5 \times 10^4$ radians per gauss-sec.)
>
> $\hbar$ = Planck's constant$/2\pi$ $(h = 6.62 \times 10^{-27}$ erg-sec.)
>
> r_0 = average distance between interacting nuclei (in cm.)

Equation 32 indicates that spin-lattice relaxation is favored by the interaction of the magnetic moments (the magnetogyric ratio is defined by $\mu/I\hbar$, in which μ is the magnetic moment of the nucleus and I is the nuclear spin), disfavored by an increase in the average distance between nuclei and proportional to the correlation time. The correlation time, τ_c, is dependent upon the viscosity of the material. (It should be clear to the student that the longer the relaxation time, the less efficient the mechanisms contributing to the relaxation.) We should thus expect a relationship between the relaxation time and the viscosity. For water at 20°, with r_0 as 1.5 A, $(1/T_1)_{\text{intra}}$ can be evaluated as 0.13 sec.$^{-1}$.

The correlation time for the intermolecular contribution to spin-lattice relaxation is derived from diffusion theory and is the time taken by a neighboring nucleus to move a distance r:

$$(33) \qquad \tau_{cj} = \frac{r^2}{12D}$$

in which D is the diffusion coefficient for the molecule which carries the nuclear magnet. Using the diffusion coefficient as defined by the Stokes–Einstein relation (see Eq. 24 for explanation of symbols)

$$(34) \qquad D = \frac{kT}{6\pi\eta a}$$

the intermolecular contribution to the spin-lattice relaxation may be evaluated from

$$(35) \qquad \left(\frac{1}{T_1}\right)_{\text{inter}} = 9\pi^2\gamma^4\hbar^2\eta \frac{N}{5kT}$$

in which N is the number of molecules per cc. and the other symbols have the usual meaning. For water at 20°C, $(1/T_1)_{\text{inter}}$ is estimated as 0.08 sec.$^{-1}$, making the total 0.21 sec.$^{-1}$. The experimental value for oxygen-free water is 0.27 sec.$^{-1}$.

$$(36) \qquad \left(\frac{1}{T_1}\right)_{\text{total}} = \left(\frac{1}{T_1}\right)_{\text{intra}} + \left(\frac{1}{T_1}\right)_{\text{inter}}$$

It may be noted that the intermolecular spin-lattice relaxation also depends upon viscosity. Both intra- and intermolecular correlation times decrease with increasing temperature (less correlation as the molecules move faster) and increase with increasing viscosity (more correlation as the resistance to a change in orientation or motion becomes greater). The theory suggests a linear relationship between the relaxation time and the ratio of viscosity and temperature, η/T, and this has been confirmed for ethanol over a considerable range of relaxation times (*318*). A number of proton spin-lattice relaxation times are listed in Table 2.3.

TABLE 2.3   *Proton Spin-Lattice Relaxation Times*[a]

Substance	T_1, Seconds	Temperature °C
Water	3.6 ± 0.2	
Ethanol	2.2	20
Acetic acid	2.4	20
Sulfuric acid	0.7	20
Glycerol[b]	0.023	20
n-Pentane	4.3	27
n-Hexane	2.0	28
Methyl iodide	3.8	29
Benzene	19.3	25
Benzene in CS_2[c]	60	25

[a] From Ref. 318.   [b] 1,2,3-trihydroxypropane.
[c] 11% by volume.

The measurement of T_1 values for the N^{14} nucleus in a number of compounds allowed the evaluation of the quadrupole correlation time, τ_q, as between 1 to 6 picoseconds (*319*). Similar values were obtained for τ_q for Cl^{35} in polychloromethanes (*320*).

$$(37) \qquad \left(\frac{1}{T_1}\right) = \frac{3}{8}\left(1 + \frac{1}{3}\eta^2\right)\left(\frac{e^2qQ}{\hbar}\right)^2 \tau_q$$

Considerable effort must still be expended upon the detailed interpretation of relaxation times. Since relaxation processes often have time constants comparable to those for the very fast reactions of intermediates, we can look forward to the application of these results to the elucidation of the mechanisms of organic reactions.

Problems

1. Derive the rate expression for the return of a monomer-dimer equilibrium after perturbation.
2. How would the treatment of processes as relaxations be affected if radiative loss (that is, phosphorescence, fluorescence) contributed to the decay of the excited state?
3. Using the data in Table 2.1, calculate dielectric relaxation times (Eq. 24, Part 2) at 25°C for the following:
   (a) Water.
   (b) Deuterium oxide.
   (c) Ammonia (at 0°).
   (d) Nitrobenzene.
   (e) Sulfuric acid.
   (f) Glycerol.
   Estimate the size of the molecule from careful drawings or models and tables of bond lengths.
4. Define T_1, the spin-lattice relaxation time.
5. Explain why dilution of benzene with carbon disulfide increases T_1 by a factor of 3 (Table 2.3).
6. Try to interpret the meaning of the T_1 for glycerol in molecular terms.

2.5   Water Structure

The solvent in the cybotactic region around a solute molecule is far from randomly distributed as a result of the interaction between the solute molecules and the solvent molecules. If we regard a particular solvent molecule as a "solute" molecule, we might then surmise that some degree of organization exists in that portion of the solvent previously referred to as "bulk solvent." In fact, the existence of short-range order in many liquids has been inferred from the results of X-ray scattering on liquids.

Let us label the particular solvent molecule as the "central" molecule within a large group of solvent molecules. The average number of molecules per unit volume in the liquid is N/V. If the solvent molecules were randomly distributed around the "central" molecule, the average number of molecules per unit volume would be the same on the microscopic scale as that found on

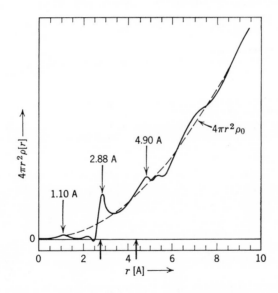

Figure 2.6   A radial distribution function for water molecules in liquid water based on X-ray diffraction at 25°C. The arrows on the abcissa at 2.75 and 4.50 A show the distances of the nearest and next-nearest neighbors in the ice structure. The maximum at 1.10 A is probably due the O—H distance. (ρ is the number of water molecules at distance r from a central molecule per cubic Angstrom; ρ_0 = average number of molecules in water per cubic Angstrom) (Ref. 324).

the macroscopic scale. The number of molecules in the spherical shell surrounding a "central" molecule (with radius r) between r and $r + dr$ is given by $(N/V) \cdot 4\pi r^2 \, dr$. The actual number of molecules in that spherical shell differs from the random number in a way that varies with the distance from the center of the "central" molecule. The function that describes the deviation from random distribution is called the radial distribution function, $g(r)$, and is defined:

$$(38) \qquad g(r) = \frac{\text{actual average number between } r \text{ and } r + dr}{\text{random average number between } r \text{ and } r + dr}$$

Number refers to the number of molecules.

The results of Danford and Levy (*324*) for X-ray scattering on water are shown in Fig. 2.6. The heavy arrows along the abscissa indicate that the

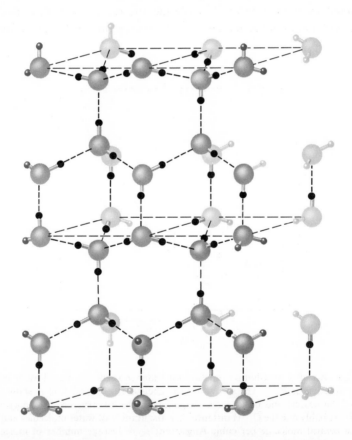

Figure 2.7 The arrangement of molecules in the ice crystal (from Ref. 326).

nearest neighbor distances in ice are not very different from those in liquid water. The $g(r)$ for water shows clearly that the distribution of nearest neighbor water molecules is not random.

The structure of ice is illustrated by a usual three-dimensional structure in Fig. 2.7. The positions of the hydrogens shown have been confirmed by a neutron-diffraction study of deuterium oxide ice (*325*) and agree with the original arguments of Pauling based on the residual entropy of ice (*326*). The remarkably open structure of ice (remember that the density of ice is only 0.92 that of water) is emphasized even more in the stereoscopic structure shown as Fig. 2.8. Not only do small molecules fit inside the ice structure, but a slightly different lattice arrangement can be stabilized by the inclusion of other molecules, which often do not interact with the polar molecules of the ice lattice except through van der Waals forces. Lattices which include other molecules in what is usually a nonintegral proportion are called "hosts." The molecules included are called "guests." Host-guest combinations which form in regular proportions are *clathrate compounds*. Typical water clathrates are xenon hydrate, $Xe \cdot 5.75\ H_2O$, chlorine hydrate, $Cl_2 \cdot 8\ H_2O$, and methane hydrate, $CH_4 \cdot 5.75\ H_2O$. The structure of methane hydrate is given in Fig. 2.9. The subject of water clathrates is thoroughly reviewed by Jeffrey and McMullan (*317*).

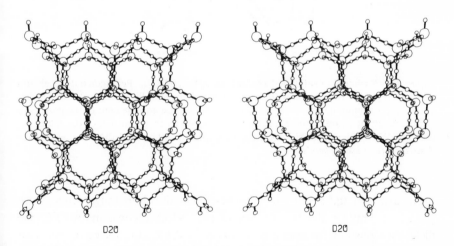

D2C   D2C

Figure 2.8 The ice structure as seen from two slightly different angles. The drawings were made by a computer and may be fused into an apparent three-dimensional image by viewing the left-hand image with the left eye and the right-hand image with the right eye. (An $8\frac{1}{2} \times 11$ inch cardboard is convenient for this purpose.) (The photograph is reprinted through the courtesy of Dr. Walter C. Hamilton of the Chemistry Department Brookhaven National Laboratory.)

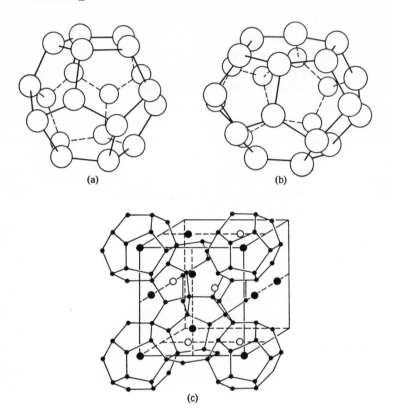

(a)   (b)

(c)

Figure 2.9 Structure of solid methane hydrate $(CH_4)_8(H_2O)_{46}$. Pentagonal dodecahedra (*a*) and polyhedra with 14 faces (*b*), consisting of tetrahedrally linked water molecules, and each containing one methane molecule. (*c*) shows the arrangement of the polyhedra in the overall structure of the gas hydrate, illustrated by the front half of the cubic unit cell (Ref. 327). (Reprinted with the permission of the authors and the publishers of the *Zeitschrift für Elektrochemie*.)

An experimental result which suggests that the short-range order in ice persists in liquid water is the value of the dielectric constant. At 0°C, the dielectric constant for water is 87.90. At −0.1°C, the dielectric constant measured for polycrystalline ice is 91.5 (*322*). Since the isolated water molecule has a relatively low dipole moment ($\mu = 1.76$ Debyes measured in benzene, *322*), the high dielectric constants of both water and ice must be due to the presence of associated forms. The similarity of the X-ray scattering patterns for water and ice suggests that the association in both cases leads to similar structures. It is thus reasonable to speak of "ice-like" structural arrangements in liquid water.

To account for the special properties of water, a number of structural models for water have been proposed. In general, these agree that there are two kinds of water molecules, those organized into clusters and those which are monomeric or n-meric, with n small. The clusters favored by Pauling (326) are structured like the water in water clathrates, with monomeric water occupying the cavities within the structure. Frank and Wen (328) proposed the idea of "flickering clusters." The clusters are short-lived, as required by the dielectric relaxation times, and would allow the unusually rapid proton and hydroxide ion transference known to occur in water (Fig. 2.10). Némethy and Scheraga (329) have tried to account for the thermodynamic properties of water in terms of large clusters and several different kinds of n-mers, with n small. Ben–Naim (330) has favored large compact clusters and monomers on the basis of thermodynamic arguments and experimental measurements of the solubility of argon in pure water and mixtures of other substances with water. Wicke (331) has written an extensive review on water structure, in which a somewhat more complicated picture is proposed. One notion worthy of attention is the possibility of hydrogen bonds which are "bent" or "curved" like those found in ice VI (a highly compressed ice) by Kamb (332). Although straight hydrogen bonds are probably the strongest, "curved" bonds of lesser stability should also form just as "curved" (or "banana") bonds connect the carbons of cyclopropane. (The "bent bond" structure for cyclopropane was proposed by Coulson and Moffitt (272) and is supported directly by the electron density maps prepared by Hartman and Hirshfeld for *cis*-1,2,3-tricyanocyclopropane (334)). Two books largely concerned with problems of water structure are available (335, 336).

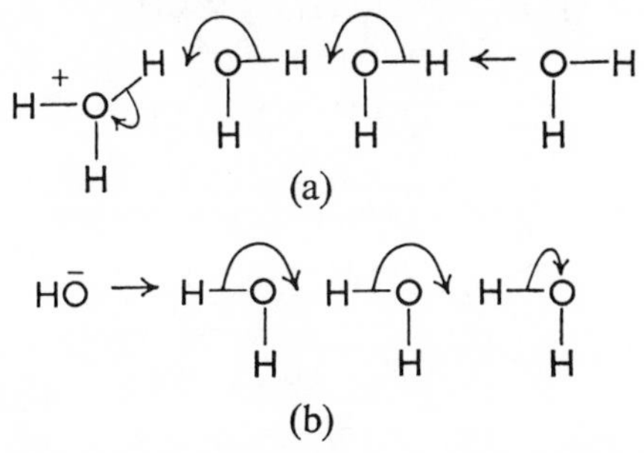

Figure 2.10 (a) Proton transference through water clusters. (b) Hydroxide ion transference through water clusters.

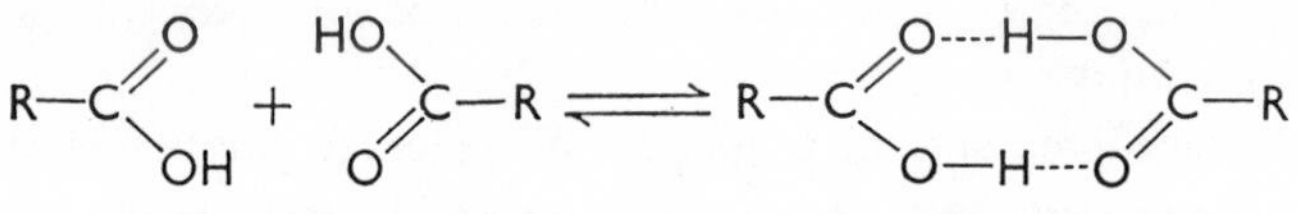

Figure 2.11   The dimerization of carboxylic acids.

The effect of organic groups, organic molecules, and ions on water structure must be understood if we are to achieve detailed understanding of the behavior and reactions of organic molecules in water as well as some comprehension of many important biological phenomena like protein folding and neurone action.

Structural effects are important for many solvents, especially those which can participate in hydrogen bonds. Particularly striking is the well-known dimerization of carboxylic acids, which is illustrated in Fig. 2.11.

Radial distribution functions for liquid alcohols (from X-ray scattering) are interpreted as indicating the presence of linear polymers of modest length, with perhaps 5 to 7 monomer units in each polymer. Apparently only two hydrogen bonds per alcohol hydroxyl group can be formed: (1) in which

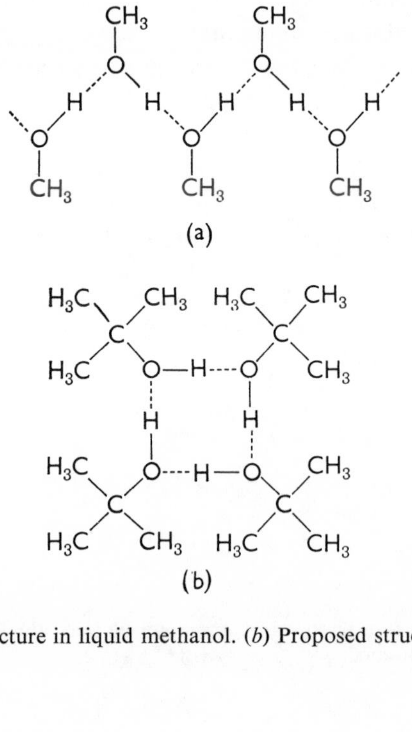

(a)

(b)

Figure 2.12   (a) Structure in liquid methanol. (b) Proposed structure of *t*-butyl alcohol tetramer.

the group is a hydrogen donor and (2) in which it is a hydrogen acceptor. The example of methanol is illustrated in Fig. 2.12*a*. Certain alcohols give rise to cyclic tetramers, like that shown for *t*-butyl alcohol in Fig. 2.12*b*. It has been suggested that cyclic *n*-mers with *n* small are present in most liquid alcohols on the grounds that the heats of fusion of many alcohols are "normal," implying that the fusion process does not involve much breaking of bonds like the hydrogen bonds which exist in the solid alcohols (*326*, *337*).

Heat evolution is observed when water is mixed with ethanol. *A priori*, the mixing process should lead to degradation of the three-dimensional order of the water clusters without replacing the two-dimensional order of the ethanol aggregates with a radically different structural order. We thus might have predicted heat absorption rather than heat evolution. Measurements indicate that a large decrease in entropy occurs on mixing. "Excess functions" are an expression of the deviation of the system from what might have been expected for the dilution of two "ideal" liquids:

$$(39) \qquad \Delta F^M = RT(x_1 \ln x_1 + x_2 \ln x_2) + RT(x_1 \ln \gamma_1 + x_2 \ln \gamma_2)$$

For ideal liquids, the activity coefficients γ_1 and γ_2 will be zero. Excess functions for the mixing of ethanol and water are shown in Fig. 2.13 as a

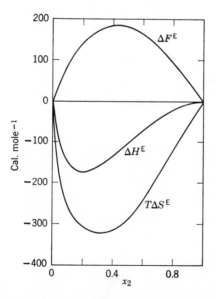

Figure 2.13 Thermodynamic excess functions for ethanol–water at 25°; x_2 = mole fraction of ethanol (from Ref. 227). (Reprinted with the permission of the authors and *Quarterly Reviews*.)

function of the mole fraction of ethanol. Note that the excess in the evolution of heat does not occur at the same composition as the maximum in entropy loss, the former occurring at $x_2 = 0.2$ and the latter at $x_2 = 0.35$.

Heat evolution on mixing ethanol and water indicates either that the strength of the individual interactions between molecules in the mixture has increased or that additional interactions have appeared. Although we might consider dipole–dipole attractions and van der Waals attractions as components of the increase in interaction energy, it seems likely that hydrogen bonding is the major factor responsible for the heat evolution. Thus, by discussing the result in terms of hydrogen bonding alone, we include these other interactions with the hydrogen bonding along with some special factors as *hydrophobic bonding*. (Hydrophobic bonding is a somewhat awkward term for the net gain in interaction energy resulting from forcing nonpolar groups in molecules bearing polar groups away from the "polar" regions in order to maximize the interaction between the polar groups. Thermodynamic data on the transfer of hydrocarbons from water to hydrocarbon solvents suggest that the positive entropy change for this process is more important than the

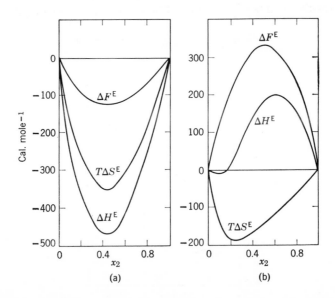

Figure 2.14 (*a*) Thermodynamic excess functions for acetone–chloroform at 25°; $x_2 =$ mole fraction chloroform. (*b*) Thermodynamic excess functions for methanol–carbon tetrachloride at 25°; $x_2 =$ mole fraction carbon tetrachloride (from Ref. 339). (Reprinted with the permission of the authors and *Quarterly Reviews*.)

enthalpy change. The entropy change arises from the release of water molecules organized around the hydrocarbon groups; the enthalpy change comes from increased interaction between polar groups.) Apparently, both more and better hydrogen bonds are formed in mixtures of ethanol and water as compared with either liquid alone, to judge from the fact that heat evolution reaches a maximum for a different composition than maximum entropy loss. The mechanism by which the additional order (increased entropy loss) is produced is not clear; it is conceivable, for example, that the extra hydrogen bonds could all be between water molecules, yielding larger clusters, rather than between water and ethanol molecules.

Excess functions are illustrated for two other cases, acetone-chloroform (Fig. 2.14*a*) and methanol–carbon tetrachloride (Fig. 2.14*b*). In contrast to the considerable heat of mixing produced in the former case, the latter occurs virtually without evolution of heat. There is, however, an appreciable initial loss of entropy as carbon tetrachloride induces additional order in the methanol.

It is easy to see that the structure of the alcohol mixed with water has much to do with the thermodynamic properties of the mixture. A comparison of the

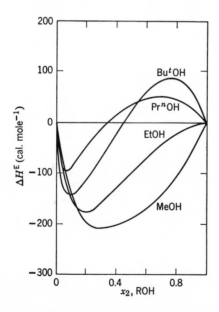

Figure 2.15 Heats of mixing (ΔH_M) of methanol, ethanol, 1-propanol, and *t*-butyl alcohol with water at 25°; x_2 = mole fraction of alcohol (from Ref. 337). (Reprinted with the permission of the authors and *Quarterly Reviews*.)

heats of mixing of methanol, ethanol, 1-propanol, and *t*-butyl alcohol with water is shown in Fig. 2.15. The curve for *t*-butyl alcohol–water mixtures is particularly interesting, with heat evolution at low alcohol concentrations and heat absorption (loss of hydrogen bonding) at high alcohol concentrations.

2.6   Solvent Polarity: Empirical Measures

The formulation of many reaction mechanisms can be aided by data on the effect of substituents or solvents on the rates and products of the reactions. In Part 1 of this book we showed how well-defined substituent effects (for example, for carbonium ion reactions, for the dissociation of benzoic acids) could be used to evaluate suggested mechanisms for many transformations. In order to make use of data on solvent effects for reaching conclusions about mechanism, we require some unambiguous way of defining what effect we expect for a given solvent. At the present time, all parameters used to describe solvents result from experimental measurements. The experimental measurement provides information about a particular process, which we may call a *model process*. This process may be macroscopic (the one that yields the dielectric constant) or microscopic (example: an electronic transition). The model process leads to a parameter that we can take as a measure of solvent polarity in those cases for which such a description is appropriate. *In order to utilize the parameter properly, we must first understand the molecular basis of the process which provided the data for defining the parameter.* We must not expect a parameter to be universal and useful for all kinds of reactions because any comparison (that is, attempted correlation) of the effect of solvent on a process of interest with a solvent parameter is, in fact, a comparison with the effect of solvent on a reference process. The model process (as long as it is microscopic) can be considered as a *probe* in the cybotactic region, a probe that sums up a wide variety of interactions including charge–dipole, dipole–dipole, hydrogen-bonding, charge–charge, dipole–induced dipole, etc. The degree of charge separation in a transition state or ground state or excited state is often the kind of information we should like to obtain, and it is for this purpose that considerable effort has been devoted to solvent parameters. Our subsequent discussion will concentrate on parameters which are mainly useful for delineating the degree of charge separation in various processes, since it is to this application that the most work has been devoted.

It is relatively easy to write *ideal extreme processes* useful as model processes on the microscopic level, once it is recognized that the larger the response of the model process to variation of the solvent, the more likely it is that unique quantities can be assigned to all solvents. The first such process is the one which converts an ion-pair (maximum interaction with the solvent) into a neutral species (zero interaction with solvent) (Eq. 40). The second process is one which transforms a neutral species into an ion-pair (Eq. 41). The hypothetical solvent parameter based on such extreme processes would be more sensitive to the nature of the solvent than any real chemical process except for those which are actually described by an equation for an extreme process.

(40) $$D^+A^- \longrightarrow D,A$$

(41) $$D,A \longrightarrow D^+,A^-$$

Two types of processes might be considered: (1) a rate process in which a transition state is formed from an initial state (2) an electronic transition in which an electron is transferred from one species to another (intermolecular charge transfer) or from one end of a molecule to another (intramolecular charge transfer). We should then search for real processes that conform as closely as possible to these types. The best-studied case of a given type is chosen as the process for measurement of solvent parameters. In other words, a case of a suitable type is used as model process, one which defines a reference system for many similar processes. (It should be clear that the "best-studied case" does not have to be the case for which there is the largest number of measurements. It should also be stated explicitly that the philosophy behind choosing the model applies to processes which do not conform to the extremes shown in Eqs. 40 and 41.)

Let us examine the two types of processes in more detail. In a rate process, the solvent is in thermal equilibrium with both the initial state and the transition state. Maximum solvent effect on a rate process could, in principle, be attained for either appearance of charge (Eq. 41) or disappearance of charge (Eq. 40). In practice, however, the solvents of interest include many in which the concentration of ion-pairs would not be equal to the stoichiometric concentration of the salt being used (due to dissociation to free ions) and thus it is not probable that a rate process which leads to the disappearance of two unit charges will be useful as a model process for defining solvent parameters. A rate process which seems to correspond to Eq. 41 is the solvolysis of t-butyl chloride, in which it is thought that a neutral initial state proceeds to a highly charged transition state (Eq. 42). Grunwald and Winstein (*338*) were the first to adopt the "best-studied case" approach for defining solvent parameters. They chose t-butyl chloride solvolysis because it was believed to be an S_N1 reaction (Hughes–Ingold terminology), S_IN (Section 1.4), or a Limiting (Lim.) reaction (Winstein–Grunwald–Jones, *61*). Although Grunwald and Winstein did not set out the formal basis for choosing a model process as we have done above, their choice of t-butyl chloride solvolysis was based on similar reasoning. The **Y**-values which are derived from the rates of reaction of *t*-butyl chloride in various solvents are defined in Eq. 43. Discussion of **Y**-values is deferred to a later place in this section.

(42)

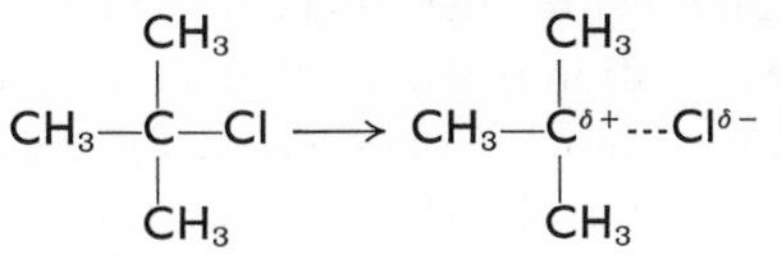

$$CH_3-\underset{\underset{CH_3}{|}}{\overset{\overset{CH_3}{|}}{C}}-Cl \longrightarrow CH_3-\underset{\underset{CH_3}{|}}{\overset{\overset{CH_3}{|}}{C}}{}^{\delta+}\cdots Cl^{\delta-}$$

(43)
$$\mathbf{Y} = \log k_{\text{solvent}}^{t\text{-butyl Cl}} - \log k_{80\% \text{ EtOH}}^{t\text{-butyl Cl}}$$

The second type of process, which one might consider for a model process, is an electronic transition. The first or second electronic transition of a species results from the absorption of a photon and the promotion of an electron to the next higher molecular orbital. An electron in a higher orbital is more weakly bound to the nuclei of a molecule and therefore has an average position which is farther from the nuclei than its average position before the transition occurred. Let us adopt 0.1 A as a reasonable estimate for the increase in average position of the electron. Since the electron changes position at the speed of light, we may estimate the time required for the electronic transition as 10^{-15} seconds (light absorption *requires* 0.001 psec.). Relaxation processes, which are responsible for changes in the orientation of one molecule with respect to another, require at least 1 picosecond (see Section 2.4). The only portion of intermolecular interaction energies, which changes as rapidly as an electronic transition, is that relatively small portion involving electronic polarization (induced changes in electron distribution within the molecule). (In Fig. 2.5, a qualitative comparison of the relative magnitudes of electronic and orientation polarization is shown. Electronic polarization would be relatively important in molecules without appreciable dipole moments). Thus, the electronic transition occurs more rapidly than the processes that allow the nuclei of the same or surrounding molecules to accommodate themselves to the changed charge distribution that might result from the electronic transition. The idea that electronic transitions occur more rapidly than motions of the nuclei has long been known as the Franck–Condon principle. The nonequilibrium excited state produced by an electronic transition can be called the "instantaneous" excited state or the "Franck–Condon state." The solvent arrangement around a solute molecule in the Franck–Condon state is the same as it was in the ground (or initial) state. Referring now to Eq. 41, we see that even though an ion-pair might be produced through light absorption by a neutral species, we would not observe an appreciable solvent effect because the transition energy would have been determined by the solvent arrangement around the ground state.

This simple (but often unappreciated) difficulty may be responsible for unexpectedly small solvent effects on electronic transitions. Thus, by the criteria we have established for the choice of a model process, we could not utilize an electronic transition that produced an ion-pair in the excited state. On the other hand, the Franck–Condon state for the destruction of an ion-pair through an electron-transfer (Eq. 40) has a solvent arrangement that is unstable, with respect to the equilibrium excited state arrangement, by an amount approximately equal to the energy of interaction of the solvent arrangement (cybotactic region) with the ground state. A process which conforms to Eq. 40 would be an excellent choice as a model process because it should be particularly sensitive to the effects of solvent. Kosower (*216*) has found that the charge-transfer light absorption band of 1-alkylpyridinium iodides is unusually sensitive to solvent (in fact, it is one of the most solvent-sensitive electronic transitions known) and has derived a solvent parameter called **Z**-value from the transition energies for 1-ethyl-4-carbomethoxy-pyridinium iodide. The discussion which follows will examine in detail the molecular basis for this solvent parameter.

The **Z**-value for a solvent is the transition energy for the longest wave-length absorption band observed for 1-ethyl-4-carbomethoxypyridinium iodide in that solvent. The defining equation is given as Eq. 44. The choice of kilocalories per mole as the energy unit is related to the usefulness of this quantity for comparisons to other chemical processes.

(44) $\mathbf{Z} = E_T$ (kilocalories/mole)

$E_T = h\nu$ (ergs/molecule)

h = Planck's constant = 6.624×10^{-27} erg-sec.

ν = frequency of photon which produces transition = c/λ with c = 2.998×10^{10} cm./sec. and λ = wavelength in cm.

To obtain E_T (kilocalories/mole), E_T (ergs/molecule) is multiplied by N (Avogadro's number) = 6.023×10^{23} molecules/mole and divided by 10^7 ergs/joule and 4184.0 kilojoules/kilocalorie. The **Z**-value is evaluated from the position of the maximum in Angstroms by Eq. 45. The electronic transition corresponding to the maximum is shown as follows:

(45) $\mathbf{Z} = 2.859 \times 10^5/\lambda$ (in angstroms)

Although this charge-transfer transition has already been discussed in Section 1.7, we shall briefly review the data which demonstrate that Eq. 46 is a proper description of the electronic transition. A process that transfers

(46)

COOCH$_3$ ... COOCH$_3$

$$\text{(46)} \quad \overset{h\nu}{\longrightarrow}$$

214

an electron to a pyridinium ring should be very sensitive to the substitution on that ring, since we should expect that substitution would affect markedly the acceptor abilities of the ring. Table 1.13 (Section 1.3) lists charge-transfer absorption bands for various 1-alkylpyridinium iodides. Variation of the 4-substituent from methyl to cyano changes the position of the charge-transfer band in a given solvent from 3590 A to 4912 A. The high sensitivity of the position of the maximum to the nature of the substituent on the ring implies very strongly that an electron-transfer process is responsible for the absorption band. Most electronic transition ($n \to \pi^*$, $\pi \to \pi^*$, etc.) are far less sensitive to the nature of the substituents than the charge-transfer transition of the pyridinium iodide. A second expectation for an electronic transition like that described in Eq. 46 is that two similar charge-transfer bands would be observed with a separation corresponding to the known separation between the two lowest states of the iodine atom. The difference between these two states ($^2P_{3/2}$ and $^2P_{1/2}$) is 21.8 kcal./mole as determined from a study of the spectrum of iodine atoms. Two similar bands are indeed observed for 1-methylpyridinium iodide in pure chloroform and the separation between these two bands is exactly 21.8 kcal./mole (*399*). The two bands observed for 1-ethyl-4-carbomethoxypyridinium iodide are separated by 28.6 kcal./mole (in 1,2-dichloroethane, the maxima are found at 4508 A and 3108 A). The fact that both bands for **214** have similar shape and the same solvent sensitivity indicates that they are the two bands expected. The reason for the deviation from the predicted value is not known but it is probable that Eq. 46 is too simple a description of the electronic transition. Nevertheless, observation of both bands suggests that the basic description of the transition is correct. We can thus state with certainty that the transition involves the loss of an electron from the iodide anion and the gain of an electron by the pyridinium ring. Kosower and Lindquist (*182*) have obtained direct evidence for Eq. 46 by showing that pyridinyl radicals are generated by flash photolysis of pyridinium iodide (Eq. 47) (see Eqs. 219–223, Section 1.7).

Finally, the high solvent sensitivity of the charge-transfer band of **214** can

(47)

only be explained in terms of a charge-transfer transition for reasons which will become apparent below. The effect of solvent on the absorption spectrum of **214** is illustrated in Fig. 2.16. The longest wavelength band, which is the charge-transfer band, shifts from 3416 A in methanol through 3591 A (ethanol), 3747 A (isopropyl alcohol), and 4005 A (acetonitrile) to 4508 A in *cis*-1,2-dichloroethylene (*55*, *216*). A special peculiarity of this transition is that the dipole moment of the excited state need not vanish completely for it to have zero interaction with the cybotactic region of the Franck–Condon state. The reason for this is that the ground state dipole is perpendicular to

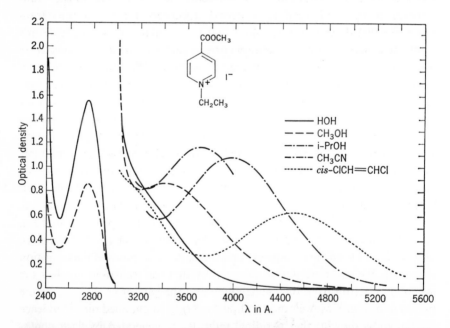

Figure 2.16 The first charge-transfer band of 1-ethyl-4-carbomethoxypyridinium iodide (**214**) in water, methanol, isopropyl alcohol, acetonitrile, and *cis*-1,2-dichloroethylene (*340*). (Reprinted with the permission of the McGraw-Hill Book Co.)

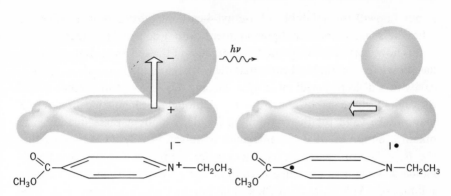

Figure 2.17 Ground and excited state dipoles of 1-ethyl-4-carbomethoxypyridinium iodide. (Reprinted with the permission of the McGraw-Hill Book Co.)

the plane of the pyridinium ring while the dipole moment of the excited state (at least that portion resulting from the pyridinyl radical) is in the plane of the ring. The change in the direction of the dipole is called a "dipole flip." The dipole moment of the cybotactic region would be parallel to the dipole moment of the ground state of the pyridinium iodide. The flip of the direction of the solute dipole upon excitation leads to an instantaneous situation in which the dipole moment of the solute is perpendicular to the dipole moment of the cybotactic region. Mutually perpendicular point dipoles do not interact. Thus, the dipole moment of Franck–Condon state of the pyridinium iodide does not exist for the dipole moment of the cybotactic region, as illustrated in Figs. 2.17 and 2.18. Although the dipole moment of the pyridinyl radical

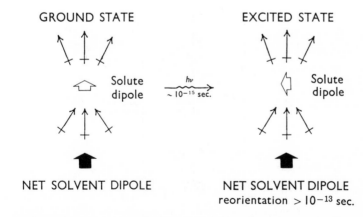

Figure 2.18 The "dipole flip" and its relationship to the solvent dipoles.

is not known, the solubility of 1-ethyl-4-carbomethoxypyridinyl radical in *n*-hexane suggests that the dipole moment cannot be very large (*136*).

It is now worth inquiring into the energetics of the solvation. Böttcher (*341*) has shown for certain ideal cases that the work required to polarize a spherical cavity in a dielectric medium is $\frac{1}{2}f\mu^2$. Placing the dipole of magnitude μ into the cavity yields a stabilization of $-f\mu^2$. Although this highly idealized model may not be valid for the pyridinium iodide, we adopt these quantities to obtain a notion of what the energetics of solvation may be. Assuming that the hypothetical gas-phase charge-transfer transition for the pyridinium iodide **214** requires the same excitation energy as that found for benzene solution (ca. 54 kcal./mole, *342*), and taking the transition energy or Z-value for water as derived below (96.4 kcal./mole), we conclude that the interaction of the ground-state ion-pair with water is 21.2 kcal./mole. This number arises from the circumstance that the destabilization of the excited state of **214** in water, with respect to the excited state in the gas phase, must be approximately equal to one half of the difference in transition energies. These relationships are illustrated in Fig. 2.19 for a series of solvents. There is little experimental information on the free energies of transfer of ion-pairs from one solvent to another (cf. *467*) although Wu and Friedman (*343*) have reported values for the heats of transfer of single ions from water to propylene carbonate.

A list of Z-values based on the longest wavelength charge-transfer band of the pyridinium iodide **214** is given in Table 2.4.

There are two limitations on the usefulness of the pyridinium iodide **214**

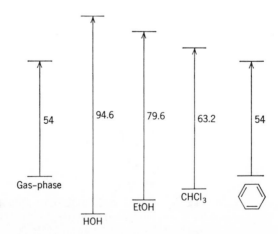

Figure 2.19 Relative transition energies for 1-ethyl-4-carbomethoxypyridinium iodide (**214**) in a series of solvents.

TABLE 2.4   *Z-Values* [a,b,c]

Solvent	Z-Value (kcal./mole)	Solvent	Z-Value (kcal./mole)
Water	94.6 [b]	Methanol: water (97.5) [i]	84.1
Methanol	83.6	(95)	84.5
Ethanol	79.6	(92.5)	84.9
1-Propanol	78.3	(90)	85.5
1-Butanol	77.7	(87.5)	85.8
Isopropyl alcohol	76.3	Ethanol: water (98) [i]	80.2
t-Butyl alcohol	71.3	(96)	80.8
Ethylene glycol	85.1	(95)	81.2
2,2,3,3-Tetrafluoropropanol-1	86.3 [j]	(92)	82.0
	96.3 [d]	(90)	82.5
2,2,3,3,4,4,5,5-Octafluoro-		(85)	83.8
pentanol-1	84.8 [j]	(80)	84.8
Chloroform (0.13 M EtOH)	63.2	(75)	85.7
Methylene chloride	64.2	(70)	8.64
Acetonitrile	71.3	Isopropyl alcohol: water	
Formamide	83.3	(95) [i]	79.3
Dimethylformamide	68.5	(90)	81.5
Dimethylsulfoxide	71.1	(80)	83.9
Hexamethylphosphoramide	62.8	*t*-Butyl alcohol: water	
Pyridine	64.0	(95) [i]	76.5
Cyclopropyl methyl ketone	65.4	(90)	80.4
Acetone	65.7	(80)	83.3
Acetic acid	79.2	Acetone: water (99) [i]	68.1
Benzene	54 [f]	(95)	72.9
N,N-Dimethylacetamide	66.9 [g]	(93)	74.8
N-Methylacetamide	77.9 [g]	(90)	76.6
Sulpholane	77.5 [g]	(85)	78.7
1,2-Dimethoxyethane	62.1 [h]	(80)	80.7
Ethoxybenzene	58.9 [k]	(75)	82.1
Tri-*n*-hexyl-*n*-heptylammonium		(70)	83.2
iodide [l]	66.4 [n]	(65)	84.3
Tri-*n*-hexyl-*n*-heptylammonium		(60)	85.5
perchlorate [m]	66.9 [n]		
Silica gel	88 [o]		

[a] Based on the longest wavelength charge-transfer absorption band of 1-ethyl-4-carbomethoxypyridinium iodide converted to kilocalories per mole.   [b] From Ref. 216, except as noted. The Z-value for water is derived from the relationships between Y-values and Z-values for a series of organic solvent: water mixtures as described in the text and Fig. 2.20.   [c] At 25°C and zero ionic strength when possible.   [d] Based on a linear relationship between E_T for the $n \to \pi^*$ transition of cyclohexanone and Z-value (Ref. 344).   [e] Ref. 345 [(CH$_3$)$_2$N]$_3$PO.   [f] Previously estimated as 62.3 according to Ref. 347 (see text, *342*).   [g] Ref. 323 (R. S. Drago and K. F. Purcell) sulpholane = tetramethylene sulfone.   [h] Ref. 346.   [i] Percentage by volume of the first-named component.   [j] Based on the charge-transfer band of 1-methyl-4-cyanopyridinium iodide and the linear relationship of the transition energies of the 1-methyl-4-cyanopyridinium iodide with Z-values in other solvents.   [k] 0.075 M chloroform (Ref. 365).   [l] m.p. 95.7° (in molten form).   [m] m.p. 100.8 (in molten form).   [n] Ref. 405.   [o] Ref. 418.

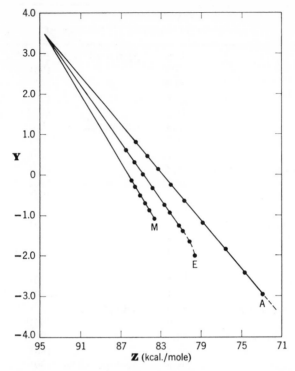

Figure 2.20 The correlation of **Y** with **Z** with methanol–water (M), ethanol–water (E), and acetone–water (A). The equations for the lines are $Y_M = 0.41632Z - 35.877$, $Y_E = 0.35338Z - 29.946$, and $Y_A = 0.29887Z - 24.758$ (*216*). (Reprinted with the permission of the *Journal of the American Chemical Society*.)

for the measurement of **Z**-values. The first is that the salt is not soluble enough in certain nonpolar solvents (for example, hexane) for direct measurement of the **Z**-value. This limitation can be circumvented in all but the most nonpolar solvents by the use of the salt, 1-ethyl-4-carbo-*t*-butoxypyridinium iodide **360**, which has greater solubility in nonpolar solvents than **214**, *as long as care is taken to extrapolate to zero ionic strength* (*342*). Extrapolation is necessary because aggregation of ion-pairs could become serious in nonpolar solvents and would lead to a higher **Z**-value. The second limitation is that the longest wavelength charge-transfer band moves to such short wavelengths in highly polar solvents that it cannot be observed underneath the much stronger $\pi \rightarrow \pi^*$ transition of the pyridinium ion. A **Z**-value for water was obtained in a straightforward way by extrapolating the **Z**-values measured for acetone–water, ethanol–water, and methanol–water mixtures to zero organic component in a plot against the Grunwald–Winstein **Y**-value (*216*).

All three correlations of **Z** and **Y** were linear and extrapolated to the same **Z**-value for water. Furthermore, the point of intersection of the three correlation lines was at the **Y**-value independently measured by Fainberg and Winstein (*352*). Although the **Z**-value for water can be regarded as firmly established, **Z**-values cannot in general be obtained directly for solvents of high polarity. Indirect means can be used, but in view of our strictures about the necessity for understanding the model process *in the solvent of interest*,

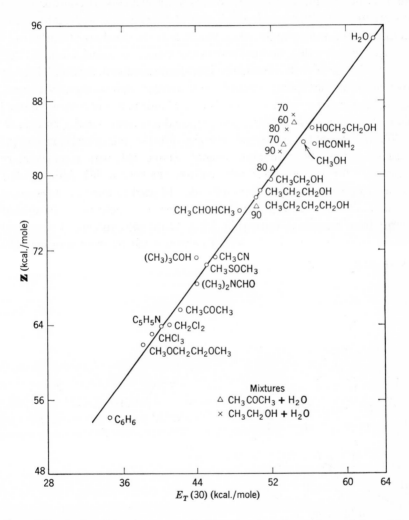

Figure 2.21 A plot of **Z**-values versus $E_T(30)$ values in various solvents (adapted from Ref. 348).

these must be used with caution. Correlations with transition energies for the $\pi \to \pi^*$ transition of pyridine-1-oxide (*216*), the transition energies of the $n \to \pi^*$ transition of cyclohexanone (*344*), and the Ω-values of Berson and co-workers (*346*) have been used to estimate **Z**-values. The correlation of **Z** and **Y** is illustrated in Fig. 2.20.

A possible way of directly measuring solvent polarity parameters for highly polar solvents would be to construct a molecule for which the solvent-sensitive absorption band is displaced to longer wavelengths. It is probably not possible to change the pyridinium iodide **214** very much by the addition of electron-withdrawing groups (which would displace the charge-transfer band to longer wavelengths), because spontaneous electron transfer would interfere with the use of such compounds. [See the discussion in Section 1.7 for an explanation of why spontaneous electron transfer (that is, thermal electron transfer) could occur much more easily than photochemical electron transfer.] Dimroth and co-workers (*348*) have proposed a solvent polarity parameter, $E_T(30)$, based on the transition energies for the intramolecular charge-transfer band of the pyridinium phenol betaine **361**, with supplementary information for the least polar solvents from the betaine **362**. Although **361** is much larger than the pyridinium iodide **214** used to measure **Z**-values, a plot of $E_T(30)$ against **Z** is fairly linear over the whole range of solvent polarity from benzene to water (Fig. 2.21). Acidic solvents cannot be studied with the betaines because the oxygen is protonated by these solvents. The $E_T(30)$-values are listed in Table 2.5.

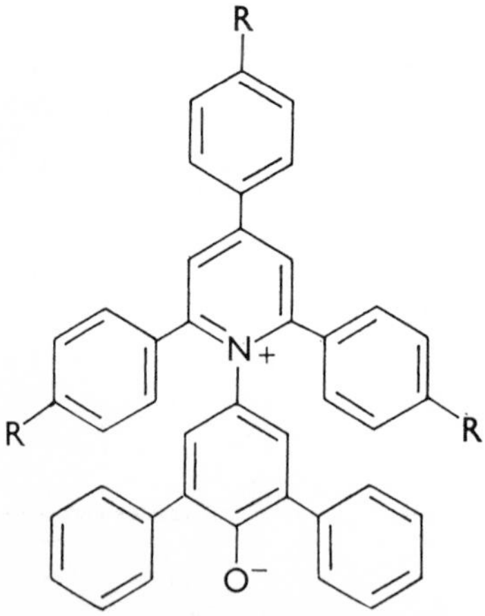

361 (R = H)
362 (R = CH₃)

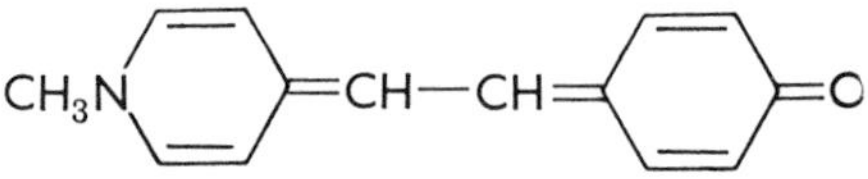

363

Brooker and his co-workers (*350*) have suggested that their early discovery of the large solvent sensitivity of the $\pi \to \pi^*$ transitions of merocyanine dyes (of which a representative is shown as **363**) (*351*) be exploited in the form of a solvent polarity parameter. These may be useful for certain special purposes (in accordance with the principle by which model processes are chosen) but uncertainty about the nature and solvation of the Franck–Condon state preclude their general application.

Determination of a solvent polarity parameter by means of a spectroscopic measurement is extremely rapid, convenient, and reasonably accurate. Parameters based on other kinds of measurements are both necessary and useful if we are to have an appropriate range of model processes. One parameter derived from measurement of reaction rates will be discussed.

The **Y**-value for a solvent is the logarithm of the rate of solvolysis of *t*-butyl chloride in that solvent minus the logarithm of the rate for the

TABLE 2.5 $E_T(30)$-*Values* [a,b]

Solvent	$E_T(30)$	Solvent	$E_T(30)$	Solvent	$E_T(30)$
H_2O	63.1	CH_3CN	46.0	2-CH_3Pyridine	38.3
$HCONH_2$	56.6	CH_3SOCH_3	45.0	$(CH_3OCH_2)_2$	38.2
$HOCH_2CH_2OH$	56.3	$C_6H_5NH_2$	44.3	$CH_3CO_2C_2H_5$	38.1
CH_3OH	55.5	Sulfolane [c]	44.0	C_6H_5Br	37.5
$HCONHCH_3$	54.1	$(CH_3)_3COH$ [d]	43.9	C_6H_5Cl	37.5
$C_2H_5OH:H_2O(80:20)$	53.6	$HCON(CH_3)_2$	43.8	THF [e]	37.4
$CH_3OCH_2CH_2OH$	52.3	CH_3COCH_3	42.2	$C_6H_5OCH_3$	37.2
CH_3CH_2OH	51.9	$C_6H_5NO_2$	42.0	2,6-$(CH_3)_2$-pyridine	36.7
$C_6H_5CH_2OH$	50.8	C_6H_5CN	42.0	1,4-dioxane	36.0
$CH_3CH_2CH_2OH$	50.7	$ClCH_2CH_2Cl$	41.9	$C_6H_5OC_6H_5$ [d]	35.3
$CH_3CH_2CH_2CH_2OH$	50.2	$C_6H_5COCH_3$	41.3	$C_2H_5OC_2H_5$	34.6
$(CH_3)_2CHOH$	48.6	CH_2Cl_2	41.1	C_6H_6	34.5
Propylene carbonate	46.6	$(CH_3)_2NCON(CH_3)_2$	41.0	$C_6H_5CH_3$	33.9
CH_3NO_2	46.3	Pyridine	40.2	CS_2	32.6
				CCl_4	32.5
				n-C_6H_{14}	30.9

[a] Ref. 348.   [b] In kcal./mole at 25°C.   [c] CH_2CH_2 SO_2 CH_2CH_2 [d] At 30°C.   [e] Tetrahydrofuran.

solvolysis of t-butyl chloride in 80% ethanol (Eq. 43). The solvolysis of t-butyl chloride is the classic example of an ionization reaction (S_IN) investigated by Hughes and Ingold (59). Winstein, Grunwald, and Jones (61) cited the fact that 2,2,2-triphenylethyl p-toluenesulfonate solvolysis (probably S_IN) has the same solvent sensitivity as the solvolysis of t-butyl chloride, making it likely that t-butyl chloride was a limiting reaction. For this reason, the solvolysis of t-butyl chloride was considered a good choice for the measurement of a rate constant which in turn would be used to define a solvent polarity parameter. It should be mentioned that t-butyl chloride has two practical disadvantages: (1) it is rather volatile [b.p. 50.8° (760 mm.)] and

TABLE 2.6   *Y-Values*[a,b]

Solvent	Y-Value	Solvent	Y-Value
$C_2H_5OH:H_2O$ (100)[c]	-2.033[d]	(50)	1.972
(98)	-1.681	(30)	2.753
(95)	-1.287	(10)	3.279
(90)	-0.747	$CH_3COOH:HCOOH$	
(80)	0.000	(100)[c,e]	-1.639
(70)	0.595	(90)[e]	-0.929
(60)	1.124	(75)[e]	-0.175
(50)	1.655	$HCOOH:H_2O$ (100)[c,e]	2.054
(45)	1.924	(50)[e]	2.546
(40)	2.196	$CH_3COOH:H_2O$[e]	
(35)	2.473	0.50 M H_2O	-1.400
(30)	2.721	2.00 M H_2O	-0.863
(25)	2.908	4.00 M H_2O	-0.404
(20)	3.051	Dioxane:H_2O (90)[c]	-2.030
(15)	3.189	(80)	-0.833
(10)	3.312	(70)	0.013
(5)	3.397	Acetone: H_2O (90)[c]	-1.856
H_2O	3.493	(80)	-0.673
$CH_3OH:H_2O$ (100)[c]	-1.090	(70)	0.130
(90)	-0.301	Formamide:H_2O (100)[c]	0.604
(80)	0.381	(80)	1.383
(70)	0.961	$(CH_3CO)_2O:CH_3COOH$	
(60)	1.492	(97.5)[c]	-3.29

[a] Ref. 352.   [b] At 25°C.   [c] Percentage by volume of first-named component.
[d] $k = 8.60 \times 10^{-8}$ sec.$^{-1}$ [e] Contained ~ 0.066 M lithium acetate and/or formate.

thus is troublesome to weigh accurately, and (2) it reacts extremely rapidly in highly polar solvents, making it difficult to obtain accurate rate constants at 25°. A list of **Y**-values is given in Table 2.6.

It was considered reasonable not long ago to assign all observed solvent effects on reaction rates to electrostatic interactions between the solute (initial state and transition state) and the solvent molecules. Hughes and Ingold *(353)* classified bimolecular (S_N2) and unimolecular (S_N1) into six charge types, as shown in Table 2.7. Although the predictions made on the basis of this classification are usually qualitatively correct, they do not permit sufficient understanding of the mechanism to be used *per se*. Winstein and Fainberg *(354)* were probably the first to demonstrate that a substantial portion of the change in rate of solvolysis of *t*-butyl chloride, with a solvent change from methanol to water, was due to the change in the free energy of solution of *t*-butyl chloride. The change in rate corresponded to a change in transition-state free energy difference from the initial state of −6.25 kcal./mole at 25°C (ΔΔF*) of which only −2.16 kcal./mole was due to the change in solvation of the transition state. Since the initial state is clearly less polar than the transition state, we might have expected a smaller change than that of the transition state *in the same direction* if only electrostatic interactions counted. The fact that the contribution of the initial state interaction with the solvent to the rate change on going from methanol to water is (a) larger than the contribution of the transition state and (b) in a direction opposite to that of the transition state requires a special explanation. Figs. 2.22*a* and 2.22*b* illustrate the thermodynamic cycle involved and how the activation parameters change with solvent composition in mixtures of ethanol and water for *t*-butyl chloride solvolysis.

TABLE 2.7   *Predicted Solvent Effects on Nucleophilic Replacements*[a]

Charge Type	Charge Distribution Initial State	Transition State	Change in Distribution[b]	Predicted Effect of Solvent on Rate
1	$Y^- + RX$	$Y^{\delta-}$---R---$X^{\delta-}$	Dispersed	Small decrease
2	$Y + RX$	$Y^{\delta+}$---R---$X^{\delta-}$	Increased	Large increase
3	$Y^- + RX^+$	$Y^{\delta-}$---R---$X^{\delta+}$	Reduced	Large decrease
4	$Y + RX^+$	$Y^{\delta+}$---R---$X^{\delta+}$	Dispersed	Small decrease
5	RX	$R^{\delta+}$---$X^{\delta-}$	Increased	Large increase
6	RX^+	$R^{\delta+}$---$X^{\delta+}$	Dispersed	Small decrease

[a] Adapted from Ref. 353.   [b] On proceeding from the initial state to the transition state.

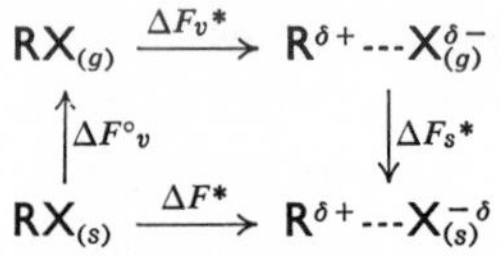

$$RX_{(g)} \xrightarrow{\Delta F_v^*} R^{\delta+}\text{---}X^{\delta-}_{(g)}$$

$$\uparrow \Delta F^\circ_v \qquad\qquad \downarrow \Delta F_s^*$$

$$RX_{(s)} \xrightarrow{\Delta F^*} R^{\delta+}\text{---}X^{-\delta}_{(s)}$$

Figure 2.22a   Thermodynamic cycle for solvolysis of *t*-butyl chloride in methanol and water (R = *t*-bu).

Fainberg and Winstein (*352*) and Hyne, Wills, and Wonkka (*355*) have emphasized the possibility that "solvent sorting" could occur in mixed solvents. Solvent sorting leads to a cybotactic region with a composition different from that of the bulk solvent. It should be emphasized that product distribution in the reaction under discussion (the solvolysis of *t*-butyl chloride) would not provide information about the solvent composition of the cybotactic region around the transition state starting from *t*-butyl chloride, but only about the transition states to product starting from the intermediate *t*-butyl carbonium ion, except in the rather unlikely circumstance that reaction of the *t*-butyl carbonium ion with the solvent in the cybotactic

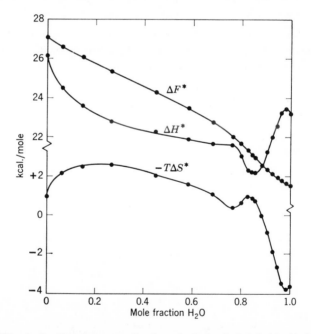

Figure 2.22b   Activation parameters for the solvolysis of *t*-butyl chloride in ethanol and water mixtures (from Ref. 354). (Reprinted with the permission of the author and the *Journal of the American Chemical Society*.)

region is so fast that this composition cannot change before the reaction occurs. Our previous discussion of relaxation processes suggests that exchanges of solvent molecules in and out of the cybotactic region are very fast but not so fast as to preclude a somewhat faster reaction of an unstable intermediate with a solvent molecule. What is not clear, however, is how solvent sorting could account for the way in which the rates, transition-state solvation energies, and ground-state solvation energies change with solvent composition. Our opinion is that solvent sorting probably does contribute to the changes observed with solvent composition but that it is not the major factor.

Arnett and his co-workers (*356, 357*) have concluded, on the basis of very careful measurements of the partial molal heat of solution of salts in mixtures of different composition, that the importance of the initial state is due to the effect of the solute on the local structure of the mixture The variation in thermodynamic parameters for the mixtures themselves has already been illustrated in Figs. 2.13 through 2.15. The added solutes contribute further changes with patterns of change that resemble those found for the two components alone. The variation of the partial molal heat of solution at infinite dilution ($\overline{H}_s$) for a series of nonelectrolytes in ethanol–water mixtures is shown in Fig. 2.23. The variation for a series of salts in ethanol–water mixtures in the value of $\overline{H}_s$ is given in Fig. 2.24. The remarkable point to be noted is that *the curves for the salts resemble those for the nonelectrolytes, except that the effects found for the nonelectrolytes are greater.* "Larger" salts yield curves which resemble those of the nonelectrolytes (Fig. 2.25). (Sodium tetraphenylboride should really have been included with the "large" salts.)

The heats of solution of the initial and transition states for *t*-butyl chloride in ethanol–water mixtures are presented in Fig. 2.26. The solvent effect on the heat of solution follows the Hughes–Ingold expectation for the transition states (Table 2.7), but it is clearly much smaller than would have been anticipated for the transition states and confusing because of the relative magnitudes of the heats of solution for the initial and transition states. The contrast with the partial molal heat of solution for the transition state for the solvolysis of methyl benzenesulfonate (data of Hyne and Robertson, *358,* as modified by Arnett and co-workers, *356*) is very striking (Fig. 2.27), since the data for the methyl derivative cover a larger range of heats of solution than the heat of solution for the transition state of *t*-butyl chloride. Although the entropy contribution to the formation of the transition state largely compensates for the deviations of $\overline{H}_s$ from being a smooth function of composition, we should not expect that there would be a fixed relationship

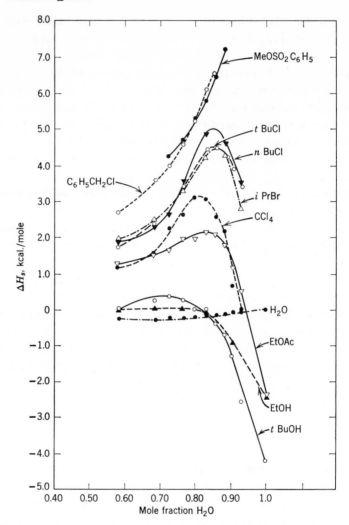

Figure 2.23 The variation in the partial molal heat of solution ($\overline{H}_s$) with the composition of ethanol–water mixtures for a series of nonelectrolytes (Ref. 356).

between the heat and entropy of solution of the transition states. Hyne, Golinkin, and Laidlaw (*364*) have found that the volume of activation for the solvolysis of *t*-butyl chloride in a series of ethanol–water mixtures reaches a maximum at about 0.3 mole fraction ethanol, in contrast to the location of the extremes for ΔH^* and ΔS^* at approximately 0.1 mole fraction ethanol (Figs. 2.22 and 2.26). The volume of activation, ΔV^*, is derived from measurements of the effect of pressure on the rate of reaction and presumably would affect ΔS^* more than ΔH^*. The smooth change of ΔF^* with solvent composition is often observed but is not a general rule, and the precise rules governing the relationship of ΔH^* and ΔS^* cannot be formulated until we know a great deal more about solvent structure, especially in mixed solvents, and the species for which we would like the rules.

In an attempt to understand in detail the molecular process of the solvolysis

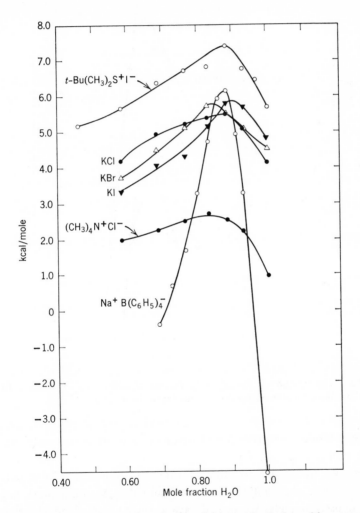

Figure 2.24 The variation in the partial molal heat of solution with composition of ethanol–water mixtures for a number of salts (Ref. 356). (All three figures reprinted with the permission of the author and the *Journal of the American Chemical Society.*)

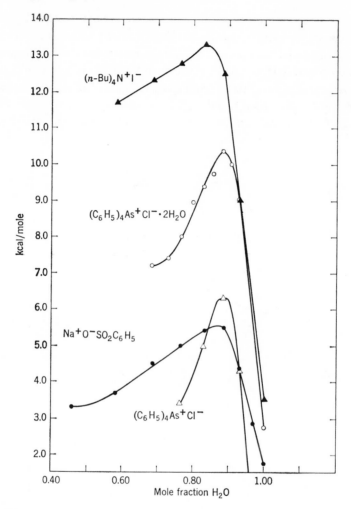

Figure 2.25 The variation in the partial molal heat of solution ($\overline{H}_s$) with solvent composition for ethanol–water mixtures for a number of large salts (Ref. 356).

of *t*-butyl chloride, we have found that simple views of solvation do not provide sufficient insight for us to be certain about our choice of cases for which we would like to utilize **Y**-values as empirical solvent polarity parameters. The thermodynamic data imply that **Y**-values must not be utilized indiscriminately. We should have a whole range of model solvolytic processes and automated techniques for measuring the required rate constants (*359*).

Model processes of many kinds can be utilized for the purpose of defining solvent polarity parameters, a subject which has been reviewed by Reichardt (*349*). Allerhand and Schleyer (*360*) studied solvent effects on the frequencies absorbed by hydrogen bonds in the infrared and proposed that G-values based on these data be utilized as solvent polarity parameters. Taft and co-workers (*43, 46*) have described the effect of solvent on the chemical shift of fluorine in fluorobenzenes as measured by n.m.r. The degree of shielding of

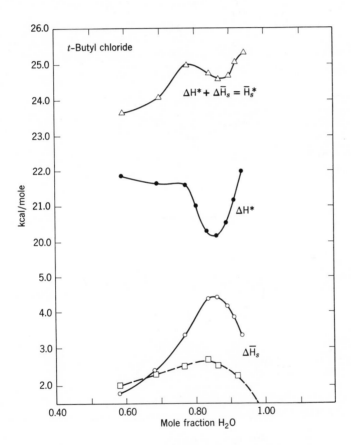

Figure 2.26 Enthalpy contributions to the ground state and transition state of *t*-butyl chloride in ethanol–water mixtures. The dashed line at the bottom is for tetramethyl-ammonium chloride. The uppermost curve represents the partial molal heat of solution for the transition state (Ref. 356). (Compare with Fig. 2.22*a*.) (Reprinted with the permission of the author and the *Journal of the American Chemical Society*.)

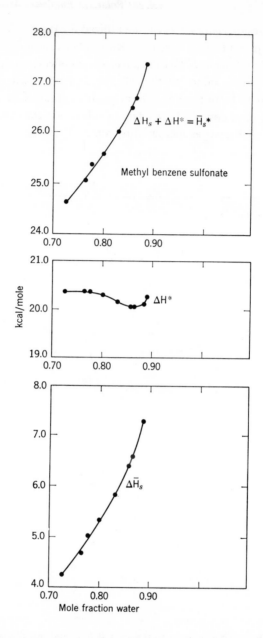

Figure 2.27 Partial molal heats of solution for the transition state and initial state of methyl benzenesulfonate. The variation of the heat of activation with solvent composition (ethanol–water mixture) is also shown (Ref. 356). (Reprinted with the permission of the author and the *Journal of the American Chemical Society*.)

the fluorine appears to be a sensitive function of the exact local environment of the fluorine, and the chemical shifts observed might provide the basis for a special kind of solvent polarity parameter. Berson and co-workers (*346*) suggested that the *exo/endo* ratio of the products formed in the reaction of cyclopentadiene and methyl acrylate is sufficiently sensitive to the nature of the solvent to be used as the basis for Ω-values. In spite of a reasonably good correlation of Ω-values with **Z**-values and the whimsical notion that ". . . a set of solvents behaves like an elephant, which can lift a log or a peanut with equal dexterity," our strictures on the use of model processes imply that Ω-values should be used only for the correlation of $[2 + 4]$ cycloadditions.

Smith, Fainberg, and Winstein (*361*) put forward the rates of ionization of *p*-methoxyneophyl tosylate (**364**) as a chemical reaction suitable for measuring solvent polarity even in fairly nonpolar solvents. However, acid-catalyzed reactions in the most nonpolar solvents used require the measurement of initial rates, and the general usefulness of k_{ion}, as the solvent parameter was called, is not clear.

364

Dubois, Goetz, and Bienvenue (*362*) formulated F-values as solvent polarity parameters based on the positions of the solvent-sensitive $n \rightarrow \pi^*$ transitions of certain aliphatic ketones. The S-values of Brownstein (*363*), which are really averages of a variety of different solvent polarity parameters including **Z** and **Y**, cannot be regarded seriously since they cannot be related to a specific model process.

Herbrandson and Neufeld (*367*) suggested that the Hildebrand–Scott solubility parameter, δ (cf. *368*) be used as a general measure of solvent effects. The parameter is defined as the square root of the molal energy of vaporization per molal volume of liquid $(-E/V^l)^{1/2}$. This parameter is thus based on the use of a solvent molecule as the probe in the cybotactic region and, in spite of the reported correlations, could not be applicable to many problems involving solutes.

Problems

1. Define radial distribution function.
2. Define clathrate compound. Are there practical or technical consequences of clathrate hydrate formation? (*Hint:* desalination, anesthesia.)
3. Draw a plausible structure for liquid acetic acid. How would the cybotactic region around ethyl tosylate look at the initial state or at the transition state?
4. Phosphoric and sulfuric acids exhibit abnormally high proton conductances. Draw structures which rationalize this fact for the pure liquids.
5. Using Fig. 2.15 as a guide, draw structures for the molecular combinations existing in alcohol–water mixtures at the mole fraction for which the greatest heat evolution occurs.
6. Define the following:
   (a) Model process.
   (b) Reference process.
   (c) Z-value.
   (d) Y-value.
   (e) Dipole flip.
   (f) $E_T(30)$-values.
   (g) Solvent sorting.
7. Give the absorption maximum for the charge-transfer band of 1-ethyl-4-carbomethoxypyridinium iodide (214) in cyclopropyl methyl ketone, acetonitrile, formamide, and water.
8. Give the molecular basis of (a) Z-values, (b) Y-values, (c) Ω-values.
9. Does solvent sorting around the transition state for ionization of *t*-butyl chloride account for the fact that the composition of the products of solvolysis in an alcohol–water mixture is different from that expected from the gross composition of the mixture?
10. What fact about salts makes more palatable the fact that the heats of solutions of salts in ethanol–water mixtures are comparable to or less than the heats of solution of nonelectrolytes?
11. Account for the change in the heat of solution of *t*-butyl chloride with variation in the composition of ethanol–water mixtures in molecular terms.
12. Comment on the statement that a solvent is like an elephant, able to lift a log or a peanut with equal dexterity.

2.7 Applications of Solvent Polarity Parameters

Correlation of a process or property with a solvent polarity parameter actually reflects a similarity between the process or property and the *model process* used to define the parameter (see Section 2.6). To the extent that we understand why the model process responds to solvent change, we may infer something about why the process or property we are interested in changes with solvent. In this section we shall indicate a few of the common kinds of correlation with empirical solvent polarity parameters.

Consider the solvolysis of *t*-butyl chloride in a series of solvents, A, B, C, . . . for which a free energy versus reaction coordinate diagram is shown in Fig. 2.28. The curves shown in the figure illustrate the free energy relationships of the initial state and transition state which lead to the solvent sensitivity expressed in the form of **Y**-values. Grunwald and Winstein (*338*) formulated an equation for correlations of solvolysis rates as shown in Eq. 48. Using

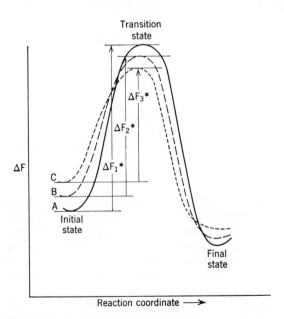

Figure 2.28 Free energy versus reaction coordinate diagram for the solvolysis of a molecule like *t*-butyl chloride in a series of solvents A, B, C, ... The effect of the solvent on the initial state is not necessarily ordered in the way indicated, but it is a function of how the halide fits into the solvent structure.

this equation, the rates of solvolysis of alkyl halides may be compared with those of *t*-butyl chloride in the form of **Y**-values.

$$(48) \qquad\qquad \log k/k_0 = m\mathbf{Y}$$

The slope of the correlation line, m, is a convenient way of expressing whether a particular alkyl halide exhibits a rate of solvolysis which is more solvent dependent or less solvent dependent than that of *t*-butyl chloride. If we examine the m values for a group of halides in ethanol–water mixtures, we find that even the small change from chloride to bromide produces a change in m from 1.000 (*t*-butyl chloride) to 0.941 (*t*-butyl bromide). Furthermore, we can see from the m values shown in Table 2.8 that the m value for a given halide is not constant but varies with the nature of the solvent pair. Winstein and his co-workers have referred to this failure of all points to fall on the

TABLE 2.8   *m-Values for Alkyl Halide Solvolysis*[a]

Compound	Solvent Mixtures[b]	m	Ref.
1-Phenylethyl chloride	10–100% C_2H_5OH—H_2O	0.966	369
	50–100% CH_3OH—H_2O	0.912	369
	0–16 M H_2O in CH_3COOH	1.136	369
	0–100% CH_3COOH—$HCOOH$	1.194	369
	10–90% dioxane—H_2O	1.136	369
1-Phenylethyl bromide	40–100% C_2H_5OH—H_2O	0.817	370
	50–100% CH_3OH—H_2O	0.843	370
	0–8 M H_2O in CH_3COOH	1.245	370
	30–90% dioxane—H_2O	1.014	370
t-Butyl bromide	40–100% C_2H_5OH—H_2O	0.941	370
	60–100% CH_3OH—H_2O	0.947	370
	0–100% CH_3COOH—$HCOOH$	0.946	370
	0–8 M H_2O in CH_3COOH	1.067	370
	40–90% dioxane—H_2O	0.921	370
Benzhydryl chloride	80–100% C_2H_5OH—H_2O	0.740	371
	90–100% CH_3OH—H_2O	0.820	371
	60–90% dioxane—H_2O	1.049	371
	0–4 M H_2O in CH_3COOH	1.561	371
Benzhydryl bromide	0–4 M H_2O in CH_3COOH	1.687	371
Trityl fluoride	40–100% C_2H_5OH—H_2O	0.890	371
	40–70% $(CH_3)_2CO$—H_2O	1.58	371
Triphenylsilyl fluoride	50–83.4% $(CH_3)_2CO$—H_2O	0.468	371

[a] At 25.0°C.   [b] Percentages by volume of first-named component.

same correlation line as "dispersion" and has ascribed its occurrence to the fact that a different blend of general and specific solvent influences interacts with the solute for each solvent pair. "Dispersion" is illustrated for 1-phenyl-ethyl chloride in Fig. 2.29.

In our discussion of *t*-butyl chloride solvolysis, we have pointed out that the major portion of the change in rate on changing solvent from methanol to water was due to a change in the free energy of the initial state. For the usual alkyl halide, the largest part of the free energy change of the initial state must be due to a change in the cybotactic region structure with additional components due to electrostatic interaction and mutual polarization. We might expect therefore that the change in the free energy of the initial

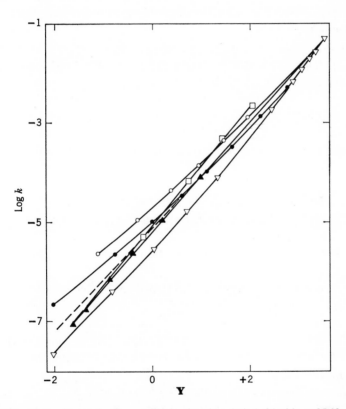

Figure 2.29 Plots of log k for the solvolysis of 1-phenylethyl chloride at 25.0° versus Y in C_2H_5OH—H_2O, ●; CH_3OH—H_2O, ○; dioxane—H_2O, ▽; CH_3COOH—H_2O, ▼; CH_3COOH—$HCOOH$, □. The dashed line is the least squares line for all of the data (from Ref. 369). (Reprinted with permission of the authors and the *Journal of the American Chemical Society*.)

state of an alkyl halide will never be exactly the same as that of *t*-butyl chloride for a given solvent change. Similar remarks apply to the transition states for which the electrostatic term is much more important. On these grounds, we might have been so pessimistic as to predict that no correlation of alkyl halide solvolysis with **Y**-values would have been found. As Fig. 2.29 demonstrates, such correlation is frequently found. We conclude that the chief element of the solvent involved in the solute-solvent interaction is the region immediately around the reaction site, that is, the *local cybotactic region*, and that this local region is modified by the remainder of the solute molecule in a way which depends upon the size and nature of the groups in the solute molecule and the nature and size of the solvent molecule or molecules. The "dispersion" observed by Fainberg and Winstein (*369, 370*) as well as by Kosower (Fig. 2.20, *216*) for plots against **Y**-values is quite understandable in these terms.

Experience with m**Y** correlations suggests that they are useful (a) for predicting rates in solvents for which direct rate determinations would be inconvenient or impossible, (b) for reaching qualitative conclusions about mechanisms of solvolysis reactions, and (c) as a means for evaluating subtle substituent effects in closely related compounds in solvolysis reactions. The **Y**-values, as well as the **Z**- and $E_T(30)$-values, provide a rational method for ordering solvents for any purpose even in the absence of good correlations with the solvent polarity parameter.

We can illustrate the estimation of a rate which would be too slow to measure conveniently by the use of a plot of **Z** against **Y** for pure solvents (Fig. 2.30) (*372*). Although the correlation is certainly not linear, it does appear to be a smooth curve which might be extrapolated to benzene (**Z** = 54). The rate thus estimated for *t*-butyl chloride ionization in benzene at $25.0°$ is 1×10^{-10} sec.$^{-1}$.

In addition to the applications mentioned for m**Y** correlations, **Z**-values (and often, $E_T(30)$-values) are useful for (a) identifying anomalous solvent effects on rate constants or electronic transitions (b) identification of electronic transitions and (c) prediction of the position of light absorption in solvents for which it is impossible or inconvenient to carry out the experimental measurement.

The quaternization of alkyl iodides is often referred to as an example of a solvent-sensitive reaction, one which would correspond to charge type 2 in Table 2.7. A large increase in rate is predicted for an increase in solvent polarity for this reaction. In fact, specific interactions of the leaving iodide ion with a number of solvents like acetone and benzonitrile cause the rate in

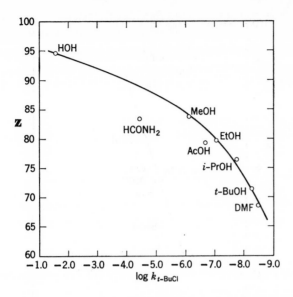

Figure 2.30 A plot of **Z**-values against the log $k_{t\text{-BuCl}}$ ($\equiv$ **Y**-value -5.033) for a series of pure solvents (Ref. 372). (By permission of the *Journal of the American Chemical Society*.)

these solvents to be particularly high and obscure what is actually a moderate solvent sensitivity. A plot of the log of the rate of the reaction of pyridine with ethyl iodide in a series of alcohols against **Z**-value indicates a modest solvent sensitivity (Fig. 2.31). The point for acetone suggests that the rate in acetone is anomalous. Acetone is an aprotic dipolar solvent (see Section 2.9). The modest solvent sensitivity of the quaternization reaction implies either that there is not a great deal of charge development in the transition state or that solvent structural effects (which would minimize the role of charge separation) dominate the solute-solvent interaction or both. The student may be interested in comparing the foregoing discussion with the more classical approach described by Wiberg (*373*).

   Identification of an electronic transition in organic molecules is usually based on absorption intensity and solvent effect. Substituent effects are also used but are more difficult to interpret except for some cases (for example, α,β-unsaturated ketones and the Woodward rules). In addition, it is necessary to synthesize several compounds in order to evaluate a substituent effect. An illustration of the effect expected for a series of solvents, A, B, C, D . . . on electronic transitions in which the excited state has a greater polarity (or

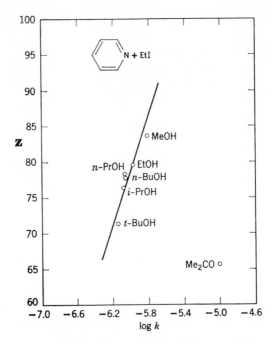

Figure 2.31 A plot of Z-value against log k for the reaction of pyridine and ethyl iodide in a series of alcoholic solvents and acetone (Ref. 372). (By permission of the *Journal of the American Chemical Society*.)

charge separation) than the ground state is given in Fig. 2.32. The important point made in this figure is that modest interaction of the solvent with the ground state in solvent D precludes the maximum possible interaction in the excited state because the electronic transition occurs much more rapidly than nuclear motion.

A brief review of the electronic transitions expected in molecules like acetone, ethylene, and mesityl oxide is now given to provide an appropriate context within which to place the discussion of solvent effects. The energy levels for acetone are indicated in Fig. 2.33. (The alkyl groups are omitted, making the diagram quite general for unconjugated carbonyl groups.) In the ground state (lower left of figure), the lowest orbital is the bonding σ. At the right of the level, occupied by two electrons, is a small orbital diagram showing the direction and signs of the orbitals that interact to form the bond. At the left of the level is a notation that indicates the signs and the direction of the orbitals of the σ-bond. As long as we do not mistake any of the signs as

Solvent

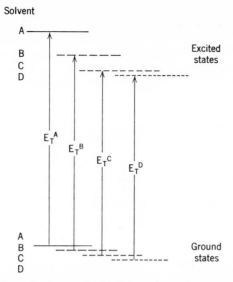

Figure 2.32 The effect of solvents (A, B, C, D, ...) on the transition energies for an electronic transition. The small difference between the levels shown for the solvents C and D in the excited state is due to the operation of the Franck–Condon principle.

indicating an *s*-orbital, this compact notation serves to tell us a great deal about the bond. (It is a condensed form of this notation, which was used in the discussion of isopolar reactions, Sections 1.8–1.9.) The second lowest level is occupied by the electrons of the π-bond. The *p–p* overlap, which leads to the π-bond, is not as effective as the overlap of the orbitals in the σ-bond. Less energy is therefore given up when the bond is formed and the level lies higher than that of the σ-bond. Compact notation for the π-bond is shown at the left of the level. Roughly speaking, the nonbonding electrons of the third oxygen *p*-orbital have not lost any energy at all and are located at a much higher level than the electrons in the π-bond. (We have shown the third oxygen orbital as *p*, although some authors have felt that it is better to consider the oxygen electrons as being in hybrid orbitals, with two pairs in sp^2-orbitals.)

If a photon of the appropriate energy strikes the acetone molecule, it may cause an *electronic transition* in which a nonbonding electron is promoted to the lowest empty orbital, the π^*-orbital. This transition is called an $n \rightarrow \pi^*$ transition and occurs at about 2789 A in hexane for acetone. If a more energetic photon is encountered by the molecule, a $\pi \rightarrow \pi^*$ transition may occur. For acetone, the $\pi \rightarrow \pi^*$ transition occurs at about 1500 A. A lower energy $n \rightarrow \sigma^*$ transition may also occur at 1800 A for acetone. The excited

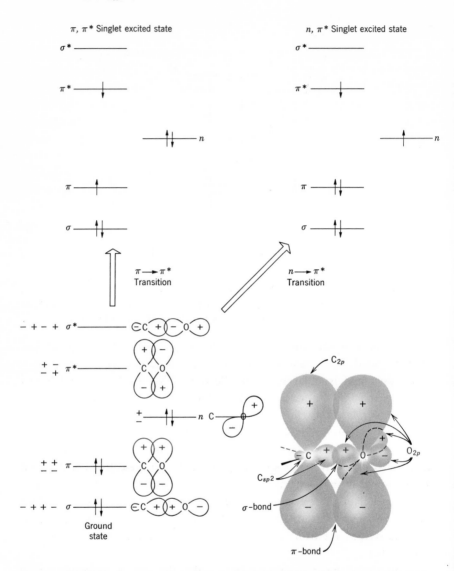

Figure 2.33 Energy levels and orbital notations for the carbonyl group. Electronic transitions to the *n, π** and *π, π** singlet excited states are shown.

states which are formed most readily arise via transitions which involve no change in multiplicity, that is, in the number of unpaired spins in the molecule. Thus, the *n,π** excited state formed by light absorption at 2865 A is a singlet state.

Energy level diagrams are shown for ethylene and mesityl oxide, $(CH_3)_2C{=}CHCOCH_3$, in Fig. 2.34. Only the π-orbitals have been indicated for mesityl oxide. The lowest energy electronic transition predicted for ethylene on the basis of the levels shown is $\pi \to \pi^*$, and this was generally accepted to be the case until the work of Robin, Hart, and Kuebler (*374*) supplied strong evidence that a weak band lying at longer wavelengths than the first strong absorption band of ethylene was $\pi \to CH^*$. (CH* represents a σ^* largely localized on the carbon–hydrogen bonds.) The arguments for the assignment are too complex to enter into in this book but imply that the simple diagrams shown in Figs. 2.33 and 2.34, with their completely independent π and σ-orbitals are too simple to explain the energy levels of real molecules. The spectra of tetramethylethylene at room temperature and at 23°K are shown in Fig. 2.35 to illustrate (a) the relative positions of the $\pi \to CH^*$ band and the strong $\pi \to \pi^*$ band, (b) the weakness of the $\pi \to CH^*$ transition in comparison to the $\pi \to \pi^*$ transition, and (c) the temperature effect on the $\pi \to CH^*$ band (movement to shorter wavelengths) which

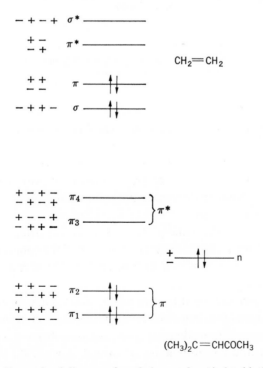

Figure 2.34 Energy level diagrams for ethylene and mesityl oxide (ground states only).

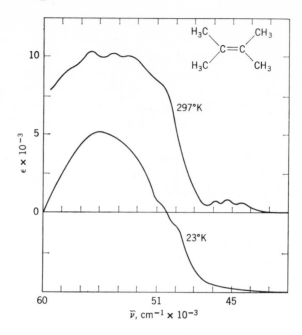

Figure 2.35 The spectrum of tetramethylethylene at 297° and 23°K. The upper spectrum is that of the vapor while the lower curve is that of a thin film in which the intensity of the curve has been adjusted to correspond to the $\pi \rightarrow \pi^*$ transition of the upper curve (Ref. 374). (By permission of the authors and the *Journal of Chemical Physics*.)

distinguishes it from the $\pi \rightarrow \pi^*$ transition. The CH* orbital as noted above arises from the σ^*-orbitals of the bonds to the carbons of the double bond mixed with some bonding character from the bond between the two carbons of the double bond. In spite of the oversimplification introduced by the diagrams, they are useful in discerning the main transitions to be expected in molecules of fair complexity.

Except for the *n* level, the π and π^* orbitals of mesityl oxide look like the π and π^* levels of butadiene. The oxygen at the end of the conjugated system in mesityl oxide, however, causes a drift of charge toward itself, especially in the excited states.

Let us first try to predict what kind of solvent effect might be expected for the $n \rightarrow \pi^*$ transitions of carbonyl compounds. In an unconjugated carbonyl compound, an $n \rightarrow \pi^*$ transition takes an electron from a nonbonding orbital on oxygen into an antibonding π^*-orbital (Fig. 2.33). The vacancy left in the nonbonding orbital is equivalent to a positive charge and the electron in π^*-orbital places excess negative charge between the carbon and oxygen. We can formulate the situation as:

$$\diagdown \!\!\!\! \underset{\diagup}{C}\!\!=\!\!O \xrightarrow{n \to \pi^*} \diagdown \!\!\!\! \underset{\diagup}{C} \!\!\overset{\cdot\cdot}{=}\!\! \bar{O} \,+$$

The ground state of acetone is polarized with a dipole moment of 2.83 D, and interacts with polar solvents in a way which places a net solvent dipole parallel to the dipole of the ketone. The excited state has a lower dipole moment than the ground state. [In the case of formaldehyde, the equilibrium excited state has a dipole moment of 1.56 D, while the ground state has a dipole moment of 2.34 D (*375*). It is likely that the Franck–Condon n,π^* state has a lower dipole moment than the equilibrium excited state. In the case of propynal (HC≡CCHO), the n,π^* excited state has a dipole moment of ca. 0.7 D in contrast to the ground state dipole moment of 2.39 D (*470*).] In addition, depending on the details of the interaction between the solvent and the carbonyl group, the excited state may be somewhat destabilized by the proximity of the positive charge in the n-orbital and the positive end of the solvent dipole.

(50)
$$C\!\!=\!\!O\cdots\overset{\delta+}{H}\!\!-\!\!\overset{\delta-}{S} \xrightarrow{n \to \pi^*} C\!\!\overset{\cdot\cdot}{=}\!\!\overset{-}{O}{}^+\cdots\overset{\delta+}{H}\!\!-\!\!\overset{\delta-}{S}$$

Both factors imply that the $n \to \pi^*$ transition would be disfavored by increased solvent polarity because the ground state would be stabilized more than the excited state. In fact, it is characteristic of carbonyl $n \to \pi^*$ transitions that the absorption band moves to shorter wavelengths if the solvent is made more polar. In many cases, the transition energy correlates with the solvent polarity parameter, the **Z**-value, as illustrated for cyclobutanone, cyclopentanone, and cyclohexanone in Fig. 2.36. The $n \to \pi^*$ transition for cyclopentanone occurs at 3001 A in isooctane and at 2808 A in water (*344*). It may be noted in Fig. 2.36 that the solvent sensitivity of the $n \to \pi^*$ transition of cyclobutanone is less than half of that of cyclopentanone.

The $\pi \to \pi^*$ transition of a simple carbonyl compound is at such short wavelengths that solvent effects have not been observed, but conjugation lowers the lowest empty π^* level and in a ketone like mesityl oxide, the $\pi \to \pi^*$ transition is the strongest and most characteristic feature of the absorption spectrum. Mesityl oxide has a dipole moment of 2.80 D in the ground state, but consists of a mixture of *s-cis* and *s-trans*-forms (**365a** and **365b**). Promotion of an electron from the highest filled π-state to the lowest unfilled π^* state places a polarizable electron at the mercy of an electronegative oxygen. The positive charge left in the π_2-orbital is relatively less

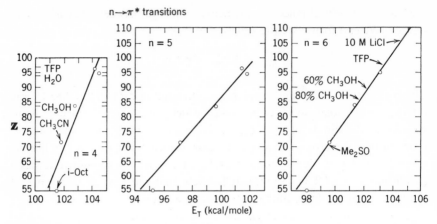

Figure 2.36 Z-values versus E_T, transition energies for the $n \to \pi^*$ transitions of cyclobutanone ($n = 4$), cyclopentanone ($n = 5$), and cyclohexanone ($n = 6$). The solvents are indicated on the figure, with TFP = 2,2,3,3-tetrafluoropropanol-1 and *i*-oct. = isooctane. The arrows on the correlation line for cyclohexanone indicate that Z-values were derived for the solvents so designated by measurement of the position of the $n \to \pi^*$ transition for cyclohexanone. The Z-value for isooctane is estimated as 53 (Ref. 344). (By permission of the *Journal of the American Chemical Society*.)

important than the positive charge left in the *n*-orbital in the $n \to \pi^*$ transition because there are three other π-electrons to shield the charge in comparison to one other *n*-electron.

We would thus expect the π,π^*-excited state of mesityl oxide would be more stabilized by polar solvents than the ground state, and that the $\pi \to \pi^*$ transition would move to longer wavelengths in more polar solvents. We might also express the capacity of the mesityl oxide system to accommodate positive charge with the resonance form **366**.

Since the position of the lowest π^* orbital in mesityl oxide is considerably below that of the π^*-orbital in acetone, we might expect the $n \rightarrow \pi^*$ transition to be shifted to longer wavelengths. Indeed, the $n \rightarrow \pi^*$ transition does occur at longer wavelengths (λ_{max} 3210 (ϵ 38) in isooctane) than that of acetone but the shift to longer wavelengths is far less than that observed for the $\pi \rightarrow \pi^*$ transition. Both $n \rightarrow \pi^*$ and $\pi \rightarrow \pi^*$ transitions show a reasonably good correlation with Z-values (Fig. 2.37). It is not possible to measure the position of the $n \rightarrow \pi^*$ transition for mesityl oxide in water because it is submerged beneath the much stronger absorption band of the $\pi \rightarrow \pi^*$ transition. The correlation with Z permits the position of the $n \rightarrow \pi^*$ absorption band to be estimated with reasonable confidence. A practical instance in which such information might be desired would be to check the appearance of a Cotton effect (ORD) or a circular dichroic maximum (CD) in an optically active α,β-unsaturated ketone.

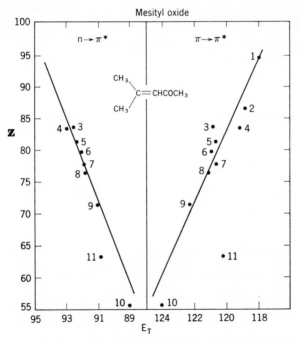

Figure 2.37 Right half: Z-values versus E_T (transition energies in kcal./mole) for the $\pi \rightarrow \pi^*$ transition of mesityl oxide, with λ_{max} 2306 A (ϵ 11900) in isooctane, estimated Z-value 53. Left half: Z-values versus the E_T for the $n \rightarrow \pi^*$ transition of mesityl oxide. The solvents are: 1 (water), 2 (2,2,3,3-tetrafluoropropanol-1), 3 (methanol), 4 (ethylene glycol), 5 (95% ethanol), 6 (ethanol), 7 (1-butanol), 8 (2-propanol), 9 (acetonitrile), 10 (isooctane), and 11 (chloroform with 0.13 M ethanol) (Ref. 347). (By permission of the *Journal of the American Chemical Society*.)

Closson and Haug (*376*) have examined the $n \to \pi^*$ transitions of carboxylate esters in different solvents and have found that these respond to a change in solvent polarity in a manner which resembles that of simple ketones. Methyl acetate, for example, has an absorption maximum at 2097 A (ϵ 57) in isooctane, at 2072 A (ϵ 57) in ethanol and at 2026 A (ϵ 61) in water. They also discovered that the size of the alkyl group had a definite effect on the position of the $n \to \pi^*$ transition. The larger the alkyl group, the longer the wavelength observed for the maximum. In isooctane, the maximum for *t*-butyl acetate occurs at 2162 A (ϵ 53). Comparison of the $n \to \pi^*$ transitions for 1-propyl acetate and 1-(2,2,3,3-tetrafluoropropyl) acetate demonstrated that an inductive effect was not responsible for the shift in maximum for *t*-butyl acetate, the two esters having maxima in isooctane at 2097 A and 2098 A. The effect has been identified by Closson and Haug as steric in origin, arising from repulsion between the carbonyl electrons and the *t*-butyl group. A particularly clear example of the operation of steric effects on $n \to \pi^*$ transitions may be seen for azoalkanes, as indicated by the maxima listed for **367**, **368**, **369**, **370**, **371**, and **372**. For other examples, see *333*. (The maxima are not sensitive to solvent.)

		$\lambda_{max}(\epsilon_{max})$	Reference
367	$CH_3N{=}NCH_3$	3500 (25)*	377
368	$CH_3CH_2CH_2N{=}NCH_2CH_3$	3595 (16)	378
369	$(CH_3)_3CN{=}NC(CH_3)_3$	3675 (14)	379

| **370** | 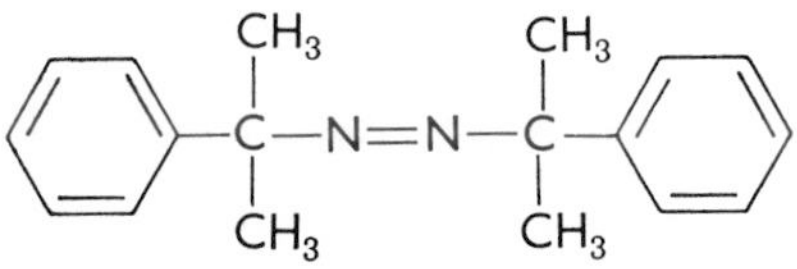 | 3670 (44) | 161 |

| **371** | 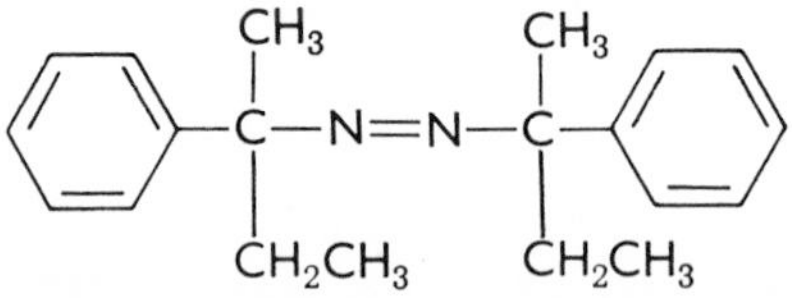 | 3750 (38) | 380 |

| **372** | 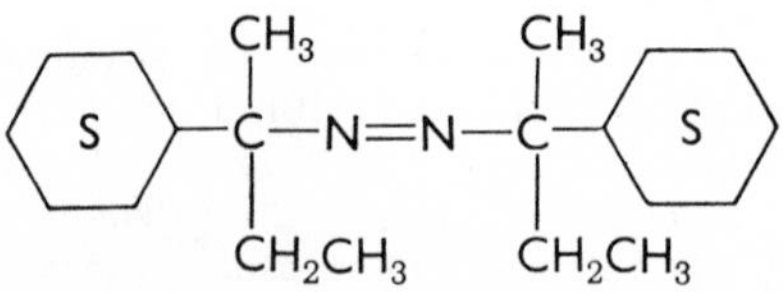 | 3815 (20) | 379 |

* In methyl chloride at $-40°C$.

The $n \rightarrow \pi^*$ transition in α,β-unsaturated esters was identified by its low intensity and its shift to shorter wavelengths with increasing solvent polarity. Ethyl acrylate has a maximum at 2430 A (ϵ 70) in isooctane which shifts to 2391 A (ϵ 92) in acetonitrile (*381*). The *t*-butyl ester of acrylic acid has an $n \rightarrow \pi^*$ transition which can be observed in a wider range of solvents than the ester, with λ_{max} 2497 A (ϵ 55) in isooctane and 2434 A (ϵ 64) in methanol. Comparison with **Z**-values shows a roughly linear correlation (*382*).

A new type of electronic transition, first found for double bonds with a certain relationship to a carbonyl group by Labhart and Wagniere (*383*), was confirmed for the molecule *trans*-5-cyclodecenone, **373**, by means of the shift to longer wavelengths induced by a change to more polar solvents (*384*). The shift was expected on the basis of the postulated charge development in the excited state. Although the Franck–Condon principle would preclude a substantial change with solvent polarity, the increase in negative charge in the region of the oxygen of the carbonyl group could lead to an increase of the interaction with the solvent already organized by the ground state dipole (**374**).

The spectroscopic shift for the solvent change from isooctane to 2,2,3,3-tetrafluoropropanol-1 is illustrated in Fig. 2.38. Wharton (*385*) later applied the same criterion to 6-methyl-5-cyclodecenone (**375**) to prove that the double bond was *trans*. He found λ_{max} 2270 A (ϵ 2750) in 2,2,3,3-tetrafluoropropanol-1 [for **165**, λ_{max} 2145 A (2300)] and 2210 A (ϵ 3050) in the less polar methanol. It should be noted that the *cis* compound related to 373 does not exhibit the special "transannular" transition which has been called a *photodesmotic* transition (*384*). (Photodesmotic implies bond formation through light absorption.)

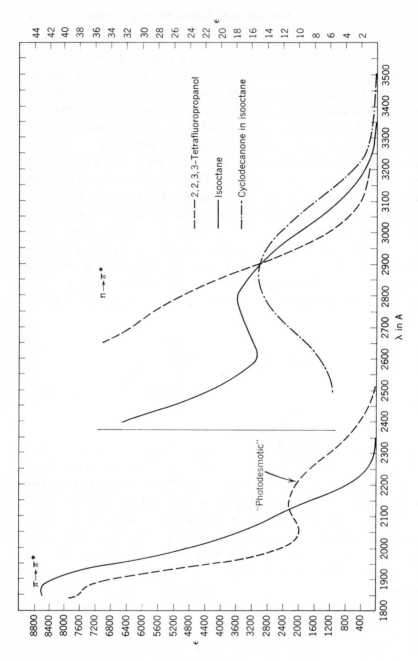

Figure 2.38 Absorption curves for *trans*-5-cyclodecanone in 2,2,3,3-tetrafluoropropanol-1 and isooctane. On the left is the region associated with the $\pi \rightarrow \pi^*$ transition for the isolated double bond and the photodesmotic transition. On the right is the region of the $n \rightarrow \pi^*$ transition. A curve for the $n \rightarrow \pi^*$ transition of cyclodecanone in isooctane is included as reference (Ref. 384). (By permission of the *Journal of the American Chemical Society*.)

Solvent effects have been used to confirm identification of $n \to \sigma^*$ transitions in halomethanes (*386, 387*).

Only a few selected illustrations of the use of solvent effects have been given. It is to be expected that much more use will be made of empirical solvent polarity parameters like the **Y**-, **Z**-, and $E_T(30)$-values as their range of validity and their usefulness becomes more widely known.

Problems

1. Give an explanation in molecular terms for the phenomenon of "dispersion" in correlations of either kinetic or spectroscopic data with solvent polarity parameters.
2. Illustrate with examples the following applications of solvent polarity parameters (examples may be sought in the literature):
   (a) Prediction of a rate.
   (b) Estimation of a spectroscopic absorption maximum.
   (c) Evidence for a mechanism.
   (d) Identification of an electronic transition.
3. Explain the following:
   (a) $n \to \pi^*$ transition.
   (b) $\pi \to \pi^*$ transition.
   (c) $\pi \to CH^*$ transition.
   (d) Photodesmotic transition.
   (e) $n \to \sigma^*$ transition.
4. Give an example of a steric effect on an electronic transition. (The steric effect may operate in either ground or excited state. Explain which state is affected the most in the example you give.)

2.8 Aprotic Dipolar Solvents

Aprotic dipolar solvents may be defined as those composed of molecules with a substantial dipole moment arising from charge separation within a group of two or three atoms. *Aprotic* molecules lack a hydrogen capable of ionization or hydrogen bonding under neutral conditions. Some of these solvents, including those which are commonly used, are listed in Table 2.9.

TABLE 2.9 *Aprotic Dipolar Solvents*

Compound	μ^a (Debyes)	Z-value[b] (kcal./mole)
Sulfur dioxide	1.62[d]	—[g]
Dimethylsulfoxide	4.3	71.1
Tetrahydrothiophene dioxide (sulfolane)	4.69	77.5
Pyridine-1-oxide[c]	4.24[f]	—
Nitrobenzene	3.99	~65.6[h]
Nitromethane	3.54[e]	~71.5[h]
Acetonitrile	3.37	71.3
Benzonitrile	4.39[e]	~65.5[h]
Dimethylformamide	3.82	68.5
Dimethylacetamide	3.79	66.9
1-Methyl-2-pyrrolidone		—
Acetone	2.72	65.7
Trimethylphosphine oxide		—
Hexamethylphosphoramide		62.8
Ethylene carbonate	4.87[i]	—[j]

[a] Ref. 389. [b] See Table 2.4. [c] m.p. 66°C. [d] Ref. 390. [e] Ref. 391. [f] Ref. 300. [g] The value reported (78.3) is probably incorrect, since the absorption coefficient for the supposed charge-transfer band is far higher than that found for pyridinium iodide charge-transfer bands in all other solvents. The most likely explanation for the absorption is that it is due to triiodide ion, I_3^-, Ref. 392. [h] From the $E_T(30)$ versus Z relationship in Fig. 2.21. [i] Ref. 433. [j] Delpuech (*434*) has used the $E_T(30)$ for propylene carbonate as a measure of solvent polarity.

The concentrated charges in the molecule of an aprotic dipolar solvent permit relatively strong interactions with solute molecules, especially those that are charged. In all cases, the negatively charged end of the solvent molecule dipole is the one which is more exposed to the molecular environment, and the strongest interactions of aprotic dipolar solvents occur with cations. The positive end of the solvent molecule dipole is much less accessible to approaching molecules than, for example, the exposed hydrogen atom of water. Anions, therefore, are less solvated (that is, far less involved in solvent molecule-anion interactions) in aprotic dipolar solvents than in protic solvents. *The decreased solvation of anions in aprotic dipolar solvents results in an increased reactivity* of anions (relative to reactivity in hydrogen-bonding solvents) towards atoms sensitive to the amount of charge concentrated in the attacking species. The change in reactivity is large enough in many cases to be called spectacular.

We must emphasize that decreased solvation of an anion in an aprotic dipolar solvent does not necessarily mean decreased solubility of the salt in the solvent. Potassium iodide, for example, is more soluble in dimethylformamide than in methanol (see Table II, *388*). Solubility equilibria in water and dimethylsulfoxide (DMSO) are compared in Eqs. 51 and 52.

(51) $$M^+X^-_{(solid)} \rightleftharpoons M^+X^-_{(H_2O)} \rightleftharpoons M^+_{(H_2O)} + X^-_{(H_2O)}$$

$$[Solid/crystal] \overset{*}{\rightleftharpoons} \left[\begin{array}{ccc} Ion\text{-}pair \\ (ionic\ aggregates) & & ions \end{array} \right]$$

(52) $$M^+X^-_{(solid)} \rightleftharpoons M^+X^-_{(DMSO)} \rightleftharpoons M^+_{(DMSO)} + X^-_{(DMSO)}$$

The relative rates of displacement of iodide ion by chloride ion from methyl iodide have been examined by Parker (*393*) in a series of solvents. The relative rates at 25° were: CH_3OH, 1, NH_2CHO, 12.5, CH_3NHCHO, 45.3, $(CH_3)_2NCHO$, 1.2×10^6, $(CH_3)_2NCOCH_3$, 7.4×10^6. We shall adopt the simple approach of assigning most of the difference in rate to a difference in solvation energies of the anion in the solvents used. (Solvation of the transition state and substrate molecule is also important; see Parker and co-workers, *435*.) This point of view is illustrated in a free energy versus reaction coordinate diagram, Fig. 2.39. It may be pointed out that the effect of solvation may be divided into two parts: (1) the energy required for the removal of a molecule from the anion so that it may approach the atom under attack and (2) an effect of the solvent upon the ability of the anion to make an attack by partially neutralizing the negative charge on the anion.

Nucleophilic aromatic substitution is accelerated by a change from a protic to an aprotic dipolar solvent. In the reaction of sodium azide with 4-fluoronitrobenzene in dimethylformamide, it was found that the rate was first order in each reactant but that no sodium fluoride precipitated. (Sodium fluoride

* Equilibrium for solution.

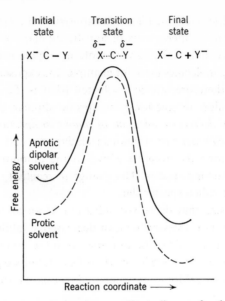

Figure 2.39 Free energy versus reaction coordinate diagram for the displacement of one anion by another anion on carbon.

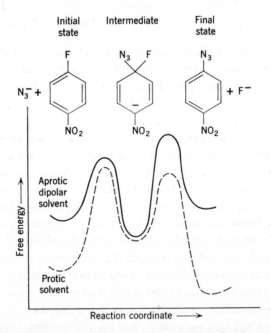

Figure 2.40 Free energy versus reaction coordinate diagram for the reaction of sodium azide with 4-fluoronitrobenzene in an aprotic dipolar solvent and in a protic solvent.

336

is almost insoluble in dimethylformamide.) The solution contained an intermediate which had λ_{max} 3970 A, although neither the starting material (for 4-fluoronitrobenzene, λ_{max} 3670 A) nor the product (4-nitrophenyl azide, λ_{max} 3610 A) absorbed at this wavelength. Addition of 5% water to the dimethylformamide solution of the intermediate precipitated sodium fluoride and gave a solution from which the product could be isolated by the addition of excess water. These observations are explained in Fig. 2.40, in which a free energy versus reaction coordinate diagram suggests that the intermediate is formed readily but that the inability of the medium to solvate the fluoride ion leads to a situation in which the intermediate is stable. Relatively few examples of moderately stable intermediates in aromatic nucleophilic substitution are known although considerable effort has been devoted to the products of addition of alkoxide to picryl ethers (for example, **376**).

$$CH_3O \quad OCH_3$$
$$N_2O \diagdown \diagup NO_2$$
$$NO_2$$

376

Miller (*394*) has attempted to analyze the course of aromatic nucleophilic substitution in a quantitative way and to rationalize the property called nucleophilicity in terms of certain well-defined properties of nucleophiles. For halide ions, the usual order of nucleophilicity is $I^- > Br^- > Cl^-$, for which the measure of nucleophilicity may be taken as the rate of a displacement reaction. On the other hand, we might have expected that the order might have been the reverse, with $Cl^- > Br^- > I^-$, from a consideration of the energies of the bonds to be formed. With the dissociation energies of the bonds as C—Cl, 83.5 kcal./mole, C—Br, 67 kcal./mole, and C—I 56 kcal./mole, as well as the assumption that the transition state for displacement occurs at a constant fraction of the final equilibrium bond distance for the X—C bond, we estimate the rate differences for halide ion and a constant substrate as follows: assume (a) the same entropy of activation for the three halide ions (b) that the transition state is unsymmetrical, with 50% of the bond to the leaving group broken and 20% of the new bond formed, and (c) that the substrate RX has a dissociation energy of 80 kcal./mole for the R—X bond. (It must be recognized that these assumptions are referred to a situation that is different from that which actually occurs in a displacement reaction. Bond dissociation energies (see discussion, Part 1, Section 1.5) refer to formation of two radical fragments. The nucleophilic replacement reaction forms an anion and the bond energy for a given degree of separation of the two partners in the bond probably differs from the bond energy for a homolytic dissociation.) These assumptions lead to the prediction that the activation energies for X^- + RX would be Cl^-, 23.3 kcal./mole, Br^-, 26.6 kcal./mole, and I^-, 28.8 kcal./mole. Winstein and co-workers (*395*) have shown that the order of reactivity is $Cl^- > Br^- > I^-$* in acetone. Weaver and Hutchison (*396*) have confirmed this order for the reaction of halide ion with methyl *p*-toluenesulfonate in DMF, and have demonstrated (through concentration dependence of rate) that ion-pairing can affect the order of reactivities observed. The rate factors are not as large as might have been expected on the basis of our crude predictions for the activation energy. It may be that polarizability plays some role in nucleophilicity: the larger the ion, the more interaction at a given distance and the more readily that anion achieves the transition state. The rate factors found for the halide ion-methyl *p*-toluenesulfonate reaction are listed in Table 2.10.

TABLE 2.10   *Lithium Halides and Methyl p-Toluenesulfonate in Dimethylformamide*[a]

Halide	Solvent	$10^3 k$, l. mol.$^{-1}$ sec.$^{-1}$
Cl^-	DMF	5.4[b]
Br^-	DMF	2.0[b]
I^-	DMF	0.6[b]
Cl^-	DMF + 5.0 M H_2O	0.12
I^-	DMF + 5.0 M H_2O	0.28

[a] Ref. 396.   [b] Extrapolated to zero salt concentration.

A study of the reaction of azide ion with 1-butyl bromide in many solvents is summarized in Table 2.11 (*397*). The reactions of sodium alkoxides with 4-fluoronitrobenzene in a series of alcohol-dimethylsulfoxide mixtures are reported to vary in rate whereby the log of the rate is linear in the dimethylsulfoxide concentration up to about 12 M (*398*), a relationship which is con-

* For the reaction of anions with *n*-butyl *p*-bromobenzenesulfonate (rate ratios $Cl^-:Br^-:I^-$, 18:4:1) with the importance of ion-pairing proven by showing that the tetra-*n*-butylammonium halide reacts more rapidly than the lithium halides.

TABLE 2.11 *Azide ion and 1-Butyl Bromide*[a,d]

Solvent	$10^2\ k$,[b] l. mol.$^{-1}$ sec.$^{-1}$	E^* kcal./mole	ΔS^* e.u.
Acetonitrile	4.31	17.1	4.2
Ethylene carbonate	0.0148	16.4	−9.2
Sulfolane[c]	0.324	15.4	−2.5
Dimethylformamide	2.37	16.5	0.3
Dimethylsulfoxide	1.14	16.9	1.6
Hexamethylphosphoramide	175.	13.4	−0.7
Methanol	0.000861	21.2	1.4
Water	0.00580	21.4	5.9
Formamide	0.00962	20.1	2.1
N-Methylacetamide	0.00735	20.1	2.2

[a] Ref. 397. [b] At 25°. [c] Tetramethylene sulfoxide. [d] Cation:sodium. Salt concentration: 0.02 M in dipolar aprotic solvents, 0.05 M in protic solvents. J. J. Delpuech, *Bull. soc. chim. France* **1966**, 1624.

sistent with steadily decreasing interaction energy for the alkoxide ion with the solvent as the dimethylsulfoxide concentration increases.

The dramatic effect of dimethylsulfoxide on the reactivity of an anion was discovered by Cram and co-workers (*399*) for the cleavage of the tertiary alkoxide **377**.

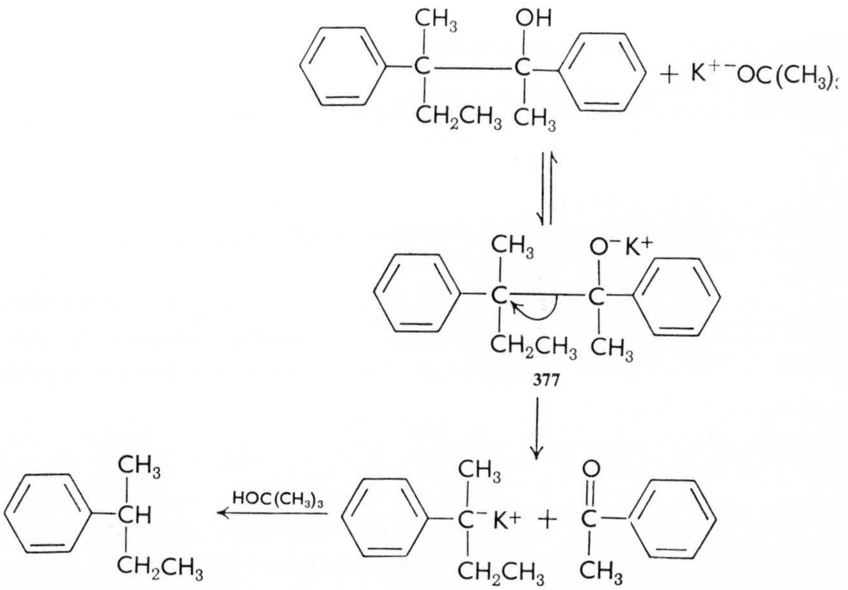

Replacement of *t*-butyl alcohol by dimethylsulfoxide as solvent for potassium *t*-butoxide led to such a large increase in rate that the reaction could be run at a temperature 150° below that of the first experiments in *t*-butyl alcohol. Similarly spectacular increases in rate were found for the transformation of a hydrazone into a hydrocarbon (the Wolff–Kishner reaction) (Eqs. 53 and 54) and for the reaction of bromobenzene with potassium *t*-butoxide, forming phenol and phenyl *t*-butyl ether (*400*).

(53) $\text{C}{=}\text{NNH}_2 \xrightarrow{B^-} \text{C}{=}\text{N}{-}\overline{\text{N}}\text{H} \xrightarrow{HB} \text{CH}{-}\text{N}{=}\text{NH}$

(54) $\text{CH}{-}\text{N}{=}\text{NH} \xrightarrow{B^-} \text{CH}{-}\text{N}{=}\text{N}^- \longrightarrow \overline{\text{C}}\text{H} \longrightarrow \text{CH}_2$

(See Eqs. 100 through 105.)

The relative rates of racemization of 2-methyl-3-phenylpropionitrile (**378**) in a series of mixtures of protic and aprotic solvents are given in Table 2.12. It is reasonable that the effect of solvent through desolvation of the basic anion should be greater for the rate of hydrogen abstraction than for many nucleophilic displacements since the anions formed by hydrogen abstraction are, in general, unstable. It is to be expected that the transition state would

TABLE 2.12   *Relative Rates of Racemization of 2-Methyl-3-Phenylpropionitrile*[a,b,c]

Solvent[d]	Relative Rate, $k_{solvent}/k_{methanol}$
100% Ethylene glycol	0.32
100% Methanol	1.0
75% Methanol-dimethylsulfoxide	32
50% Methanol-dimethylsulfoxide	160
24% Methanol-dimethylsulfoxide	4900
10% Methanol-dimethylsulfoxide	1300×10^2
3% Methanol-dimethylsulfoxide	1400×10^3
1.5% Methanol-dimethylsulfoxide	5000×10^4
2% Methanol-sulfolane[e]	7800×10
t-Butyl alcohol, 0.01 M H_2O	1400×10^3
t-Butyl alcohol, 0.003 M H_2O	4200×10^3

[a] From Ref. 10.   [b] Potassium alkoxides.   [c] At 25°.   [d] Percentage by weight of first-named component given.   [e] Tetramethylenesulfoxide.

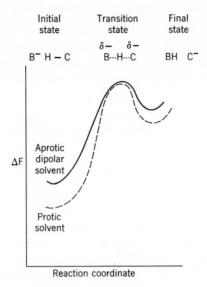

Figure 2.41 A free energy versus reaction coordinate diagram for the removal of a proton from a carbon–hydrogen bond by a base.

be close in energy to the final state, that is, the anion. A greater degree of bond breaking would be expected at the transition state and, therefore, a greater fraction of the difference between the free energy of the anion in a protic solvent and an aprotic dipolar solvent would be utilized to drive the reaction forward. A free energy versus reaction coordinate diagram for this situation is shown in Fig. 2.41.

Halide ions, including fluoride ions are not only better nucleophiles in aprotic dipolar solvents than in protic solvents, but halide ions can also serve as bases, as in the elimination of hydrogen chloride from 2-chloro-2-methyl-cyclohexanone with lithium chloride in dimethylformamide (*401*).

(55)

Estimations of single ion hydration energies have been made by various authors (see summary by Rosseinsky, *402*). If, as we have assumed, all of the rate effects are due to the lack of anion solvation in aprotic dipolar solvents, even the maximum rate factor (ca. 10^8, although Cram (*10*) quotes a factor of 10^{13} for the change from potassium methoxide-methanol to potassium *t*-butoxide-0.9 M *t*-butyl alcohol-dimethylsulfoxide for the rate of racemization of 1-phenyl-1-methoxyethane-1-*d*) could be accounted for by a modest decrease in the free energy of solvation of the ion. Hydration free energies, for example, vary from 60 to 100 kcal./mole for the halide ions (*402*).

378

Many of the molecules classified as aprotic dipolar components of solvents serve as donors in so-called adduct compounds. Dimethyl sulfoxide forms a crystalline compound with boron trifluoride, for example. A huge variety of other compounds of this genre and a critical discussion of their structure and properties has been published by Lindqvist (*403*).

The accessibility of the negatively charged atom in the molecules of aprotic dipolar solvents makes them favorably constituted for interaction with cations. Accessibility of the charge poses the possibility of the participation of aprotic dipolar molecules in nucleophilic displacements (S_DN reactions, Section 1.4) or elimination reactions. Smith and Winstein (*404*) reported that dimethyl sulfoxide reacts about ten times as rapidly as ethanol with ethyl tosylate. The rate factors observed for many of the reactions previously discussed in this section are much larger than ten, so that there is little chance of confusing reaction of a substrate with the solvent with acceleration of a reaction not involving the solvent. Nevertheless, the reaction of the solvent is not to be ignored in those cases for which "aprotic dipolar acceleration" is small. Two different products of the reaction of methyl tosylate and dimethyl sulfoxide are possible:

(56) $(CH_3)_2SO + CH_3OSO_2C_6H_4CH_3 \rightleftharpoons (CH_3)_2\overset{+}{S}OCH_3 \quad {}^-OSO_2C_6H_4CH_3$

(57) $(CH_3)_2SO + CH_3OSO_2C_6H_4CH_3 \longrightarrow (CH_3)_3\overset{+}{S}{=}O \quad {}^-OSO_2C_6H_4CH_3$

Too little is known about the structure of aprotic dipolar solvents to consider its role at this time.

2.9   Salt Effects

The effects of the charged species derived from salts on the properties of molecules in solution and on the rates of the reactions of molecules in solution are important to understand and are sometimes of appreciable magnitude. In Fig. 2.42, we illustrate two of the most significant factors in the operation of "salt effects." A molecule or transition state may interact with separated ions, the free energy of the system decreasing in a manner dependent upon the details of the interaction. Often, the key question is whether similar or opposite charges are proximate for a given pair. The interaction of single ions with neutral, dipolar, or charged species is illustrated on the left side of Figs. 2.42a, b, and c. (To preserve electrical neutrality, the *gegen-* or counter-ion must also be present.) Oppositely charged ions may associate, forming ion-pairs. Ion-pairs, in general, will interact more weakly with solutes or solvents than ions with the possible exception of dipolar molecules or transition states, in which the solute or solvent dipole has an appropriate geometry (right side, Figs. 2.42a, b, and c).

Understanding salt effects should thus be possible if we could understand (a) how single ions interact with other molecules and (b) how counter-ions affect the interactions of an ion, either at a great distance or at a range small

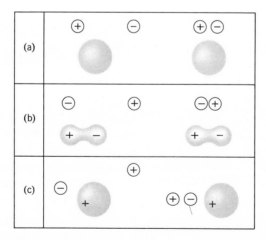

Figure 2.42   Interaction of charged species with solute or solvent molecules. (*a*) Neutral molecule. (*b*) Dipolar molecule. (*c*) Charged species. (The molecules may also be considered as transition states.)

enough for the combination to be defined as an ion-pair. Unfortunately, our understanding of these factors is rather limited. We shall discuss certain aspects of the behavior of salts and ions which should be significant in physical organic chemistry.

The oppositely charged partners in a salt (the gegen-ions) attract one another according to Coulomb's law, Eq. 58. (Species with the same charge repel one another with the same dependence.) The charge on a given ion is indicated by z_i, the unit charge by e, the distance between the ions as r and the medium property which controls the strength of the interaction as D, the dielectric constant.

(58)
$$E = \frac{z_1 z_2 e^2}{Dr}$$

We might first try to find out what the average distance between the ions is for various (1–1) salt concentrations. This can be done easily be dividing the solution up into little cubes and putting one ion in each. The number of particles per mole of salt is 12.0×10^{23} and this may be divided by the number of cubic angstroms per liter (10^{27}) to yield the reciprocal of the cube of the average distance between ions. The average distances for salt concentrations between 1 M and 10^{-7} M are listed in Table 2.13.

If we assume that positive ions alternate with negative ions in the array of cubes that contain the salt we have put into the solution, the arrangement of the ions is like that of an extended sodium chloride lattice. The average interaction energy per ion-pair is obtained from Eq. 58 by multiplying by the Madelung constant for sodium chloride (this corrects for the contributions of the other ions). Although it is quite clear that the dielectric constant parameter used in Eq. 58 is not valid for describing the interactions of ions in solutions at distances that are comparable to twice the radius of the cybotactic region (ca. 10 A), we have calculated the interaction energies for water (D = 78) and acetic acid (D = 6) for the purpose of comparing the average interaction energy per ion-pair with the average kinetic energy per particle ($\frac{3}{2}RT$ for a mole of particles). Below the range of interaction energies that are significant with respect to thermal energies, the motions of the ions will be determined largely by their thermal energy. In aqueous solution, the concentration at which thermal energy of the ions is primarily responsible for their behavior is about 10^{-3} M. In a low dielectric constant solvent like acetic acid, interionic attraction is important even at 10^{-6} M. These figures are given in Table 2.13.

The *lattice model* just described for a solution of 1–1 electrolytes would

TABLE 2.13   *Interionic Distances and Interaction Energies*

Concentration (M)	Average Distance between ions (A) (r)[a]	Interaction Energy (kcal./mole)[b] E	E	Fraction of Translational Energy (n)[c]	
		$(D = 78)$	$(D = 6)$	$(D = 78)$	$(D = 6)$
1	9.4	0.79	10.4	0.89	11.7
10^{-1}	21.2	0.35	4.6	0.39	5.2
10^{-2}	43.6	0.17	2.3	0.19	2.6
10^{-3}	94	0.09	1.0	0.10	1.1
10^{-4}	212	0.04	0.46	0.05	0.52
10^{-5}	436	0.02	0.23	0.02	0.26
10^{-6}	940	0.008	0.11	0.01	0.11
10^{-7}	2120	0.004	0.05	0.005	0.06

[a] Number of ions/cubic angstroms $= 1/r^3$ (univalent ions).   [b] $E = (1.75\ e^2/Dr) \cdot$ 332. The last factor converts the charge in e.s.u. (4.80×10^{-10} e.s.u.) per unit of separation (10^{-8} cm.) into kilocalories per mole through the factors 6.02×10^{23} molecules per mole, 10^{-7} joules per erg, and 4186 joules per kilocalorie.   [c] At 25°C, the average translational energy per particle per mole is 0.98 kcal./mole ($\frac{3}{2}RT$). The average interaction energy/average translational energy $= n$.

predict a cube root dependence of the log of the activity coefficient for an ion on the concentration, because this is the way in which the interionic attraction varies. Frank (*410*), in fact, insists that an equation like Eq. 59 is more reasonable than one which utilizes the square-root dependence derived from the Debye–Hückel theory.

$$(59) \qquad \log \gamma = a - bc^{1/3} \qquad (C < 0.02\ M)$$

$$\gamma = \text{activity coefficient}$$

The classical treatment of interionic attraction is that of Debye and Hückel. In their approach, the distribution of ions around a central ion j is described by a Boltzmann distribution and the interaction energy of these ions with the central ion is given by a potential function times the charge. Taking the Poisson equation for the mean electrostatic potential yielded the differential equation

(60)
$$\nabla^2 \psi_j = -\frac{4\pi e}{D} \sum_i z_i \rho_i e^{-z_i e \psi_j(r)/kT}$$

ψ_j = potential produced by the ion j

∇^2 = an operator $\dfrac{\partial^2}{\partial x^2} + \dfrac{\partial^2}{\partial y^2} + \dfrac{\partial^2}{\partial z^2}$

e = charge on an electron

D = dielectric constant

z_i = charge on ion i

ρ_i = density of ions of type i

This equation cannot be solved analytically but the exponential can be expanded through the approximation

(61)
$$e^x = 1 + x$$
(x must be small)

and the resulting linearized equations can be solved analytically. The activity coefficient expression

(62)
$$-\ln \gamma_i = \frac{z_i^2 \alpha \sqrt{\mu}}{1 + \beta a \sqrt{\mu}}$$

α, β = constants characteristic of a given solvent and temperature

a = distance of closest approach of ion i to the central ion j

μ = ionic strength

is derived through a fairly lengthy development and a number of approximations (408). In very dilute solutions, the so-called "limiting law" is obtained because the denominator approaches unity.

(63)
$$-\ln \gamma_i = z_i^2 \alpha \sqrt{\mu}$$

For the reaction of an ion A with an ion B, the effect of ionic strength is given approximately by

(64)
$$\ln \frac{k}{k_0} = 2 z_A z_B \alpha \sqrt{\mu}$$

with α in water equal to 0.509 (2.303). It is important to remember that the approximation (Eq. 61) used to derive the expressions for the activity coefficient limits the validity of these expressions to dilute solutions (x, small).

According to Eq. 64, the logarithm of rate constants for the reactions of ions should be related to the square root of the ionic strength (Eq. 65) with a slope dependent in sign and magnitude on the nature of the reactants.

$$(65) \qquad \mu = \frac{1}{2} \sum_i c_i z_i^2$$

Correlations with Eq. 64 have been reviewed by Davies (*409*) who assigns all deviations from a linear correlation to the effects of specific ionic association, but such a conclusion is probably too simple in view of the approximations already incorporated into the Debye–Hückel approach.

Any specific interaction that favors association of ions will cause deviations from the predictions of the limiting law (Eq. 63). Coordination of an anion in the first coordination sphere of a cation is usually the result of an interaction greater than that expected on purely electrostatic grounds and would cause a deviation from the limiting law. An especially important specific interaction is that recognized by Diamond (*406*) as being important in the behavior of salts which are composed of both large cations and large anions. Such ions would tend to pair much more than expected on purely electrostatic grounds because of the extra interaction energy of "hydrophobic bonding." In essence, the ions are driven from the water phase into a close association with one another because of the great preference of water molecules for one another and for incorporation in the "iceberg" structures (or clusters) present in the purely aqueous region. A comparison of micelle formation, which is also due to hydrophobic bonding, and hydrophobic ion-pairing is shown in Fig. 2.43. Hydrophobic ion-pairing may be significant in the behavior of the intimate ion-pairs derived from certain alkyl arenesulfonates, in the sense that collapse pathways (return to starting ester, rearrangement, or elimination) within the ion-pair may be favored over those reaction pathways that lead to dissociation of the ion-pair partners into separate ions.

Even in the absence of specific interactions between ions, the fact that real ions are not small hard spheres will result in interactions in concentrated solutions of salts, which are not described by the approaches used in the Debye–Hückel formulation. In addition, the molecular nature of the solvent and saturation of its response to an electric field will cause deviations from Debye–Hückel behavior, which would be hard to evaluate. The electric field at the surface of a small cation is approximately 10^8 V/cm., a field which is far greater than that necessary to completely orient a nearby dipole. (Remember that the dielectric constant reflects the reorientation of solvent dipoles in

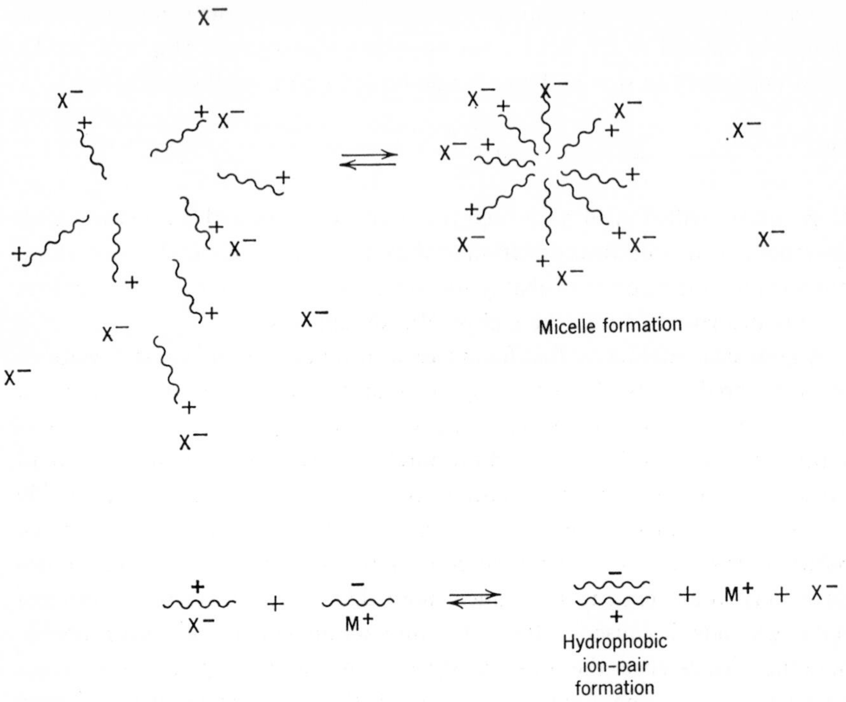

Figure 2.43 A comparison of micelle formation with hydrophobic ion-pair formation.

response to an external electric field.) Microwave techniques have made it possible to measure the dielectric constant of a medium with a conductivity too large to be treated by the usual method. A list of molar depressions of dielectric constants in aqueous solutions is set forth in Table 2.14. A one-molar solution of lanthanum trichloride would have a dielectric constant of 34 in contrast to the 78 found for water itself, *assuming* that the change in dielectric constant is linear in concentration. This is unlikely to be true for any solutions other than moderately dilute ones.

Organic solvents almost all have dielectric constants lower than that of water (hydrogen cyanide, formamide, and N-methylformamide are notable exceptions; see Table 2.1) and it would be expected on the basis of the Coulomb law that ionic association in organic solvents would be quite a bit more important than in water. Not only would ion-pairs form, but higher aggregates could also be present in solution. (Many salts, of course, are not soluble in organic solvents.) The salt, tetraisoamylammonium thiocyanate,

TABLE 2.14 *Molar Depression of Dielectric Constant of Water*[a,b,c]

Substance	δ (l. mol.$^{-1}$)	Substance	δ (l. mol.$^{-1}$)
HCl	-10	NaI	-7.5
LiCl	-7	KI	-8
NaCl	-5.5	$MgCl_2$	-15
KCl	-5	$BaCl_2$	-14
RbCl	-5	$LaCl_3$	-22
NaF	-6	NaOH	-10.5
KF	-6.5	Na_2SO_4	-11

[a] As quoted in Ref. 310 from the data of J. B. Hasted, D. M. Ritson, and C. H. Collie, *J. Chem. Phys.*, **16**, 1 (1948). [b] At 25°. [c] The defining equation for δ is $D = D_{H_2O} + 2\delta c$, where c is the concentration of the electrolyte in moles/liter.

$(C_5H_{11})_4N^+SCN^-$, exists almost entirely in the form of ion-pairs in benzene at 25° at a total salt concentration of 1×10^{-6} M. The dissociation constant reported for the ion-pairs is 5.6×10^{-18} (*407*). At concentrations above micromolar, ion-triplets and higher aggregates are indicated by an examination of the freezing point depression at the higher concentrations. However, dielectric relaxation measurements by Davies and Williams (*445, 446*) on solutions of tetraalkylammonium salts in benzene-xylene mixtures suggest that only ion-pairs are present up to concentrations of ca. 0.01 M and that the aggregation is only apparent. Direct empirical evidence that the presence of the salt can influence the behavior of the solution as a solvent is derived from measurements of the Z-value for chloroform containing 0.13 M ethanol with a wide range of concentrations of the pyridinium iodide (**214**) used for the measurement of Z-value. As one can see from the data given in Table 2.15, the absorption coefficient for the pyridinium iodide charge-transfer band does not change very much over the range of concentrations used, suggesting that the Z-value indeed measures the average molecular environment seen by the pyridinium iodide ion-pairs, and that this average environment simply contains more and more ion-pairs as the concentration of salt is increased.

Molten salts as solvents have been reviewed by Bloom and Hastie (*411*). *A priori* one might have expected that a molten salt would have provided an unusually polar environment for a solute. Gordon (*405*), an advocate of low-melting organic salts as solvents, has measured the Z-values of tri-*n*-hexyl-*n*-heptylammonium iodide and perchlorate as 66.4 and 66.9, respectively. By the criterion of Z-value, at least, these salts are only slightly more polar than acetone (**Z** 65.7), probably because the large alkyl groups shield the positive charges from the test solute ion-pair.

TABLE 2.15   *Z-Value Variation with Salt Concentration in Chloroform*[a,b,c]

Concentration, 10^3 moles/liter	λ_{max}, Å	$\epsilon_{apparent}$	**Z**-Value
54.8	3990	1410	71.6
6.07	4150	1021	68.9
5.48	4150	1186	68.9
1.26	4338	1090	65.9
0.548	4418	1113	64.6
0.110	4470	1136	63.9
0.0219	4489	1233	63.7

[a] Ref. 216.   [b] At 25°.   [c] Solvent contained 0.13 Methanol.

Complete derivations of the Debye–Hückel equations are given by Hill (*408*) and Robinson and Stokes (*310*). Critical discussion of the Debye–Hückel approach, as well as other aspects of the chemical physics of ionic solutions, appears in a symposium volume (*410*), in which the papers of Poirier, Frank, Fuoss, and Friedman are worth special attention.

Empirical relationships like that of Setschenow (*412*)

(66) $\log \gamma = K_s c_s$ (**K** = constant, c = concentration of salt s)

have been utilized to examine the effect of aqueous electrolytes on the activity coefficients of the initial and transition states of t-butyl chloride by Clarke and Taft (*413*) and the effect of electrolytes on the solubility (and therefore the activity coefficient) of acetyltetraglycine ethyl ester (**171**) by Robinson and Jencks (*414*).

$$CH_3CONHCH_2CONHCH_2CONHCH_2CONHCH_2COOC_2H_5$$
379

The current trend is to utilize techniques like nuclear magnetic resonance (for the measurement of relaxation processes, exchange processes, and conformational averaging processes) to acquire detailed information on the behavior of the molecules in the solvent in the presence and absence of electrolytes *(417)*. Eventually one might hope to combine such information with deductions about the thermodynamics of single ions (Rosseinsky, *402*; Noyes, *415*), including the electron (Jortner and Noyes, *416*). Relatively little has been done along these lines for organic solvents, although Friedman and his co-workers have published some studies of salts in propylenecarbonate *(343)*.

2.10 Reaction Partners

The pathway for many reactions proceeds through intermediates stable enough to be classified as discrete species, yet so unstable that much of the evidence concerning them is indirect. Among these unstable intermediates may be placed *reaction partners*, which we define as any pair [... triplet, quadruplet ...] of species that form one or more associated species and for which the formation of the associated species appears to be responsible for some characteristic of the reaction pathway. Characteristics of the reaction pathway, which might indicate the intermediacy of reaction partners, are product distributions, reaction rates, isotope distribution in products, product stereochemistry, and environmental effects on rate. The behavior of reaction partners is illustrated by the results obtained by Lyon and Levy for the photolysis of a mixture of azomethane, $CH_3N{=}NCH_3$, and hexadeutero-azomethane, $CD_3N{=}NCD_3$ in isooctane (*419*). On the naïve basis that photolysis leads to free radicals, a mixture of CH_3CH_3, CH_3CD_3, and CD_3CD_3 should have been isolated. Instead, only CH_3CH_3 and CD_3CD_3 were found, showing that the original radical partners had a strong preference for one another. Since the formation of radicals in azoalkane photolyses may be demonstrated readily in the gas phase, the experimental result is explained by the trapping of the initially formed free radicals in a *solvent cage*, within which the radicals react to give the observed products. Formation of CH_3CD_3 would have required liberation of the methyl radicals from the solvent cage (Eq. 70).

(67) $CH_3N{=}NCH_3 \longrightarrow \overline{CH_3{\cdot}\quad N_2\quad CH_3{\cdot}}$

(68) $\overline{CH_3{\cdot}\quad N_2\quad CH_3{\cdot}} \longrightarrow \overline{CH_3{\cdot}\quad CH_3{\cdot}} + N_2$

(69) $\overline{CH_3{\cdot}\quad CH_3{\cdot}} \longrightarrow CH_3CH_3$

(70) $\overline{CH_3{\cdot}\quad CH_3{\cdot}} \longrightarrow CH_3{\cdot} + CH_3{\cdot}$

Four varieties of reaction partners may be expected in principle as illustrated in Fig. 2.44. These are the cage pair, the extended cage pair (in which one solvent molecule is between the partners), the solvent-separated pair (in which two solvent molecules are between the partners), and the cybotactic region pair (in which three solvent molecules may be between the partners). Somewhat more complicated classifications might be made for three reaction partners. The combination of two methyl radicals and a nitrogen molecule shown in Eq. 67 could be regarded as an extended cage pair in which the nitrogen molecule takes the place of a solvent molecule, or

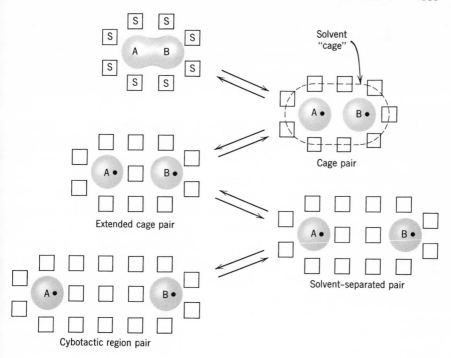

Figure 2.44 Varieties of reaction partners. From top to bottom are illustrated the cage pair, the extended cage pair, the solvent-separated pair, and the cybotactic region pair. For charged species in nonpolar solvents, it might be necessary to consider additional types.

as a special kind of cage pair (since the nitrogen molecule is much smaller than the isooctane molecule, a larger interaction between the partners could be expected).

The reaction partners may be radicals, a cation and anion (that is, an ion-pair), and a radical cation and an anion radical (that is, a diradical ion-pair). These are illustrated in Eqs. 71 through 73. Two names in common usage for ion-pairs are indicated in Eq. 72.

(71) $\quad AB \rightleftarrows \overline{A\cdot \ .B} \rightleftarrows A\cdot + B\cdot \longrightarrow$ products

(72) $\quad AB \rightleftarrows \underset{\substack{\text{Intimate}\\\text{ion-pair}}}{\overline{A^+B^-}} \rightleftarrows \underset{\substack{\text{Solvent-separated}\\\text{ion-pair}}}{\overline{A^+ \parallel B^-}} \rightleftarrows A^+ + B^- \longrightarrow$ products

(73) $\quad A,B \rightleftarrows \underset{\substack{\text{diradical}\\\text{ion-pair}}}{\overline{A\cdot^+ \ {}^-\!\cdot B}} \rightleftarrows A\cdot^+ + B\cdot^- \longrightarrow$ products

$\quad\quad\quad \updownarrow$

$\quad\quad A + B$

The line over the molecular pairs (for example, $\overline{A\cdot\ \ \cdot B}$) indicates that the two species are within a solvent cage. The line does not here define which kind of cage (see below). The rationale behind the categories of reaction partners shown in Fig. 2.44 is as follows: for interspecies distances greater than that defined by the cybotactic region, solute species and their coterie of solvent molecules should behave in an independent way. The degree to which behavior is independent will be influenced by the presence of charges, the dielectric constant of the medium between the cybotactic regions of two species, the temperature, and the nature of the solvent molecule. In many cases, however, pairs that are in contact at the limit of their cybotactic regions (first coordination sphere plus second solvent shell; see Fig. 2.20) can be regarded as independent, that is, pairs separated by at least four solvent molecules are not counted as pairs.

Noyes (*420*) has discussed some of the interesting theoretical and kinetic problems which arise from the nonequilibrium distribution of A and B (Fig. 2.44). Corrections to ordinary kinetic equations might be necessary for very fast reactions of A or B, perhaps those with half-lives on the order of 1000 psec. (10^{-9} seconds). Such "reactions" as diffusion of A away from B, or the turning around of a solvent molecule near A are fast enough so that the presence of B will influence the rates.

Our discussion of reaction partners will be limited primarily to radical pairs and ion-pairs. Diradical ion-pairs have scarcely been investigated but are mentioned briefly in Part 1 (Section 1.7).

The azo compound, azoisobutyronitrile (**42**), is a widely used initiator for polymerization reactions and decomposes in most solvents with an activation energy of about 31 kcal./mole. (A useful and more extensive discussion of all aspects of radical reactions and chemistry will be found in the book by Pryor, *422*.) The extended radical pair produced by the first step can disappear in two ways: (1) either forming a radical pair or (2) forming a solvent-separated radical pair. [The number of molecules (solvent or inert partners) between the pairs of interest are indicated by "V's" in the line which represents the cage.]

The radical pair (Eq. 75), produced by the diffusion of the nitrogen into the

(74) $(CH_3)_2C(CN)-N{=}N-(CN)C(CH_3)_2$
　　　　　　42

$$\longrightarrow \overline{(CH_3)_2C(CN)\cdot\ \ \overset{V}{N_2}\ \ \cdot(CN)C(CH_3)_2}$$

(75) $\overline{(CH_3)_2C(CN)\cdot\ \ \overset{V}{N_2}\ \ \cdot(CN)C(CH_3)_2} \longrightarrow \overline{(CH_3)_2C(CN)\cdot\ \ \cdot(CN)C(CH_3)_2}$

(76) $\overline{(CH_3)_2C(CN)\cdot \overset{v}{N_2} \cdot (CN)C(CH_3)_2}$

$\longrightarrow \overline{(CH_3)_2C(CN)\cdot \overset{vv}{N_2} \textit{i-o} \cdot (CN)C(CH_3)_2}$

i-o = isooctane

solvent, can disappear in three ways: (2) to give the dimer, tetramethyl-succinonitrile (**380**), (2) to give the dimer, the ketenimine **381**, and (3) to yield an extended radical pair, with an isooctane molecule separating the reaction partners. These processes are shown in Eq. 77.

(77)

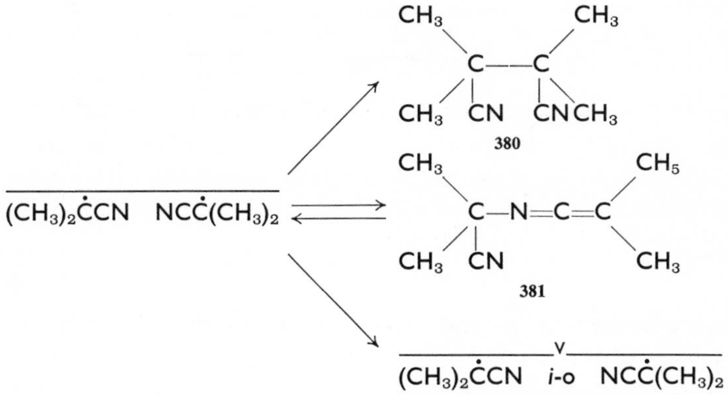

$$(CH_3)_2\overset{\cdot}{C}CN \quad NC\overset{\cdot}{C}(CH_3)_2 \rightleftharpoons$$

A complication in these considerations, which has not yet been mentioned, is that the radical pairs may be either singlet or triplet. The weak interaction between spins, which might exist in the extended radical pair, would not cause a sufficient difference between singlet and triplet levels for one to be preferred. The rate of spin interconversion in radical pairs could be low enough to affect the fate of the radicals. (Turro (*423*) cites 5×10^7 sec.$^{-1}$ as the rate of intersystem crossing from the excited singlet of 1-chloronaphthalene to the π,π^* triplet) (see Part 1, Section 1.6.)

In carbon tetrachloride, the azo compound **42** yields almost exclusively the dinitrile **380**. (The ketenimine is unstable and dissociates to yield a radical pair.) The cyanoisopropyl radical, $(CH_3)_2CCN\cdot$, is therefore a poor halogen abstractor. If 1-butanethiol is added to the solution, the yield of dimer is diminished with the formation of *n*-butyl disulfide and isobutyronitrile.

(78) $(CH_3)_2CCN\cdot + BuSH \longrightarrow (CH_3)_2CHCN + BuS\cdot$

(79) $BuS\cdot + BuS\cdot \longrightarrow BuSSBu$

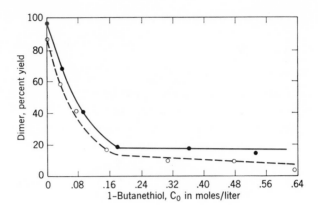

Figure 2.45 The yield of tetramethylsuccinonitrile (**380**) (radical dimer) from the thermal decomposition of azoisobutyronitrile (**42**) in (*a*) •———• carbon tetrachloride and (*b*) —o—°—o— toluene as a function of 1-butanethiol concentration. The concentration of azo compound was 0.2 M (Ref. 424). (Reprinted with the permission of the authors and the *Journal of the American Chemical Society*.)

At equimolar butanethiol and azoisobutyronitrile (0.2 M, for this example), the yield of dimer is only 20%. Further increases in the concentration of butanethiol have no effect on the dimer yield, at least up to 0.6 M butanethiol (Fig. 2.45) (*424*). This result is interpreted to mean that 20% of the radicals do not escape from a solvent cage, provided that all of the reacting azo compound decomposed via radicals. A cyclic transition state, proceeding via a *cis*-azo derivative, could also explain the formation of a product that cannot be intercepted by *scavenger* molecules. [A scavenger is a species that reacts quite readily with radicals to give a much less reactive species. If the scavenger is a singlet molecule, the product is a more stable (less reactive) radical. If the scavenger is a stable radical (diphenylpicrylhydrazyl or galvinoxyl), the product is a singlet molecule.] The cyclic mechanism is illustrated in Eqs. 80, 81, and 82.

Trapp and Hammond (*425*) have shown that liquid bromine as a solvent eliminates completely the formation of the dimer **381**, and Waits and Hammond (*426*) have found little to indicate that bromine reacts directly with a related azodinitrile. Thus, a high concentration of bromine scavenges all the radical pairs, and a cyclic mechanism for this series of compounds is unlikely. Furthermore, the results on gas-phase decomposition of azo compounds suggest that all of the reaction proceeds via intermediate free radicals (for example, *419*). Each substrate type (and perhaps each particular sub-

$$(80) \qquad \underset{R}{\overset{R}{\diagdown}} N{=}N^{\diagup R} \longrightarrow \underset{R}{\overset{R}{\diagdown}} N{=}N \diagdown R$$

$$(81) \qquad \underset{R}{\overset{R}{\diagdown}} N{=}N \diagdown R \longrightarrow \underset{R\cdots\cdots\cdots R}{N{\equiv}N} \longrightarrow N_2 + R{-}R$$

$$(82) \qquad \underset{N{\equiv}C}{\overset{N{=}N}{\underset{R}{\diagup}}\ \underset{R'}{\diagdown}} \longrightarrow \underset{N{\equiv}C}{\overset{N{\equiv}N}{R\ \ R'}} \longrightarrow R{-}N{=}C{=}R'$$

strate within a given series) must be investigated for the possible incursion of a cyclic reaction that could simulate a reaction which proceeded through caged pairs. How can one then be sure that a cyclic reaction has not occurred? The cyclic reaction should be less sensitive to substituent and medium effects than a reaction which proceeds through pairs. Unfortunately, radical reactions are not very sensitive to medium effects, and this criterion is not therefore a good one for distinguishing cyclic reactions from cage reactions. Substituent effect should be an effective criterion, since a cyclic transition state ought to be fairly insensitive to the nature of substituents on the system undergoing reaction. Transition states which produce radicals should have a moderate sensitivity to the nature of substituents. Thus, a determination of the variation in the extent of dimer formation for a change in substitution on the system being studied *might* provide a way to differentiate cyclic and noncyclic transition states. We assume that interception of the radical intermediates by scavenger will not be affected in exactly the same way by a change in substituent as the reaction within a cage.

It is likely that cyclic reactions are unimportant in most cases because there is no reason for a sharp change in mechanism for the change to extra-cage reactions (clearly radical) to intra-cage reactions. We shall discuss intra-cage reactions in terms of radical intermediates.

One way of investigating the behavior of cage radicals is to vary the "strength" of the cage. Cooling the system to 77°K freezes the cage and restricts the molecules completely to intra-cage reactions. Increasing the viscosity at higher temperatures has a similar effect, as shown by the comparison Traylor and his co-workers (*366*) have made for the decompositions of di-*t*-butyl peroxide (**211**), di-*t*-butyl hyponitrite (**209**), and di-*t*-butyl peroxalate (**210**). The extent of intra-cage reaction varies with the number of "extra" molecules between the *t*-butoxy radicals, but the importance of the cage is

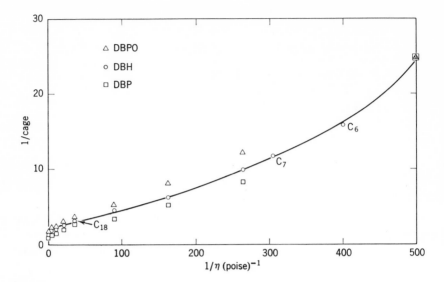

Figure 2.46 A plot of the reciprocal of the percentage of cage reaction versus the reciprocal of the square root of the viscosity for △ DBPO, which is di-*t*-butyl peroxalate (**210**), ⊙ DBH, di-*t*-butyl hyponitrite (**209**), and ⊡ DBP, di-*t*-butyl peroxide (**211**). (Courtesy of Professor T. G. Traylor.)

shown in the fact that even when there are two molecules between the combining radicals, a large proportion of the reaction is intra-cage (Fig. 2.46). The components of the three cages are shown below.

$$211 \longrightarrow \overline{(CH_3)_3CO\cdot \quad \cdot OC(CH_3)_3}$$

$$209 \longrightarrow \overline{(CH_3)_3CO\cdot \quad \overset{v}{N_2} \quad \cdot OC(CH_3)_3}$$

$$210 \longrightarrow \overline{(CH_3)_3CO\cdot \quad O_2C \overset{vv}{\quad} CO_2 \quad \cdot OC(CH_3)_3}$$

Photolysis of azoethane under various conditions (liquid solution or glasses) forms ethylene, ethane and butane (*427*). In most of the experiments, ethane or ethylene were produced in equal amounts, suggesting a disproportion of ethyl radicals within a cage.

(83)
$$\begin{array}{ll} H \quad \cdot CH_2CH_3 & + CH_3CH_3 \\ \diagup & \\ CH_2CH_2\cdot & \longrightarrow CH_2{=}CH_2 \end{array}$$

Another interpretation is possible. If the ethylazo radical, formed by cleavage of one bond (C—N bond energy, 73 kcal./mole, $n \rightarrow \pi^*$ transition produced by light absorption corresponds to 80 kcal./mole), reacts with an ethyl radical, ethane and ethylene could form.

(84) $\quad$ $CH_3CH_2N{=}NCH_2CH_3 \longrightarrow \overline{CH_3CH_2N{=}N\cdot \quad \cdot CH_2CH_3}$

$$(85) \quad \begin{array}{c} H \\ | \\ CH_2CH_2{-}N{=}N\cdot \end{array} \overset{\cdot CH_2CH_3}{\longrightarrow} \begin{array}{c} H{-}{-}{-}\cdot CH_2CH_3 \\ \vdots \\ CH_2{=}{=}{=}CH_2{-}{-}{-}N{\equiv}{\equiv}N\cdot \end{array} \longrightarrow \begin{array}{c} CH_3CH_3 \\ \\ CH_2{=}CH_2 \end{array} + N_2$$

Although we have expressed some doubt about the stability of an azo radical like $(CH_3)_2C(CN)N{=}N\cdot$ (in Section 1.6), an azo radical, which could not give rise to a moderately stable radical with spin centered on carbon, might have greater *relative* stability.

Radical reaction partners may give rise to dimers, to the products of disproportionation, or to the products which form from the radicals that escape from the cage. The work of Bartlett and McBride (*715*) has shown (Section 1.6) that complete stereospecificity of radical recombination to dimers may be observed for a suitably large radical in a glass at a low temperature. Most of the parameters that control the behavior of radical reaction partners have not been evaluated, but will no doubt require a study of what we might call relaxation of the radical species within the cage and relaxation of either the component groups or the molecules of the solvent cage.

The significance of ion-pair intermediates in carbonium ion reactions was first shown clearly by Young, Winstein, and Goering (*428*) for the solvolysis of α,α-dimethylallyl chloride (**382**) in acetic acid. The formation of dimethylallyl acetate is accompanied by isomerization to γ,γ-dimethylallyl chloride. The starting tertiary chloride does not rearrange as a pure liquid, showing that the isomerization, like the formation of acetate product, requires the presence of the solvent. Added chloride has no effect on the rate of acetate formation or isomerization, indicating that the reaction does not proceed through a carbonium ion which subsequently reacts with chloride ion or acetate ion to form the products. An intermediate, which could be responsible for these findings, is an ion-pair. If we make the further assumption that the ion-pair intermediate is a cage-pair (no solvent molecule between the cation and anion), it seems certain that the anion must be much closer to one end of the allylic system than the other. We may call such an ion-pair *localized*. Localized ion-pairs will have electron-distributions within the delocalized partner (for example, the allylic cation) which are different from the electron-distributions within the same partner surrounded only by solvent molecules. Shandala, Waight, and Weinstock (*429*) have suggested that a localized ion-pair is responsible for the racemization that accompanies the isomerization of optically active 1-phenylallyl chloride to cinnamyl chloride. The mechanism for the solvolysis and isomerization of α,α-dimethylallyl chloride is shown in Eqs. 64 and 65. Isomerization is not observed in ethanol which implies that the ion-pair intermediate is more susceptible to dissociation in ethanol which has a higher dielectric constant than acetic acid.

(86)

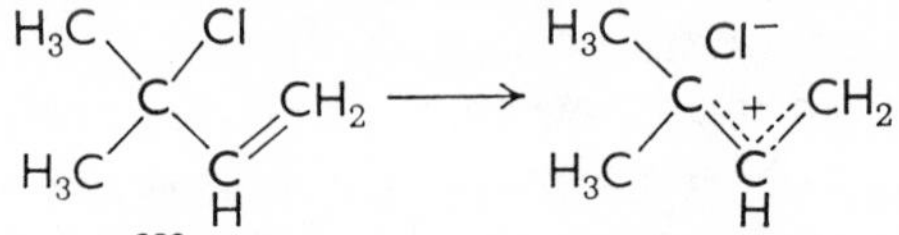

382

(87)

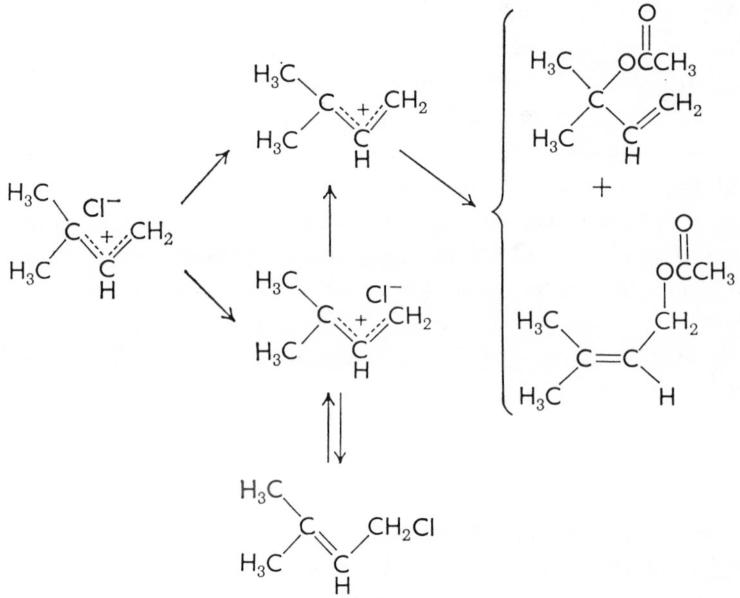

A "special salt effect" discovered by Winstein and his co-workers (*430*) in the acetolysis of a number of alkyl arenesulfonates led to the proposal that at least two types of ion-pairs were required to explain the facts about certain solvolyses. The special salt effect is the two- to threefold increase in rate of solvolysis as measured by titration of acid produced by very small concentrations of lithium perchlorate (as low as 4×10^{-5} M for the acetolysis of cholesteryl *p*-toluenesulfonate, *431*). We shall illustrate the possibility of multiple ion-pair intermediates with the case of *threo*-3-*p*-anisyl-2-butyl arenesulfonates investigated by Winstein and Robinson (*432*) after a brief review of another system which solvolyzes through ion-pairs.

The solvolysis of *exo*-norbornyl *p*-bromobenzenesulfonate (**163**) in acetic acid can be followed by titration of the excess sodium acetate present in the medium. (Sodium acetate is a strong base in acetic acid.) The solvolysis of optically active *exo*-norbornyl *p*-bromobenzenesulfonate in acetic acid can be followed polarimetrically. (Most measurements were made using visible light, mostly the sodium D line. The availability of instruments for the measurement of optical rotatory dispersion makes possible optical rotation measurements at any wavelength for which solvent light absorption does not interfere. Optical rotations can become quite large in the ultraviolet, making it possible to use dilute solutions.) Winstein and Trifan (*436*) made the interesting discovery that the rate followed polarimetrically was greater than the rate followed titrimetrically. Recovery of the starting ester after partial reaction demonstrated that racemization had occurred more rapidly than solvolysis. Racemization, a process accompanying solvolysis, resembled the isomerization accompanying the solvolysis of α,α-dimethylallyl chloride, and could be explained through the intervention of an ion-pair intermediate. Either the racemization of **163** or the isomerization of **382** can be called "internal return." *Internal return* can be defined as a reaction which forms a covalent bond from reaction partners derived from the original reactant. The racemization and solvolysis of **163** are illustrated in Fig. 2.47. It is probable that the nature of the solvation around the carbonium ion center affects the degree of delocalization in bonds that help to satisfy the electron demand of the carbonium ion. For further details on equilibrating nonclassical carbonium ions, see Part 1, Section 1.5.

Ion-pairs were utilized in the mechanism explaining the finding that the racemization rate for optically active *threo*-3-phenyl-2-butyl *p*-toluenesulfonate (*threo*-**150**) was higher than the solvolysis rate. A modification of the scheme of Cram (*437*), including equilibration between two enantiomeric equilibrating nonclassical ions, is shown in Fig. 2.48.

The rate constant, k_α, which characterizes the polarimetric rate of disappearance of such compounds as optically active **163** in acetic acid, is increased by lithium perchlorate in a way that is described by the empirical Eq. 88 (*438*), the constant b varying from 10–40 for secondary arenesulfonates.

(88) $$k_\alpha = k_\alpha^0[1 + b(\mathrm{LiClO_4})]$$

The constant b is different for *p*-toluenesulfonates and *p*-bromobenzenesulfonates. The low concentration dependence of the rate [$\log \gamma = f(\log c_{\mathrm{salt}})$; compare with Eqs. 59 and 64] suggests that the observed salt effects are due

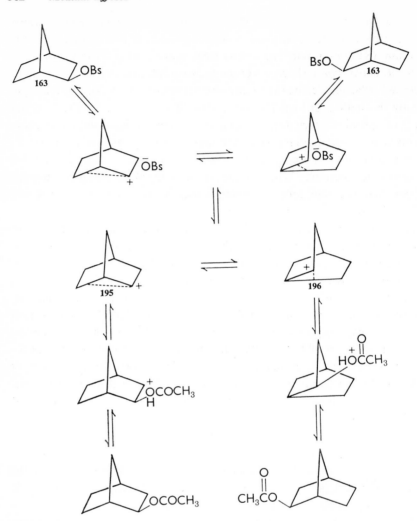

Figure 2.47 The racemization and solvolysis of *exo*-norbornyl *p*-bromobenzene-sulfonate (**163**) in acetic acid.

to ion-pairs, as one might expect for the low dielectric constant of acetic acid ($D = 6$). However, plots of $\log k$ against salt concentration are almost as linear as those shown in Fig. 2.49.

The rate constant, k_t, which is derived from the titrimetric rate of disappearance, is also increased by lithium perchlorate for acetolyses in a way described by Eq. 89, a relationship similar to Eq. 88 except for the constant.

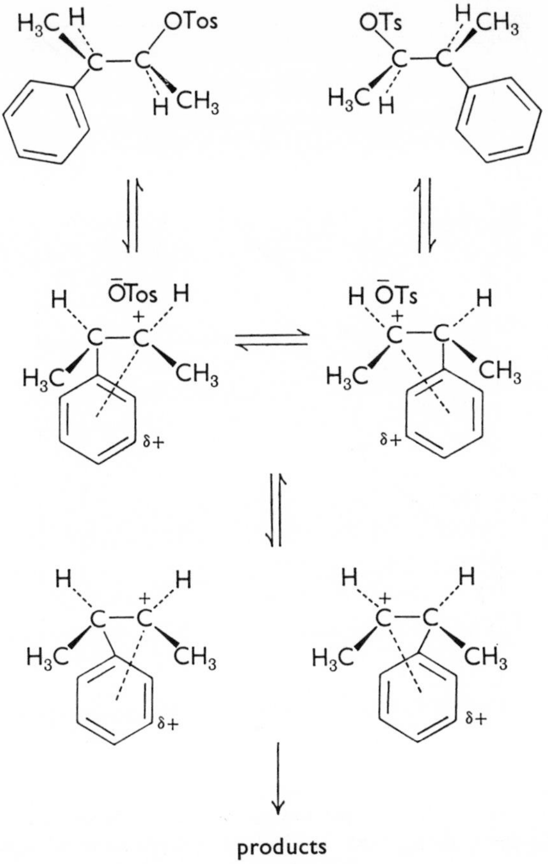

Figure 2.48 The solvolysis and racemization of *threo*-3-phenyl-2-butyl *p*-toluene-sulfonate (**150**).

The titrimetric rate constants for the acetolysis of compounds like **163** and **150** are correlated by:

$$(89) \qquad k_t = k_t^0[1 + b(\text{LiClO}_4)]$$

In a few cases, like *threo*-3-*p*-anisyl-2-butyl *p*-toluenesulfonate (**383**), cholesteryl *p*-toluenesulfonate (**97**) and several others summarized in Table 2.16, the value of the titrimetric rate constant predicted at zero salt concentration (k_{ext}^0) is two to three times greater than the titrimetric rate constant actually measured by experiment (k_t^0). In sharp contrast to the discrepancy found for the titrimetric rate constant, the polarimetric rate constant (k_α^0)

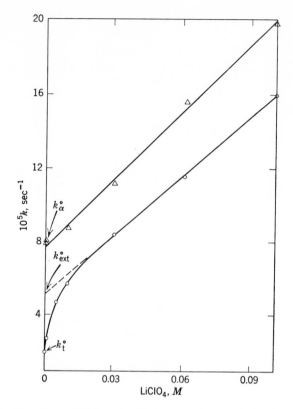

Figure 2.49   The effect of lithium perchlorate on the acetolysis of *threo*-3-*p*-anisyl-2-butyl *p*-bromobenzenesulfonate (**383**) at 25° (*432*). (Reproduced with permission from the *Journal of the American Chemical Society*.)

predicted from Eq. 88 is that found by experiment. Winstein and co-workers concluded that the strikingly rapid rise in titrimetric rate constant for low lithium perchlorate concentrations (the "special salt effect") coupled with the linear behavior of the polarimetric rate constant demanded an extra intermediate in solvolysis which they identified as a "solvent-separated" ion-pair. The rate constants for **383** as a function of lithium perchlorate concentration in acetic acid are shown in Fig. 2.49.

The polarimetric rate constant measures the formation of ion-pairs, which Winstein calls "intimate" ion-pairs. The titrimetric rate constant indicates how fast protons are generated from the combination of acetic acid with the cationic portion of the ion-pair or a carbonium ion. The special salt effect indicates that there is a reservoir of intermediate which does not participate

TABLE 2.16 *Salt Effects in Acetolysis of Arenesulfonates*[a]

	Temperature °C	Salt Effect Parameter (b)[b,c]	$(LiClO_4)_{1/2}$[d]	k^0_{ext}/k^0_t [e]
exo-Norbornyl OBs[f] (**163**)	25	38	—	1.0[h]
threo-3-Phenyl-2-butyl OTs[g]	50	37	—	1.0[h]
1-*p*-Anisyl-2-propyl OTs[g]	50	27	3×10^{-3}	2.4
3-*p*-Anisyl-2-butyl OBs[f] (**383**)	25	18	4×10^{-3}	3.1
2-*p*-Anisylethyl OTs[g]	50	11	3.4×10^{-4}	3.3
Cholesteryl OTs[g] (**97**)	50	28	4×10^{-5}	2.3
2-(2,4-Dimethoxyphenyl-)-ethyl OBs[f]	50	12	8×10^{-5}	2.2

[a] Ref. 432. [b] Eq. 2-89. [c] $LiClO_4$. [d] Concentration of $LiClO_4$ required to raise the titrimetric constant to half of the extrapolated constant (k^0_{ext}) based on Eq. 89. [e] See Fig. 2.49. [f] *p*-Bromobenzenesulfonate. [g] *p*-Toluenesulfonate. [h] No special salt effect.

in racemization, but which can generate protons at a higher rate than observed in the absence of lithium perchlorate. The mechanism by which the additional intermediate responds to the presence of the lithium perchlorate is through formation of a solvent-separated perchlorate ion-pair. It seems reasonable that the perchlorate anion would have a lower tendency to return to intimate ion-pair than arenesulfonate ions. Ehret and Winstein (*439*) have obtained good kinetic evidence for the formation of cholesteryl perchlorate in the perchloric acid catalyzed rearrangement of 3,5-cyclocholestan-6β-yl acetate (**101** acetate). Furthermore, Winstein, Klinedinst, and Clippinger (*440*) have been able to demonstrate a parallelism in the salt effects produced by lithium bromide and lithium perchlorate on the acetolysis of **383** (the same k^0_{ext} from both at 25°). The bromide ion acts as an efficient scavenger for solvent-separated ion-pairs, forming the bromide corresponding to **383**. A complete mechanistic scheme for the reactions of **383** is shown in Fig. 2.50.

The "intimate" ion-pair solvolysis intermediate is, in all probability, to be identified with the cage pair of Fig. 2.44, and would, in our terminology, be called a cage ion-pair. The solvent-separated ion-pair may be equivalent to an extended cage pair or a solvent-separated pair, with the former preferred. There is no experimental evidence on the structure of these ion-pairs, so that we shall often use the term introduced by Winstein to describe ion-pairs that have one or more solvent molecules between the partners, but we shall utilize

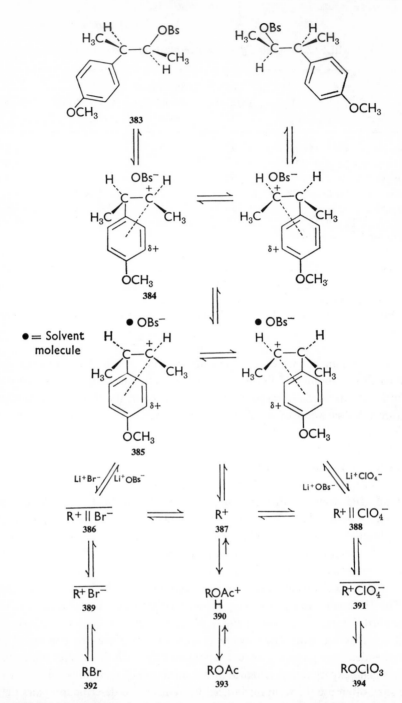

Figure 2.50 Mechanistic scheme for the acetolysis of *threo*-3-*p*-anisyl-2-butyl *p*-bromo-benzenesulfonate (**383**).

the expression *cage ion-pair* in the sense of intimate ion-pair. The general equilibria and the symbols used are shown in Eq. 90, which is almost the same as Eq. 72.

(90) $RX \rightleftharpoons \overline{R^+X^-} \rightleftharpoons \overline{R^+ \parallel X^-} \rightleftharpoons R^+ + X^- \longrightarrow$ products

                       Cage   Solvent-
                 ion-pair   separated
                               ion-pair

An amazing amount of information about ion-pairs involving free radicals can be obtained from a study of electron paramagnetic resonance (e.p.r.) spectra. Additional insight is gained from a study of ultraviolet and visible spectra. These spectroscopic studies confirm the existence of several kinds of ion-pairs. Adam and Weissmann (*441*) discovered that the sodium ketyl of benzophenone had an e.p.r. spectrum with lines that could only be explained if interaction with sodium were involved. The way in which the interaction with sodium is exhibited is in the splitting observed in the hyperfine e.p.r. spectrum.

An unpaired electron in a magnetic field can occupy (crudely speaking) two possible energy levels, one in which the spin is aligned with the field and one in which the spin is counter to the field. Observing the e.p.r. spectrum involves detecting transitions between these two levels. The level of the unpaired electron may be split into these two levels (labeled $+1/2$ and $-1/2$) by an external magnetic field and split further by the magnetic field of a nucleus with a magnetic moment. Three nuclei with nuclear spins of $1/2$ (H^1, F^{19}, and C^{13}) are shown in Fig. 2.51*a*. An expanded version of the energy level-splitting diagram is shown in Part 3, Section 3.2. The magnitude of the splitting produced by a nucleus is dependent on the size of its magnetic moment and the extent to which it "sees" the electron. For example, two possible structures for the methyl radical are shown in Fig. 2.51*b*. The unpaired electron in a tetrahedral methyl radical would occupy an sp^3-orbital and would spend 25% of its time in an orbital with considerable density at the carbon nucleus. The coupling constant for an electron in a carbon $2s$ orbital has been estimated as 300 gauss. The coupling constant estimated for a C^{13} nucleus in a tetrahedral methyl radical would be at least 75 gauss. The unpaired electron in a *planar* methyl radical would be in a *p*-orbital and would, in the limit, spend no time near the carbon nucleus. The coupling constant would not be zero, however, since the orbital occupied by the electron would not be purely *p* and some effect of the carbon-13 nucleus would be transmitted by spin polarization (Fig. 2.51*c*). The coupling constant observed for C^{13} in a methyl radical by McConnell and his co-workers is

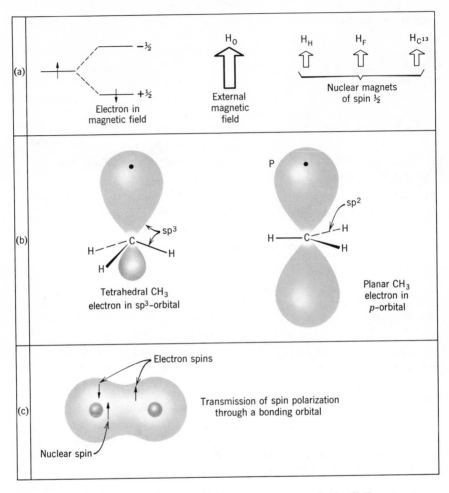

Figure 2.51 (*a*) Splitting of electron energy levels by magnetic fields. (*b*) Two structures for methyl radical. (*c*) Spin polarization of bonding orbital.

about 41 gauss (*134*), of which the greater portion should probably be ascribed to spin polarization.

Splitting in an e.p.r. spectrum thus provides insight into how much time the unpaired electron spends near a particular nucleus. Sodium-23 has a nucleus with a nuclear spin of 3/2 (see Appendix A, *442*) and would produce a four-line pattern. Finding such a pattern in the sodium ketyl of benzophenone (*395*) demonstrated that the unpaired electron spent part of its time near the sodium nucleus. Only direct contact between the partners in a cage ion-pair could account for the results.

(91) $$(C_6H_5)_2C{=}O + Na \longrightarrow (C_6H_5)_2\overset{\cdot}{C}{=}O^-Na^+$$

$$395$$

The structure of the cage ion-pair varies with the solvent for a given cation-anion combination. Hirota (*443*) finds that the sodium splitting in sodium anthracenide in tetrahydrofuran (THF) is 1.55 gauss, but 2.9 gauss in dibutyl ether (DBE). Part of the difference may be ascribed to the fact that THF can interact with the sodium cation more effectively than DBE, reducing the demand on the electron present in the anthracenide portion of the ion-pair. It is unlikely, however, that the solvation factor could account for all of the variation in sodium splitting and some structural difference (that is, average distance between cation and anion) in the ion-pair is no doubt responsible.

The electron distribution within the ketyl radical anion varies with the strength of the interaction between the metal cation and the oxygen. Hirota (*444*) measured the C^{13}-splitting at the carbonyl carbon in a series of metal benzophenone ketyls and showed that the greater the electrostatic attraction was between the metal cation and the oxygen, the more spin density there was on the carbonyl carbon. Small cations had a greater effect than large cations. We may express this change in electron distribution by writing the resonance forms:

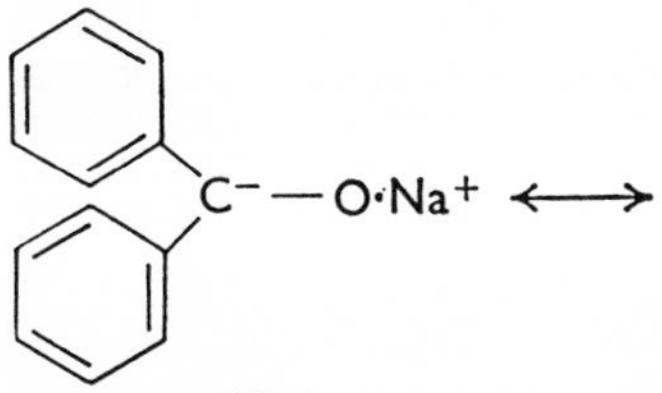

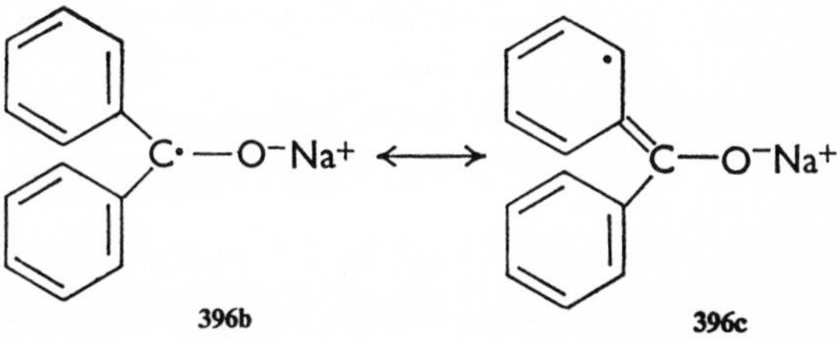

The magnitude of the sodium splitting for sodium anthracenide (Eq. 92) varies markedly with temperature (*443*), changing from 1.55 gauss in 2-methyl-tetrahydrofuran (MTHF) at 50°C to 0.50 gauss at −90°C. A plot of the coupling constant (a_{Na}) against temperature varies in a way expected for an equilibrium (Fig. 2.52). The marked temperature sensitivity of the sodium coupling constant was first reported by Atherton and Weissman for sodium naphthalenide (*447*). The phenomenon was originally interpreted as the result of an increase with temperature in the time spent by the sodium ion near positions of appreciable spin density, with the most stable position identified as the node of zero spin density between the 9 and 10 carbons of the naphthalenide ions. Hirota and Kreilick (*448*) have suggested that an equilibrium between two kinds of ion-pairs, a cage ion-pair and a solvent-separated ion-pair, was more reasonable as an explanation for the observation that the outer lines of the sodium quartet broadened before the inner lines changed as the temperature was lowered.

(92)

The larger the cation, the smaller the electrostatic attraction between the cation and the anion, with the result that smaller couplings to the alkali metal cation would be observed. Smaller coupling constants should be found for larger alkali metal cations, in any case, since the density of the acceptor *s* orbital at the nucleus decreases with increasing atomic number. Figure 2.52 illustrates the variation in the coupling constant for cesium and potassium anthracenides. These are considerably smaller than the sodium couplings. Unlike the sodium coupling constant, the splittings rise slightly with decreasing temperature. Larger alkali cations would gain less from increased solvation with the change from a cage ion-pair to a solvent-separated ion-pair. The cage ion-pairs derived from cesium and potassium are apparently more

TABLE 2.17   *Thermodynamic Quantities for the Conversion of Cage Ion-Pairs to Solvent-separated Ion-pairs* [a]

	Sodium Anthracenide		Sodium Naphthalenide	Sodium Fluorenylide [b]
	MTHF	THF-MTHF	THF	THF
$\Delta H°$ (kcal./mole)	-4.6 ± 0.3	-5.6 ± 0.4	-4.7 ± 0.3	-7.6
$\Delta S°$ (e.u.)	-23 ± 5	-23 ± 6	-20 ± 5	ca. -25

[a] Ref. 443.   [b] Ref. 455.

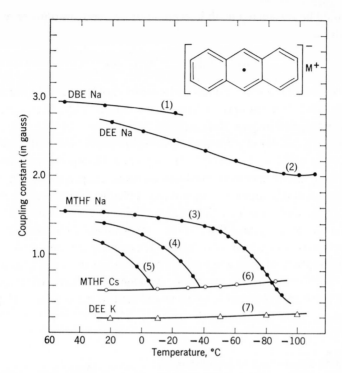

Figure 2.52 The temperature dependence of the alkali metal coupling constants for anthracenide ions: —●— sodium, ····△···· potassium, ---○--- cesium. The solvents used were (1) DBE = di-*n*-butyl ether, (2) DEE = diethyl ether, (3) MTHF = 2-methyltetrahydrofuran, (4) 65% MTHF + 35% THF = tetrahydrofuran, (5) 35% MTHF + 65% THF, (6) MTHF, (7) DEE (*443*). (Reproduced with permission of the authors and the *Journal of Physical Chemistry*.)

stable than "looser" ion pairs over the whole range of temperature open to investigation.

The apparently surprising conclusion that the cage ion-pair is more stable than the solvent-separated ion-pair at high temperatures (for sodium anthracenide) is reasonable (even if not predictable) in terms of the interaction of solvent with the sodium ion in the two forms. Hirota (*443*) has derived thermodynamic quantities for the equilibrium shown in Eq. 93 by using the splitting constants as a measure of the concentration of the different forms. These are listed in Table 2.17. The electron-transfer reaction between anthracenide ions and anthracene (*443*) and that between naphthalene and naphthalenide ions (*449*) is slowed by a factor of 100 compared to the rate in dimethoxyethane (DME) by ion-pairing. The possible intervention of ion pairs should be considered in all interpretations of electron-transfer reactions in all solvents.

(93) $$\overline{\text{ArH}\cdot{}^-\text{Na}^+} \; \rightleftharpoons \; \overline{\text{ArH}\cdot{}^{-\text{V}}\text{Na}^+}$$

Other details about e.p.r. studies on ion-pairs should be sought in the work of Hirota (*450*), Symons (*451*), Chang and Johnson (*452*), Luckhurst (*453*), and Atherton and Goggins (*454*).

Hogen-Esch and Smid (*455*) examined the ultraviolet and visible spectrum of sodium fluorenylide (Eq. 94) in THF and made the important observations that changing the temperature produces a change in spectrum characteristic of the formation of another species but that a change in the concentration by a factor of 100 did not change the relative heights of the maxima at 3560 and 3730 A at any temperature. The spectroscopic changes are illustrated in Fig. 2.53. The two species which participate in the equilibrium must thus have the same composition since changing the concentration does not change their relative contributions to the spectrum. An equilibrium between a cage ion-pair and a solvent-separated ion-pair would lead to these results. The effect of the cation on the spectrum of the cage ion-pair is considerable as shown in

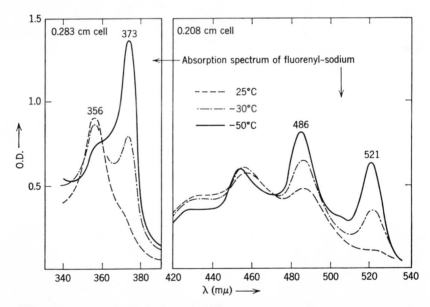

Figure 2.53   The effect of temperature on the absorption spectrum of sodium fluorenylide in THF (*455*). (Reprinted with permission of the authors and the *Journal of the American Chemical Society.*)

TABLE 2.18   *Dependence of the Position of Absorption Maximum on Cation Radius for Fluorenylide Ion-pairs*[a,b]

Cation	r, Å[e]	λ_{max}, A
Li^+	0.60	3490
Na^+	0.96	3560
K^+	1.33	3620
Cs^+	1.66	3640
$n\text{-}Bu_4N^{+}$ [c]	3.5	3680
$\overline{M^{+}}^{V}$ [d]	~4.5	3730
Free anion	∞	3740

[a] Ref. 455. [b] In THF at 25°. [c] Tetra-*n*-butyl-ammonium ion. [d] Signifies solvent-separated ion-pair. [e] Cation radius.

Table 2.18. The solvent-separated ion-pair has a spectrum which is independent of the cation.

The reactivity of the polystyrene anion ("living polymer anion") depends on the counter-ion and the solvent. In dioxane, the propagation rates for

(94)

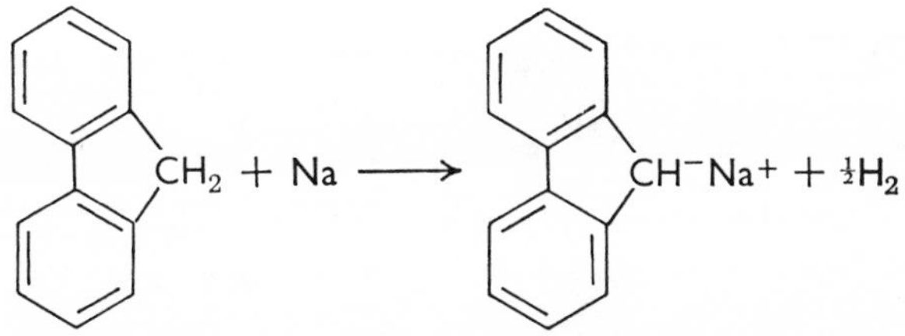

(95)

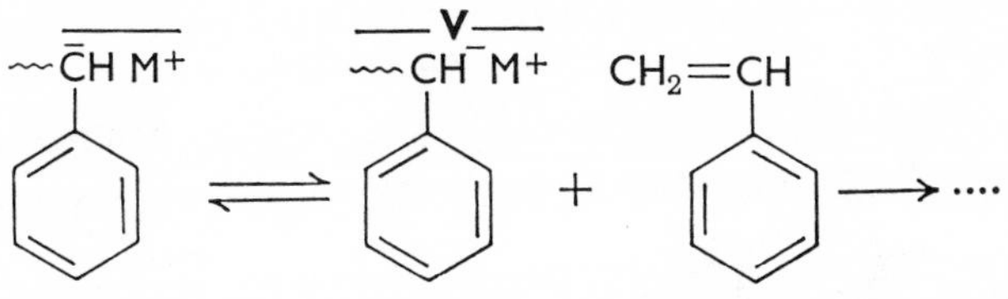

styrene increase with the size of the counter ion, from 0.9 l. mole^{-1} sec.$^{-1}$ for lithium to 24.5 l. mole^{-1} sec.$^{-1}$ for cesium, the order expected if the electrostatic stabilization of the cage ion-pair controlled the ease of dissociation to the more reactive solvent-separated ion-pair. In tetrahydrofuran, the rates

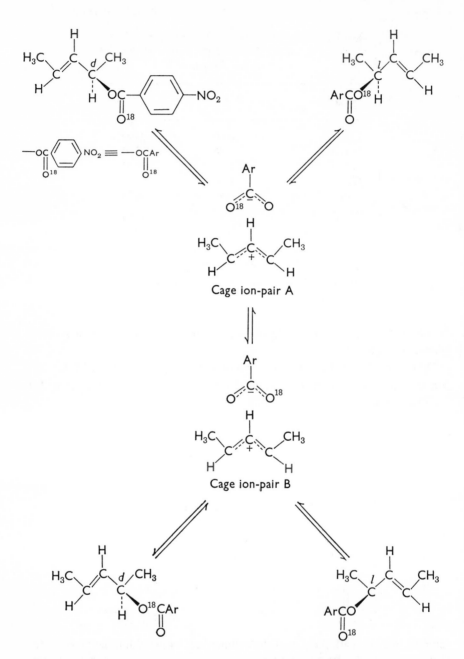

Figure 2.54 Mechanism for the racemization and O^{18}-equilibration accompanying the solvolysis of *trans-α*, *γ*-dimethylallyl *p*-nitrobenzoate in 60% or 90% acetone (*457*) [*d*- and *l*- are arbitrary designations to differentiate the enantiomers].

change from 160 l. mole^{-1} sec.$^{-1}$ for lithium to 22 l. mole^{-1} sec.$^{-1}$ for cesium, in accord with what might be expected for the relative amounts of cage ion-pair and solvent-separated ion-pairs (456). The large cesium ion is not as well solvated as the small lithium ion and produces a lower proportion of the reactive solvent-separated ion-pairs. In Fig. 2.52, the failure of the cesium splitting constant to change with temperature for e.p.r. spectra of cesium anthracenide is clearly shown and is understandable if the cesium salt is present as cage ion-pairs with little tendency to dissociate.

The discussion of ion-pairs will be concluded by brief descriptions of a number of reactions, for which the intervention of ion-pairs must be postulated to explain the results. The examples are varied and suggest that a detailed understanding of the chemistry of ion-pairs is required in preparative organic as well as physical organic chemistry.

Goering, Pombo, and McMichael (457) investigated the *trans*-α,γ-dimethyl-allyl *p*-nitrobenzoate. Racemization of the optically active ester in 60% (or 90%) acetone proceeded at the same rate as equilibration of an O^{18}-label between the carbonyl-O^{18} and the ether-O^{18}. However, reresolution of racemic alcohol obtained from recovered ester demonstrated that bonding of the oxygen of the carboxylate ion to the allylic cation occurred preferentially between proximate atoms. In the mechanism shown in Fig. 2.54, the latter result implies that conversion of ion-pair A to ion-pair B is slower than collapse to ester. [Note that both partners are *ambident*, capable of reaction at two sites.]

Alcohols react with thionyl chloride to form a chlorosulfite (Eq. 96). The chlorosulfite group is an extremely good leaving group, and it is difficult to isolate the chlorosulfite derivatives of any but those alkyl groups which are poorest at supporting the acquisition of a positive charge. Under the usual reaction conditions (excess thionyl chloride in pure form), it is difficult to establish the pathway by which the products are formed. In ether solution with equimolar thionyl chloride, an approach first applied by Kosower and Winstein to 3,5-cyclocholestan-6β-ol (**101**) (*102, 105*), reaction proceeds through cage ion-pairs. It is interesting that the major product [**133**/**132** ∼ 5] is the one in which the chloride group is attached to a position away from the atom near which it was first located in the initial ion-pair (see the scheme outlined in Fig. 2.55). It is not known whether the chlorosulfite ion rotated before losing sulfur dioxide or whether the chloride ion-pair should have been counted as one ion-pair or as two localized ion-pairs that equilibrate with great rapidity. Of these possibilities, rotation of the chlorosulfite ion seems

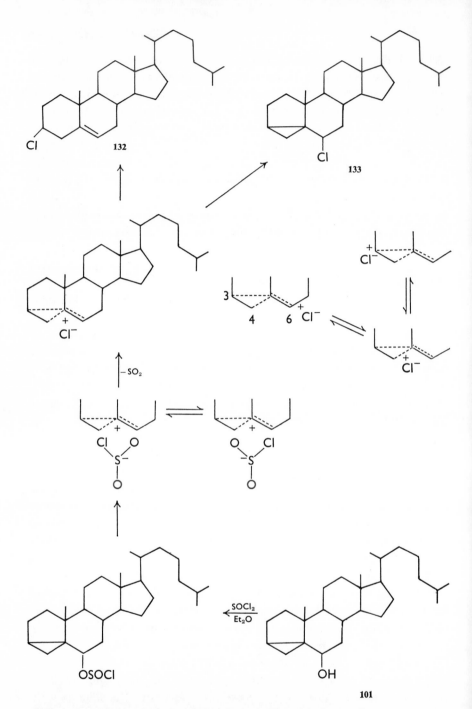

Figure 2.55 Scheme for the formation of cholesteryl chloride and 3,5-cyclocholestan‾ 6β-yl chloride from 3,5-cyclocholestan-6β-ol (**101**) (*102, 105*).

the more reasonable. If the localized ion-pairs are not completely interconvertible before collapse to covalent chlorides, the product ratios (for reaction at the two reactive positions, 3 and 6) may not reflect the intrinsic reactivity of the ion.

$$\text{(96)} \qquad \text{ROH} + \text{SOCl}_2 \longrightarrow \text{ROSOCl} + \text{HCl}$$
$$\text{ROSOCl} \longrightarrow \text{RCl} + \text{SO}_2$$

White and Elliger (*458*) utilized internal return from an ambident ion-pair to convert alcohols to amines, as shown in Eq. 97. Benzhydrol was converted in 76% yield to benzhydryl dimethylamine (Eq. 98). The pathway of the reaction is similar to that of formation of benzhydryl isothiocyanate from benzhydryl thiocyanate studied by Fava and co-workers (*459*) (Eq. 99).

(97) $\text{ROH} + \text{R}'_2\text{NSO}_2\text{Cl} \longrightarrow \text{ROSO}_2\text{NR}'_2 \longrightarrow \text{R}^+\bar{\text{O}}\text{SO}_2\text{NR}'_2$

$$\longrightarrow \text{R}^+ \overset{\text{R}'}{\underset{\text{R}'}{\text{N}}}\bar{\text{SO}}_3 \longrightarrow \text{RNR}'_2$$

(98)

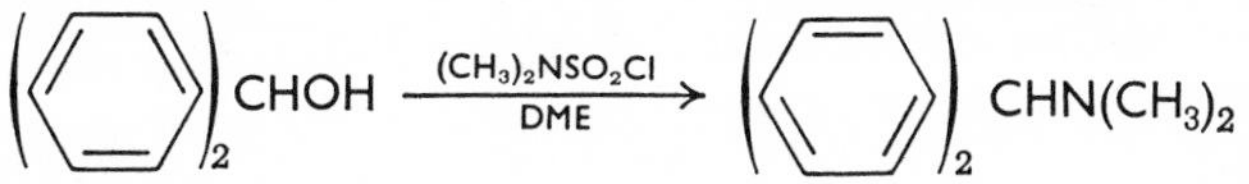

(99)

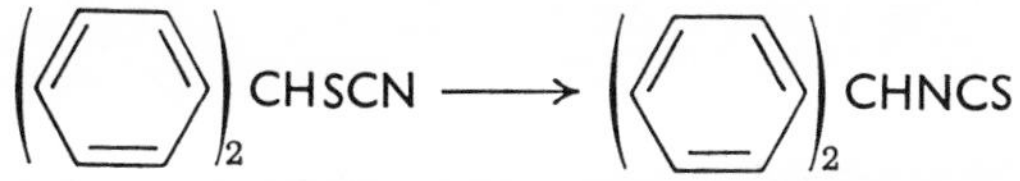

Cram and his co-workers (see the summary in *10*) have reported that optically active 2(*N*,*N*-dimethylcarbamido)-9-methylfluorene (**397**) labeled with deuterium in the 9-position exchanges far more rapidly with ammonia in THF than it loses optical activity. The intermediate ion-pair contains an ammonium ion which can rotate more rapidly than the fluorenylide anion can extract a proton (or deuteron). The exchange and racemization are shown in Fig. 2.56.

Walborsky and his students (*460*) have added greatly to our knowledge of the stereochemistry of the reaction of the ion-pairs present in organometallic derivatives, such as organolithium compounds and Grignard reagents, with

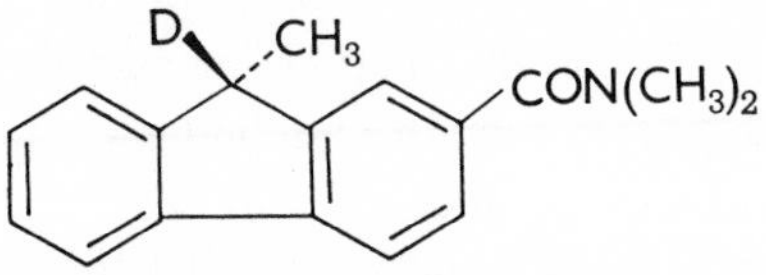

397

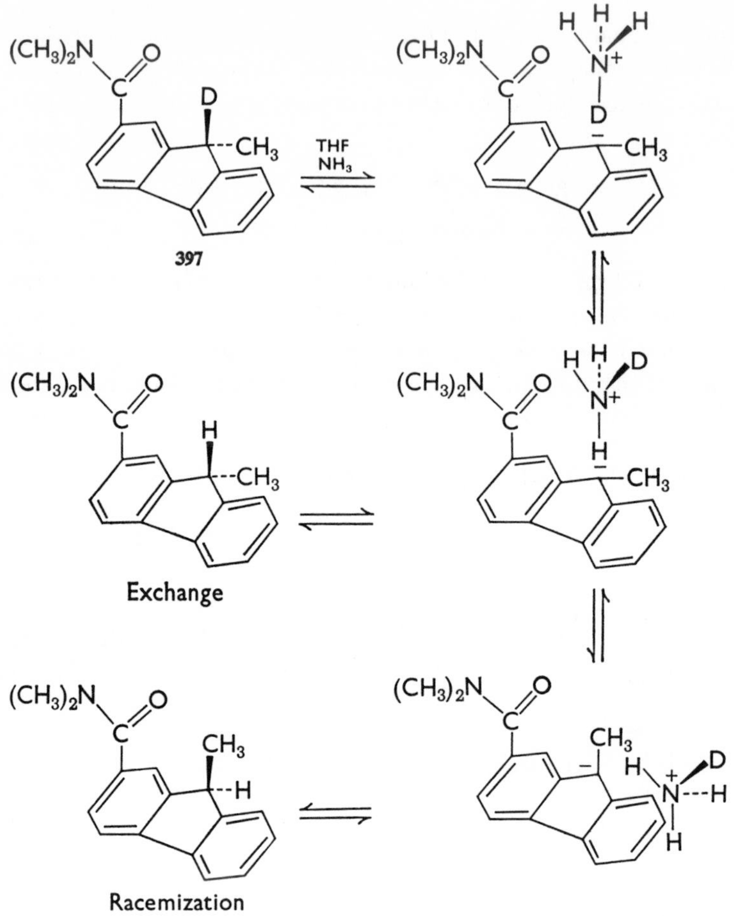

Figure 2.56 Exchange and racemization produced by the action of ammonia on 2-(*N,N*-dimethylcarbamido)-9-methylfluorene-9-*d* (**397**) at 145° in THF (*10*).

studies of the reactions 2,2-diphenyl-1-methylcyclopropyl bromide (**398**). Cyclopropyl magnesium bromide and cyclopropyl lithium form and react with predominant retention of configuration (Fig. 2.57). Primary Grignard reagents (which, according to the work of Stucky and Rundle, *461*, on the crystal structure of phenylmagnesium bromide dietherate, must be alkyl-magnesium halides) invert configuration quite rapidly as determined by n.m.r. studies on 3,3-dimethylbutyl magnesium chloride in diethyl ether (*462*). Whiteside and Roberts (*463*) have found that secondary alkyl magnesium halides invert much more slowly and probably do so in a bimolecular reaction with another alkyl magnesium halide. The relatively rapid racemization of

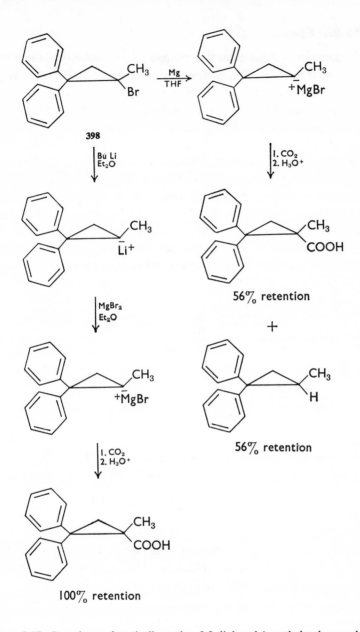

Figure 2.57 Reactions of optically active 2,2-diphenyl-1-methylcyclopropyl bromide (**398**) through lithium and bromomagnesium ion-pairs. Formation of the cyclopropyl magnesium bromide from the bromide and magnesium probably proceeds via charge-transfer to the magnesium in the solid and therefore involves a radical-like intermediate with modest configurational stability (*460*).

sec-butyl lithium at $-8°$ indicates that configurational stability of the lithium alkyls must be lower than that of the alkyl magnesium halides. Cram (*10*) notes that rates of inversion of organometallic compounds decrease from lithium to magnesium to aluminum to mercury. It is likely that the mechanisms of inversion change with the cation so that direct comparisons are extremely difficult to make. Knowledge of the behavior of ion-pairs from other studies, especially for those derivatives studied by e.p.r., should aid research on organic derivatives of Group I and Group II cations.

The creation of desired reaction partners can be favored by the use of charged micelles, as pointed out by Winters and Grunwald (*464*) and supported by the investigations of Cordes and co-workers (*465*).

The transformation of hydrazones into hydrocarbons (the "Wolff–Kishner reaction") proceeds via solvent-mediated transfer of a proton from nitrogen to carbon.

(100)
$$\underset{R}{\overset{R}{\diagdown}}C{=}NNH_2 \xrightarrow[\substack{ROH \\ 200°}]{RO^-} \underset{R}{\overset{R}{\diagdown}}CH_2 + N_2$$

(101)
$$\underset{R}{\overset{R}{\diagdown}}C{=}NNH_2 \xrightarrow{RO^-} \underset{R}{\overset{R}{\diagdown}}C{-}N{=}N^- \xrightarrow{ROH} \underset{R}{\overset{R}{\diagdown}}CH_2 + N_2$$

The hydrazone anion is relatively stable in an aprotic dipolar solvent like dimethyl sulfoxide, according to Szmant and Roman (*471*).

(102)
$$\underset{R}{\overset{R}{\diagdown}}C{=}NNH_2 \xrightarrow[CH_3SOCH_3]{^-CH_2SOCH_3} \underset{R}{\overset{R}{\diagdown}}C{=}N\bar{N}H$$

The ion which forms by rearrangement is known to be unstable from the results of Kosower and Huang (*472, 666*) who generated phenyldiimide anion from phenyldiimide (**399**) and hydroxide ion.

(103)
$$\left[\underset{R}{\overset{R}{\diagdown}}C{=}N\bar{N}H \longleftrightarrow \underset{R}{\overset{R}{\diagdown}}\bar{C}{-}N{=}NH \right] \xrightarrow{ROH} \underset{R}{\overset{R}{\diagdown}}C{-}\overset{H}{\underset{}{N}}{=}NH$$

$$\longrightarrow \underset{R}{\overset{R}{\diagdown}}C{-}\overset{H}{\underset{}{N}}{=}N^-$$

(104)

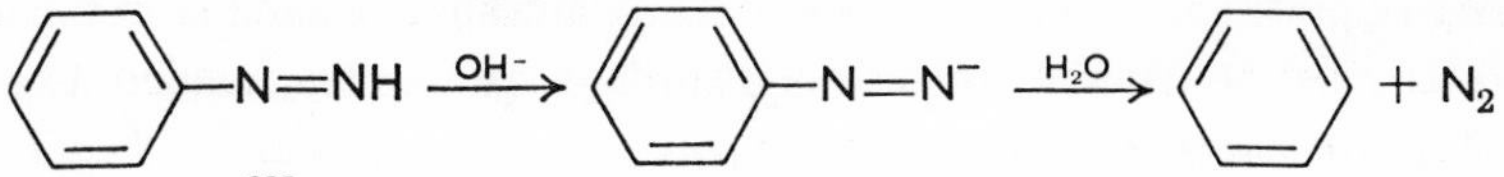

399

An unusually efficient conversion of benzophenone hydrazone into diphenylmethane is effected by potassium *t*-butoxide in dimethyl sulfoxide at 25° (*473*). Since the hydrazone anion (Eq. 102) is stable in the absence of a proton donor, the rapid overall reaction (Eq. 100) must be due to the presence

(105)

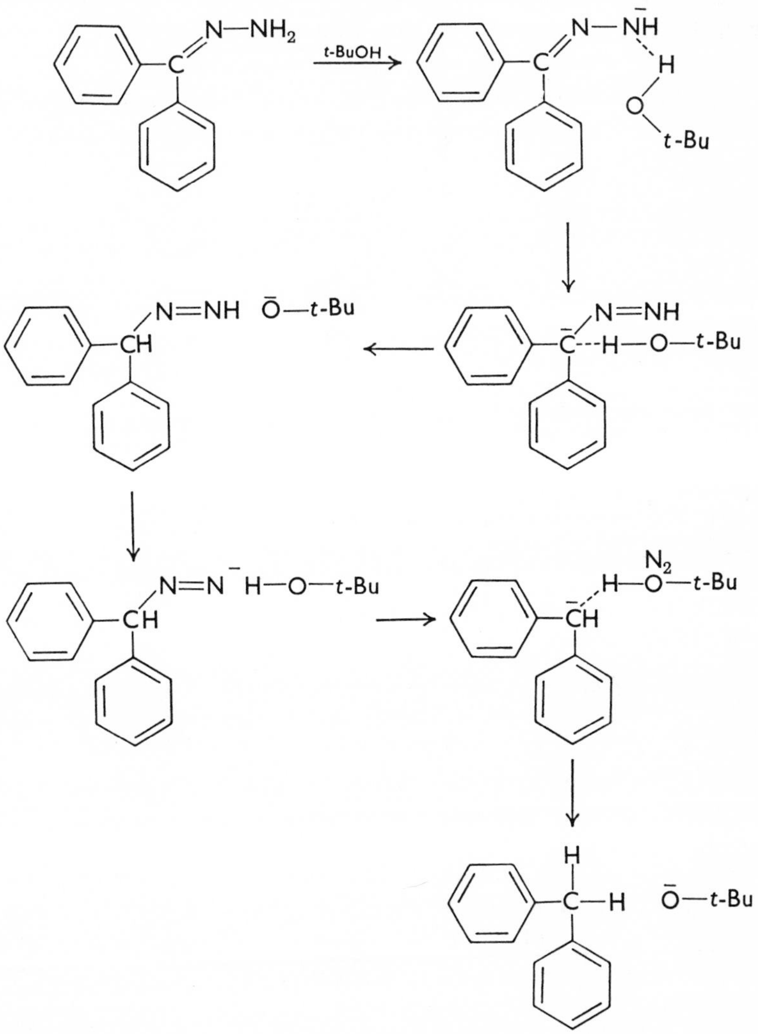

of a *t*-butyl alcohol molecule in the immediate environment of the hydrazone anion. The *t*-butyl alcohol molecule and hydrazone anion constitute a pair of reaction partners that react within a solvent cage to yield diimide with unusual facility (Eq. 103). This reaction is an example of the great importance of the local environment and the significance of reaction partners in determining the rates of reactions. The conversion of the benzophenone hydrazone into diphenylmethane is summarized in the following equations.

The study of reaction partners and their role in many reactions will be an important part of physical organic chemistry. To summarize their behavior in the briefest possible way, we may write:

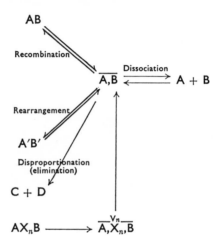

Problems

1. Compare two aprotic dipolar solvents with two hydroxylic solvents with respect to the solvation of sodium iodide, using approximately correct size parameters to draw the cybotactic regions.

2. Why is *N*-methylacetamide so different from *N,N*-dimethylacetamide for the displacement of iodide ion from methyl iodide by chloride ion? (Relative rate k_{DMA}/k_{NMA} about 10^5.)

3. Sodium azide reacts with 4-fluoronitrobenzene in dimethylformamide to form a compound which remains in solution. Addition of water (5%) precipitates sodium fluoride. Explain the nature of the compounds formed and draw a free energy versus reaction coordinate diagram for the reaction.

4. How can one reverse the usual order of nucleophilicity of the halide ions: $I^- > Br^- > Cl^-$? Why is this possible?

5. Give the product of the reaction between lithium chloride and 2-chloro-2-methylcyclohexanone in dimethylformamide.

6. Plot the relative rate of racemization of 2-methyl-3-phenylpropionitrile in methanolic solvents (Table 2.12) against % methanol, concentration methanol, and log concentration methanol.

7. Using the lattice model for solutions, calculate the concentrations at which interionic attraction becomes less than 10% of kinetic energy for uni-univalent salts in acetonitrile, methanol, ethanol, and benzene.

8. Give some examples of hydrophobic ion-pairing.

9. Define the following:
   (a) Aprotic dipolar solvent.
   (b) Hydrophobic ion-pairing.
   (c) Reaction partners.
   (d) Cage effects.
   (e) Scavenger.

10. What are the products of photolysis of a (1:1) mixture of $CH_3N{=}NCH_3$ and $CD_3N{=}NCD_3$ in isooctane solution? How would the product composition change if the photolysis were carried to only 50% completion? Would the results change if the reaction were carried out in the gas phase?

11. Define the following terms:
    (a) Cage pair.
    (b) Extended cage pair.
    (c) Solvent-separated pair.
    (d) Cybotactic region pair.
    (e) Intimate ion-pair.
    (f) Solvent-separated ion-pair.

12. Write a complete scheme for the decomposition of the unknown diacyl hyponitrite **A**. Would you expect this compound to be more readily decomposed than di-*t*-butyl hyponitrite? Why? Suppose the *t*-butyl group in **A** were replaced by a tertiary alkyl group which was part of a polymer chain. How would the course of the reaction depend upon the nature of the polymer?

$$(CH_3)_3CO\overset{\displaystyle O}{\overset{\displaystyle \|}{C}}ON{=}NO\overset{\displaystyle O}{\overset{\displaystyle \|}{C}}OC(CH_3)_3$$

A

How would you prepare compound **A**?

13. Why does the yield of tetramethylsuccinonitrile in the decomposition of azoisobutyronitrile depend upon the concentration of added 1-butanethiol?

14. Give the products of solvolysis of α,α-dimethylallyl chloride in acetic acid. Write a complete scheme for their formation.

15. Define the following terms:
    (a) Special salt effect.
    (b) Internal return.
    (c) Living polymer anion.
16. Draw a detailed scheme (like Fig. 2.50) for cholesteryl tosylate solvolysis in acetic acid. Show which portions apply to k_t^0, k_{ext}°. What process corresponds to racemization in the *threo*-3-*p*-ansiyl-2-butyl brosylate solvolysis in acetic acid?
17. Write resonance forms to express the origin of the sodium splitting in the e.p.r. spectrum of the sodium ketyl of benzophenone.
18. Why does the sodium splitting of sodium anthracenide vary with temperature?
19. Explain the effect of solvent on the reactivity of the lithium "living" polystyrene anion combination. (The rate of reaction with styrene increases by a factor of about 180 on changing the solvent from dioxane to tetrahydrofuran.)
20. Explain why it might be difficult to achieve quantitative rearrangement of carbonyl-O^{18} *trans*-α,γ-dimethylallyl *p*-nitrobenzoate to the ether-O^{18} derivative. What would the stereochemical consequences of this rearrangement be? (*Hint:* Use free energy versus reaction coordinate diagrams and good judgement.)
21. Rationalize *in detail* the formation of 3,5-*cyclo*cholestan-6β-yl chloride and cholesteryl chloride from 3,5-*cyclo*cholestan-6β-ol and thionyl chloride in ether. Why could pure thionyl chloride not be used? What purpose does the ether serve? Could cholesterol be used as starting material?
22. Show how to convert optically active 2,2-diphenyl-1-methyl-cyclopropyl bromide into the corresponding carboxylic acid with 100% retention of stereochemistry. Why is the reaction sequence successful?
23. Using the summary scheme expressed in Eq. 106 (Part 2), and information for any place in this book or elsewhere, give a complete example for the following:
    (a) A,B   Radical pair.
    (b) A,B   Ion-pair (organic cation).
    (c) A,B   Ion-pair (organic anion).
    (d) A,B   Diradical ion-pair.

PART THREE

Reaction Intermediates and Unusual Molecules

„כבוד אלהים הסתר דבר

וכבוד מלכים חקור דבר"

Proverbs 25: 2

3.0 Introduction

Many years ago, Lapworth (*500*) demonstrated that the bromination of acetone proceeded through an *intermediate enol* or *enolate* ion. The rate of bromination depended upon acetone and catalyst (base or acid) and was independent of the bromine concentration (Eqs. 1 and 2).

$$(1) \quad CH_3COCH_3 + B: \ \rightleftharpoons \ CH_2{=}\overset{\overset{\displaystyle OH}{|}}{C}{-}CH_3 \ \rightleftharpoons \ CH_2{=}\overset{\overset{\displaystyle O^-}{|}}{C}{-}CH_3$$

$$(2) \quad CH_2{=}\overset{\overset{\displaystyle OH}{|}}{C}{-}CH_3 + Br_2 \ \longrightarrow \ BrCH_2COCH_3 + HBr$$

Although the utility of the mechanism for halogenation of ketones was clear, interest in intermediates did not become general until much later, probably because efficient methods for the detection of intermediates were not available. Indirect approaches predominated for the identification of reaction intermediates: the carbonium ion in "S_N1" reactions (Ingold, *59*), the tetrahedral intermediate in ester hydrolysis (use of O^{18} by Bender, *501*), radicals in abnormal addition of hydrogen bromide (*676*). Eventually the teachings of physical organic chemistry permeated most of organic chemistry, and attention shifted from gross mechanism (that is, are reactions free radical or ionic?) to the properties of the intermediates themselves. The development of many new techniques and instruments for the study of intermediates aided in this shift of emphasis, and an affluent economy made possible widespread use and application of many of the developments. The scientific advances, which contributed to the changes in organic chemistry, are summarized in Table 3.1 under the headings of production technique (for the generation of intermediates), storage techniques (for the retention of intermediates so that they may be further studied), and detection methods (for the observation of intermediates of various stabilities).

The third part of the book has been limited to *charged species* (carbonium ions and carbanions) and *radicals* (free radicals, radical ions, diradicals, methylenes, radical dimers). Other exciting areas might have been treated if space and time had permitted. For example, the study of *strained molecules* is extremely active and interesting for both mechanism and synthesis. Although the beautifully symmetric and symbolic tetrahedrane (**400**) has not yet been prepared, noteworthy strained molecules include benzyne (**401**),

TABLE 3.1   *Summary of Improvements*[a]

Production Technique	Storage Techniques	Detection Methods
Irradiation (steady-state and flash)	Matrix isolation	Vapor-phase chromatography
Visible	Inert gas	Spectra
Ultraviolet	Clathrate	Mass; Infrared;
X-ray	Crystal	Visible; Ultraviolet;
Electron pulse	Vacuum line	Fluorescence;
	technique	Phosphorescence;
Flow systems/jet		Electron paramagnetic
mixers		resonance;
		Nuclear magnetic
		resonance;
Improved chemistry		Optical rotatory
New reactions		dispersion;
Special solvents		Circular dichroism
		Isotopic labeling

[a] Examples are through fall, 1966. These lists are not intended to be exhaustive, and the student is urged to search for citations if lacking and to add details to any of the entries. Relaxation methods (temperature jump, pressure jump, electric field pulse, sound absorption) are very important but involve the detection (by some of the methods shown above) of changes in an equilibrium situation. It will not be obvious to students schooled in well-equipped undergraduate laboratories (and possessing some background and experience in many of the techniques and methods mentioned above) how drastic the change in organic chemical research was for the decade from 1950 to 1960.

[2.2]paracyclophane (**402**), bicyclobutane (**403**), cubane (**404**), hexahelicene (**405**), prismane (**406**), benzvalene (**407**), quadricyclane (**408**), cyclopropanone (**409**), tricyclo[2.2.0.0^{2,6}]hexane (**410**), bicyclo[2.1.0]pentene-2 (**411**), and bicyclo[2.2.0]hexa-2,5-diene (**412**). Several general discussions of ring strain are available (*701–703*).

The complete replacement of the hydrogen in hydrocarbons by fluorine to form perfluoroorganic compounds has been productive of materials with new and unusual chemical and physical properties. The principle of replacing all of the hydrogens in a hydrocarbon has been extended to other substituents to find out whether other *per-compounds* possess unusual properties. Per-cyanoethylene (**413**) (tetracyanoethylene, TCNE) is one of the best known materials resulting from such research. Others include pentacyanocyclopenta-

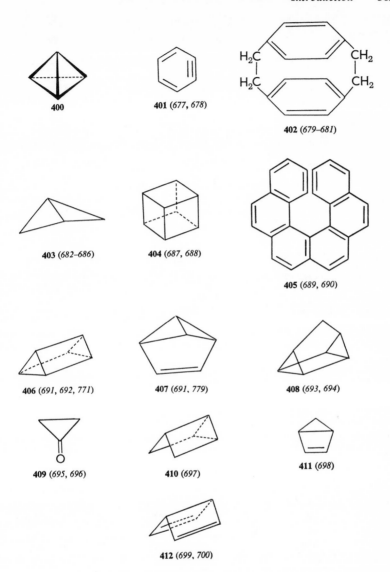

400

401 *(677, 678)*

H_2C CH_2
H_2C CH_2

402 *(679–681)*

403 *(682–686)*

404 *(687, 688)*

405 *(689, 690)*

406 *(691, 692, 771)*

407 *(691, 779)*

408 *(693, 694)*

O

409 *(695, 696)*

410 *(697)*

411 *(698)*

412 *(699, 700)*

dienide ion (**414**), *tetrakis*-(dimethylamino)methane (**415**), *tetrakis*-(dimethyl-amino)-ethylene (**416**), tetramethoxyethylene (**417**), and trichlorocyclo-propenium ion (**418**).

An area that is just beginning to feel the pressure of proliferation from its application to organic molecules is that of the chemistry of *excited states*, which could include those produced by photochemists, mass spectrometrists,

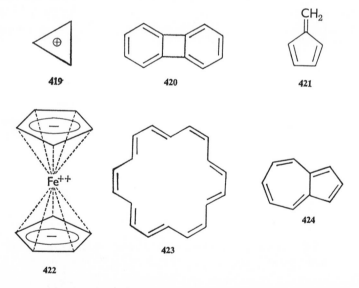

$(NC)_2C{=}C(CN)_2$

413 *(704)*

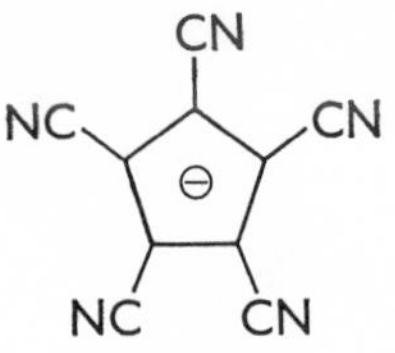

414 *(254)*

$[(CH_3)_2N]_4C$

415 *(705)*

$[(CH_3)_2N]_2C{=}C[N(CH_3)_2]_2$

416 *(706, 707)*

$(CH_3O)_2C{=}C(OCH_3)_2$

417 *(708)*

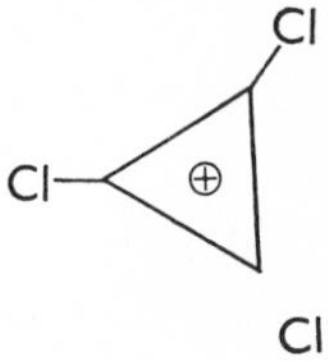

418 *(709)*

and those who study the interaction of high-energy radiation and matter. *Nonbenzenoid aromatic hydrocarbons* have been reviewed by Lloyd *(710)* in an excellent survey which covers cyclopropenium ions (**419**), biphenylene (**420**), fulvene (**421**), ferrocene (**422**), annulenes (for example, **423**), azulene (**424**), and many others.

419

420

421

422

423

424

Some of the factors that affect the path of an organic molecule over a free energy surface in a reaction are summarized in a free energy versus reaction coordinate diagram in Fig. 3.1. It is obvious that our understanding of such

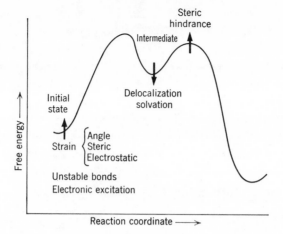

Figure 3.1   Free energy versus reaction coordinate diagram illustrating the factors which result in survival of an intermediate: its ease of formation from an initial state and the relative difficulty with which it proceeds to final product.

diagrams (and their physical counterparts—real chemical reactions) will be increased by the acquisition of knowledge about intermediates. The following discussion (in Sections 3.1 and 3.2) is designed to illustrate some of the methods used for studying intermediates, some of the structural factors affecting their properties, and some of the phenomena, including (where desirable) chemical reactions in which these intermediates are significant.

3.1 Charged Species

Some of the charged species which may serve as intermediates in organic chemistry are listed in Tables 3.2 and 3.3. We shall briefly discuss some general aspects of the stability of charged species, mostly as the ideas are applicable to carbon species. The remainder of this section is devoted to some ground-state properties of carbonium ions. Carbanions are only mentioned at the end because most of the important principles governing the

TABLE 3.2 *Electron-deficient Species*

Species	Formula	Example
Carbonium ion	R_3C^+	$(CH_3)_2CH^+$
Oxocarbonium ion (acylium ion)	RCO^+	CH_3CO^+
Nitrenium ion	$R_2\ddot{N}^+$	$(CH_3)_2N^+$
Oxonitrenium ion (nitrosonium ion)	$O{=}\ddot{N}^+$	NO^+
Oxenium ion	$R\ddot{\ddot{O}}^+$	CH_3O^+
Radical cation	$M\cdot^+$	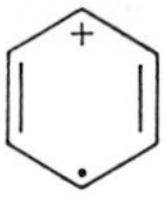

TABLE 3.3 *Electron-excess Species*

Species	Formula	Example
Carbanion	$R_3C:^-$	$CH_3{}^-$
Amide ion	$R_2\ddot{N}:^-$	$(CH_3)_2N:^-$
Alkoxide ion	$R\ddot{\ddot{O}}:^-$	CH_3O^-
Radical anion	$M\cdot^-$	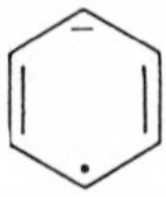
Electron (solvated)[a]	e_{solv}^-	e_{aq}^-

[a] See Ref. 544.

stability of carbanions have been taken up in the discussion of acidity. An excellent and complete description of the physical organic chemistry of carbanions is given in the book by Cram, *10*.

As an element in the middle of the first row of the periodic table, carbon is not especially effective at accepting electrons or at donating electrons. The "electronegativity" of carbon is about halfway between that of lithium and that of fluorine. The *electronegativity* of an element according to Mulliken is proportional to the sum of its electron affinity (ability to acquire an extra electron) and its ionization potential (energy required to remove an electron). The Pauling electronegativity is based on the deviation of the bond energy of a molecule AB from the geometric mean of the bond energies for the molecules AA and BB, and is thus proportional to the contribution of ionic structures like A^+B^- to the stability of AB. (A complete discussion of electronegativity will be found in Cotton and Wilkinson, *545*.)

In order to stabilize a charged carbon species (either a carbanion or a carbonium ion), it is necessary to enhance the electron affinity or to decrease the ionization potential. A variety of effects may be utilized to this end. Conjugation *delocalizes* either the positive or the negative charge, distributing that charge either to other atoms or to atoms that are more effective than carbon at maintaining the charge. The *inductive effect* operates through the bonds to the carbon atom which bears the charge. In favorable cases (the monohydroperfluorocarbons, Section 1.2, Part 1), the charge-carrying capacity of a carbon can be tremendously enhanced. The *hybridization* of the orbital that carries the charge has an important effect on its electronegativity. The higher the percentage of *s*-character, the greater the capacity of the orbital to sustain a negative charge since the *s*-orbital on the average is close to the nucleus of the atom.

Another important factor that contributes to the stability of an intermediate is its reactivity towards other molecules. Steric hindrance to reaction will, in effect, lengthen the survival time of an intermediate, that is, make it appear more stable (Fig. 3.1), even though its thermodynamic stability might not be unusual in comparison to related molecules.

Carbonium ions are generated in three ways: (a) heterolytic cleavage of a bond, (b) removal of an electron from a free radical, and (c) reaction of neutral molecule with a suitably charged species like a proton (Eqs. 3 through 5). Route (a) includes the classical methods of solvolysis and treatment of an amine with nitrous acid, as well as the more recent approach of hydride transfer to a reactive carbonium ion and solvolysis of alkyl mercuric derivatives (Eqs. 6 through 8).

(3) $$RX \longrightarrow R^+ + X^-$$

(4) $$R\cdot + M^{+n} \longrightarrow R^+ + M^{+n-1}$$

(5) $$R_2C{=}CR_2 + H^+ \longrightarrow R_2C^+{-}CHR_2$$

(6) $$(CH_3)_3CCl \longrightarrow (CH_3)_3C^+ + Cl^-$$

(7)

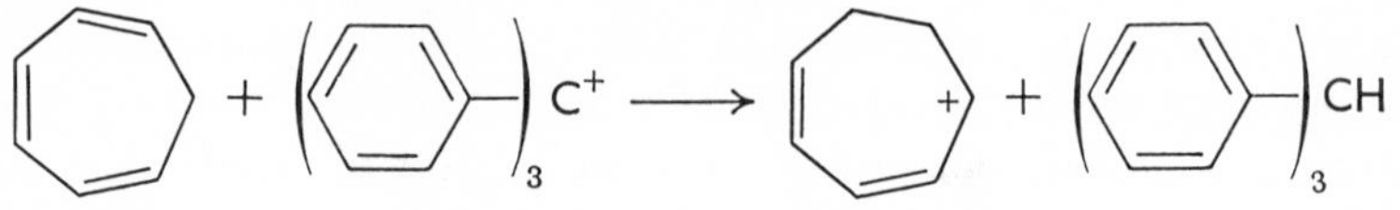

(8) $$(CH_3)_3CHg^+ \longrightarrow (CH_3)_3C^+ + Hg^0$$

Olah and his co-workers (*502–507*) have utilized the strongest known "Lewis acid" systems for the generation of secondary and tertiary alkyl carbonium ions and have examined their n.m.r. and ultraviolet spectra. Pure antimony pentafluoride (for example, *502*), fluorosulfonic acid (FSO₃H) and antimony pentafluoride (*503*), and hydrogen fluoride and antimony pentafluoride (*504*) are among the systems used. Fluorosulfonic acid is thought to be one of the strongest pure acids known.

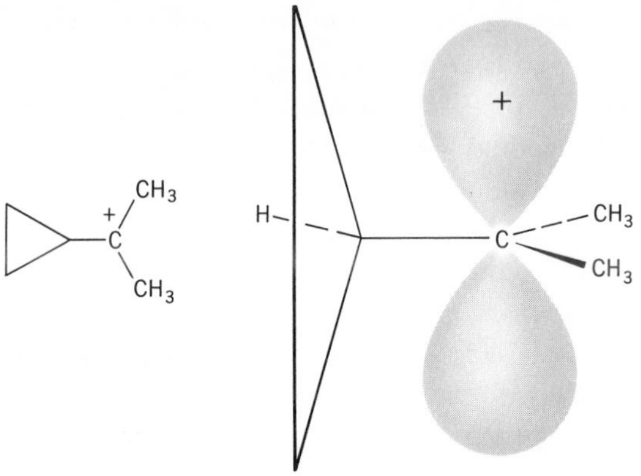

The n.m.r. (nuclear magnetic resonance) spectrum not only provides direct evidence for the structure of the carbonium ion, but also yields data on the delocalization of the charge and the rates of internal rearrangements within the carbonium ion. In a general way, the position of an n.m.r. absorption for a given atom [normally recorded as a chemical shift relative to a standard which for hydrogen is usually tetramethylsilane, (CH₃)₄Si] will depend on the electron density around that atom. High electron density will shield the atom from the external field and a higher field will thus be required to observe the absorption at fixed frequency. Low electron density will "deshield" the atom and allow the absorption to be observed at lower magnetic fields. In homologous series, the relative chemical shifts for similar protons will indicate reasonably well the extent to which positive charge is concentrated at a particular center, since the effects of other shielding and deshielding mechanisms will be minimized. (For further discussion of n.m.r. theory and practice, see Jackman, *509*, Pople, Schneider, and Bernstein, *318*, and Emsley, Feeney, and Sutcliffe, *442*.) We may translate observations on chemical shifts of different hydrogens into conclusions about the degree of delocalization of positive charge (see Table 3.8). Lowering the temperature at which an n.m.r. spectrum is measured often results in the appearance of numerous new lines. The usual reason for the change in the spectrum is that some process, which averaged the field seen by a particular hydrogen, has been decreased sufficiently in rate so that hydrogens that were equivalent at a higher temperature now sense different degrees of shielding for a given external field. We shall mention a case of this type (the norbornyl cation) below and utilize such findings in other cases.

Both *n*-propyl and isopropyl fluorides dissolve in antimony pentafluoride to form solutions for which identical n.m.r. spectra were found. All four C_4-fluorides (*n*-butyl, isobutyl, *sec*-butyl, and *t*-butyl) exhibited the same n.m.r. spectrum in antimony pentafluoride solution. Since the n.m.r. spectrum for the C_3-case was clearly that of isopropyl carbonium ion (two sets of peaks with an area ratio of 6:1) and markedly different from that for isopropyl fluoride, the *n*-propyl compound must have rearranged, perhaps through the *n*-propyl carbonium ion (*502*). The n.m.r. spectrum for the C_4-fluorides in SbF_5 had one peak at a position quite different from that of the peak for *t*-butyl fluoride. Clearly, all of the ions from C_4 fluorides had rearranged to the *t*-butyl carbonium ion. As the data in Table 3.4 illustrate, the effect of a neighboring positive charge on the chemical shift of the hydrogens in the carbonium ions is very great.

The ^{13}CH coupling constants (J^{13}_{CH}) for the methyl groups of the isopropyl and *t*-butyl carbonium ions are the same (130 c.p.s.) and only slightly different from the coupling constants of the same groups in the corresponding fluorides (127 and 128 c.p.s. for the C_3 and C_4 fluorides respectively). In Table 1.5 a coupling constant of 125 c.p.s. is shown for methane and is thus "normal" for an sp^3-bond to hydrogen. The relationship of *s*-character to J^{13}_{CH} is shown in Fig. 1.6 (Section 1.2) and presumably depends upon the fact that *s*-orbitals have electron density at the nucleus, providing a mechanism for the transmission of spin polarization from the carbon nucleus to the

TABLE 3.4   *N.M.R. Chemical Shift Data for Isopropyl and t-Butyl Carbonium Ions*

$(CH_3)_2CH^{+a}$	δ, p.p.m.[b]	$(CH_3)_2CHF^c$	δ, p.p.m.[b]
2-H	-13.5	2-H	-4.64
1-H	-5.06	1-H	-1.23
$(CH_3)_3C^{+a}$		$(CH_3)_3CF^d$	
1-H	-4.35	1-H	-1.30

[a] Generated from the corresponding fluoride in antimony penta-fluoride, Ref. 502.   [b] In parts per million downfield from the signal for TMS (tetramethylsilane).   [c] Neat liquid.

hydrogen nucleus. Although such a relationship cannot be taken literally as a measure of hybridization, the coupling constants do seem to be strongly influenced by such hybridization. (To be exact, the electron distributions, which are expressed in terms of hybrid orbitals, have a marked effect upon the manner in which the carbon-13 and hydrogen nuclear spins interact.) It is particularly striking, therefore, that the [13]CH coupling constant for the central carbon of the isopropyl carbonium ion is 168 c.p.s., greater than the value of 151 c.p.s. for isopropyl fluoride. [^{13}C-enriched chloride was used to

TABLE 3.5   *Coupling Constants ($J_{13_{CH}}$) for Some Substituted Methanes*[a]

Methane Derivative	$J_{13_{CH}}$ c.p.s.
CH_3CN	136
CH_3F	149
CH_3Cl	150
CH_3I	151
CH_3Br	152
CH_2Cl_2	178
$CHBr_3$	206
$CHCl_3$	209

[a] Ref. 510.

generate the carbonium ion in SbF_5 (*511*).] If taken at face value in terms of the linear relationship shown in Fig. 1.6, the coupling constant corresponds to an orbital bonded to the hydrogen of sp^2. There is an effect of substituents on the value of J^{13}_{CH} which is related in part to the polarity of the substituent (Table 3.5). Nevertheless, it is likely that isopropyl and *t*-butyl carbonium ions are planar species with a hybridization at the central carbon of sp^2, in which the positive charge at the central carbon has little effect as an electron-withdrawing substituent.

The formation of the isopropyl and *t*-butyl carbonium ions is shown in Eqs. 9 and 10.

(9) $\qquad (CH_3)_2CHF + SbF_5 \longrightarrow (CH_3)_2CH^+SbF_6^-$

(10) $\qquad (CH_3)_3CF + SbF_5 \longrightarrow (CH_3)_3C^+SbF_6^-$

The gross chemistry of the *t*-butyl carbonium ion (which Olah prefers to call the trimethylcarbonium ion) is about what one would expect as illustrated in Eqs. 11 through 17.

(11) $(CH_3)_3C^+SbF_6^- + H_2O \longrightarrow (CH_3)_3COH + HSbF_6$

(12) $(CH_3)_3C^+SbF_6^- + ROH \longrightarrow (CH_3)_3COR + HSbF_6$ $\quad (R = CH_3, CH_3CH_2)$

(13) $(CH_3)_3C^+SbF_6^- + CH_3COOH \longrightarrow (CH_3)_3COOCCH_3 + HSbF_6$

(14) $(CH_3)_3C^+SbF_6 + H_2S \longrightarrow (CH_3)_3CSH + [(CH_3)_3C]_2S + HSbF_6$

(15) $(CH_3)_3C^+SbF_6^- \xrightarrow{1.CO}_{2.H_2O} (CH_3)_3CCOOH + HSbF_6$

(16) $\qquad (CH_3)_3C^+SbF_6 + \bigcirc \xrightarrow{SO_2} \bigcirc{-}C(CH_3)_3$

(17) $CH_2{=}C(CH_3)_2 + (CH_3)_3C^+SbF_6^- \xrightarrow[-78°]{CH_2Cl_2 + CH_2{=}CHCl}$ polymer
$\qquad\qquad\qquad$ Catalytic $\qquad\qquad\qquad\qquad\qquad$ [Very rapid]
$\qquad\qquad\qquad$ amount in SO_2

Delocalization of the positive charge of a carbonium ion creates a system which is more stable than an ion with a localized positive charge. It is possible to obtain the n.m.r. spectra of the allyl and 2-methylallyl carbonium ions, generated from the corresponding fluorides with antimony pentafluoride in sulfur dioxide at $-60°$ (*512*). (Eqs. 18 and 19.) The n.m.r. chemical shifts are shown in Table 3.6.

TABLE 3.6　*N.M.R. Chemical Shift Data for Allylic Halides*

Carbonium Ion	δ, p.p.m.[a]	Halide		δ, p.p.m.[a]
$(CH_2\text{---}CH\text{---}CH_2)^{+\ b,c}$		$CH_2=CH-CH_2F^{\ c}$		
423　1-H(CH₂)	−8.97	**424**	*trans*-3-H	−5.14
2-H(CH)	−9.64		*cis*-3-H	−5.01
			2-H	−5.52
			1-H	−4.56

$(CH_2\text{---}C\text{---}CH_2)^{+\ b,c}$
　　　|
　　CH_3

$CH_2=C-CH_2F$
　　　|
　　CH_3

425　1-H(CH₂)	−8.95	**426**	*trans*-3-H	−4.81
2-CH₃	−3.85		*cis*-3-H	−4.69
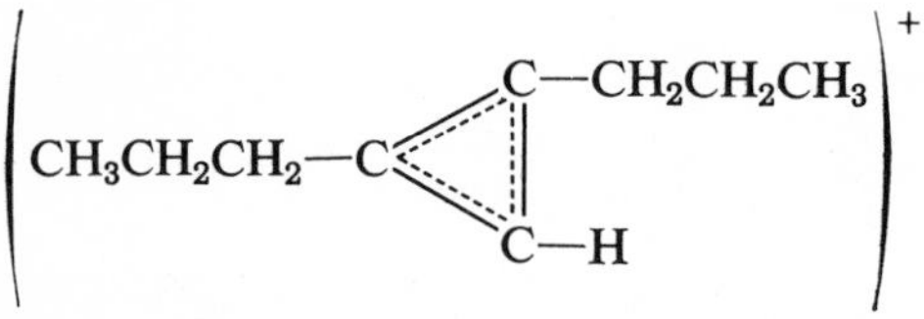			2-CH₃	−1.47
			1-H	−4.32

$$\left(\ CH_3CH_2CH_2-C \overset{C-CH_2CH_2CH_3}{\underset{C-H}{\lessgtr}}\ \right)^{+\ d}$$

427　3-H(CH)	−10.3 [e]			
1′-H(CH₂)	−3.15			
2′-H(CH₂)	−1.88			
3′-H(CH₃)	−1.01			

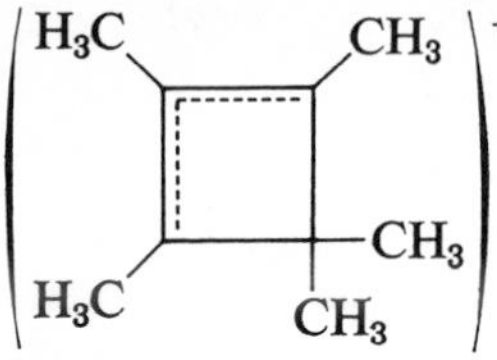

$$\left(\ \begin{array}{c} H_3C \quad\quad CH_3 \\ \square \\ H_3C \quad\quad CH_3 \end{array}\ -CH_3 \right)^{+\ f,g}$$

$$\begin{array}{c} H_3C \quad\quad CH_3 \\ \overset{2\quad 1}{\underset{3\quad 4}{}}\!-Br \\ H_3C \quad\quad CH_3 \end{array}\ -CH_3$$

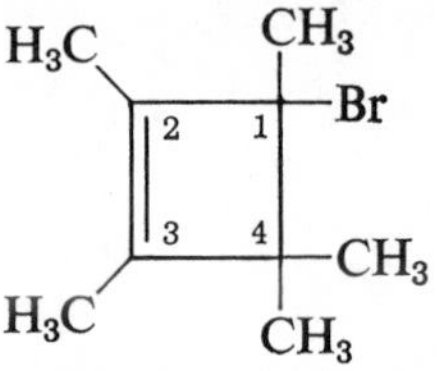

428　4,4-CH₃	−1.60	**429**　4,4-CH₃		−1.17
1,3-CH₃	−2.64	2,3-CH₃		−1.68
2-CH₃	−2.37	1-CH₃		−1.55

[a] In parts per million downfield from TMS.　[b] Generated with SbF₅ in SO₂ at −60°.
[c] Ref. 512.　[d] Ref. 513 (in trifluoroacetic acid).　[e] Original data referenced with benzene internally and corrected to TMS in Ref. 512.　[f] Ref. 514.　[g] As tetrachloroaluminate salt in CH₂Cl₂.

$$(18)\qquad CH_2=CHCH_2F\ \xrightarrow[-60°]{\ SbF_5\ /\ SO_2\ }\ [CH_2\text{---}CH\text{---}CH_2]^+SbF_6^-$$

$$(19)\qquad CH_2=\underset{\underset{CH_3}{|}}{C}-CH_2F\ \xrightarrow[-60°]{\ SbF_5\ /\ SO_2\ }\ [CH_2\text{---}\underset{\underset{CH_3}{|}}{C}\text{---}CH_2]^+SbF_6^-$$

Delocalization of the charge diminishes the effect of the positive charge on the chemical shift. The hydrogens on the ends of the allyl cation appear in the n.m.r. spectrum at 4–4.5 p.p.m. lower than their position in the n.m.r. spectrum of allyl fluoride, in contrast to the shift of 9 p.p.m. observed for the change from isopropyl fluoride to isopropyl carbonium ion. The shifts found for the α-methylenes in the 1,2-di-*n*-propylcyclopropenium ion (**427**) and the 1,3-methyl groups of the pentamethylcyclobutenyl carbonium (**428**) are clearly smaller than that found for the methyl groups of the *t*-butyl carbonium ion, indicating that the deshielding produced by the positive charge is diminished by delocalization.

A surprising facet of the n.m.r. spectra of all the allylic carbonium ions is the marked change in the chemical shift of hydrogens and alkyl groups attached to the central carbon of the cation. The central carbon, according to the usual valence bond formulations (**423a** $\leftrightarrow$ **423b**), carries no positive charge.

$$CH_2{=}CHCH_2^+ \longleftrightarrow \overset{+}{CH_2}{-}CH{=}CH_2$$

423a   423b

The central hydrogen of the allyl cation (2-H in Table 3.6) is shifted slightly more than the end hydrogens, from -5.52 p.p.m. to -9.64 p.p.m. The central methyl group of the methallyl cation and the 2-methyl group of the pentamethylcyclobutenyl cation are both displaced. A number of theoretical calculations of the charge distribution in the allyl cation (Hirst and Linnett, *515* and Simonetta and Heilbronner, *516*) indicate that a substantial positive charge is located at the central carbon atom. Even though few chemical experiments would directly suggest such a conclusion, the n.m.r. spectra are in accord with a formulation such as **430a** or **430b**.

430a   430b

There is little doubt that "1,3-interaction" is extremely important in cyclopropenium ions (**431a** $\leftrightarrow$ **431b** $\leftrightarrow$ **431c**).

431a   431b   431c

The ease of ring-opening of cyclopropyl cations [see Section 1.9] to allyl cations is consistent with these formulations.

Sorensen (*517*) has prepared the series of polyenylic carbonium ions from the trienylic, **432**, through the tetraenylic, **433**, to the pentaenylic (**434**), and confirmed that the displacement of the chemical shift for a methyl group or a vinylic hydrogen decreases as the concentration of the positive charge on the atom to which the group is bonded decreases. A comparison of the n.m.r.

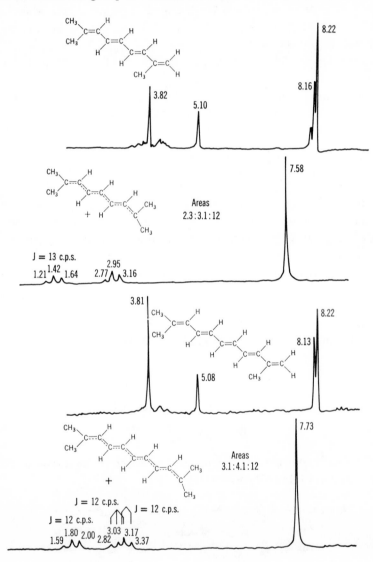

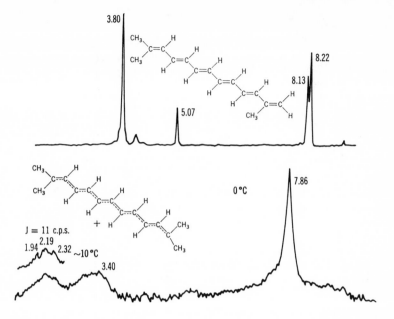

Figure 3.2 N.m.r. spectra of the trienylic cation **432**, the tetraenylic cation **433**, and the pentaenylic cation **434**, along with n.m.r. spectra of the polyenes, from which they were derived by solution in sulfuric acid. The spectrum of the **434** cation is broadened by the presence of a paramagnetic oxidation product (*517*). (Reprinted with permission of the author and the *Journal of the American Chemical Society*.)

spectra of the polyenes and the corresponding carbonium ions obtained by dissolution in strong acid (sulfuric acid or perfluorobutyric acid) is shown in Fig. 3.2. Deno and his co-workers (see the review on carbonium ions, *518*) have affirmed and others have confirmed the extreme care that must be taken in preparing solutions of carbonium ions in strong acids. Normally, almost all alkenes or polyenes are highly reactive towards carbonium ions. If the protonation step (or dehydration step if alcohols are used as ion precursors) is not carried out so as to keep the concentration of the carbonium ion low at the point where mixing of the precursor with the strong acid is effected, polymer or polymeric carbonium ions will be the chief products.

Sorensen has also succeeded in preparing the divinyl dienylic carbonium ion, **435** (*519*) and the trivinyl carbonium ion, **436** (*520*). The remarkably simple n.m.r. spectrum of the trivinyl ion **436** is illustrated along with that of its precursor tetraene (**437**) in Fig. 3.3. A comparison of vinyl carbonium

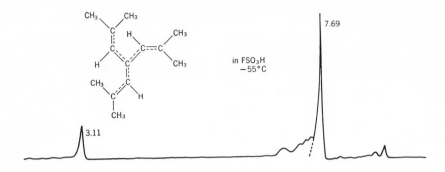

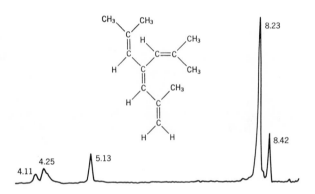

Figure 3.3 The n.m.r. spectrum of the trivinyl carbonium ion **436** and the precursor tetraene **437**, from which it was derived by solution in fluorosulfonic acid at −55° (*520*). (Reprinted by permission of the author and the *Canadian Journal of Chemistry*.)

ions in Table 3.7 illustrates again how delocalization decreases the effect of a positive charge on the chemical shift for a particular group or atom.

The special role of the cyclopropyl ring in stabilizing adjacent positive charge was suggested by Roberts and co-workers (*522*) on the basis of the reactivities of cyclopropylcarbinyl derivatives. (See Section 1.5.) Deno, Richey, and co-workers (*100, 523*) have found that the tricyclopropylmethyl carbonium ion, **117**, may be readily generated from the alcohol with trifluoro-acetic acid at −25°. The high reactivity found for tricyclopropylcarbinyl derivatives by Hart and his students (*98, 99*, see Part 1, Section 1.5) is accord with considerable stability for the intermediate ion. In fact, the tricyclo-

TABLE 3.7   *Comparison of N.M.R. Data for Vinyl Carbonium Ions*[a]

Ion	Protons	Chemical Shift[b]
$\left[(CH_3)_2C\text{---}CH\text{---}C(CH_3)_2\right]^+$ **434a**	12 Methyl 1 Alkene	-2.96[c] -7.74
$\left[(CH_3)_2C\text{---}CH\text{---}CH\text{---}CH\text{---}C(CH_3)_2\right]^+$ **435**	12 Methyl 2 Alkene	-2.65[d] -7.10[d]
$\left[\begin{array}{c}(CH_3)_2C\text{---}CH\text{---}C\text{---}CH\text{---}C(CH_3)_2 \\ \text{CH} \\ C(CH_3)_2\end{array}\right]^+$ **436**	18 Methyl 3 Alkene	-2.35 -6.89

[a] From Ref. 520.   [b] In p.p.m. from TMS.   [c] From Ref. 521.   [d] Average positions.

propylmethyl carbonium ion is half-formed from the alcohol in 22% sulfuric acid whereas the triphenylmethyl carbonium ion is half-formed from the carbinol only in 50% sulfuric acid. A direct indication of delocalization is the chemical shift found for the cyclopropyl hydrogens in the n.m.r. spectra of a series of carbonium ions bearing, respectively, one, two, and three cyclopropyl groups on the carbon that carries the positive charge in a formal sense. Thus for the 2-cyclopropyl-2-propyl carbonium ion (**438**) the shift (from TMS) for the ring hydrogens is 3.4 to 4.0 p.p.m. (*524*), for the dicyclopropylmethyl carbonium ion (*524*), the shift is 2.8 to 3.5 p.p.m., and for the tricyclopropyl-methyl carbonium ion, the shift is 2.26 p.p.m. (*523*). In the latter case, both α- and β-hydrogens exhibit the same chemical shift, a circumstance which is probably a matter of coincidence rather than the result of a special structure for the ion or an unexpected exchange process that equalizes the chemical shifts of all of the hydrogens. The chemical shifts of the two methyl groups of the ion **438** are *not equivalent*, with signals that are separated by 0.54 p.p.m. (*524*). A structure in which the plane of the cyclopropyl group is perpendicular to the plane of the sp^2-orbitals around the formally positive central carbon could account for this result. The structure is illustrated as **439**. The n.m.r. spectrum was measured in a mixture of thionyl chlorofluoride, antimony pentafluoride, and sulfur dioxide at $-75°$. Warming to $-30°$ resulted in the destruction of the ion without any sign in the n.m.r. spectrum that coalescence of the methyl signals had begun to occur. The stabilization produced by interaction of the cyclopropyl group with the *p*-orbital of the carbonium ion center is so stereospecific that rotation of the group attached to the cyclopropane ring does not occur readily. The solvolytic reactivity of a *bis*cyclopropylcarbinyl system (**440**) with a geometric arrangement that favors the formation of a transition state, in which the cyclopropyl groups are perpendicular to the developing carbonium ion center, is appreciably higher than that of open chain analogs (*525*).

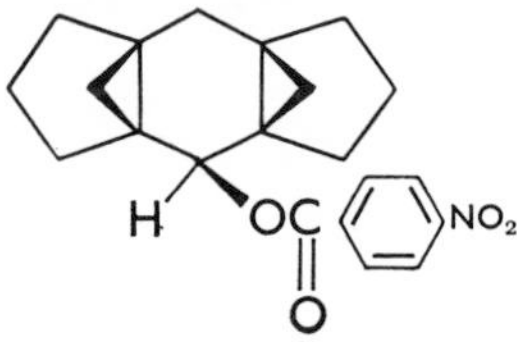

440

Oxocarbonium ions like the acetyl ion **440** can be generated from acetyl fluoride with strong Lewis acids, for example, antimony pentafluoride (*505, 526*).

$$CH_3CO^+$$
440

The n.m.r. spectrum of the acetyl ion (which Olah designates as the methyl oxocarbonium ion) has a methyl resonance at -4.08 p.p.m., considerably farther downfield than the methyl resonance in acetyl fluoride at -2.18 p.p.m. The crystal structure of acetyl hexafluoroantimonate has been determined by Boer (*527*). The bond from the methyl group to the positively charged carbon (1.38 A) is definitely shorter than might have been expected for an sp^3-sp

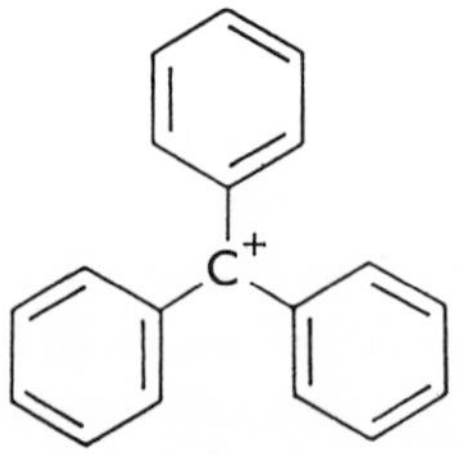

78

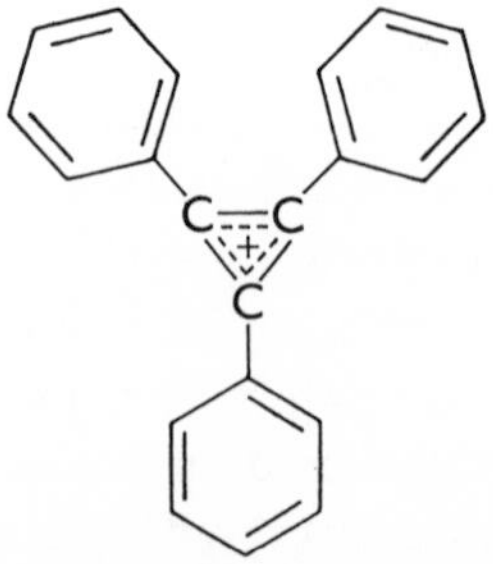

441

bond (1.46 A, Table 1.6). The carbon–oxygen distance (1.12 A) is quite close to the carbon–oxygen distance in carbon monoxide (1.13 A) and considerably lower than that found in aldehydes and ketones (1.20 A). A comparable shortening of the bond to a formally positive carbon atom has been observed for the triphenylcarbonium ion **78** (*528*), but the shortening is not as extreme in the triphenylcyclopropenium ion **441** (*529*).

Well-authenticated examples of *bis*-carbonium ions are known. An ion which bears a direct relationship to the triphenylcarbonium ion **78** is that derived from a derivative of *p*-xylene, **442** (*530*).

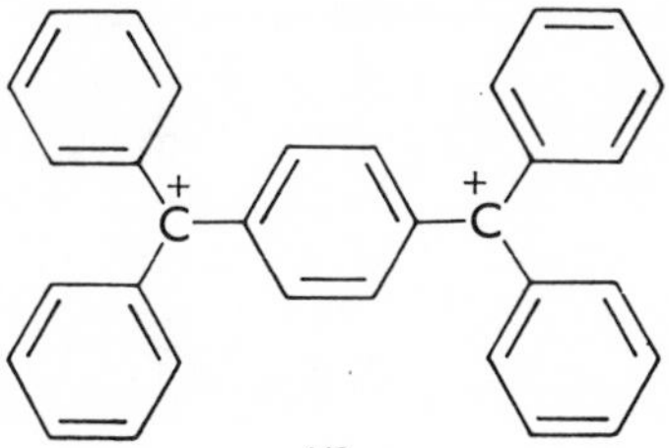

442

The n.m.r. spectra of two aliphatic *bis*-carbonium ions, **443** and **444**, have been reported (*711*).

$$(CH_3)_2\overset{+}{C}CH_2CH_2\overset{+}{C}(CH_3)_2 \qquad (CH_3)_2\overset{+}{C}CH_2CH_2CH_2\overset{+}{C}(CH_3)_2$$

443 **444**

The second positive charge does not influence the n.m.r. shifts very greatly, and the chemical shift for the methyl group for **443** relative to tetramethyl-silane in antimony pentafluoride-sulfur dioxide at low temperature is -4.24 p.p.m., almost the same as that found for the methyl group in the *t*-butyl carbonium ion (-4.35 p.p.m.). *Bis*-oxocarbonium ions (for example, **445**) are also accessible through the techniques used for the alkyl carbonium ions described in this section (*531*).

445

The cycloheptatrienylium ion, **446**, was predicted by molecular orbital theory to be very stable. Salts of **446**, variously called tropenium or tropylium salts, were actually prepared at the end of the last century by Merling (*532*) but not recognized as such until Doering and Knox (*533*) and Dauben and his co-workers (*534*) proved their structure and investigated their behavior.

TABLE 3.8   *Chemical Shifts in the N.M.R. Spectra of Stable Hydrocarbon Ions*[a]

Ion	π-Charge Difference from Benzene	Observed Shift, δ p.p.m.[b]	Observed Shift, δ p.p.m. (Corrected)[b,c]	Chemical Shift Per Unit Charge[d]
Cyclopentadienide (**6a**)	+0.200	+1.73	+1.43	7.15
Tropylium (**446**)	−0.143	−1.87	−1.59	11.13
Cyclooctatetraene dianion (**447**)	+0.250	+1.58	+2.42	9.70

[a] Adapted from Ref. 535.   [b] In p.p.m. from an internal benzene reference. To estimate the shifts from TMS, assume that benzene hydrogens are 7.27 p.p.m. downfield from TMS. The latter values will only be *rough estimates.*   [c] Corrected for solvent shift and ring current.   [d] The average shift per unit charge (9.3 p.p.m.) derived from these three numbers is in qualitative agreement with such estimates for other systems.

A preparative method has been illustrated in Eq. 7 (*534*). A comparison of the n.m.r. positions for the hydrogens of the tropylium ion with the hydrogens of benzene, cyclopentadienide anion (**6a**), and cyclooctatetraene dianion (**447**) is given in Table 3.8. Reasonable uniformity is found for the effect of charge at a given position on the resonance of a hydrogen attached to that position.

      446   **6a**   **447**

The cycloheptatrienylium ion is, in fact, so stable that ionization in the mass spectrometer of many different C_7H_8 isomers yields an ion, $C_7H_7^+$ which, from its own cracking pattern, is **446**. Ions which were long thought to be benzyl carbonium ions, generated from toluene in the mass spectrometer, were shown by Myerson and his co-workers (*536*) to be tropylium on the basis of the even distribution of deuterium isotope in the cracking products of the $C_7H_7^+$ ion regardless of the position of the detuerium in the original toluene. Among the other sources for **446** are cycloheptatriene (**18**), bicycloheptadiene (**448**), quadricyclane (**408**), methylfulvene (**449**), 1,6-heptadiyne (**450**), and toluene (**16**).

18   448   408   449 $HC{\equiv}C(CH_2)_3C{\equiv}CH$ 450   16

Rearrangement of the benzyl carbonium ion to the cycloheptatrienylium ion apparently does not take place readily in solution, probably because the energy required to overcome the extra stabilization produced by solvation is too great. (In Part 1, the fact that the ionization potential of benzyl radicals was much more substituent-sensitive than the solvolysis of benzyl halides was rationalized in the same way.)

Addition of a proton to cyclooctatetraene (**451**) produces the monohomotropylium ion, **452**, for which the structure is based on: (a) the n.m.r. spectrum, in which there are four absorption regions at -8.6, -6.6, -5.2, and $+0.6$ p.p.m. with area ratios of $5:2:1:1$ and (b) the electronic spectrum which resembles that of the tropylium ion [λ_{max} 2325 A (ϵ_{max} 32,300) and 3130 A (30,000) for **452** versus 2170 A (40,700) and 2735 (4260) for **446**] more than that of a heptatrienylium ion (λ_{max} 4700 A). The interesting part of the n.m.r. spectrum is the fact that the two "aliphatic" protons give fairly sharp resonance lines separated by 5.8 p.p.m. The average of the two aliphatic positions (-2.3 p.p.m.) is reasonable for protons on an alkyl group alpha to a delocalized carbonium ion (compare with **436**, Table 3.7). To explain the huge difference in the positions of the two "aliphatic" protons, Keller and Pettit (*537, 538*) and Winstein, Kreiter, and Braumann (*539*) have proposed that a "ring current" in the tropylium portion of the homotropylium ion creates a large difference in the magnetic environments of the "inside" and "outside" protons. Since the presence of ring currents is characteristic of closed circuit "aromatic" nuclei, the homotropylium ion **452** is thus considered to be "aromatic" and, therefore, "nonclassical" (as opposed to the "classical," that is, formulation **453**) (*518*). Although the effect of possible charge at the "aliphatic" carbon is not known (*539*), **452** is probably to be preferred to **453** as a formula for the homotropylium ion.

452   453

Winstein and co-workers have also found that protonation occurs first on the "inside" and has measured the rate of equilibration of inside and outside protons by using initially deuterated **452**. The rate at $32°$ was 6.1×10^{-4} sec.$^{-1}$, corresponding to a free energy of activation of 22.3 kcal./mole. The conversion of **454a** to **454b** was presumed to proceed via the planar ion **455**. It is not known whether or not there is any proton transfer from one inside position to another. Such internal transfers would require a transition state like **206**, and must be slow since the aliphatic and aromatic hydrogens are quite distinct in the n.m.r. spectrum.

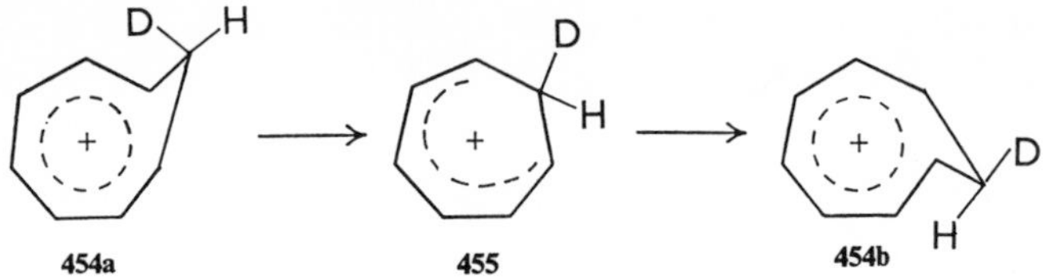

454a   455   454b

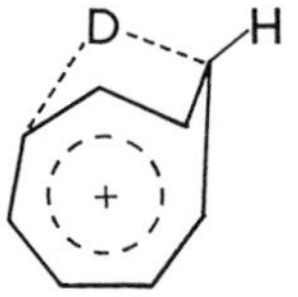

456

The high reactivity of *anti*-7-norbornenyl *p*-toluenesulfonate (**457**) in comparison with that of 7-norbornyl *p*-toluenesulfonate (**458**) with $k_{457}/k_{458} = 10^{11}$ led to the suggestion that a nonclassical carbonium ion **459** was an intermediate in solvolysis, arising through a transition state which resembled the intermediate (cf. *540*).

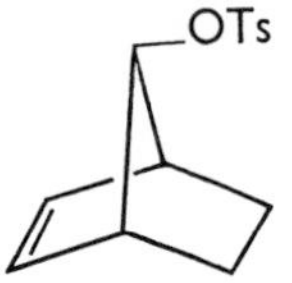

457 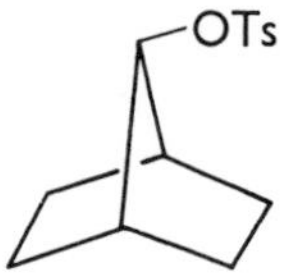   458 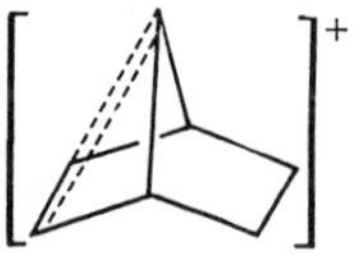   459

The intermediate carbonium ion has been generated from the alcohol **460** by solution in fluorosulfonic acid at $-78°$ (*541*; see also *540*). The chemical shifts found for the cation **461** are compared to the shifts for the 7-methyl cation **462** and the 7-hydroxy cation **463**.

N.m.r. chemical shifts are given in p.p.m. from tetramethylsilane reference.

Only one resonance for the hydrogens attached to the double bond appears in the n.m.r. spectra of the ions **461–463**. It follows that only one symmetrical

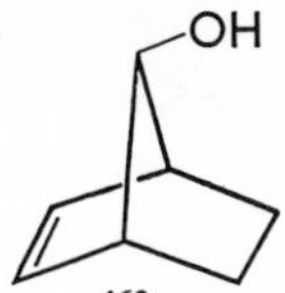

460

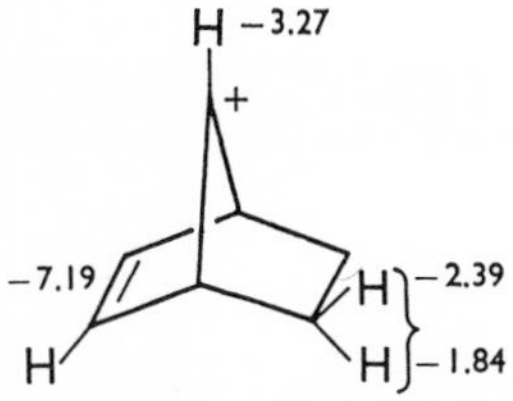

H −3.27

−7.19

H

461

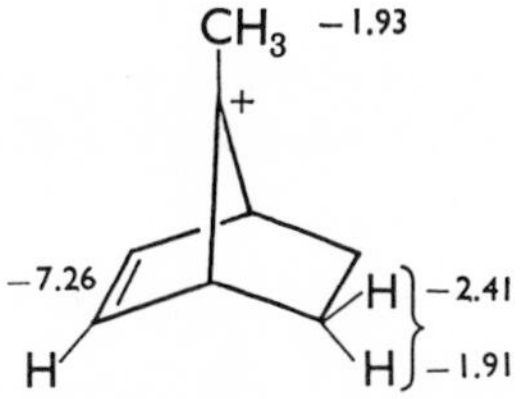

CH₃ −1.93

−7.26

H

462

OH

−6.77

H

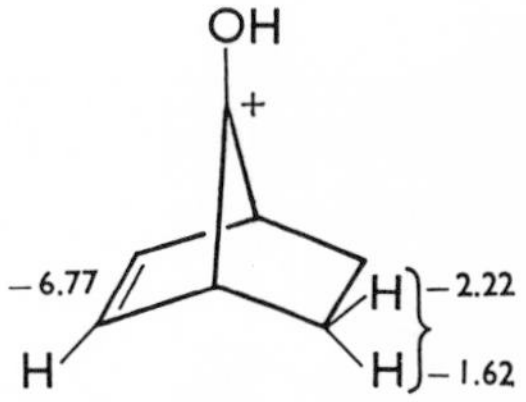

463

structure is required to explain the spectra of the ions or that two inter-converting ions are involved. For these cases, we think it simpler to represent the ion as **464** (see discussion, Section 1.5) which is transformed readily into one of the two possible interconverting ions **465a** and **465b**.

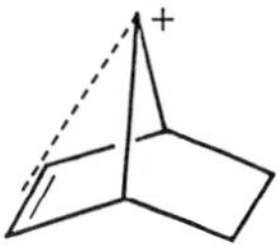

464 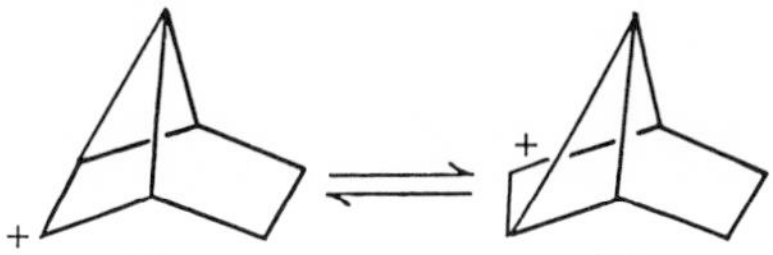   465a   465b

The temperature dependence of the n.m.r. spectrum of the norbornyl cation is illustrated in Fig. 3.4 (*542, 543*). The details of the interpretation have already been presented in Section 1.5 and Fig. 1.30.

As our understanding of the behavior of carbonium ions increases, our criteria for the evaluations of mechanisms of S_IN reactions are augmented. For example, Streitwieser and Stang (*543*) utilized the fact that an isopropyl carbonium ion could be generated without worry about rapid interchange between the hydrogens on C_1 and C_2 to investigate the alkylation of benzene with isopropyl alcohol and boron trifluoride. Optically active 2-propanol-1-d_3 (**466**) and boron trifluoride in benzene yielded almost completely racemic 2-phenylpropane-1-d_3 (**467**), indicating that the equivalent of a free carbonium ion had been generated as an intermediate (**468**). (A pair of ion pairs, **469a** and **469b**, would also yield racemic product).

The ground state properties of carbanions have been intensively studied in recent years. The factors affecting the stability of carbanions are summarized

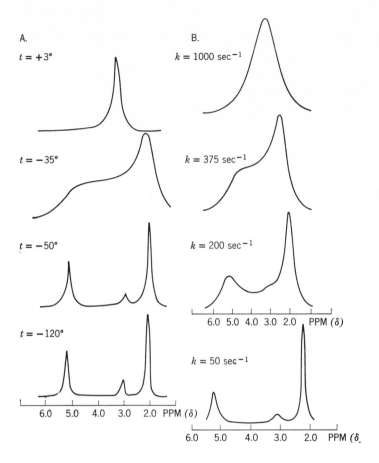

Figure 3.4 Observed (A column) and calculated (B column) n.m.r. spectra of the 2-norbornyl cation at various temperatures. The rate constants signify various rates for 3.2-hydride shifts (*542*). (Reprinted with permission of the authors and the *Journal of the American Chemical Society.*)

410

in Section 1.2, Part 1. Only a few interesting examples of carbanions and their derivatives will be cited here. Many of the more reactive carbanions may be generated and retained in stable form only in nonpolar solvents so that carbanions are normally examined in the form of the derivatives, the ion-pairs. An interesting example of how carbanion behavior depends upon solvent and gegenion was discovered by Maercker and Roberts (*772*). Cyclopropylcarbinyl Grignard and cyclopropylcarbinyllithium readily rearrange to the corresponding allylcarbinylderivatives (*773, 774*) (**470** → **471**; **472** → **473**).

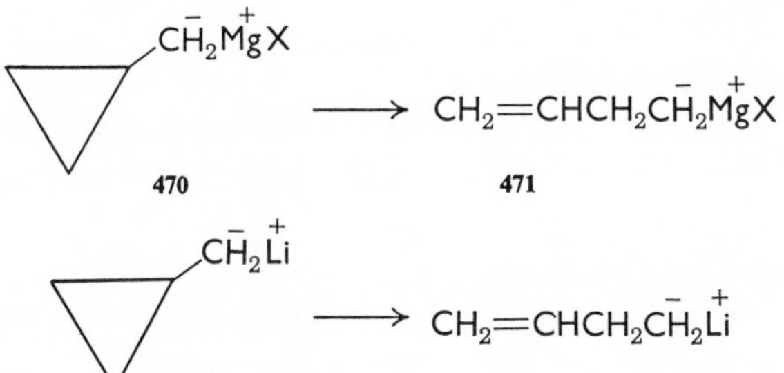

Addition of two phenyl groups to the carbinyl carbon should stabilize the negative charge at that center. It was found that the potassium or sodium cation in ether stabilized the negative charge in diphenyl cyclopropyl carbinyl anion in ether solution (prepared via **474** → **475**) so that the cyclopropyl ring was retained in the ion-pair.

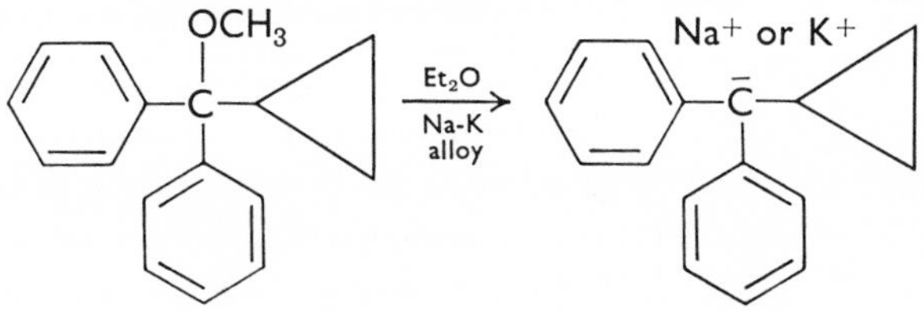

Replacement of the potassium ion with lithium by treatment with lithium bromide led to complete rearrangement, the characteristic red color of the anion present in **475** being replaced by a colorless solution that contained the isomeric allylcarbinyl lithium derivative **476**. Addition of tetrahydrofuran to a solution of the colorless salt **476** caused the immediate reappearance of the red color, due to the diphenyl cyclopropyl carbinyl anion lithium salt **477**.

The reverse rearrangement (**477 → 476**) represents a remarkable example of the importance of solvent in controlling the properties of ion-pairs.

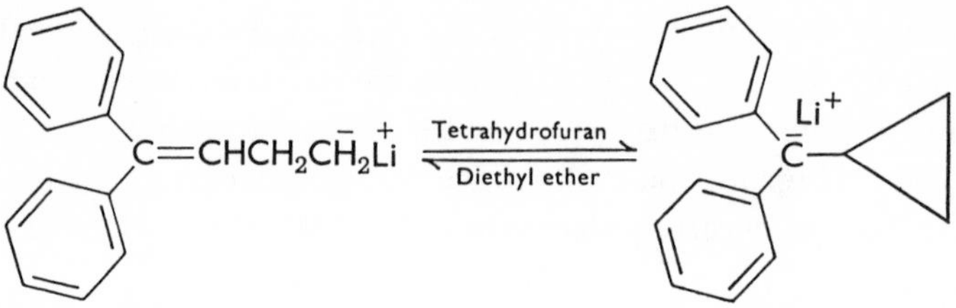

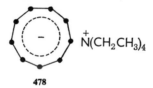

Tetrahydrofuran
Diethyl ether

476   477

Salts of the cyclononatetraenyl anion have been prepared by Katz and Garratt (*546*) and LaLancette and Benson (*547*) and the tetraethylammonium salt isolated (*546*) (**478**). The n.m.r. spectrum of the anion exhibits only one peak with a position slightly dependent on the cation and solvent. In dimethyl sulfoxide-d_6, the peak appears at -6.82 p.p.m. A single peak indicates that all of the hydrogens are equivalent. As Katz and Garratt pointed out, the position of the peak is approximately that expected for an anion with a ring current (for explanation of this term, see *509*) like that of cyclooctatetraene dianion **447** (Table 3.8) but with only 0.11 excess negative charge on each carbon atom.

$\overset{+}{N}(CH_2CH_3)_4$

478

The anion of **478** fits the prediction made on the basis of the Hückel $4n + 2$ rule that 10π-electron systems should be stable. (The extreme instability of the unsubstituted cyclopentadecaene **479**, reported by van Tamelen and Burkoth (*775*), must be ascribed to angle strain which overcomes the stabilization of the π-electron system or to hydrogen–hydrogen repulsion in the isomer **480**.)

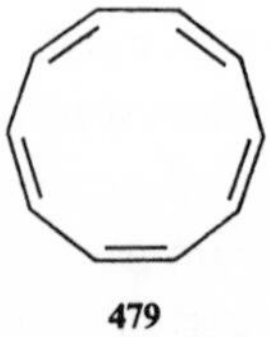

H   H

479 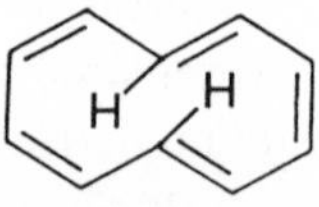   480

An experiment in which **478** was equilibrated with **6** suggested that **478** was comparable in stability to **6a** (*547*), a conclusion that must be regarded with some caution, since it is unlikely that cyclononatetraene **481** is unlikely to be planar and, on this count alone, must be less stable than cyclopentadiene.

(20)

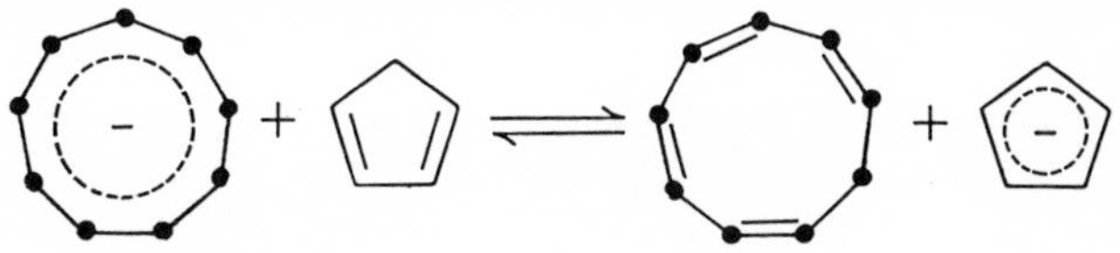

| | 478 | 6 | 481 | 6a |

Krieghoff and Cowan (*548*) generated *exo-* and *endo-*norbornyl Grignard reagents in n.m.r. tubes from *exo-* and *endo-*norbornyl chlorides and obtained the same mixture of Grignard reagents from either starting material.

(21)

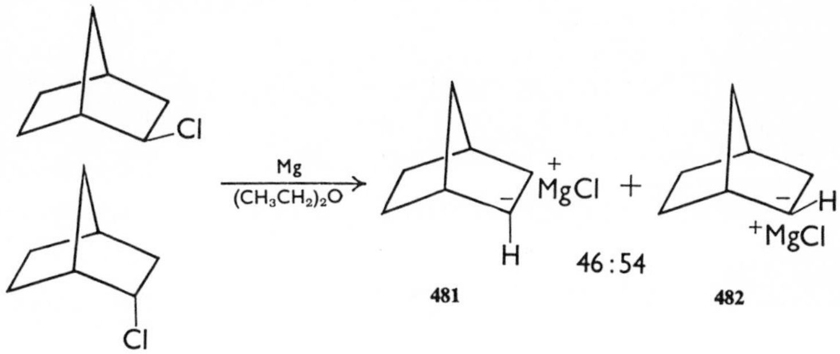

They assigned high-field multiplets in the n.m.r. spectrum at -0.12 p.p.m. to the *exo-*hydrogen at 2- of the *endo-*Grignard, and at 0.32 p.p.m. to the *endo-*hydrogen of the *exo-*Grignard. The difference between the two n.m.r. peaks is 0.44 p.p.m., well within the range (0.40 to 0.48 p.p.m.) usually observed for such hydrogens. In both cases, a shift of more than 4 p.p.m. to higher field, with respect to the corresponding hydrogens in the norbornyl chlorides, was in agreement with a concentrated negative charge present at the carbon and shielding the hydrogen atom attached to the 2-carbon. No temperature effect ($-40°$ to $+80°$) on the n.m.r. spectrum was found, indicating that the *exo-* and *endo-*Grignard reagents are not isomerizing rapidly. Jensen and Nakamaye (*776*) found that the pure *endo*, prepared by destruction of the *exo-*isomer with benzophenone, reforms the equilibrium mixture of *exo-* and *endo-*Grignard reagents in 1 day. Slow interconversion has been observed for other secondary Grignard reagents (for example, 3,3-dimethyl-cyclobutyl Grignard) although interconversion of primary Grignard reagents is fairly rapid (*549*).

Carbonation of the mixture of *exo*- and *endo*-norbornyl Grignard reagents yielded a mixture of the corresponding carboxylic acids. The ratio of *exo*- to *endo*-product was about the same as the ratio of isomers in the Grignard reagent and was not changed by varying the temperature at which the carbonation was carried out (*776*, but compare with *550*). The reactions of **481** and **482** to yield **483** and **484** are thus stereospecific, a conclusion confirmed by the formation of almost pure **484** from pure **482**, prepared as described above.

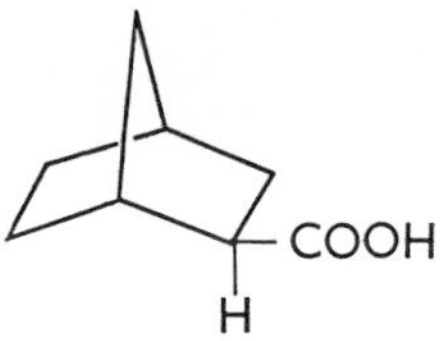

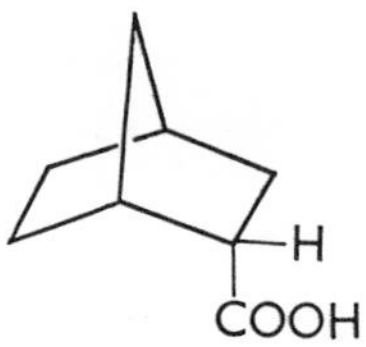

Waack and co-workers (*551*) investigated the C^{13} n.m.r. of the series of alkyl lithiums, benzyl lithium **485**, benzyhydryl lithium **486**, and triphenyl-methyl lithium **487**.

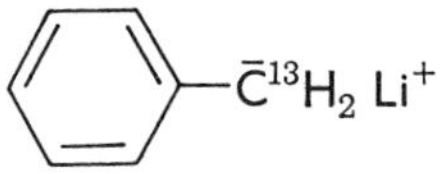

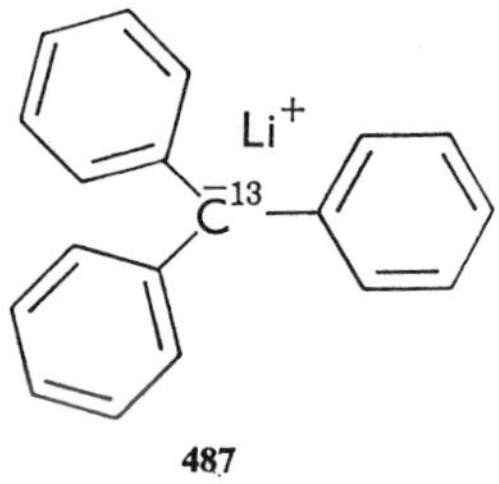

The Carbon labeled C^{13} is 58% enriched with that isotope.

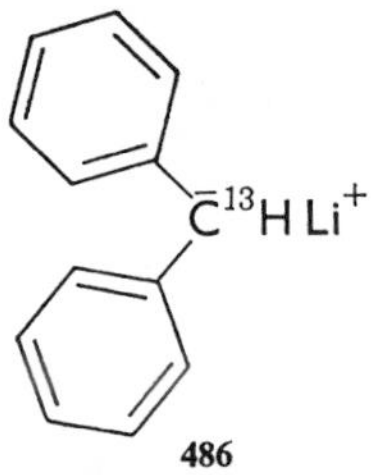

On the basis of a net downfield shift of the C^{13}-resonance with respect to the C^{13} signal in the hydrocarbon precursors, they concluded that the hybridization at the central carbon was *sp²*. Had the hybridization in the lithium derivatives been the same as that in the hydrocarbon precursors, an upfield shift would have been expected due to the extra shielding at C^{13}-carbon produced by the anion.

Carbonium ions and carbanions are intermediates in countless reactions. Specific studies designed to elucidate the behavior of these intermediates can only serve to sharpen our knowledge of the overall mechanisms of reactions proceeding through these species as intermediates.

Problems

1. Try to present a one-line summary of an application of each "improvement" cited in Table 3.1.
2. Draw an n.m.r. spectrum for the ion, which results from the solution of the following halides in antimony pentafluoride–sulfur dioxide at low temperature.
   (a) *n*-Propyl fluoride.
   (b) Isopropyl fluoride.
   (c) *sec.*-Butyl fluoride.
   (d) Isobutyl fluoride.
   (e) Allyl fluoride.
   (f) 2-Methylallyl fluoride.
3. Tabulate the n.m.r. shifts for hydrogens attached directly to the cationic center of carbonium ions and explain the relative magnitudes of the shifts. Make a similar table of methyl group positions.
4. Give an explanation for the fact that a *bis*-carbonium ion is not very different from a *mono*-carbonium ion, with respect to the chemical shift of a methyl group attached to the carbonium ion center.
5. Rationalize the behavior of the ion-pairs derived from diphenyl cyclopropyl carbinyl anion in terms of the properties of ion-pairs described in Section 2.10.
6. Write transition states for the formation of *exo*- and *endo*-norbornyl carboxylic acids from the Grignard reagents.
7. Explain the downfield shift for the C^{13} n.m.r. for the anions **485–487** (with respect to the hydrocarbon precursors as references).

3.2 Radicals

A radical is a species with an unpaired electron. Certain intermediates with more than one unpaired electron (polyradicals, triplet species) and with no unpaired electrons (singlet species related to triplet species including diamagnetic radical dimers) are conveniently discussed along with free radicals. Table 3.9 presents a general list of radical and related intermediates.

TABLE 3.9 *Radical Species and Related Intermediates*

Species	Formula	Example
Free radical	$R\cdot$	$CH_3CH_2\cdot{}^{b}$, $NF_2\cdot{}^{c}$
Methylene[a] (triplet)	$R_2\overset{\bullet}{C}$	$\overset{\bullet}{C}H_2\cdot{}^{d}$
(singlet)	$R_2C:$	$CH_2:{}^{d}$
Nitrene (triplet)	$R\overset{\bullet}{N}\cdot$	$N\overset{\bullet}{C}N\cdot{}^{e}$
(singlet)	$RN:$	$CH_3CH_2OOCN:{}^{f}$
Free radical dimers (covalent)	$R{-}R$	$F_2NNF_2{}^{c}$
(diamagnetic)	$(R\cdot)_2$	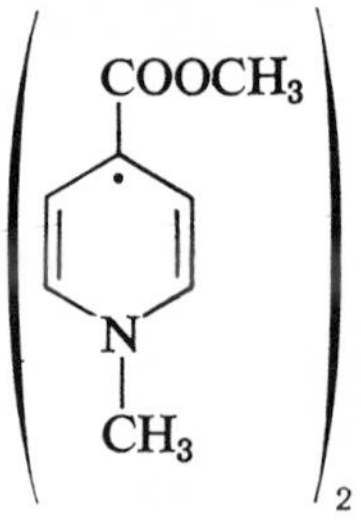

---

[a] Hine (Ref. 555) has continued the *Chemical Abstracts* practice of basing the name of the "divalent carbon" species on the parent hydrocarbon, methane. Kirmse (Ref. 556) prefers the name *carbene* for the same species and, indeed, has included this word in the title of his book. As Doering and Knox (Ref. 557) mentioned in footnote 9 of their article on carbalkoxycarbene, the name carbene was the result of a brief collaboration between R. B. Woodward, S. Winstein, and W. v. E. Doering in 1951. [b] Ref. 558. [c] Ref. 559. [d] Ref. 560. [e] Ref. 561. [f] Ref. 562. [g] Ref. 209.

In a magnetic field, the energy of the free electron is altered (see Fig. 2.51 and discussion, Section 2.10, Part 2). Two energy states are possible, a lower one in which the spin of the electron is aligned with the external field and a higher one in which the spin is opposed to the applied field. If the electron is also near a nucleus with a magnetic moment (see Appendix A, *442* and the same table in Ref. 552), the energy levels are altered (*split*) further. The case of hydrogen atom is illustrated in Fig. 3.5. The *splitting* of the energy levels of the electron will vary according to how much the nucleus "sees" the electron, or how much the spins of a bonding pair are polarized by a nucleus, so that the farther one, in turn, might interact with a free electron (see Fig. 2.51 for an illustration). Transitions between the energy levels thus produced according to the selection rules, $\Delta m_s = \pm 1$, $\Delta m_I = 0$ (m_s = electron spin, m_I = nuclear spin quantum numbers), produce the spectrum observed with an e.p.r. (electron paramagnetic resonance) spectrometer. The e.p.r. spectrum reflects in an *approximate* way the *spin density* distribution in a radical

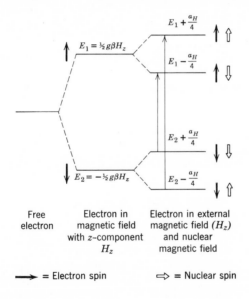

Free electron

Electron in magnetic field with z-component H_z

Electron in external magnetic field (H_z) and nuclear magnetic field

$\longrightarrow$ = Electron spin $\Rightarrow$ = Nuclear spin

Figure 3.5 Behavior of the energy level of the electron on a hydrogen atom in a magnetic field: $\downarrow$ = electron spin; $\Downarrow$ = nuclear spin; g = Landé g-factor = 2.002319 for unbound electrons; β = Bohr magneton = $eh/2m_ec$ (e = charge of electron, $\hbar$ = Planck's constant, h divided by 2π, m_e = mass of electron, c = speed of light). The vertical arrow represents the transitions which would be observed for an external magnetic field H with z-component H_2. The splitting constant (coupling constant) is the difference between these two transitions. It should be clear that a/4 is the energy level change produced by the hydrogen nucleus.

molecule and is thus an important clue to the structure and nature of the radical. The planar nature of the methyl radical, as we have already pointed out (Part 1, Section 1.6; Part 2, Section 2.10), was determined by an analysis

TABLE 3.10   *Electron Paramagnetic Resonance Properties of Free Radicals*

Radical[a] (Formula)	(Name)	Coupling (Splitting) Constants (In gauss)	Ref.
$H \cdot ^1$	Hydrogen atom **488**	508	563
$Li \cdot ^6$	Lithium atom **489**	81	564
$Na \cdot ^{23}$	Sodium atom **490**	632	565
$K \cdot ^{39}$	Potassium atom **491**	165	566
$Cs \cdot ^{133}$	Cesium atom **492**	3280	567
$N^{14}O \cdot ^{16}$	Nitric oxide **493**	(N^{14}) 14.3	568
$\cdot C^{12}N^{14}$	Cyanide radical **494**	(N^{14}) 174	569
$CH_3 \cdot$	Methyl radical[g] **495**	(H^1) 23	558
		(C^{13}) 41	134
$CH_3CH_2 \cdot$	Ethyl radical[g] **496**	$(\alpha\text{-}H^1)$ 22.4	558
		$(\beta\text{-}H^1)$ 26.9	558
$(CH_3)_2CH \cdot$	Isopropyl radical[g] **497**	$(\alpha\text{-}H^1)$ 22.1	558
		$(\beta\text{-}H^1)$ 24.7	558
$(CH_3)_3C \cdot$	*t*-Butyl radical[g] **498**	(H^1) 22.7	558
$HC{\equiv}C \cdot$	Ethynyl radical[e] **499**	(H^1) 16.1	570
$CH_2{=}CH \cdot$	Vinyl radical[f] **500**	$(\alpha\text{-}H^1)$ 16	570
		$(cis\text{-}\beta\text{-}H^1)$ 68 [b]	570
		$(trans\text{-}\beta\text{-}H^1)$ 34 [b]	570
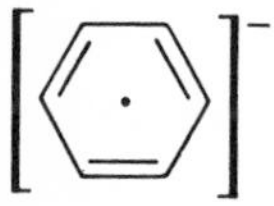	Benzene radical anion[h] **501**	(H^1) 3.75 [c]	571
		(C^{13}) 2.8	572
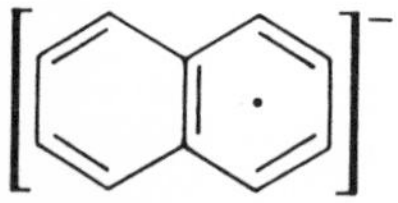	Naphthalene radical anion **213**	$(\alpha\text{-}H^1)$ 4.95	447
		$(\beta\text{-}H^1)$ 1.87	447
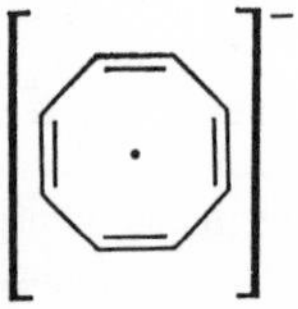	Cycloöctatetraene radical anion **503**	(H^1) 3.23 [d]	574

TABLE 3.10 (*Continued*)

Structure	Name	Coupling	Ref.
	Pyrazine radical anion **504**	(H^1) 2.66 (N^{14}) 7.22	575 575
	1,4-Dihydropyrazine radical cation **505**	(N^{14}) 7.60 (H^1) 3.26 (HN—H^1) 8.30	576 576 576
	2,3,5,6-Tetramethyl-1,4-dihydropyrazine radical cation **506**	(N^{14}) 6.64 (HN—H^1) 6.95 (CH$_3$—H^1) 2.53	577 577 577
	tetrakis(-dimethyl-amino)-ethylene radical cation^i **507**	(N^{14}) 4.85 (A—H^1) 3.28 (B—H^1) 2.84	578 578 578
	Triethylenediamine radical cation **508**	(N^{14}) 17.0 (H^1) 7.3	581 581
	Triphenylmethyl radical **509**	(C^{13}) 26	583
	Triphenylphosphine radical cation **510**	(P^{31}) 2.3	582
	1,1,4,4-Tetramethyl-2-tetrazene radical cation^j **511**	(1,4-N^{14}) 10.9 (2,3-N^{14}) 1.1 (A—H^1) 10.5 (B—H^1) 11.7	584 584 584 584

TABLE 3.10 (*Continued*)

Radical[a] (Formula)	(Name)	Coupling (Splitting) Constants (In gauss)	Ref.
	Cyclopropyl radical **512**	(α-H^1) 6.5 (β-H^1) 23.4	558 558
	Cyclohexadienyl radical **513**	(CH$_2$—H^1) 47.7 (2-H^1) 8.99 (3-H^1) 2.65 (4-H^1) 13.0	558 558 558 558
	Cyclobutyl radical **514**	(α-H^1) 21.2 (β-H^1) 36.7	558 558

[a] Ground state of free radicals.   [b] *cis-* = *cis-* to hydrogen on α-carbon; *trans-* = *trans-* to hydrogen on α-carbon. The usage in Ref. 570 is opposite to that given here, the reference location for *cis-* or *trans-* being the free electron.   [c] The hydrogen coupling constant of the benzene radical anion has a value which depends upon temperature to a slight extent, with the coupling increasing as the temperature decreases (*573*). This is reflected, as reported in the reference, in the total splitting (that is, the width of the e.p.r. spectrum), which changes from 22.4 gauss (at $-60°$) to 22.9 gauss (at $-130°$). The total width of the e.p.r. spectrum of other cyclic radicals is definitely greater than that of the benzene radical anion, ranging from 25.7 gauss for C$_8$H$_8^-$ (the cyclooctatetraene radical anion, *574*) through C$_7$H$_7\cdot$ (tropyl radical) **515** to 30.0 gauss for the C$_5$H$_5\cdot$ radical (cyclopentadienyl radical) **516**. See also Ref. 580 in which the variation in the width of the e.p.r. spectrum of heterocyclic radical anions is discussed.   [d] Cyclo-öctatetraene radical anion is readily reduced to the dianion. Complexing of the dianion with alkali metal ions (at least, in the solvents that can be used for the reductions) is strong and, for example, the reduction potential of the radical anion is decreased by 0.14 v in the presence of tetra-*n*-butylammonium cation (*579*). Disproportionation of the radical anion into dianion and cycloöctatetraene occurs readily in the presence of alkali metal cations (*574*), but *not* in the presence of tetra-*n*-butylammonium cation (*579*).   [e] Generated by the photolysis of acetylene in an argon matrix at 4°K.   [f] Generated by the addition of a hydrogen atom (derived from the photolysis of hydrogen iodide) to ethylene in an argon matrix at 4°K.   [g] Generated by irradiation of a hydro-carbon or a hydrocarbon mixture at low temperatures with a 2.8 MeV electron beam. The sample is held within the cavity of an e.p.r. spectrometer and the e.p.r. spectrum is monitored during irradiation.   [h] From alkali metal (for example, potassium) in 1,2-dimethoxyethane at $-80°$ [i] Through electrochemical oxidation at -0.75 v (versus aqueous saturated calomel electrode) in acetonitrile containing tetraethylammonium perchlorate.   [j] Formed by oxidation with tetranitromethane or by electrochemical oxidation in acetone at $-30°$.

of the e.p.r. spectrum of the C^{13}-derivative. A series of radicals for which e.p.r. splitting constants are of some interest is presented in Table 3.10. A detailed discussion of the e.p.r. phenomenon (measurement and applications) is beyond the scope of this book, but can be found in the books by Bersohn and Baird (*553*), by Carrington and Maclachlan (*554*), and the review by Symons (*597*).

The coupling constant for the electron and the hydrogen nucleus in a hydrogen atom is somewhat larger than 500 gauss, while that for a hydrogen nucleus and a neighboring free electron in an orbital on carbon is about 23 gauss. Thus, separating the hydrogen nucleus from the free electron by one bond has a very great effect on the magnetic interaction of that nucleus with the unpaired electron. The coupling constant actually increases if another bond is placed in between the hydrogen and the unpaired electron in many radicals. For the β-hydrogens of the ethyl radical, the coupling constant is 26.9 gauss. Coupling constants for hydrogens that are farther away than the β-position are usually quite small in saturated radicals. The special character of the β-hydrogens is usually attributed to hyperconjugation, equivalent to writing the valence bond structures:

$$\underset{496a}{\overset{\overset{\displaystyle H}{\overset{|}{}}}{\dot{C}H_2{-}CH_2\cdot}} \quad \longleftrightarrow \quad \underset{496b}{\overset{\displaystyle H\cdot}{CH_2{=}CH_2}}$$

One of the largest values known for this type of coupling constant is that for the hydrogens of the methylene group in the cyclohexadienyl radical (**513**) (Table 3.10). Nordio, Pavan, and Giacometti state that hyperconjugation accounts for the 47.7 gauss coupling constant observed by Fessenden and Schuler (*558*) and present molecular orbital calculations in support of this assertion (*585*). The cyclobutyl radical **514** also exhibits a rather high value for the coupling constant of the β-hydrogens (36.7 gauss), hyperconjugation supposedly being enhanced by the relatively rigid nature of the four-membered ring in comparison with open-chain systems, for which the coupling constants of the β-hydrogens are about 23–27 gauss.

Although it is clear that the calculations can be adjusted to yield coupling constants in reasonably good agreement with the experimental results, it is uncertain whether the "hyperconjugation-explanation" is the sole answer to such problems in magnetic interaction.

Substitution of alkyl groups has little effect on the coupling constants of hydrogen on the α-position of alkyl radicals (22–23 gauss) and relatively little effect on the coupling constants for the β-hydrogens (as stated above: 23–27 gauss). A change in hybridization, however, has a marked influence. For the α-hydrogens of the vinyl and cyclopropyl radical, the coupling constants are 16 and 6.5 gauss, respectively. The β-hydrogens, in contrast, of the vinyl radical couple quite strongly to the unpaired electron, especially that hydrogen which is *trans*- to the unpaired electron.

The structure of the vinyl radical **500**, CH_2=CH·, might be written as in **520** (hydrogen bonded to an *sp*-orbital) or as in two interconverting forms,

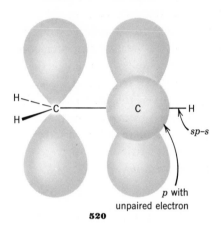

520

517a and **517b** (hydrogen bonded to an *sp²*-orbital). At 4.2°K, the two β-hydrogens

are clearly different, but at ca. 90°K (in liquid ethylene), the vinyl e.p.r. spectrum is simpler than at 4.2°K and can be accounted for in terms of the equilibration of **517a** and **517b**. Chemical evidence for an equilibrium of the type **517a** ⇌ **517b** lies in the finding by Sargent (*780*) that the naphthalene radical anion reduces *cis*- and *trans*-3-chloro-3-hexenes to somewhat different mixtures of *cis*- and *trans*-3-hexenes. In the e.p.r. spectrum of the cyclopropyl radical **512**, the signals for the β-hydrogens show that these are all equivalent, presumably indicating that the cyclopropyl radical is not conformationally stable and interconverts between two forms, **518a** and **518b**, or exists as a single form **519**.

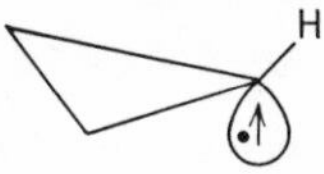

518a  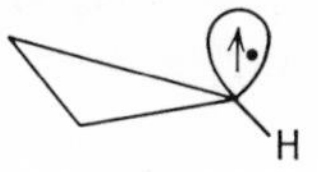   518b 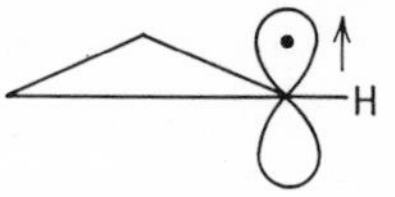   519

The coupling constant for the β-hydrogen of ethynyl radical (16.1 gauss) is markedly lower than that for the β-hydrogens of either vinyl or saturated alkyl radicals.

Spin density distribution in the naphthalene radical anion corresponds roughly to what one might expect on the basis of valence bond forms, **521** and **522**.

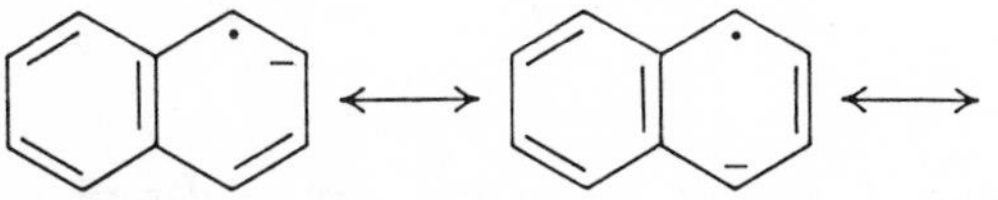

521

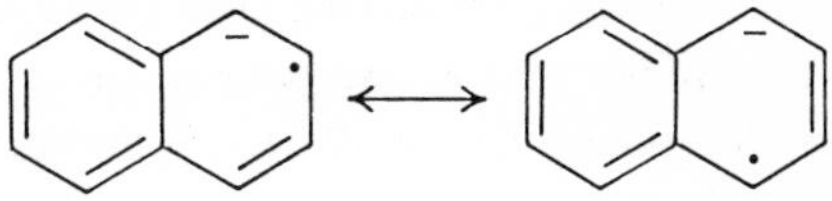

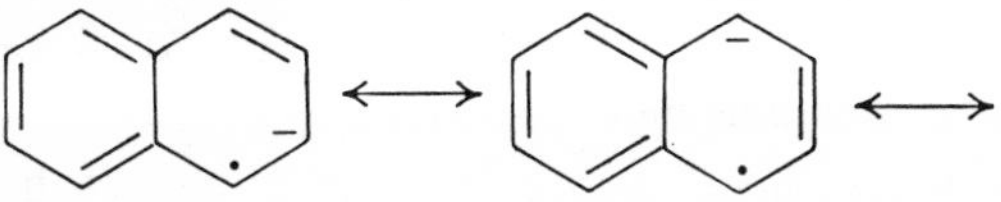

522

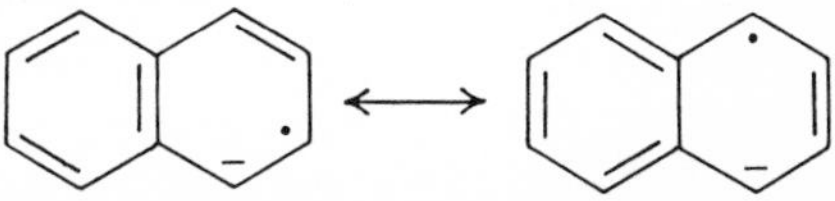

The occurrence of two kinds of hydrogen signals in the e.p.r. spectra of the radical cations **507** and **511** indicates that rotation around the bonds connecting the dimethylamino groups to the rest of the molecule is slower than the time scale for the e.p.r. measurement (ca. 10^{-8} seconds). The difference in the splitting constants observed for the hydrogens is due to the difference in the environments.

An extensive table of the splitting constants of radical ions has been compiled by Bowers (*586*). A number of entries (cyclopropane radical anion, adamantane radical anion, etc.) are erroneous (*587*).

The survival of free radicals depends upon intrinsic stability and steric

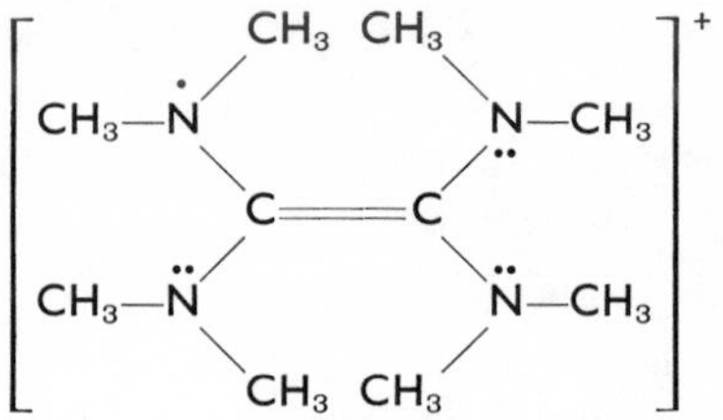

507

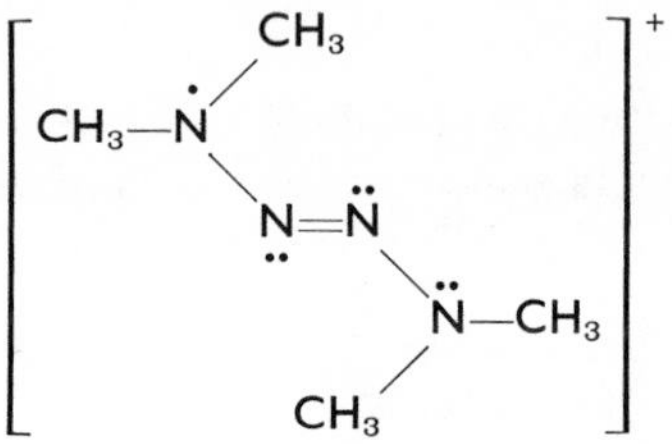

511

hindrance to dimerization. Intrinsic stability is another way of describing relative lack of reactivity. It is convenient to be able to examine the properties of radicals that are stable enough (that is, unreactive enough) to be isolated in the pure form (see Part 1, Section 1.6). The stability of free radicals like the red liquid, di-*t*-butyl nitroxide (**218**) (*137*), has been attributed to steric hindrance. Dupeyre and Rassat (*588*) noted that unstable nitroxides have a hydrogen on the α-carbon and reasoned that a stable nitroxide could be prepared from a molecule in which a double bond to nitrogen would be prohibited by "Bredt's rule" (no double bond to a bridgehead in polycyclic molecules). The nitroxide **523** ("norpseudopelletierine-*N*-oxyl" or 9-aza-3-

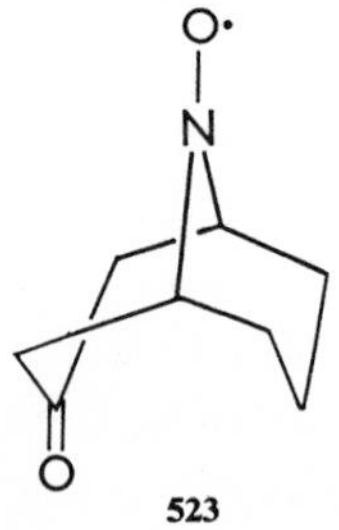

523

(22)

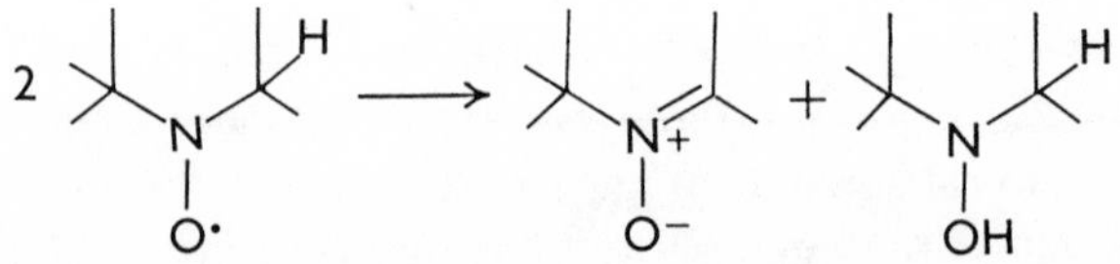

ketobicyclo[3.3.1]nonane-9-oxyl) was prepared by oxidation of the corresponding imine and was stable under neutral conditions. The instability of other nitroxides (for example, dimethyl nitroxide) was therefore attributed to a disproportionation reaction (Eq. 22).

Brière, Lemaire, and Rassat (*591*) found that the light absorption of the nitroxide **524** (2,2,6,6-piperid-4-one-1-oxyl) in the visible region had a maximum that varied with solvent. The transition energies for the maximum gave a linear correlation with the solvent polarity standard, **Z**-value (see Section 2.6). No particular variation in stability, as the solvents were changed in polarity, was noted, arguing against the possibility of an electron-transfer mechanism (see Part 1, Section 1.7). A hydrogen abstraction reaction is thus a reasonable possibility for the disproportionation reaction (Eq. 23). Lack of an α-hydrogen could therefore account for the stability of the purple gas, *bis*(trifluoromethyl) nitroxide **525** (*589, 590*).

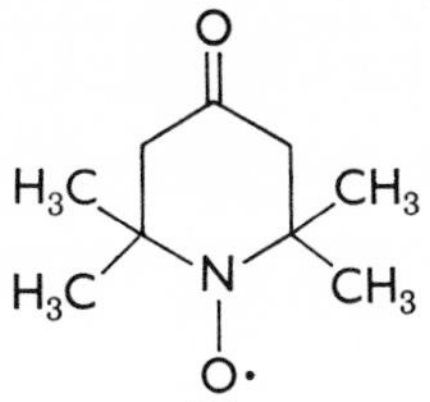

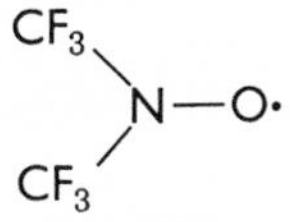

(23)

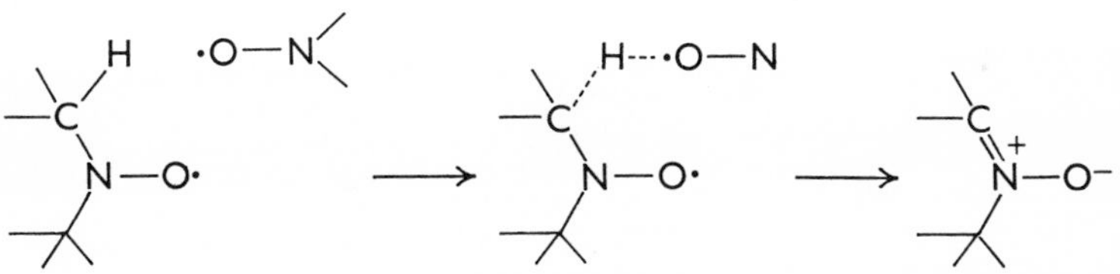

Polyradicals containing the nitroxide moiety have been synthesized by Lemaire, Rassat, and co-workers (*592*) and Rozantsev and Golubev (*593*). The diradicals **526** (*592*) and the tetraradicals **528** and **529** (*593*) were readily prepared by esterification of the hydroxy compound (**530**) derived through reduction of the keto radical **524**. The diradical **527** was prepared from **524** by reaction with hydrazine.

The striking fact about the e.p.r. spectra (room temperature) of the diradicals and tetraradicals like **527, 528,** and **529** is that the free electron on an individual nitroxide moiety interacts with all of the nitrogen nuclei in the molecule. Nitroxide e.p.r. spectra can be quite simple, as shown in Fig. 3.6*a* for both the simple nitroxide **524** and the *bis*-nitroxide **526**. Only three major

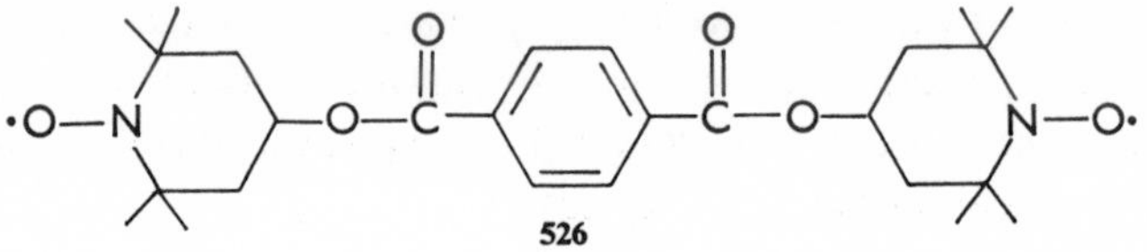

526

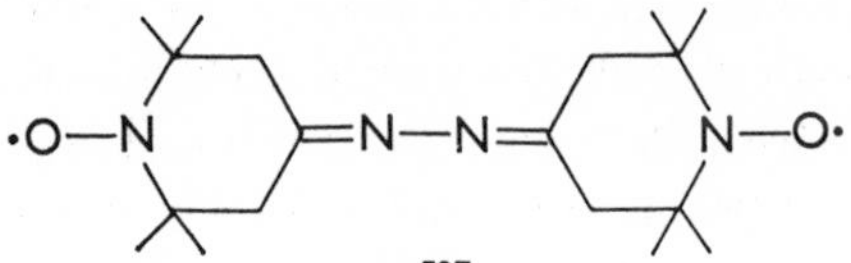

527

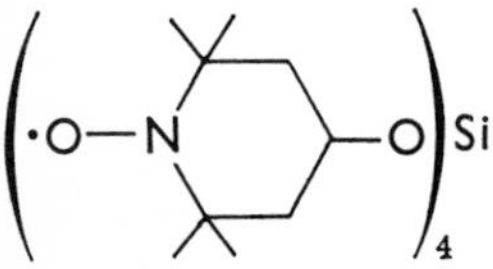

528

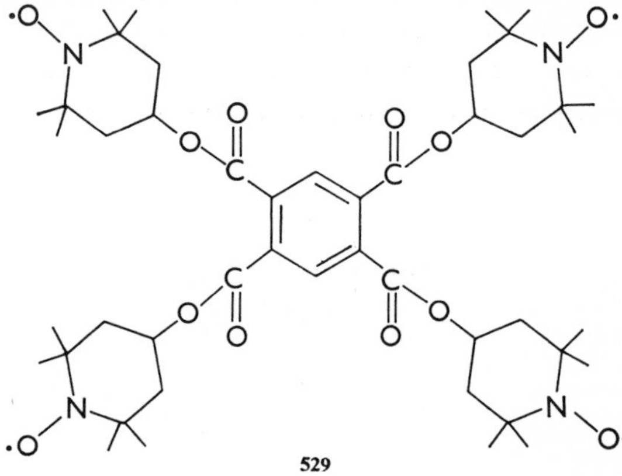

529

lines can be seen, the coupling constant being 15.6 gauss. The diradical **527**, in contrast, has five lines in its e.p.r. spectrum, with a separation of 7.4 gauss. The tetraradical **528** has nine lines in its spectrum, with a separation of 3.9 gauss (Figs. 3.6*b* and 3.6*c*). The additional lines in the e.p.r. spectrum can only mean that the free electron in one part of the polyradical is interacting with the nitrogen nuclei in the rest of the molecule by a weak interaction (spin exchange). The distance over which such exchange is reasonably

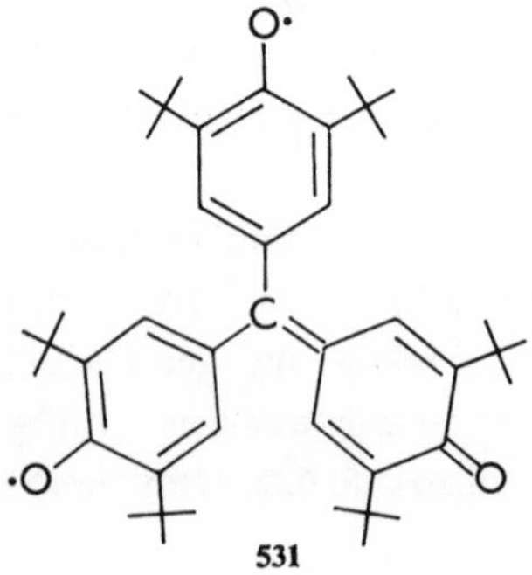

531

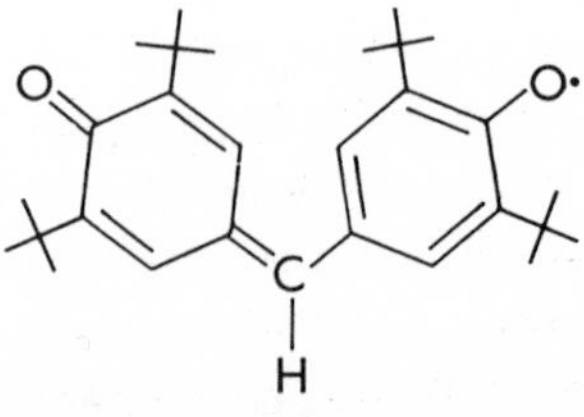

224

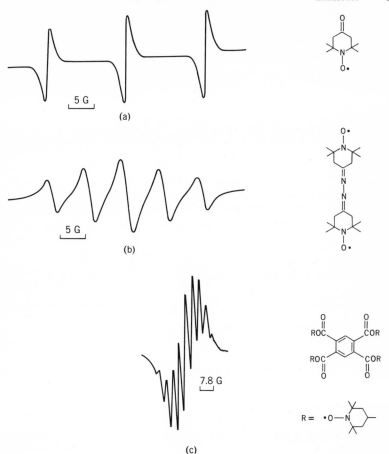

Figure 3.6 (*a*) The e.p.r. spectrum of the diradical **526** (identical to that of mono-radical **524**). (*b*) The e.p.r. spectrum of diradical **527** (both from Ref. 592 and reprinted with the permission of the *Bulletin de la Societe Chimique de France*). (*c*) The e.p.r. spectrum of tetraradical **529** (reprinted from Ref. 593 with permission of Consultants Bureau).

effective is 10 A or less, for when the distance is increased to 17 A as in diradical **526**, the e.p.r. spectrum shows only the three lines expected for a completely local interaction.

The diradical **531** synthesized by Yang and Castro (*594*) will here remain unnamed, according to standard nomenclature, as advised by Bartlett for the case of galvinoxyl (**224**) as follows (*595*): "We are aware of a body of competent opinion deploring all trivial names and of a rising tide of acronymy . . . believing that nomenclature, like the sabbath, was made for man and not *vice versa*, we use a euphonious nickname without apology."

Figure 3.7 (*a*) The change in the energies of a free electron with spin parallel to the external field (lower line) or spin opposite to the external field (upper line). The transition, from spin state, $m_s = +1/2$ to the upper state, $m_s = -1/2$, obeys the selection rule, $\Delta m_s = 1$ and occurs in a field of about 3400 gauss for a radiation frequency of 9500 megacycles (or 9500 MHz). (*b*) Energy level behavior with varying magnetic field for a system of two spins that do not interact. (*c*) Energy level behavior for two interacting spins. The parameter D measures the spin interaction along a main axis of the radical; E reflects interaction in the two directions perpendicular to the main axis. Two transitions in the simplest case would be observed above and below 3400 gauss with the election rule. $\Delta m_s = 1$. The greater the interaction of the two spins, the greater will be the difference in the positions of the two transitions. Another transition, characteristic of the triplet state, can often be found near 1500 gauss with the selection rule $\Delta m_s = 2$. This transition could only occur in a system with strongly interacting spins because it involves simultaneous flipping of two spins. Note that, in every case, the energy of the transition (the length of the arrow) is the same.

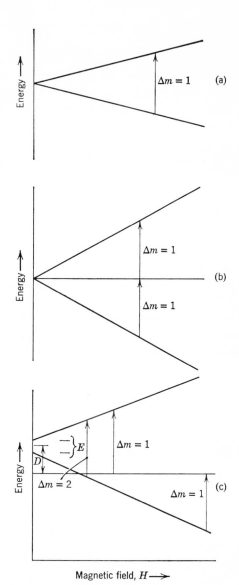

$\Delta m = 1$ (a)

$\Delta m = 1$

$\Delta m = 1$ (b)

E

D

$\Delta m = 1$

$\Delta m = 2$

$\Delta m = 1$ (c)

Magnetic field, $H \longrightarrow$

The diradical **531** in 2-methyltetrahydrofuran solution at room temperature shows seven lines with a separation of 0.86 gauss indicating a coupling of the free electron to six hydrogens (*596*). The low temperature spectrum will be discussed below.

The splitting of the energy levels for an electron in a magnetic field (Fig. 3.5) is a function of the strength of the magnetic field. This point is shown graphically in Fig. 3.7a. In the case of a diradical in which there is no interaction between the spins of the two electrons, the total spin can assume three values, corresponding to $m_s = +1$, $m_s = 0$, and $m_s = -1$. The energies of the three levels will vary with the strength of the imposed field (Fig. 3.7b). For a diradical in which the interaction of the two spins is appreciable, the energy levels change in a way characterized by two parameters, D and E. Since the interaction of the two spins leads to a separation of the energy levels (spins parallel or opposite) even in the absence of an external magnetic field, these parameters are called the zero-field parameters. The parameter D measures the spin interaction along a particular molecular axis (the z-axis, perpendicular to the ring plane, in the case of aromatic molecules) and E refers to spin interaction along the x- and y-axes. Molecules with two unpaired electrons are all diradicals, and those in which there is appreciable interaction between the two electrons can be called triplet molecules. (There is some disagreement on how strong the interaction should be before applying the name of triplet state to a particular diradical.) The variation in the energy levels for a triplet molecule with the strength of the magnetic field is shown in Fig. 3.7c. For a discussion of the theory of the triplet state e.p.r. spectra and their interpretation, the student is referred to Wasserman, Snyder, and Yager (*598*).

Hutchison and Magnum (*599*) devised the experimental approach that made possible the initial studies of the triplet states of organic molecules, by means of electron paramagnetic resonance. Naphthalene (**212**) was introduced as a "guest" into a crystal "host" of durene **532**. Irradiation produced the triplet state of naphthalene, stable at low temperatures (Eq. 24). The host provided both orientation and dilution for the paramagnetic triplet.

The triplet of phenanthrene **535** can be produced in a diphenyl **536** host.

By diluting the naphthalene with durene (1,2,4,5-tetramethylbenzene), the triplet concentration was lowered, so that the triplet molecules did not interact with one another. Using durene as the medium made it possible to define the geometric relationship of the naphthalene triplet and the external field, since durene had a known crystal structure. The two $\Delta m_s = 1$ lines of the naphthalene triplet are extremely sensitive to the relative orientations of the

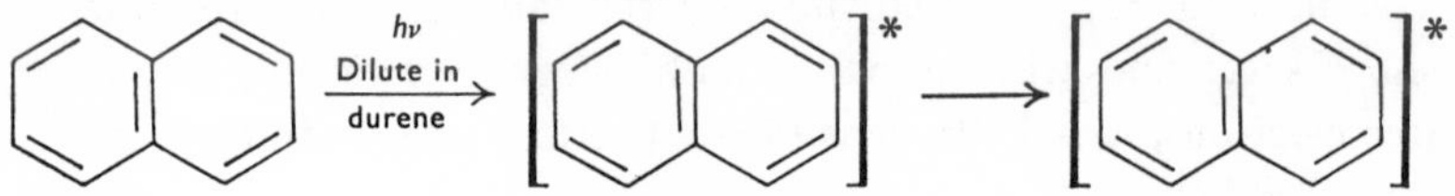

Excited singlet
533

Triplet
534

(24)

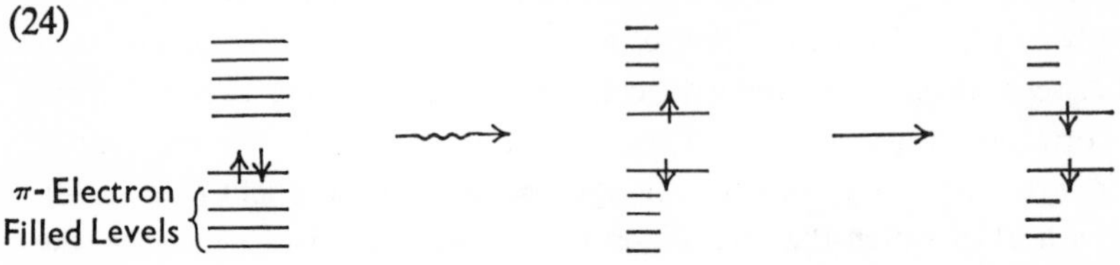

π- Electron Filled Levels

molecule and the external magnetic field, varying almost 2000 gauss for a change of 45° in angle. As stated in Fig. 3.5, the transition energy for an e.p.r. line is equivalent to $g\beta H$. With the external field parallel to the z-axis of naphthalene, the separation between the two e.p.r. lines is 2136 gauss, which is equal to $2D$. The Bohr magneton, β, defined in Fig. 3.5, has the value 0.927×10^{-20} erg/gauss. The value of $2D$ is, thus after converting into wavenumbers with the relationship $E = hc\nu$, 0.20 cm.$^{-1}$. The value of D for naphthalene is 0.10 cm.$^{-1}$.

Although the study of guest triplets in host crystals is an elegant and precise method for obtaining information about the triplet state of many molecules, it is not generally applicable because a host with a well-defined crystal structure is not available for every molecule and it is often impossible for practical reasons (for example, instability of the diradical) to prepare the appropriate combination. The discovery by van der Waals and de Groot (*600*) that the $\Delta m_s = 2$ transition could be observed for randomly oriented molecules and the extension of the e.p.r. observations for such molecule to the $\Delta m_s = 1$ transitions by Wasserman, Snyder, and Yager (*598*) made it possible to study triplets in glasses. [A glass is an amorphous (*noncrystalline*), usually clear, substance prepared by cooling such liquids as 2-methyltetrahydrofuran, molten boric acid, etc.] A whole variety of triplets have been studied in glasses. Parameters for a number of triplet species are listed in Table 3.11. A derivative spectrum for the triplet diradical, **537**, is shown in Fig. 3.8 (*601*).

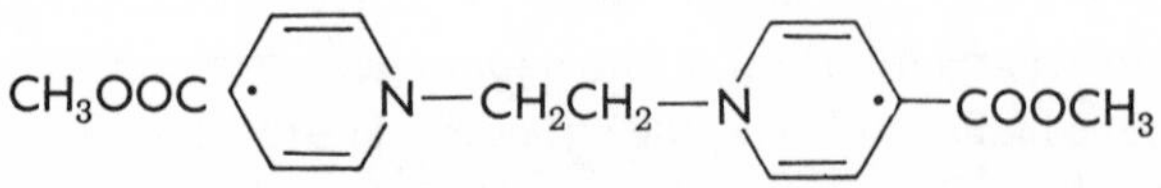

CH_3OOC — N—CH_2CH_2—N — $COOCH_3$

537

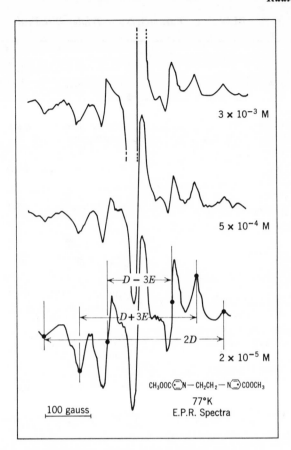

Figure 3.8 E.p.r. spectra of three different concentrations of the pyridinyl diradical **537** in 2-methyltetrahydrofuran glass at 77°K. The $D - 3E$, $D + 3E$, and $2D$ separations are marked. The strong signal in the center (at ca. 3240 gauss) is due to the monoradical ends of diradical polymer of the type $\uparrow \cdot PyC_2Py \downarrow \uparrow PyC_2Py \cdot \uparrow$ (Ref. 601).

The e.p.r. spectrum of the diradical **531** in 2-methyltetrahydrofuran at about 110°K reveals two pairs of lines around the signal for a monoradical. The inner lines are separated by 38 gauss; assuming that the inner lines are separated by $D - 3E$, the corresponding D parameter is the smallest listed in Table 3.11 (about 0.003 cm.$^{-1}$). D is a function of $1/r^3$, in which r is the average distance between spins (*554*). Kreilick (*596*) has estimated that the D value for the diradical **531** corresponds to an average separation between the spins of about 9 A, implying that the two free electrons in diradical **531** are almost completely localized on the oxygen atoms.

TABLE 3.11 *Parameters for Triplet Diradicals*

Diradical (Formula)	(Name)	Parameters D $\quad$ E (in cm.$^{-1}$)		Ref.
HC$\equiv$C$\dot{\text{C}}$H[a] (538)	Ethynylmethylene (propargylene)	0.628	0	602
CH$_3$C$\equiv$C$\dot{\text{C}}$H[a] (539)	(1-Propynyl)methylene	0.626	0	602
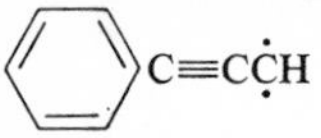 C$_6$H$_5$—C$\equiv$C$\dot{\text{C}}$H (540)[a]	(2-Phenylethynyl)-methylene	0.541	0.0035	602
CH$_3$C$\equiv$C—C$\equiv$C$\dot{\text{C}}$H (541)[a]	(1-Penta-1,3-diinyl)-methylene	0.609	0	602
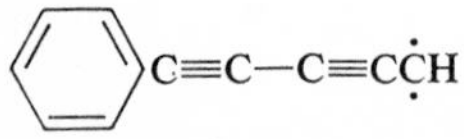 C$_6$H$_5$—C$\equiv$C—C$\equiv$C$\dot{\text{C}}$H (542)[a]	1-(4-Phenylbuta-1,3-diinyl)methylene	0.553	0	602
(CH$_3$)$_3$CC$\equiv$C—C$\equiv$C$\dot{\text{C}}$H (543)[a]	1-(5,5-Dimethylhexa-1,3-diinyl)methylene	0.606	0	602
N$\equiv$C$\dot{\text{C}}$H (544)[a]	Cyanomethylene	0.863	0	602
$\dot{\text{C}}$H$_2$ (545)[b]	Methylene	(1.017)[c]	0	603,604
$\bar{\text{N}}$=$\overset{+}{\text{N}}$=$\dot{\text{C}}$ (546)[d,t]	Diazomethylene	1.153	0	606
N$\equiv$CN : (547)[e,t]	Cyanonitrene	1.544[f]	0	606
N$\equiv$C$\dot{\text{C}}$C$\equiv$N (548)[g]	Dicyanomethylene	1.002	0[h]	606
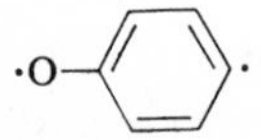 ·O—C$_6$H$_4$—· (549)[i]	4-Oxylphenylradical	0.318	0.0055	609
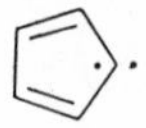 (550)[j]	Cyclopentadienylene	0.409	0.0120	610
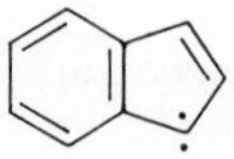 (551)[j]	Indenylidene	0.378	0.0160	610

TABLE 3.11 (*Continued*)

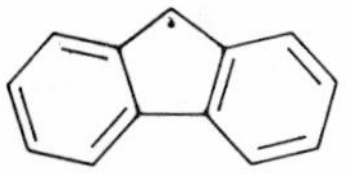 (552)[j]	Fluorenylidene	0.408	0.0283	611,612
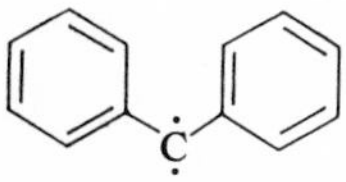 (553)[j]	Diphenylmethylene	0.406	0.0194	612,613
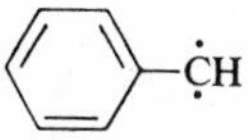 ĊH (554)[j]	Phenylmethylene	0.515	0.0251	612
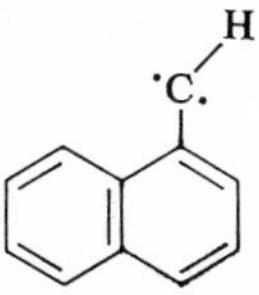 (555)[j]	*anti*-1-Naphthyl-methylene	0.456	0.0202	614
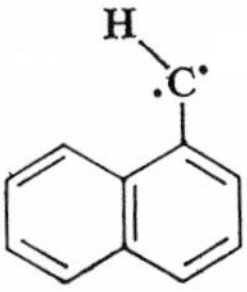 (556)[j]	*syn*-1-Naphthyl-methylene	0.435	0.208	614
Ṅ H(557)	Nitrene[k]	1.86[l]	(0)[m]	615
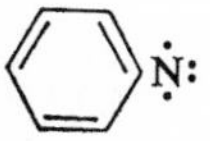 Ṅ: (558)	Phenylnitrene	1.00	0	616,617
$(CH_3)_3C\ddot{N}$: (559)[n]	*t*-Butylnitrene	1.625	0	616
$CH_3SO_2\ddot{N}$: (560)	Methylsulfonylnitrene	1.581	0.0036	616
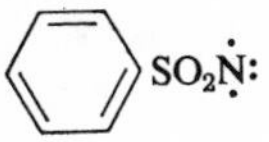 $SO_2\ddot{N}$: (564)[n]	Benzenesulfonylnitrene	1.45	—	621
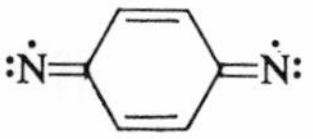 :Ṅ ═══ Ṅ: (561)[n]	Quinone diimine diradical	0.0675	0	618
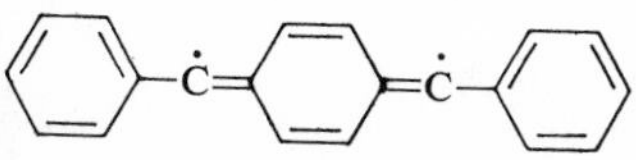 (565)[j]	1,4-*bis*-Phenylidene-*bis*-(phenylmethyl radical)[q]	0.0513	0	618

433

TABLE 3.11 (*Continued*)

Diradical (Formula)	(Name)	Parameters D E (in cm.$^{-1}$)	Ref.
(562)^o	*bis*-Galvinoxyl^r	0.005 —	619
CH$_3$OOC⟨·⟩NCH$_2$CH$_2$N⟨·⟩COOCH$_3$ **(537)**^{p}	"1-2-1"-Diradical^s	0.0178 0.0017	601
[CH$_3$OOC⟨·⟩NCH(CH$_3$)$_2$]$_2$ **(563)**	1-Isopropyl-4-carbo-methoxypyridinyl diradical dimer	0.006 —	620
(531)	—^{r}	0.003 —	596
(566)	Pentachlorocyclo-pentadienyl cation radical	0.150 0	622 782
(585A)	Dibenzo[*a,d*]cyclo-heptenylidene	0.379 0.0162	781
(585B)	Tribenzo[*a,c,e*]cyclo-heptenylidene	0.422 0.0195	781

In general, the data in Table 3.11 reveal that spin–spin interaction in triplet diradicals follows roughly what we might expect for delocalization of the free electrons into conjugated systems. Thus ethynylmethylene (**538**) has a higher D (0.628 cm.$^{-1}$) than the diradical **540**, in which a hydrogen has been replaced by a phenyl group (D = 0.541). The e.p.r. spectrum for methylene has not been observed in spite of much effort and the D for this has only been calculated or estimated by a number of extrapolation procedures. If a D of 1.0 is approximately correct for methylene, conjugation of a cyano group allows the spins to be farther apart and cyanomethylene (**544**) has a D of 0.863. Further conjugation with a phenyl group (D of **554** is 0.515) or two phenyl groups (D of **553** is 0.406) increases the separation of the spins.

---

[a] Generated by photolysis of the diazo compound in polychlorotrifluoroethylene at 77°K.   [b] The ground state of methylene is triplet and linear, according to the detailed structure of the 1415 A absorption band discovered by Herzberg and Shoosmith (Ref. 605). The ground state assignment was made because the intensity of the band rises under conditions that favor the decay of more excited species after flash photolysis. [c] Calculated from theory including spin-spin interaction (Ref. 603) and spin-orbit interaction (Ref. 604).   [d] From photolysis of cyanogen azide in a fluorocarbon matrix at 77°K using radiation with λ > 3000 A followed by a brief irradiation with λ < 3000 A (see footnote t).   [e] Like d, but omitting the second irradiation (see footnote t). [f] Gas-phase spectroscopic results of Herzberg and Travis (Ref. 607) indicate that D is 1.567 cm.$^{-1}$. D is thus almost independent of environment.   [g] From photolysis of diazodicyanomethane (Ref. 608).   [h] $E = 0.0033$ cm.$^{-1}$ for dicyanomethylene in a hexafluorobenzene matrix indicating a 10–15° deviation from linearity of the molecule. [i] From photolysis of 1,4-benzenediazooxide, prepared from 4-aminophenol by diazotization.   [j] Generated by photolysis of the diazo compounds in various matrices or glasses.   [k] Also called imine radical.   [l] Spectroscopic results.   [m] Calculated.   [n] From photolysis of azides.   [o] From lead dioxide treatment of the phenol.   [p] Through reduction of the *bis*-pyridinium iodide with sodium amalgam in acetonitrile.   [q] Described as 1,4-phenylene *bis*-(phenylmethylene) in Ref. 618.   [r] See text for comment on nomenclature.   [s] 1,2-ethylene *bis*-(4-carbomethoxypyridinyl).   [t] Milligan and Jacox report in Ref. 632 that NCN is produced through photolysis of cyanogen azide through both the 2750 A and 2200 A absorption bands. The long wavelength absorption band may produce a triplet excited state of CNN_3 and the short wavelength band produces a singlet excited state. The excited states are assigned on the basis of intensity, with singlet → triplet being weak and "forbidden" and singlet → singlet being strong and allowed. The formation of CNN from NCN occurs through photolysis of the latter to carbon atoms in a ^1D state and nitrogen. Reaction of the excited carbon atoms with nitrogen produces CNN. The ^1D state of carbon has a half-life of 15 seconds in a cold matrix according to the work of Skell and Engel (Ref. 633). Analysis of the infrared spectrum of NCN in an argon matrix indicates that the stretching force constant for the carbon–nitrogen double bond approximates that for a double bond, based on the weak 2672 cm.$^{-1}$ which might be expected for a symmetrical A=B=A species.

Nitrogen has a higher nuclear charge, and the electrons are on the average somewhat closer to the nucleus and to each other around nitrogen than around carbon. The spin–spin interaction in nitrene (**557**) is reflected in a D of 1.86 cm.$^{-1}$ and other nitrenes (**558–560, 564**) also have high D values. The "dinitrene" (**561**) generated by photolysis of 1,4-diazidobenzene has a very small D value, showing that the free electrons are localized in nonbonding orbitals on the nitrogens and that the species is better considered as a diradical rather than a dinitrene.

Wasserman and co-workers (*611*) examined the hydrogen hyperfine splitting in the e.p.r. spectrum of phenylmethylene (**554**) with C^{13} at the methylene carbon and concluded that the phenyl-C—H angle was 140–150° rather than 180° because the splitting was much lower than expected (**554a**).

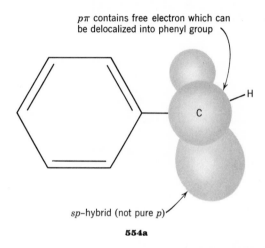

$p\pi$ contains free electron which can be delocalized into phenyl group

sp–hybrid (not pure p)

H

C

554a

The bent structure for triplet arylmethylenes has been confirmed by the work of Trozzolo, Wasserman, and Yager (*614*). In a suitable arylmethylene, the in-plane electron will differ in its interaction with the $p\pi$-electron on the proximate ring positions, if those positions differ in spin density. Two isomers of 1-naphthylmethylene (**555** and **556**) can be produced by photolysis of the corresponding diazo compound. Higher spin density at the 8-position in a 1-napththylmethylene results in a slightly greater D-value for the isomer called *anti*.

An unusual phenomenon which has been observed for a number of organic radicals is that of the formation of diamagnetic radical dimers which do not have a new covalent bond as would be expected in the usual dimerization of radicals. The evidence in many cases of diamagnetic radical dimerization rests upon the fact that the spectrum of the dimer is not very different from

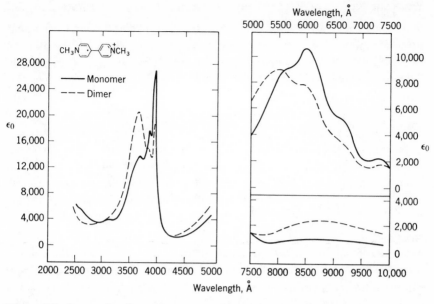

Figure 3.9 Spectra for the monomer and dimer of methylviologen radical cation (**567**) in aqueous solution (from Ref. 623). (Reprinted with permission of the *Journal of the American Chemical Society*.)

that of the monomer. The spectroscopic changes are illustrated for the case of methylviologen cation radical (**567**) (Eq. 25) in Fig. 3.9 (*623*). The lithium salt of the tetracyanoquinodimethane radical anion (**568**) has been investigated by Boyd and Phillips (*624*) (Eq. 26) and the dimerization of 1-methyl-4-carbomethoxypyridinyl (**280** ⇌ **279**, see Part 1, Section 1.8) by Itoh and Nagakura (*209, 787*).

(25) $2\ CH_3\overset{+}{N}$⟨⟩•⟨⟩NCH_3 $\underset{}{\overset{H_2O}{\rightleftharpoons}}$ $\left[CH_3\overset{+}{N}⟨⟩•⟨⟩NCH_3 \right]_2$

567

(26) 2 ⟨⟩ $\rightleftharpoons$ $\left[⟨⟩ \right]_2$ with substituents •$C(CN)_2$ and $^-C(CN)_2$

568

Waits and Kosower (*620*) have found that a small amount of triplet dimer **502** is in equilibrium with the singlet (diamagnetic) dimer in the case of the pyridinyl radicals, as shown in Eq. 27. The ketyl dimers discovered by Hirota and Weissman (*627*), however, are paramagnetic. For sodium fluorenone ketyl dimer a D of 0.0092 is found.

(27)

$$Py \cdot + Py \cdot \xrightarrow{K_1} (Py \cdot)_2 \xrightarrow{K_2} (Py \cdot)_2$$

$K_1 \sim 10^4 \text{ l. mol}^{-1} \textbf{(280)}$ **502**

$K_2 \ll K_1$ (At 77°K)

$R = (CH_3)_2CH$

$R = CH_3, CH_3CH_2, (CH_3)_2CH$

For many years, the e.p.r. signals found for Chichibabin's hydrocarbon (**569**) were interpreted as those of a diradical (**570**) in equilibrium with the quinoid form **569** (*625*). Waring and Sloan (*626*) discovered that the e.p.r. signal from **569** does not change instantaneously on sudden cooling, implying that a chemical change rather than a rearrangement of electrons produced the change from paramagnetic to diamagnetic species. Furthermore, no $\Delta m_s = 2$ transition was found at low temperature. A dimer of the diradical (**571** or **572**) would account for the results for **569** and possibly for many of the other diradicals referred to by Waring and Sloan. Ikegami and Kosower (*601*) have found that diradical 1-2-1 (**237**) has an e.p.r. spectrum which exhibits more hyperfine structure on a weaker signal at high concentrations than at low concentrations, the reverse of what is usually found for radical solutions. The dimerization equilibrium for **237** diradical is given in Eq. 38. [See Fig. 3.8 for an illustration of how the "monoradical" concentration (that is, **537a**) changes with gross concentration.]

(28)   1-2-1 + 1-2-1 $\rightleftharpoons$ Dimer (diamagnetic complex with paramagnetic ends)

(537)   (537)   537a

Py· —Py·

Py· —Py·

The strength of radical–radical association is known in so few cases that it is difficult to draw any conclusions concerning the driving force for the process. The constants for the dimerization of viologen radical cation (Eq. 25) and tetracyanoquinodimethane radical anion (Eq. 26) are about 1000 l. mole^{-1}. In both cases, association occurs to a much smaller extent in

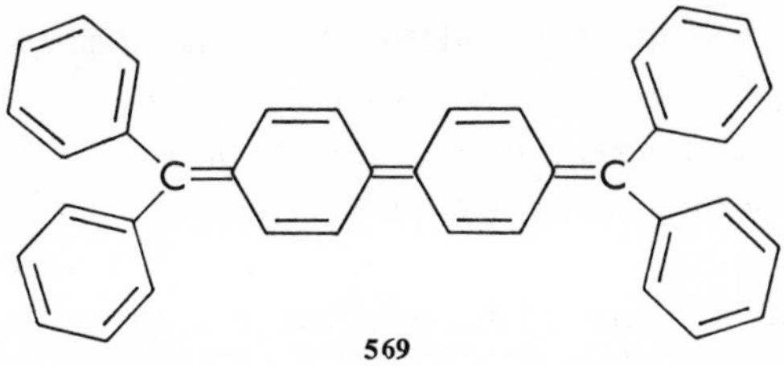

569

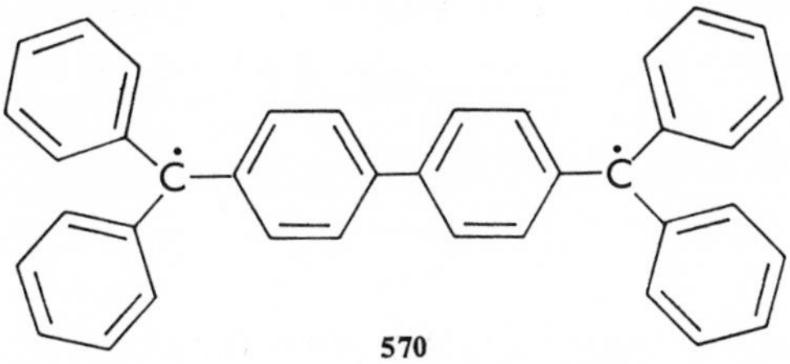

570

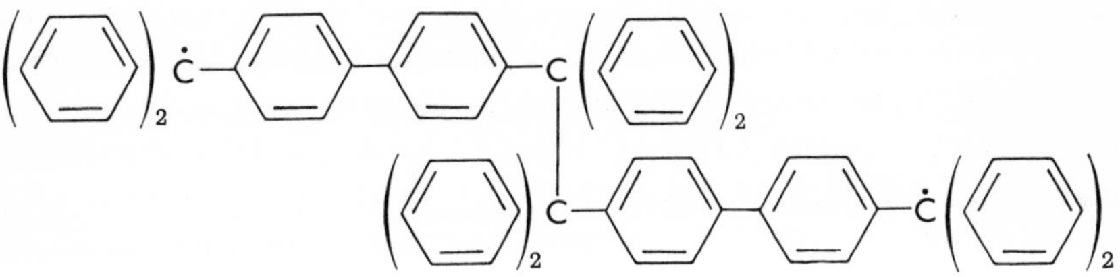

571

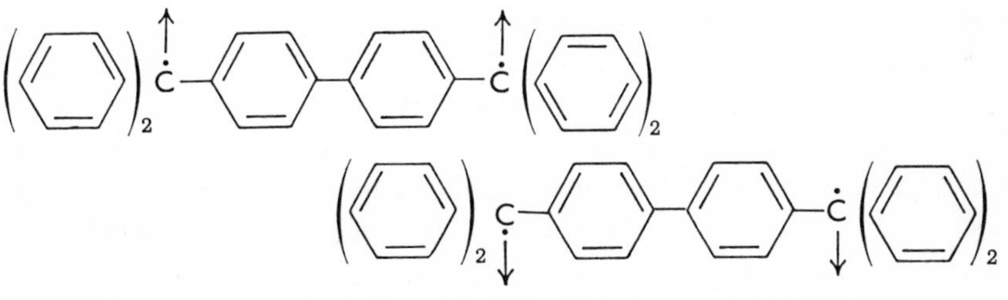

572

organic solvents than in water, implying that a substantial portion of the driving force is due to "hydrophobic bonding" (see Part 2, Sections 2.5 and 2.9). The equilibrium constant for the dimerization of 1-methyl-4-carbo-methoxypyridinyl radical to diamagnetic dimers in isopentane is 10^4 l. mole^{-1} (Eq. 27). Pending further work, interaction energies favoring radical–radical association of between 1 to 4 kcal./mole should be held possible. This factor has already been considered in connection with the discussion of the cycloadditions via diradical intermediates investigated by Bartlett and Montgomery (*209*) (Section 1.8). We might further expect radical–radical interactions to be important in the reactions of triplet methylenes.

The formation of methylenes must be considered first in any discussion of their chemistry because, in many cases, the precise nature of the reactive species is not known and is inferred either from the method of preparation or the mode of reaction. A general equation for the formation of methylenes can be written (Eq. 29), but it is probably conceptually clearer to subdivide the general equation for the elimination of XY into three groups.

(29)

$$\underset{Y}{\overset{X}{\diagdown C \diagup}} \longrightarrow \diagdown C :$$

The *ionic approach* to methylenes (Eq. 30) is illustrated by the formation of dichloromethylene (**573**) from treatment of chloroform with hydroxide ion, first proven by the studies of Hine (*635*) (Eqs. 31, 32). The two steps in the reaction have very different substituent sensitivities. The rate of anion formation (which can be measured by deuterium exchange) is very fast for iodoform (CHI_3) and bromoform ($CHBr_3$) (k about 1 l. mole^{-1} sec.$^{-1}$ at $0°$ in water), intermediate for fluorodibromomethane and for chloroform ($CHCl_3$) (36.0 and 8.2×10^{-3} l. mole^{-1} sec.$^{-1}$, respectively) and undetectable for fluoroform (CHF_3) under the conditions used (*555*) (cf. *26*). In contrast, the net rate for the two steps leading to dihalomethylene (equivalent to the overall rate of hydrolysis, since the reactive methylene disappears quickly under the conditions used) decreases from 1×10^{-8} l. mole^{-1} sec.$^{-1}$ for iodoform to 2.77×10^{-3} l. mole^{-1} sec.$^{-1}$ for fluorodibromomethane ($CHBr_2F$) ($0°$, H_2O). The compounds $CHBrF_2$ and $CHIF_2$ do not show any deuterium exchange in base and yet hydrolyze readily, with rate constants of 2.08 and 9.60×10^{-3} l. mole^{-1} sec.$^{-1}$ for water at $0°$. Hine and Langford (*636*) concluded that a concerted α-elimination must be written for the latter two compounds (Eq. 33).

(30) $B + HCXYZ \longrightarrow BH + {}^-CXYZ \longrightarrow Z^- + :CXY$

(31) $OH^- + CHCl_3 \longrightarrow CCl_3{}^-$

(32) $CCl_3{}^- \longrightarrow :CCl_2 \ (\mathbf{573}) + Cl^-$

(33) $OH^- \longrightarrow H{-}\underset{F}{\overset{F}{C}}{-}I \longrightarrow H_2O + I^- + :CF_2$

Thus, it may be inferred that fluorine is far more effective than iodine for the stabilization of the dihalomethylene.

Other methods for generating the intermediate anion can, under the appropriate conditions (aprotic medium), produce dihalomethylenes, as in the decarboxylation of trichloroacetate anion (*637*).

(34)

$$Cl_3C-COO^- \longrightarrow Cl^- + :CCl_2 + CO_2$$

It is likely that the decarboxylation is concerted according to the results of Hine and Duffey (*638*) who obtained a poor yield of haloform on decarboxylation of chlorodifluoroacetate ion:

(35)

$$ClCF_2-COO^- \longrightarrow Cl^- + :CF_2 + CO_2$$

The *diradical approach* to methylenes (Eq. 36) can be illustrated by the benzophenone-sensitized photolysis of diazomethane (*639*). Light absorption by benzophenone in the region of the $n \rightarrow \pi^*$ transition (Fig. 2.33) produces the n,π^* excited singlet, the lowest excited state in the set of states called the singlet manifold. "*Crossing-over*" from the n,π^* singlet to the n,π^* triplet produces the *lowest state* in the triplet manifold, a state which is incidentally considerably more stable than the n,π^* singlet (69 versus 74 kcal./mole above the singlet ground state) (*423*). The triplet n,π^* benzophenone behaves like a diradical and reacts with diazomethane to produce triplet diazomethane (Eqs. 37, 38, and 39). Triplet diazomethane decomposes into triplet methylene (Eq. 39).

(36)

$$\begin{array}{c} \underset{Y}{\overset{X}{\diagdown}}C \xrightarrow[\text{diradical}]{h\nu \text{ or}} \left[\underset{Y}{\overset{X}{\diagdown}}C\right]^* \longrightarrow \diagdown C: + XY \\ \text{Triplet} \qquad\qquad \text{Triplet} \end{array}$$

The n,π^* triplet state usually has a lower energy than the n,π^* singlet state primarily because the electrostatic repulsion between the electrons is greater in the singlet than in the triplet state. The same statement may be made about π,π^* triplet and singlet states, such as those derived from ethylene. The antiparallel spins of the electrons in an excited singlet allow them to (fractionally)

(37)

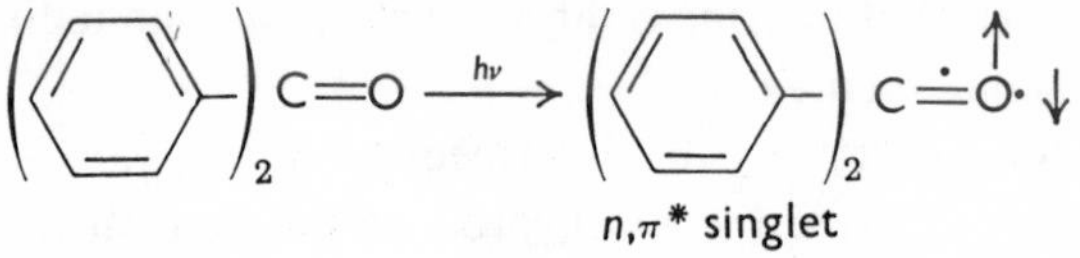

n,π^* singlet

(38)

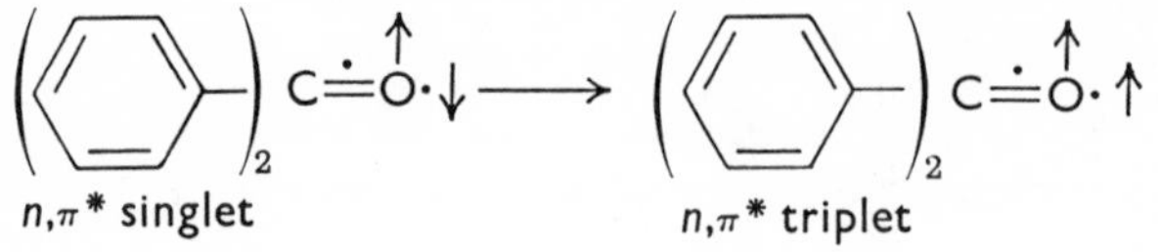

n,π^* singlet n,π^* triplet

(39)

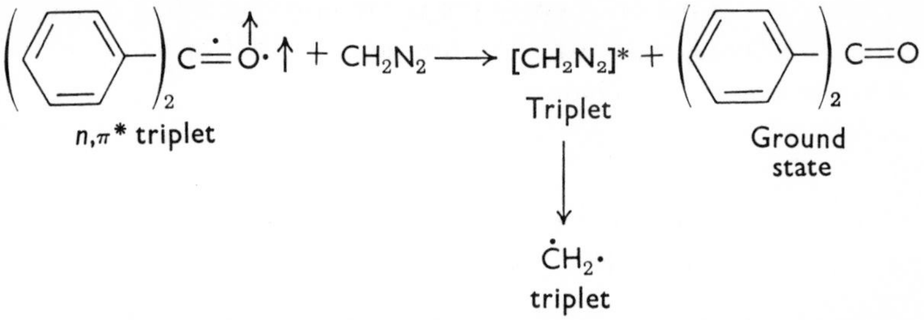

n,π^* triplet   Triplet   Ground
                                                  state

$\dot{C}H_2\cdot$
triplet

occupy one another's orbitals to a greater extent than in the triplet. This is
equivalent to saying that electron correlation results in a greater electron–
electron separation in triplet states than in singlet states. Correlation of
electron distribution (position of one electron being dependent on the

$\xrightarrow{h\nu}$ [574]* $\longrightarrow$ [574]*

π,π^* singlet π,π^* triplet

574

(40)

Phenylmethylene **OR** Benzaldehyde
triplet   triplet
554   **575**

$(CH_3)_2C{=}CH_2$

576   **577**

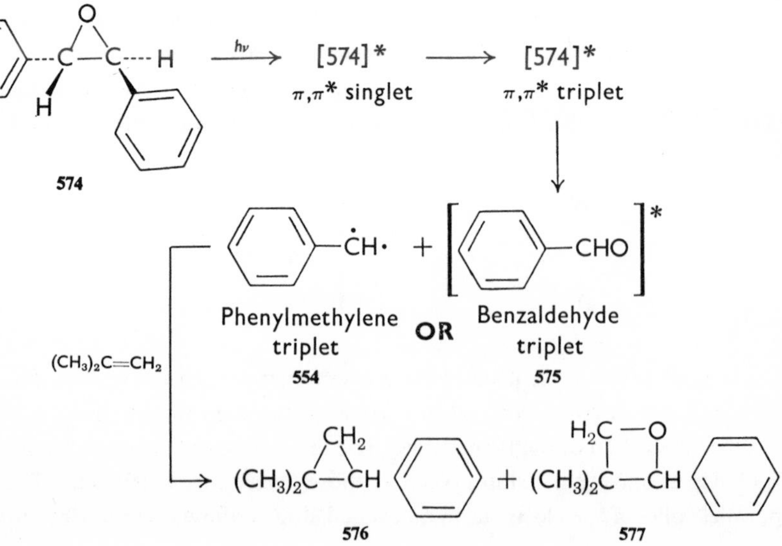

position of the other electron in a two-electron case) arises from the fact that electrons have the same (negative) charge. (For further discussion on this point, see *554*.)

The useful and novel photolysis of epoxides discovered by Kristinsson and Griffin (*640*), illustrated for the formation of phenylmethylene from stilbene oxide, may proceed by way of a triplet π,π^* state.

The *isopolar approach* to methylenes can be illustrated by the thermal decomposition of *tris*-(trifluoromethyl)difluorophosphorane found by Mahler (*641*) (Eq. 41).

(41)
$$(CF_3)_3PF_2 \xrightarrow{120°} PF_5 + 3:CF_2$$

578   579

Trichloromethyl-trichlorosilane decomposes at 250° to yield dichloromethylene (*642*). Presumably, the driving forces for each of these reactions is the formation of a strong bond, either the silicon–chlorine bond or the phosphorus–fluorine bond.

(42)
$$Cl_3CSiCl_3 \xrightarrow{250°} SiCl_4 + :CCl_2$$

573

Many reactions do not proceed by way of methylene intermediates but through closely related derivatives which can be called *methylenoid*. (One common usage for this type of intermediate is *carbenoid*, that is, carbene-like or methylene-like. See Footnote a, Table 3.9.) The methylenoid derivatives react to provide a methylene group to another molecule and differ in reactivity and specificity from free methylenes. The best known example of such a reagent is iodomethylzinc iodide, discovered and applied by Simmons and Smith (*643*) and often called the Simmons–Smith reagent (Eq. 43). The reagent reacts with cyclohexene to form bicyclo[4.1.0]heptane in good yield (Eq. 44).

(43)
$$CH_2I_2 \xrightarrow[\substack{Couple \\ Et_2O}]{Zn-Cu} ICH_2ZnI$$

580   581

(44)

582   583

The Simmons–Smith reagent is much more stable than the methylenoid compounds, dichloromethyl lithium prepared by Köbrich and Merkle (*644*) by treatment of dichloromethane with butyl lithium in tetrahydrofuran between $-65°$ and $-100°$ (Eq. 45), and trichloromethyl lithium, derived in a similar way from tetrachloromethane (Eq. 46) (*645, 646*). These are reactive towards alkenes at low temperatures but can be characterized by reaction with carbon dioxide to yield the corresponding carboxylic acids. Warming the solutions to $-65°$ or $-30°$ (depending on the compound) caused rapid, exothermic decomposition and methylene formation could be shown through the formation of cyclopropanes from alkenes present during decomposition.

(45) $n\text{-}C_4H_9Li + CH_2Cl_2 \xrightarrow[-100°]{THF} Li^+\bar{C}HCl_2$ **584**

(46) $n\text{-}C_4H_9Li + CCl_4 \xrightarrow[-105°]{THF} Li^+CCl_3$ **585**

Mercury derivatives, for example, trichloromethyl phenylmercury, $CCl_3HgC_6H_5$, are much less reactive as methylenoid reagents than the zinc derivatives, but Seyferth and co-workers (*647*) have shown that dichloromethylene formation can be induced by iodide ion.

There are three possible general routes for methylene reactions via: (a) triplet methylene, (b) singlet methylene, or (c) methylenoid intermediates. How can one decide which intermediate or intermediates is participating in a given reaction? Skell and Woodworth (*628*) suggested that the degree of stereospecificity of the reaction of methylenes with alkenes could be used to decide if the intermediate had been singlet or triplet. It was expected that singlet methylene would add stereospecifically and that triplet methylene would add nonstereospecifically. As Gaspar and Hammond (*560*) have pointed out, stereospecific addition of a singlet methylene is good intuition rather than rigorous prediction. A singlet methylene is, in a sense, a carbanion and carbonium ion. The addition of this species, utilizing, for example, the empty orbital (carbonium ion) produces an ion pair (Eq. 47). The ion-pair may or may not be in a position to collapse so rapidly that rotation around

(47)

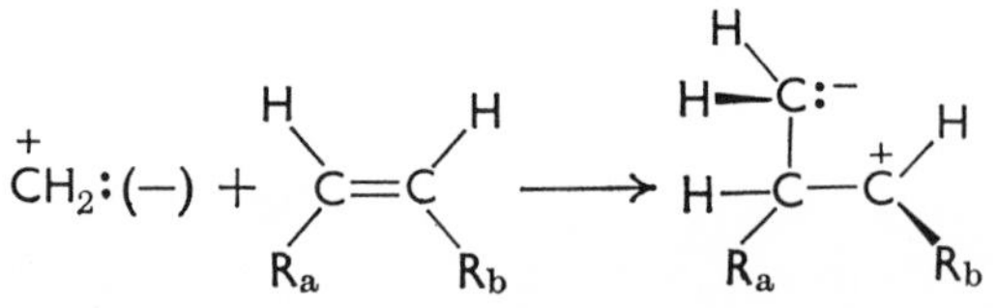

(48)

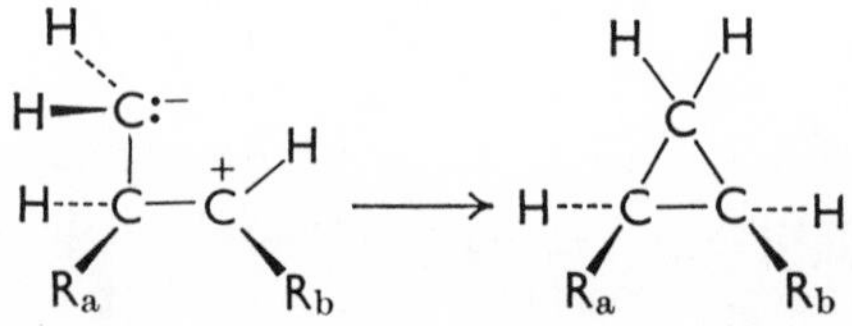

the single bond which belonged to the alkene is possible (Eq. 48). We can easily imagine that the nonstereospecific addition of a singlet methylene would be observed for the reaction of an appropriately substituted alkene with an appropriately substituted methylene. Another difficulty with the use of the criterion of stereospecific addition is that there is little information on the singlet–triplet separation for most methylenes. Thus, an intermediate may be generated as a singlet but react as a triplet.

Triplet methylenes, which are diradicals, should add in two steps. The first reaction yields a diradical and the second produces the observed product, a cyclopropane (or cyclopropanes). The possibilities inherent in this pathway are outlined in Fig. 3.10. However, in spite of the feeling that rotation around

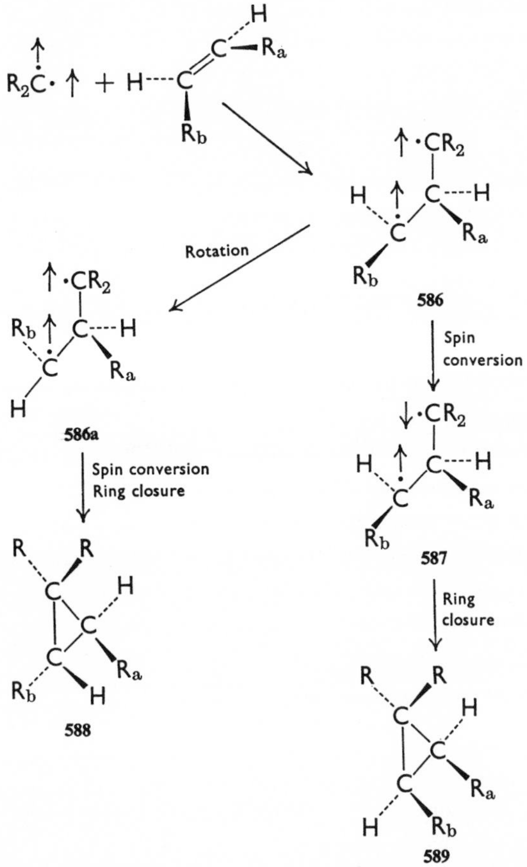

Figure 3.10 Reaction of triplet methylene with alkene in two steps to produce a cyclopropane derivative.

a single bond (**586** → **586a**) should be much faster than spin conversion, there is no firm data on this point for the methylenes of chemical interest. In addition, radical–radical interaction could preserve stereoechemistry so that a triplet methylene might add stereospecifically.*

A further problem in the interpretation of the results of addition exists because singlet methylene produces a cyclopropane with more than enough excess energy to undergo further reaction, even to isomerize. The energetics for the reaction are shown in Eq. 49. The activation energy for the isomerization is 65 kcal./mole. The problem is discussed in great detail by Frey (*648*) and is important for gas-phase reactions. In the liquid phase, collisional deactivation is very efficient.

$$
(49) \qquad CH_2{=}CH_2 + CH_2 \longrightarrow CH_2\underset{}{\overset{\overset{\displaystyle CH_2}{\diagup\ \diagdown}}{\rule{2cm}{0pt}}}CH_2
$$

$$
\quad +12.5 \qquad +86 \qquad\qquad +12.7 \qquad \Delta H = -86
$$

(Heats of formation are given in kcal./mole.)

Another factor which might contribute to the structure of the diradical intermediate **586a** (Fig. 3.10) is resonance of the type proposed by Bader and Generosa (*634*) as indicated by the structures **590a** ↔ **590b** ↔ **590c**.

$$
\begin{array}{ccc}
\cdot CH_2 & CH_2\cdot & CH_2 \\
\diagup & \diagup & \diagup\ \diagdown \\
\cdot CH_2{-}CH_2 & CH_2{-}CH_2\cdot & CH_2\cdot\ \ CH_2\cdot \\
\textbf{590a} & \textbf{590b} & \textbf{590c}
\end{array}
$$

The mechanistic details for the addition of methylenes to alkenes are not certain, but it is likely that the view of Closs and Moss (*649*) [that a whole range of mechanisms will be found (from free methylenes to methylenoid displacement reactions)] shall be confirmed.

Skell and Garner (*629*) proposed that the relative reactivities of alkenes towards methylenes be adopted as a second criterion for judging the nature of the methylene intermediate. A representative group of relative rates for dibromomethylene, dichloromethylene, bromine, and trichloromethyl radical reactions with alkenes is given in Table 3.12. It is not surprising that reactions like bromine addition exhibit far more sensitivity to substituent effects than radical addition, since carbonium ions vary far more in stability with substitution than radicals. With these limited data, it appears that (a) methylenes are

---

* Stereospecific addition of dibenzo[*a,d*]cycloheptenylidene (**585A**) and tribenzo[*a,c,e*]cycloheptenylidene (**585B**) to *cis*- and *trans*-2-butenes has been reported (*669*). These methylenes have triplet ground states; e.p.r. spectra at 77°K yielded D and E values close to those for diphenylmethylene (**553**) (*781*) (see Table 3.11).

TABLE 3.12   *Relative Rates of Alkene Reactions*

Alkene	$:CBr_2$[a]	$:CCl_2$[a]	Br_2[b]	$\cdot CCl_3$[c]
$(CH_3)_2C{=}C(CH_3)_2$	35	288	14,000	—
$(CH_3)_2C{=}CHCH_3$	39	126	1800[d]	1.0
cis-$CH_3CH{=}CHCH_2CH_3$	—	9	630	—
trans-$CH_3CH{=}CHCH_2CH_3$	—	12	40	—
$CH_2{=}CHCH_2CH_2CH_2CH_3$	1.0	1.0	1.0	1.1

[a] Ref. 650.   [b] Refs. 630, 631, 651.   [c] Ref. 629.   [d] For *cis*-3-methyl-2-pentene.

far less discriminating than bromine, but act in a parallel fashion as electrophilic reagents, and (b) dichloromethylene is more stable and, therefore, more discriminating than dibromomethylene toward alkenes. It is likely that both dichloromethylene and dibromomethylene (and many other methylenes) are much more reactive than molecular bromine. Even the reaction of tetramethylethylene with bromine has a rate constant (*ca.* 4×10^5 l. mole^{-1} sec.$^{-1}$), which is far less than that for a diffusion-controlled reaction. If the rate constants for the reaction of methylenes approach those for diffusion-controlled reactions, little difference would be expected between the rates for different alkenes. A better notion of the electrophilic character of methylenes might have been obtained from a series of less reactive alkenes. Some care would then have to be exercised in the choice of a method for the generation of the methylene intermediate, since Doering and Hoffmann (*652*) have observed that side-reactions under the usual conditions (*t*-butoxide and chloroform) prevent the study of the reactions of less reactive alkenes.

The addition to alkenes is probably the most widely used reaction of methylenes. A second major pathway for the reaction of methylenes was elucidated by Doering and co-workers (*653*) as an insertion reaction. This type of reaction was first discovered by Meerwein and his students (*654*) who found that photolysis of diazomethane in diethyl ether, isopropyl alcohol, or tetrahydrofuran led to all possible insertion products. The general equation for insertion into a carbon–hydrogen bond is

$$(50) \qquad \overset{\diagdown}{\underset{\diagup}{-C}}-H + :CH_2 \longrightarrow \overset{\diagdown}{\underset{\diagup}{-C}}-CH_3$$

The special character of insertion is best illustrated with the experiments of Doering and Prinzbach (*655*) on the reaction of methylene with 2-methyl-(1-C^{14})propene (**591**). Even in the gas-phase, only 8% of the labeled carbon

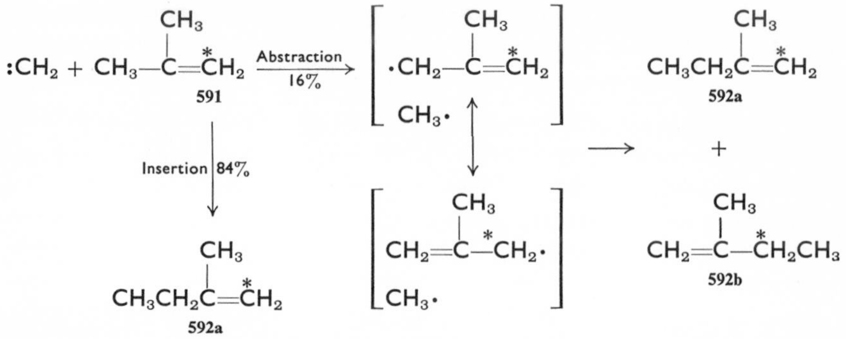

Figure 3.11 The reaction of methylene with 2-methyl-1-C^{14}-propene (Ref. 655). (The * indicates the position of the radioactive carbon atom.)

appeared in the 3-position of the 2-methyl-1-butene product although a radical pathway would have produced 50% of such labeled material (Fig. 3.11). In the liquid phase, methylene (from photolysis of diazomethane) reacted with **591** to yield only 4% of "radical-pathway" products. An alternative route (*655*) to rearranged products through "hot" cyclopropane might also be written (Fig. 3.12), the analogy to the isomerization of cyclopropane to propene standing as a relevant example.

Applying the ideas of Berson and co-workers for nucleophilic substitution (*656*) (see Part 1, Section 1.4) to the methylene insertion reaction, we might predict that singlet methylenes would give rise to the three-center transition state suggested by Doering and Knox (*657*) by acting as electrophilic attacking reagents in an S_DE reaction, and that triplet methylenes would form a

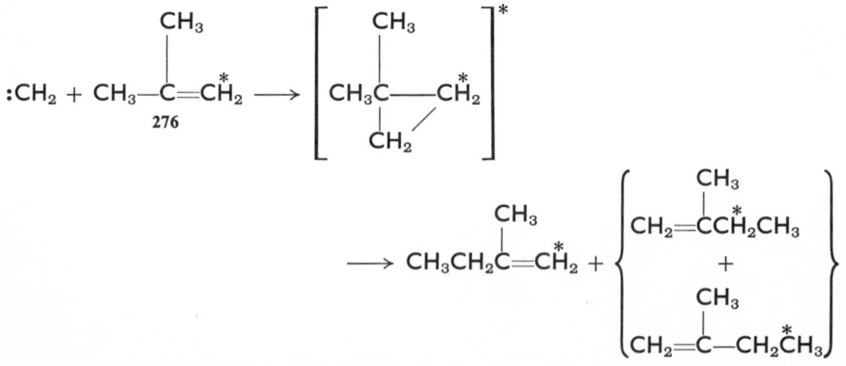

Figure 3.12 Alternate pathway to explain the products derived from the reaction of methylene with 2-methyl-1-C^{14}-propene (Ref. 655). (The * indicates the position of the radioactive carbon atom.)

linear transition state, leading to abstraction rather than insertion. Recapitulating the basic idea briefly, a system of three orbitals (ABC) will produce three levels: bonding, nonbonding, and antibonding. For a triangular arrangement of the three orbitals, one may achieve extra stabilization of the bonding state through 1,3-overlap if only two electrons are present in these levels. This is the case for electrophilic substitution, in which A^+ attacks BC. The nonbonding level is raised far more than the bonding level is lowered by the introduction of another electron (or two electrons) into the system, and the triangular arrangement is no longer the favored one.

The equivalent of insertion can be attained by a two-stage mechanism, in which radical abstraction is followed by radical–radical reaction to form a covalent bond.

(51)
$$\cdot CR_2 + X\!-\!\overset{|}{\underset{|}{C}}\!\!\diagdown \longrightarrow \diagup\!\!\overset{|}{\underset{|}{C}}\cdot \quad \cdot CR_2 \atop X$$

(52)
$$\diagup\!\!\overset{|}{\underset{|}{C}}\cdot \quad \cdot \underset{X}{CR_2} \longrightarrow \diagup\!\!\overset{|}{\underset{|}{C}}\!-\!\underset{X}{CR_2}$$

The reaction of methylene with optically active 2-chlorobutane leads to insertion product with 90% racemization (*658*).

(53)
$$:CH_2 + CH_3CH_2\overset{\underset{\textstyle |}{Cl}}{\underset{593}{C}}HCH_3 \longrightarrow CH_3CH_2\underset{594}{CH}\diagup^{CH_2Cl}_{\diagdown CH_3}$$

A chain reaction can be initiated by the reaction of methylene with tetrachloromethane, leading to pentaerythrityl tetrachloride **596** as the major product (*660*). Intramolecular migration of chlorine (Eq. 56) must be rather rapid, probably faster than the migration of phenyl in the 2,2,2-triphenylethyl radical **597**, reported by Kaplan (*659*) who trapped **597** as 1,1,1-triphenylethane with triphenyltin hydride.

(54) $\quad :CH_2 + CCl_4 \longrightarrow \cdot CH_2Cl + \cdot CCl_3$

(55) $\quad \cdot CCl_3 + CH_2N_2 \longrightarrow N_2 + \cdot CH_2CCl_3$

(56) $\quad \cdot CH_2CCl_3 \longrightarrow ClCH_2\underset{\cdot}{C}Cl_2$

(57) $\quad ClCH_2\underset{\cdot}{C}Cl_2 + CH_2N_2 \longrightarrow ClCH_2\overset{\overset{\textstyle CH_2\cdot}{|}}{\underset{\underset{\textstyle Cl}{|}}{C}}Cl$

(58) 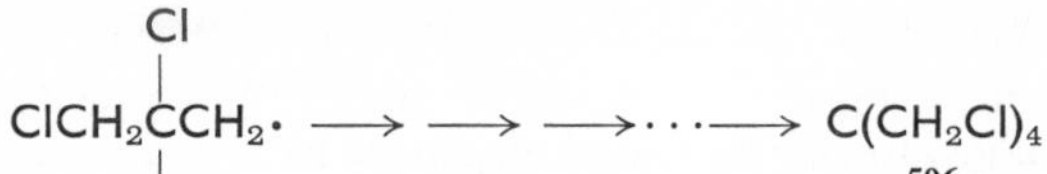
$$ClCH_2\overset{\displaystyle Cl}{\underset{\displaystyle Cl}{C}}CH_2\cdot \longrightarrow \longrightarrow \longrightarrow \cdots \longrightarrow C(CH_2Cl)_4$$
596

Straightforward abstraction is a reaction of methylene as shown through the formation of CH_4 and CH_3D from the reaction of methylene with $(CD_3)_3CH$ investigated by Halberstadt and McNesby (*661*). In this case, the assumption is made that intramolecular redistribution of energy would have made possible the formation of much CD_3H and CD_4, along with other products, if an insertion product with excess energy had been the first product of the reaction.

The stereochemistry of the insertion of cyanonitrene in different solvents has been utilized by Anastassiou (*662*) to demonstrate what is probably a difference in the reaction pathways for singlet and triplet cyanonitrenes. Anastassiou, Simmons, and Marsh (*663*) had found that *cis*- and *trans*-1,2-dimethylcyclohexanes reacted with cyanonitrene [generated by thermal decomposition of cyanogen azide (*664*)] to give cyanamides with the original stereochemistry of the substrate, preserved for the major products derived from insertion at the tertiary hydrogens.

(59)

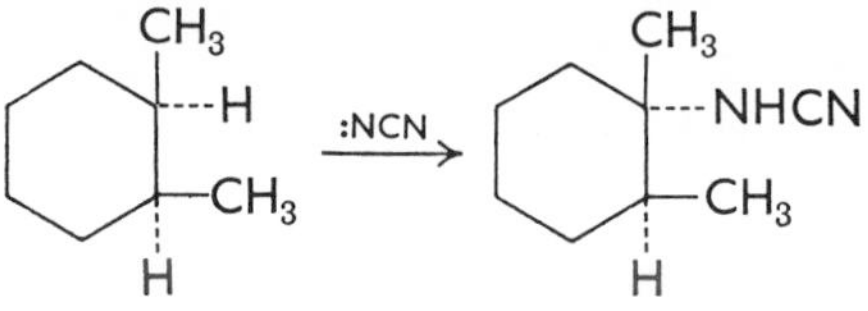

597

(60)

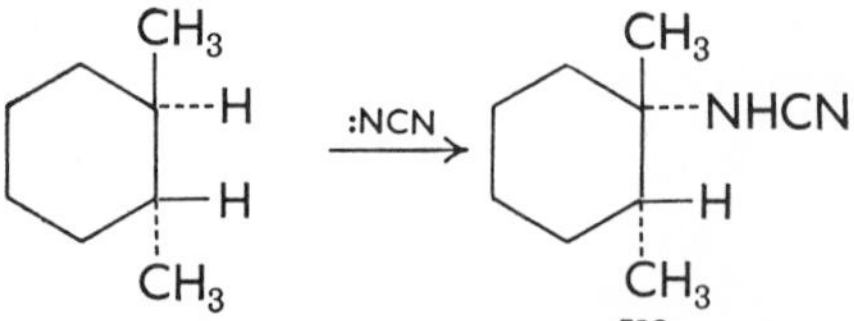

598

Diluting the dimethylcyclohexanes with dichloromethane caused the formation of considerable amounts of the "other" isomer in the reaction, and the use of dibromomethane produced equal amounts of both isomers. It is known that heavy atoms favor singlet–triplet (or triplet–singlet) transitions [as in the use of ethyl iodide for the direct observation in spectra of singlet–triplet transitions (*665*)] and the loss of stereochemical specificity in the cyanonitrene insertion reaction is attributed to the conversion of the initially formed singlet cyanonitrene to a triplet cyanonitrene. The triplet cyano-nitrene, as we have already indicated, might be expected to react through the intermediate formation of free radicals and thus not react in a stereospecific manner. Lwowski and McConaghy (*562*) have identified two kinds of car-bethoxynitrene in addition reactions.

The electrophilic character of the methylene species, which effects the insertion reaction, is illustrated by the relative rates of insertion of dicyano-methylene (**548**) into the primary, secondary, and tertiary carbon–hydrogen bonds of *n*-butane and isobutane (*667*).

(61) $(NC)_2C: + CH_3CH_2CH_2CH_3$

$(NC)_2\bar{C} - \overset{+}{N}\equiv N$ **548**

(62) $(NC)_2C: + CH_3CHCH_3$
$\qquad\qquad\qquad\quad |$
$\qquad\qquad\qquad\quad CH_3$

$\overset{9\%}{CH_3CH_2CH_2CH_2CH(CN)_2} + \overset{27\%}{CH_3CH_2CHCH_3}$
$\qquad\qquad\qquad\qquad\qquad\qquad\qquad\qquad |$
$\qquad\qquad\qquad\qquad\qquad\qquad\qquad\quad CH(CN)_2$

$\overset{7\%}{(CH_3)_3CCH(CN)_2} + \overset{7\%}{(CH_3)_2CHCH_2CH(CN)_2} +$ 6%

$$CH_3 \quad CH_2 \quad CN$$
$$C{-}{-}{-}C$$
$$CH_3 \qquad\quad CN$$

After correcting for the numbers of the different kinds of bonds, the relative rates of attack on primary, secondary, and tertiary C—H bonds were evaluated as 1:4.6:12.0. An order of this kind would be in agreement with either the development of radical character at the carbon which loses the hydrogen or with the acquisition of a modest amount of positive charge. Either radical attack or electrophilic attack would be consistent with relative reactivities in the insertion reaction. However, we have already given the theoretical reasons for preferring that direct insertion (no kinetically discrete intermediate formed) involve the methylene as an electrophilic reagent, and we must therefore conclude that such insertion does indeed involve the singlet methylene. It is of some interest to compare the processes of addition and insertion. For the isomeric 2-butenes, addition is the favored reaction if the methylene is singlet. Dilution of the reaction mixture with cyclohexane per-mits the singlet methylene to form the triplet methylene. The latter yields very little insertion product, as shown by the data in Table 3.13.

A reaction which appears to proceed via a singlet electrophilic tetraphenyl-cyclopentadienylene is the formation of the pyridinium 2,3,4,5-tetraphenyl-cyclopentadienylide from the corresponding diazo compound (Eq. 63). Sterically hindered pyridine derivatives can be successfully used in the reaction, but the analogous preparation of pyridinium cyclopentadienylide (36) fails (668). The latter is of interest because it photolyzes to yield, like the diazo compound (599), the diradical 550, and eventually the hydrocarbon, fulvalene (600) (24, 670, 671).

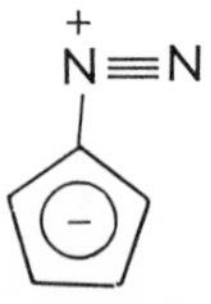

(63)

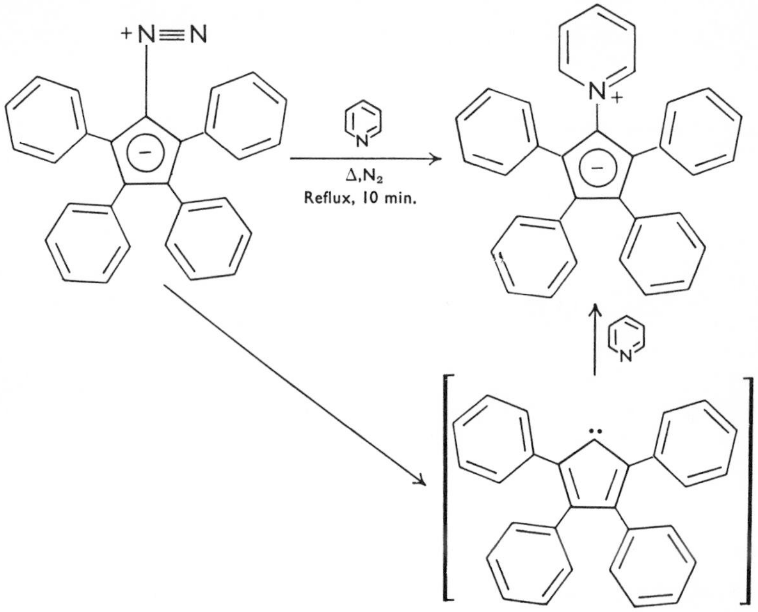

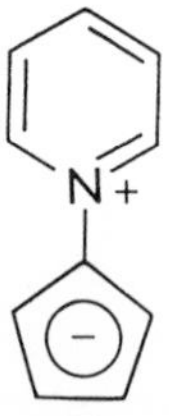

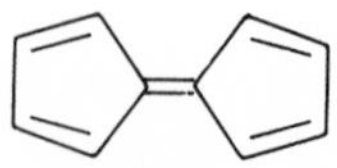

Skell and his co-workers (672) have ingeniously devised methods for the study of C_3 (601) by condensing this *bis*-methylene with an unreactive hydrocarbon on a cold surface (77°K), the C_3 source being a carbon arc. The

TABLE 3.13   *Addition and Insertion of Dicyanomethylene*[f]

Olefin	Dilution[a]	Addition Products[b]  NC CN / Me Me *cis*	 NC CN / Me Me *trans*	Ratio of Addition to Insertion[c]
cis-2-Butene	Neat	92	8	92:8
	1:10	60	40	94:6
	1:100	30	70	>98:2[e]
trans-2-Butene	Neat	6	94	88:12[d]
	1:10	22	78	94:6
	1:100	30	70	>98:2[e]

[a] Ratio of 2-butene to cyclohexane.   [b] Relative ratio determined gas chromatographically; uncorrected for possible differences in thermal conductivity.   [c] Ratio of *cis*- and *trans*-2,3-dimethyl-1,1-dicyanocyclopropanes to 2-butenylmalonitriles.   [d] The value of 12% includes an impurity of unknown structure which may not be an insertion product.   [e] No 2-butenylmalononitriles could be detected; limit of detection ca. 2%.   [f] From Ref. 667.

presence of C_3 in carbon vapor is well established (*673*), and it is present in appreciable concentrations.

$$:C=C=C:$$
601

The reaction of C_3 with both *cis*- and *trans*-2-butenes is stereospecific. Since the ground state of C_3 had been shown to be singlet by spectroscopic studies, it was reasonable to assume that the stereospecific reaction was due to the reaction of the singlet. This conclusion was strengthened by the finding that a very unstable excited state of C_3 can be detected through reaction with alkenes if the reactants are mixed before condensation on the cold surface. The unstable state reacts nonstereospecifically.

The reaction of ground state C_3 with *cis*-2-butene is illustrated, with a shorthand for the product shown as **602a**.

$:C=C=C:$ + (structure) → (structure)

(64)

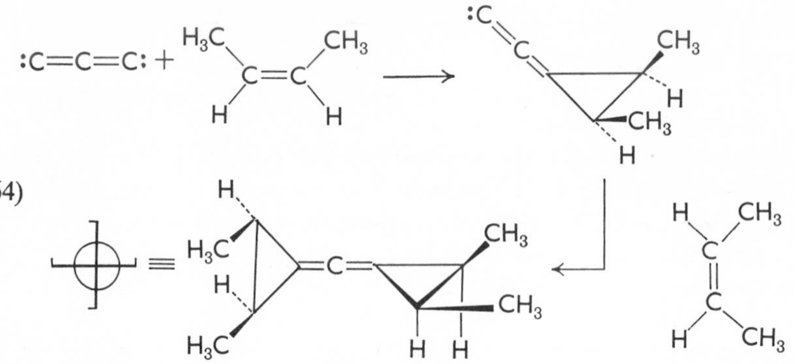

(structures)   602a   602

Skell and his students (*633, 674, 675*) have also examined the reaction of the ground and several excited states of carbon atoms with alkenes and saturated hydrocarbons.

This section has been devoted largely to the physical properties of radicals and species closely related to radicals. The chemistry of methylenes has also been discussed in this part of the book rather than in Part 1 because the chief questions in methylene chemistry are related to the question of singlet or triplet character for the intermediates. The rich yield of information from examination of the intermediates, mostly as a result of the technique of electron paramagnetic resonance, promises a great deal in the way of understanding the mechanisms of reactions in which these intermediates are formed.

An understanding of the nature and behavior of intermediates must be counted as one of the major responsibilities of those engaged in chemical pursuits, and not one of the least for those interested in physical organic chemistry. If we ration our devotion to chemistry, and satisfy ourselves only with the *nourriture necessaire* of those compounds that we require for one reason or another, we might find ourselves in the unfortunate position of Freeman:

> ... but she had stepped among the statues, and when he vainly
> sought her in the veiled mist that had risen from the lake,
> still calling her name, Freeman embraced only moonlit stone.
>
> *The Lady of the Lake*, B. Malamud

Problems

1. Define the following terms:
   (a) Free radical.
   (b) Methylene.

(c) Nitrene.

(d) Free radical dimer.

2. Draw an energy level diagram for the transitions that might be observed in a magnetic resonance study of the species H_2^+.

3. Explain qualitatively the α-hydrogen splittings observed for the vinyl and cyclopropyl radicals in comparison to the methyl radical. Consider the structures given for the cyclopropyl radical and try to choose which is the more likely on the basis of the splitting constant.

4. Compare the nitrogen splittings in **507** and **508** and explain why one is so much larger than the other. Might there be chemical consequences of this difference?

5. Explain the spin density distribution in naphthalene radical anion on the basis of valence bond resonance forms. (Remember that the splitting of energy levels by hydrogens is very much influenced by the local spin density at the carbon to which that hydrogen is attached.)

6. Write a chemical reaction of a nitroxide radical and cite an example that is unable to undergo the reaction because of some unique characteristic of the molecule. Name that characteristic and explain how it prevents the reaction.

7. Design some nitroxide radicals, giving sensible syntheses, in which there are (a) two nitroxide radicals less than 15 A from one another and (b) three nitroxide radicals less than 14 A average distance from one another.

8. Explain the following:

   (a) Zero-field splitting.

   (b) Parameters D and E in interpretation of triplet spectra.

   (c) Generation of naphthalene triplet.

   (d) Diamagnetic diradical dimers.

   (e) Covalent radical dimers.

   (f) Paramagnetic diradical dimers.

9. Explain qualitatively the magnitudes of D for the following triplets in comparison to the D for methylene:

   (a) Propargylene **538**.

   (b) Cyclopentadienylene **550**.

   (c) Nitrene.

   (d) Quinone diimine diradical **561**.

   (e) *bis*-Galvinoxyl **562**.

10. Explain why it is reasonable that the *syn*- and *anti*-isomers of 1-naphthylmethylene should differ slightly in the D values assigned to their e.p.r. spectra.

11. Write diamagnetic diradical dimerization equilibria for the following and explain the thermodynamic reason for the association.

    (a) 1-Methyl-4-carbomethoxypyridinyl.

    (b) Methylviologen cation radical.

    (c) Tetracyanoquinodimethane anion radical.

12. Explain the paramagnetism of Chichibabin's hydrocarbon.

13. Write equations for the formation of the following:
    (a) Methylene.
    (b) Dichloromethylene.
    (c) Cyclopentadienylene.
    (d) A methylene from an epoxide.
    (e) Difluoromethylene.
14. What is the Simmons–Smith reagent? Give three applications of its use.
15. Show, with an example, how one might decide whether or not a triplet or a singlet methylene was an intermediate in a reaction.
16. Give the evidence for the direct insertion reaction of methylenes.
17. What is the product and mechanism of formation of the product from the reaction of diazomethane and carbon tetrachloride?
18. Write the products of reaction of cyanonitrene with *cis-* and *trans-*1,2-dimethylcyclohexane. Do the reaction conditions affect the nature of the products?
19. Write the product(s) of reaction of the *bis-*methylene C_3 with the following:
    (a) *cis-*2-Butene.
    (b) *trans-*2-Butene.
    (c) Cyclopropene.
    (d) Ethylene.
    (e) The product derived from ethylene.

REFERENCES

1. K. B. Wiberg, *"Physical Organic Chemistry,"* John Wiley and Sons, New York, 1964, 591 pp.
2. L. P. Hammett, *"Physical Organic Chemistry,"* McGraw–Hill Book Co., New York, 1940, 404 pp.
3. J. N. Brønsted and K. J. Pedersen, *Z. Physikal. Chem.*, **108**, 185 (1924).
4. R. P. Bell, *"The Proton in Chemistry,"* Methuen and Co., London, 1959, pp. 155–182.
5. J. B. Conant and G. W. Wheland, *J. Am. Chem. Soc.*, **54**, 1212 (1932).
6. W. K. McEwen, *J. Am. Chem. Soc.*, **58**, 1124 (1936).
7. A. I. Shatenshteĭn, *Advances in Phys. Org. Chem.*, **1**, 156 (1963).
8. A. Streitwieser, Jr., R. A. Caldwell, R. G. Lawler, and G. R. Ziegler, *J. Am. Chem. Soc.*, **87**, 5399 (1965) and previous papers.
9. A. Streitwieser, Jr., University of California, Berkeley, personal communication.
10. D. J. Cram, *"Fundamentals of Carbanion Chemistry,"* Academic Press, New York, 1965, 289 pp.
11. A. Streitwieser, Jr., R. G. Lawler, and C. Perrin, *J. Am. Chem. Soc.*, **87**, 5583 (1965).
12. G. S. Hammond, *J. Am. Chem. Soc.*, **77**, 334 (1955).
13. A. Streitwieser, Jr., J. I. Braumann, J. H. Hammons, and A. H. Pudjaatmaka, *J. Am. Chem. Soc.*, **87**, 384 (1965).
14. V. R. Sandel and H. H. Freedman, *J. Am. Chem. Soc.*, **85**, 2328 (1963).
15. C. A. Coulson, *"Valence,"* 2nd ed., Chapter VIII, Oxford Univ. Press, New York, 1963.
16. H. J. Bernstein, *Trans. Farad. Soc.*, **57**, 1649 (1961).
17. M. J. S. Dewar and H. N. Schmeising, *Tetrahedron*, **11**, 96 (1960).
18. A. Streitwieser, Jr., and R. G. Lawler, *J. Am. Chem. Soc.*, **87**, 5388 (1965).
19. P. Haake and J. Mantecon, *J. Am. Chem. Soc.*, **86**, 5230 (1964).
20. T. J. Katz and P. J. Garratt, *J. Am. Chem. Soc.*, **85**, 2852 (1963).
21. E. A. LaLancette and R. E. Benson, *J. Am. Chem. Soc.*, **85**, 2853 (1963); **87**, 1941 (1965).
22. R. G. Pearson and R. L. Dillon, *J. Am. Chem. Soc.*, **75**, 2439 (1953).
23. Z. Arnold and J. Zemlicka, *Coll. Czech. Chem. Commun.*, **25**, 1319 (1960).
24. E. M. Kosower and B. G. Ramsey, *J. Am. Chem. Soc.*, **81**, 856 (1959).
25. H. Dauben, University of Washington, personal communication.
26. S. Andreades, *J. Am. Chem. Soc.*, **86**, 2003 (1964).
27. R. G. Pearson, *J. Am. Chem. Soc.*, **85**, 3533 (1963).
28. D. H. Busch, footnote 2 in Ref. 27.
29. J. O. Edwards, *J. Am. Chem. Soc.*, **76**, 1540 (1954).
30. G. S. Reddy and J. H. Goldstein, *J. Mol. Spectroscopy*, **8**, 475 (1962).
31. N. Muller and D. E. Pritchard, *J. Chem. Phys.*, **31**, 768 (1959).
32. J. N. Shoolery, *J. Chem. Phys.*, **31**, 1427 (1959).

33. J. D. Roberts and W. T. Moreland, *J. Am. Chem. Soc.*, **75**, 2167 (1953).
34. H. D. Holtz and L. M. Stock, *J. Am. Chem. Soc.*, **86**, 5188 (1964).
35. C. D. Ritchie and W. F. Sager, *Progress in Phys. Org. Chem.*, **2**, 323 (1964).
36. R. W. Taft, in *Steric Effects in Organic Chemistry*, M. S. Newman, ed., John Wiley and Sons, New York, 1956, Chap. 13.
37. W. A. Sheppard, *J. Am. Chem. Soc.*, **87**, 2410 (1965).
38. R. W. Taft, Jr., *J. Am. Chem. Soc.*, **79**, 1045 (1957).
39. H. C. Brown and Y. Okamoto, *J. Am. Chem. Soc.*, **80**, 4979 (1958).
40. A. I. Biggs and R. A. Robinson, *J. Chem. Soc.*, **81**, 388 (1961).
41. R. W. Taft, Jr., and I. C. Lewis, *J. Am. Chem. Soc.*, **81**, 5343 (1959).
42. E. S. Lewis and M. D. Johnson, *J. Am. Chem. Soc.*, **81**, 2070 (1959).
43. R. W. Taft, E. Price, I. R. Fox, I. C. Lewis, K. K. Anderson, and G. T. Davis, *J. Am. Chem. Soc.*, **85**, 709 (1963).
44. H. S. Gutowsky, D. W. McCall, B. R. McGarvey, and L. H. Meyer, *J. Am. Chem. Soc.*, **74**, 4809 (1952).
45. L. H. Meyer and H. S. Gutowsky, *J. Phys. Chem.*, **57**, 481 (1953).
46. R. W. Taft, E. Price, I. R. Fox, I. C. Lewis, K. K. Andersen, and G. T. Davis, *J. Am. Chem. Soc.*, **85**, 3146 (1963).
47. S. Ehrenson, *Progress in Phys. Org. Chem.*, **2**, 195 (1964).
48. A. G. Harrison, P. Kenarle and F. P. Lossing, *J. Am. Chem. Soc.*, **83**, 777 (1961).
49. J. C. McGowan, T. Powell, and R. Raw, *J. Chem. Soc.*, **1959**, 3103.
50. E. M. Kosower, *Progress in Phys. Org. Chem.*, **3**, 81 (1965).
51. M. A. DaRooge and L. R. Mahoney, *J. Org. Chem.*, **32**, 1 (1967).
52. E. L. Eliel, "*Stereochemistry of Carbon Compounds*," McGraw–Hill Book Co., New York, 1962, 486 pp.
53. C. G. Swain, W. H. Stockmayer, and J. T. Clarke, *J. Am. Chem. Soc.*, **72**, 5426 (1950).
54. R. W. Taft, R. H. Martin, and F. W. Lampe, *J. Am. Chem. Soc.*, **87**, 2490 (1965).
55. E. M. Kosower, D. Hofmann, and K. Wallenfels, *J. Am. Chem. Soc.*, **84**, 2755 (1962).
56. F. Gerson and E. Heilbronner, *Helv. Chim. Acta*, **42**, 1877 (1959).
57. R. Grinter and E. Heilbronner, *Helv. Chim. Acta*, **40**, 2496 (1962).
58. P. R. Wells, *Chem. Revs.*, **63**, 171 (1963).
59. C. K. Ingold, "*Structure and Mechanism in Organic Chemistry*," Cornell University Press, Ithaca, 1953.
60. A. Streitwieser, Jr., "*Solvolytic Displacement Reactions*," McGraw–Hill Book Co., New York, 1962.
61. S. Winstein, E. Grunwald, and H. W. Jones, *J. Am. Chem. Soc.*, **73**, 2700 (1951).
62. J. O. Edwards, *J. Am. Chem. Soc.*, **78**, 1819 (1956).
63. S. Winstein, S. Smith, and D. Darwish, *Tetrahedron Letters*, 24 (1959).
64. A. Fava and A. Iliceto, *J. Am. Chem. Soc.*, **80**, 3478 (1958).
65. A. Streitwieser, Jr., "*Molecular Orbital Theory for Organic Chemists*," John Wiley and Sons, New York, 1961, 489 pp.

66. W. A. Pryor and H. Guard, *J. Am. Chem. Soc.*, **86**, 1150 (1964).
67. G. A. Wiley, R. L. Hershkowitz, B. M. Rein, and B. C. Chung, *J. Am. Chem. Soc.*, **86**, 964 (1964).
68. G. A. Wiley, B. M. Rein, and R. L. Hershkowitz, *Tetrahedron Letters*, No. 36, 2509 (1964).
69. I. P. Fisher, J. B. Homer, and F. P. Lossing, *J. Am. Chem. Soc.*, **87**, 957 (1965).
70. I. P. Fisher, I. F. Palmer, and F. P. Lossing, *J. Am. Chem. Soc.*, **86**, 2741 (1964).
71. A. Maccoll, *Advances in Phys. Org. Chem.*, **3**, 91 (1965).
72. H. Martin, R. Hoffmann, and A. Maccoll, *J. Am. Chem. Soc.*, **87**, 3774 (1965).
73. S. Winstein and H. Marshall, *J. Am. Chem. Soc.*, **74**, 1120 (1952).
74. E. F. Caldin, "*Fast Reactions in Solution*," John Wiley and Sons, New York, 1964, 306 pp.
75. P. D. Bartlett and L. H. Knox, *J. Am. Chem. Soc.*, **61**, 3184 (1939).
76. R. C. Fort, Jr., and P. v. R. Schleyer, *J. Am. Chem. Soc.*, **86**, 4194 (1964).
77. P. v. R. Schleyer, R. C. Fort, Jr., W. E. Watts, M. B. Comisarow, and G. A. Olah, *J. Am. Chem. Soc.*, **86**, 4195 (1964).
78. S. Winstein, E. Grunwald, and L. L. Ingraham, *J. Am. Chem. Soc.*, **70**, 821 (1948).
79. B. Capon, *Quart. Revs.*, **18**, 45 (1964).
80. S. Winstein, A. Allred, R. F. Heck, and R. Glick, *Tetrahedron*, **3**, 1 (1958).
81. S. Winstein and E. Grunwald, *J. Am. Chem. Soc.*, **70**, 828 (1948).
82. S. W. Benson, *J. Chem. Educ.*, **42**, 502 (1965).
83. R. M. Roberts, J. Corse, R. Boschan, D. Seymour, and S. Winstein, *J. Am. Chem. Soc.*, **80**, 1247 (1958).
84. P. Bruylants and A. Dewael, *Bull. Classe Sci. Acad. Roy. Belg.*, [5] **14**, 140 (1928).
85. H. K. Hall, Jr., *J. Org. Chem.*, **29**, 3539 (1964).
86. J. D. S. Ritter and S. I. Miller, *J. Am. Chem. Soc.*, **86**, 1507 (1964).
87. C. A. Grob, "*Theoretical Organic Chemistry*," Butterworth Scientific Publications, London, 1959, p. 114.
88. C. A. Grob and W. Schwarz, *Helv. Chim. Acta*, **47**, 1870 (1964).
89. S. Winstein and H. J. Lucas, *J. Am. Chem. Soc.*, **61**, 1576, 2845 (1939).
90. S. Winstein and R. F. Heck, *J. Am. Chem. Soc.*, **74**, 5584 (1952).
91. S. Winstein, H. V. Hess, and R. E. Buckles, *J. Am. Chem. Soc.*, **64**, 2796 (1942).
92. S. Winstein and R. E. Buckles, *J. Am. Chem. Soc.*, **65**, 613 (1943).
93. S. Winstein and R. Boschan, *J. Am. Chem. Soc.*, **72**, 4669 (1950).
94. J. B. Rogan, *J. Org. Chem.*, **27**, 3910 (1962).
95. E. M. Kosower and S. Winstein, *J. Am. Chem. Soc.*, **78**, 4347 (1956).
96. G. Whitham, *Proc. Chem. Soc.*, **1961**, 422.
97. J. D. Roberts and R. H. Mazur, *J. Am. Chem. Soc.*, **73**, 2509 (1951).
98. H. Hart and G. M. Sandri, *J. Am. Chem. Soc.*, **81**, 320 (1959).
99. H. Hart and P. A. Law, *J. Am. Chem. Soc.*, **86**, 1957 (1964).

100. N. C. Deno, H. G. Richey, J. S. Liu, J. D. Hodge, J. J. Houser, and M. J. Wisotsky, *J. Am. Chem. Soc.*, **84**, 2016 (1962).

101. S. Winstein and R. Adams, *J. Am. Chem. Soc.*, **70**, 835 (1948).

102. E. M. Kosower, Ph.D. Thesis, Univ. Calif., Los Angeles, 1952.

103. C. W. Shoppee and G. H. Williams, *J. Chem. Soc.*, **1955**, 686.

104. E. M. Kosower and M. Ito, *Proc. Chem. Soc.*, **1962**, 25.

105. E. M. Kosower and S. Winstein, *J. Am. Chem. Soc.*, **78**, 4354 (1956).

106. S. Winstein and E. M. Kosower, *J. Am. Chem. Soc.*, **81**, 4399 (1959).

107. H. Meerwein and K. van Emster, *Ber.*, **55**, 2500 (1922).

108. T. P. Neville, E. de Salas, and C. L. Wilson, *J. Chem. Soc.*, **1939**, 1188.

109. L. Pauling, "*The Nature of the Chemical Bond*," 3rd ed., Cornell Univ. Press, Ithaca, New York, 1960, 644 pp.

110. S. Winstein and D. Trifan, *J. Am. Chem. Soc.*, **74**, 1147, 1154 (1952).

111. H. C. Brown, K. J. Morgan, and F. J. Chloupek, *J. Am. Chem. Soc.*, **87**, 2137 (1965).

112. H. C. Brown, "*The Transition State*," Special Publ. No. **16**, The Chemical Society, London, 1962, p. 140.

113. S. Winstein and B. K. Morse, *J. Am. Chem. Soc.*, **74**, 1133 (1952).

114. K. L. Servis and J. D. Roberts, *J. Am. Chem. Soc.*, **86**, 3773 (1964).

115. G. LeNy, *Compt. Rend.*, **251**, 1526 (1960).

116. M. C. Flowers and H. M. Frey, *Proc. Roy. Soc.*, **257A**, 121 (1960).

117. H. C. Brown and F. J. Chloupek, *J. Am. Chem. Soc.*, **85**, 2322 (1963).

118. A. Colter, E. C. Friedrich, N. J. Holness, and S. Winstein, *J. Am. Chem. Soc.*, **87**, 378 (1965).

119. P. v. R. Schleyer, M. M. Donaldson, and W. E. Watts, *J. Am. Chem. Soc.*, **87**, 375 (1965).

120. P. G. Gassman and J. L. Marshall, *J. Am. Chem. Soc.*, **87**, 4648 (1965).

121. T. G. Traylor and C. L. Perrin, *J. Am. Chem. Soc.*, **88**, 4934 (1966).

122. P. D. Bartlett, S. Bank, R. J. Crawford, and G. H. Schmid, *J. Am. Chem. Soc.*, **87**, 1288 (1965).

123. G. A. Olah, E. Namanworth, M. B. Comisarow and B. Ramsey, *J. Am. Chem. Soc.*, **89**, 711 (1967).

124. D. J. Cram, *J. Am. Chem. Soc.*, **86**, 3767 (1964).

125. P. D. Bartlett and G. D. Sargent, *J. Am. Chem. Soc.*, **87**, 1297 (1965).

126. R. G. Lawton, *J. Am. Chem. Soc.*, **83**, 2399 (1961).

127. F. Brown, E. D. Hughes, C. K. Ingold, and J. F. Smith, *Nature*, **168**, 65 (1951).

128. O. Diels and K. Alder, *Ann.*, **460**, 98 (1928).

129. P. v. R. Schleyer, *J. Am. Chem. Soc.*, **86**, 1854 (1964).

130. C. S. Foote, *Tetrahedron Letters*, No. **9**, 579 (1963).

131. P. v. R. Schleyer, *J. Am. Chem. Soc.*, **86**, 1856 (1964).

132. P. D. Bartlett, W. D. Closson, and T. J. Cogdell, *J. Am. Chem. Soc.*, **87**, 1308 (1965).

133. R. Baird and S. Winstein, *J. Am. Chem. Soc.*, **85**, 567 (1963).

134. T. Cole, D. E. Pritchard, N. Davidson, and H. M. McConnell, *Mol. Phys.*, **1**, 406 (1958).

135. G. A. Olah, M. B. Comisarow and E. Namanworth, *J. Am. Chem. Soc.*, **89**, in press (1967).
136. E. M. Kosower and E. J. Poziomek, *J. Am. Chem. Soc.*, **86**, 5515 (1964).
137. A. K. Hoffmann and A. T. Henderson, *J. Am. Chem. Soc.*, **83**, 4671 (1961).
138. C. D. Cook, D. A. Kuhn, and P. Fianu, *J. Am. Chem. Soc.*, **78**, 2002 (1956).
139. E. Müller and K. Ley, *Chem. Ber.*, **88**, 601 (1955).
140. E. M. Kosower and E. J. Poziomek, *J. Am. Chem. Soc.*, **85**, 2035 (1963).
141. M. C. Kloetzel, H. L. Holmes, Chapters 1 and 2, *Org. Reacts.*, **4**, John Wiley and Sons, New York, 1948.
142. K. Ziegler, P. Orth, and K. Weber, *Ann.*, **504**, 131 (1933).
143. S. W. Benson, "*The Foundations of Chemical Kinetics,*" McGraw–Hill Book Co., New York, 1960, 703 pp.
144. H. E. Bent and G. R. Cuthbertson, *J. Am. Chem. Soc.*, **58**, 170 (1936).
145. P. L. Hanst and J. G. Calvert, *J. Am. Chem. Soc.*, **63**, 104 (1959).
146. P. D. Bartlett and T. G. Traylor, *J. Am. Chem. Soc.*, **85**, 2407 (1963).
147. A. Factor, C. A. Russell, and T. G. Traylor, *J. Am. Chem. Soc.*, **87**, 3692 (1965).
148. T. G. Traylor and C. A. Russell, *J. Am. Chem. Soc.*, **87**, 3698 (1965).
149. R. Hiatt and T. G. Traylor, *J. Am. Chem. Soc.*, **87**, 3766 (1965).
150. P. D. Bartlett and R. R. Hiatt, *J. Am. Chem. Soc.*, **80**, 1398 (1958).
151. P. D. Bartlett and C. Rüchardt, *J. Am. Chem. Soc.*, **82**, 1756 (1960).
152. P. D. Bartlett and H. Minato, *J. Am. Chem. Soc.*, **85**, 1858 (1963).
153. C. S. Foote, *J. Am. Chem. Soc.*, **86**, 1853 (1964).
154. R. J. Crawford and A. Mishra, *J. Am. Chem. Soc.*, **88**, 3963 (1966).
155. P. D. Bartlett, "*Non-Classical Carbonium Ions,*" W. A. Benjamin, New York, 1965, 559 pp.
156. A. Streitwieser, Jr., and J. H. Hammons, *Progress in Phys. Org. Chem.*, **3**, 41 (1965).
157. R. H. Boyd, *J. Phys. Chem.*, **67**, 737 (1963).
158. S. G. Cohen and C. H. Wang, *J. Am. Chem. Soc.*, **75**, 5504 (1953).
159. C. G. Overberger and A. V. DiGuilio, *J. Am. Chem. Soc.*, **81**, 2154 (1959).
160. S. Seltzer and F. T. Dunne, *J. Am. Chem. Soc.*, **87**, 2628 (1965).
161. S. F. Nelsen and P. D. Bartlett, *J. Am. Chem. Soc.*, **88**, 137 (1966).
162. P. Scheiner, *J. Am. Chem. Soc.*, **88**, 4759 (1966).
163. W. F. Libby, *J. Phys. Chem.*, **56**, 863 (1952).
164. H. Taube, "Mechanisms of Redox Reactions of Simple Chemistry," *Adv. in Inorg. Chem. and Radiochem.*, **1**, 1 (1959).
165. E. S. Gould and H. Taube, *J. Am. Chem. Soc.*, **86**, 1318 (1964).
166. R. D. Butler and H. Taube, *J. Am. Chem. Soc.*, **87**, 5597 (1965).
167. E. S. Gould, *J. Am. Chem. Soc.*, **87**, 4730 (1965).
168. D. H. Huchital and H. Taube, *J. Am. Chem. Soc.*, **87**, 5371 (1965).
169. H. von Hartel and M. Polyani, *Z. Physik. Chem.*, **11B**, 97 (1930).
170. H. Von Hartel, N. Meer, and M. Polyani, *Z. Physik. Chem.*, **19B**, 139 (1932).
171. D. R. Hershbach, *Discussions Faraday Soc.*, **33**, 149 (1962).
172. M. Szwarc, "*The Transition State,*" Special Publ. No. **16**, The Chemical Society, London, 1962, p. 101.

173. C. Walling, "*Free Radicals in Solution*," John Wiley and Sons, Inc., New York, 1957.
174. J. Halpern and J. P. Maher, *J. Am. Chem. Soc.*, **87**, 5361 (1965).
175. E. M. Kosower and I. Schwager, *J. Am. Chem. Soc.*, **86**, 5528 (1965).
176. J. L. Kurz, R. Hutton, and F. H. Westheimer, *J. Am. Chem. Soc.*, **83**, 584 (1961).
177. C. E. Castro and W. C. Kray, Jr., *J. Am. Chem. Soc.*, **85**, 2768 (1963).
178. W. C. Kray, Jr., and C. E. Castro, *J. Am. Chem. Soc.*, **86**, 4603 (1964).
179. F. A. L. Anet and E. Leblanc, *J. Am. Chem. Soc.*, **79**, 2649 (1957).
180. O. Neunhoeffer and H. Haase, *Ber.*, **91**, 1801 (1958).
181. A. A. Zavitsas and S. Seltzer, *J. Am. Chem. Soc.*, **86**, 1265 (1964).
182. E. M. Kosower and L. Lindqvist, *Tetrahedron Letters*, No. **50**, 4481 (1965).
183. T. L. Cottrell, "*The Strengths of Chemical Bonds*," 2nd ed., Butterworths Scientific Publications, London, 1958, p. 203.
184. Yu. G. Papulov, *J. Structural Chem. USSR*, **4**, 561 (1964) (English translation).
185. P. B. Ayscough and K. E. Russell, *Can. J. Chem.*, **43**, 3039 (1965).
186. F. W. Lampe, J. L. Franklin, and F. H. Field, *Progress in Reaction Kinetics*, Pergamon Press, Oxford, **1**, 87–88 (1961).
187. E. S. Lewis and L. Funderburk, *J. Am. Chem. Soc.*, **89**, 2322 (1967).
188. W. Brackman, *Rec. Trav. Chim.*, **68**, 147 (1949).
189. R. S. Mulliken, *J. Am. Chem. Soc.*, **74**, 811 (1952).
190. R. S. Mulliken, *J. Chim. Phys.*, **61**, 20 (1964).
191. G. Briegleb, "*Elektronen-Donator-Acceptor-Komplexe*," Springer–Verlag, Berlin, 1961, 279 pp.
192. L. J. Andrews and R. M. Keefer, "*Molecular Complexes in Organic Chemistry*," Holden–Day, San Francisco, 1964, 196 pp.
193. K. Toyoda and W. B. Person, *J. Am. Chem. Soc.*, **88**, 1629 (1966).
194. H. McConnell, J. S. Ham, and J. R. Platt, *J. Chem. Phys.*, **21**, 66 (1953).
195. R. S. Mulliken and W. B. Person, *Ann. Rev. Phys. Chem.*, **13**, 107 (1962).
196. J. K. Williams, D. W. Wiley, and B. McCusick, *J. Am. Chem. Soc.*, **84**, 2210 (1962).
197. N. C. Yang and Y. Gaoni, *J. Am. Chem. Soc.*, **86**, 5023 (1964).
198. W. v. E. Doering, footnote 7 in Ref. 230.
199. R. B. Woodward and R. Hoffmann, *J. Am. Chem. Soc.*, **87**, 395 (1965).
200. R. Hoffmann and R. B. Woodward, *J. Am. Chem. Soc.*, **87**, 2046 (1965).
201. R. B. Woodward and R. Hoffmann, *J. Am. Chem. Soc.*, **87**, 2511 (1965).
202. R. Hoffmann and R. B. Woodward, *J. Am. Chem. Soc.*, **87**, 4388 (1965).
203. R. Hoffmann and R. B. Woodward, *J. Am. Chem. Soc.*, **87**, 4389 (1965).
204. H. C. Longuet–Higgins and E. W. Abrahamson, *J. Am. Chem. Soc.*, **87**, 2045 (1965).
205. J. D. Roberts and C. M. Sharts, *Org. Reactions*, **12**, 1 (1962).
206. P. D. Bartlett, L. K. Montgomery, and B. Seidel, *J. Am. Chem. Soc.*, **86**, 616 (1964).
207. L. K. Montgomery, K. Schueller, and P. D. Bartlett, *J. Am. Chem. Soc.*, **86**, 622 (1964).

208. P. D. Bartlett and L. K. Montgomery, *J. Am. Chem. Soc.*, **86**, 628 (1964).
209. M. Itoh and S. Nagakura, *Tetrahedron Letters*, No. **2**, 227 (1966).
210. S. W. Benson, *J. Chem. Phys.*, **34**, 521 (1961); **38**, 18 (1963).
211. R. B. Turner, "*Theoretical Organic Chemistry*," Butterworth Scientific Publications, London, 1959, p. 67.
212. E. M. Kosower, Y. Ikegami, and H. P. Waits, unpublished results.
213. R. Huisgen, *Angew. Chemie*, **75**, 604 (1963).
214. R. Huisgen, *Angew. Chemie*, **75**, 742 (1963).
215. A. Cairncross and E. P. Blanchard, Jr., *J. Am. Chem. Soc.*, **88**, 496 (1966).
216. E. M. Kosower, *J. Am. Chem. Soc.*, **80**, 3253 (1958).
217. H. Seidl, footnote 12 in Ref. 214.
218. P. B. Ayscough, B. R. Brook, and H. E. Evans, *J. Phys. Chem.*, **68**, 3889 (1964).
219. J. A. Berson and A. Remanick, *J. Am. Chem. Soc.*, **83**, 4947 (1961).
220. S. Seltzer, *J. Am. Chem. Soc.*, **87**, 1534 (1965).
221. E. A. Halevi, *Progress in Phys. Org. Chem.*, **1**, 109 (1963).
222. R. B. Woodward and T. J. Katz, *Tetrahedron*, **5**, 70 (1959).
223. L. Watts, J. D. Fitzpatrick, and R. Pettit, *J. Am. Chem. Soc.*, **87**, 3253 (1965).
224. L. Watts, J. D. Fitzpatrick, and R. Pettit, *J. Am. Chem. Soc.*, **88**, 624 (1966).
225. E. Havinga and J. L. M. A. Schlatman, *Tetrahedron*, **16**, 151 (1961).
226. E. Vogel, *Ann.*, **615**, 14 (1958).
227. R. Criegee, as cited on p. 38, *Chem. Engr. News*, Mar. 22, 1965.
228. E. N. Marvel, G. Caple, and B. Schatz, *Tetrahedron Letters*, No. **7**, 385 (1965).
229. P. v. R. Schleyer, G. W. Van Dine, U. Schollkopf, and J. Paust, *J. Am. Chem. Soc.*, **88**, 2868 (1966).
230. S. J. Rhoads, "*Molecular Rearrangements*," Chapt. 11, Vol. 1, p. 655, J. Wiley and Sons-Interscience, New York.
231. A. C. Cope, A. C. Haven, Jr., F. L. Ramp, and E. R. Trumbull, *J. Am. Chem. Soc.*, **74**, 4867 (1952).
232. R. W. Murray and M. L. Kaplan, *J. Am. Chem. Soc.*, **88**, 3527 (1966).
233. A. P. Ter Borg and H. Kloosterziel, *Rec. Trav. Chim.*, **82**, 741 (1963).
234. A. P. Ter Borg, H. Kloosterziel, and N. Van Meurs, *Rec. Trav. Chim.*, **82**, 717 (1963).
235. T. Nozoe and K. Takahashi, *Bull. Chem. Soc. Japan*, **38**, 665 (1965).
236. W. N. White and B. E. Norcross, *J. Am. Chem. Soc.*, **83**, 1968 (1961).
237. W. N. White and B. E. Norcross, *J. Am. Chem. Soc.*, **83**, 3265 (1961).
238. W. N. White and C. D. Slater, *J. Org. Chem.*, **26**, 3631 (1961).
239. W. N. White and C. D. Slater, *J. Org. Chem.*, **27**, 2908 (1962).
240. E. Vogel, *Angew. Chem.*, **72**, 21 (1960).
241. E. Vogel, *Ann.*, **615**, 1 (1958).
242. W. v. E. Doering and W. R. Roth, *Tetrahedron*, **19**, 720 (1963).
243. E. Vogel, W. Grimme, and E. Dinné, *Angew. Chem.*, **75**, 1103 (1963).
244. M. Saunders, *Tetrahedron Letters*, 1699 (1963).
245. J. B. Lambert, *Tetrahedron Letters*, No. **27**, 1901 (1963).

246. W. v. E. Doering and W. Roth, *Tetrahedron*, **18**, 67 (1962).
247. M. S. Newman, ed., "*Steric Effects in Organic Chemistry*," J. Wiley and Sons, New York, 1956, 710 pp.
248. J. D. Roberts and V. C. Chambers, *J. Am. Chem. Soc.*, **73**, 5034 (1951).
249. E. L. Eliel, N. L. Allinger, S. J. Angyal, and G. A. Morrison, "*Conformational Analysis*," J. Wiley and Sons-Interscience, New York, 1965, 524 pp.
250. J. Lederberg, *Proc. Nat'l. Acad. Sci., U.S.*, **53**, 134 (1965).
251. O. Bastiansen and A. de Meijere, *Angew. Chem.*, **78**, 142 (1966).
252. W. v. E. Doering and E. F. Schoenewaldt, *J. Am. Chem. Soc.*, **73**, 2333 (1951).
253. W. v. E. Doering, M. Levitz, A. Sayigh, M. Sprecher, and W. P. Whelan, Jr., *J. Am. Chem. Soc.*, **75**, 1008 (1953).
254. O. W. Webster, *J. Am. Chem. Soc.*, **88**, 3046 (1966).
255. J. A. Landgrebe and R. H. Rynbrant, *J. Org. Chem.*, **31**, 2585 (1966).
256. A. Escoffier, "*Ma Cuisine*," p. 5, Flammarion, Paris, 1934.
257. J. Hine, "*Physical Organic Chemistry*," McGraw–Hill Book Co., New York, 2nd ed., 1962, 552 pp.
258. E. S. Gould, "*Mechanism and Structure in Organic Chemistry*," H. Holt, New York, 1959, 778 pp.
259. J. N. Brønsted, *Rec. Trav. Chim.*, **42**, 718 (1923).
260. M. Eigen, *Angew. Chem. Intern. Ed.*, **3**, 1 (1964).
261. M. S. Matheson, p. 45 in Ref. 544.
262. F. S. Lee and G. B. Carpenter, *J. Phys. Chem.*, **63**, 279 (1959).
263. G. C. Pimentel and A. L. McClellan, "*The Hydrogen Bond*," W. H. Freeman and Co., San Francisco, 1960, 475 pp.
264. R. P. Bell, *Advances in Phys. Org. Chem.*, **4**, 1 (1966).
265. T. C. Bruice and S. J. Benkovic, *Bioorganic Mechanisms*, Vol. 1, W. A. Benjamin, 1966, 362 pp.
266. D. E. Applequist and D. F. O'Brien, *J. Am. Chem. Soc.*, **85**, 743 (1963).
267. R. M. Salinger and R. E. Dessy, *Tetrahedron Letters*, No. **11**, 729 (1963).
268. V. I. Slovetskii, L. V. Okhlobystina, A. A. Fainzil'berg, A. I. Ivanov, L. I. Biryukova, and S. S. Novikov, *Izv. Akad. Nauk. SSSR. Ser. Khim. No. 11*, *Engl. transl.*, **1965**, 2032.
269. E. B. Wilson, Jr., J. C. Decius, and P. C. Cross, "*Molecular Vibrations*," McGraw–Hill Book Co., New York, 1955, 388 pp.
270. P. C. Lauterbur, in "*Determination of Organic Structures by Physical Methods*," Vol. 2, pp. 483–506, Academic Press, New York, 1962.
271. A. N. Douglas, *J. Chem. Phys.*, **45**, 3465 (1966).
272. C. A. Coulson and W. Moffitt, *Phil Mag.*, **40**, 1 (1949).
273. A. Almenningen, B. Andersen, and M. Traetteberg, *Acta Chem. Scand.*, **18**, 603 (1964).
274. M. Saunders and E. H. Gold, *J. Am. Chem. Soc.*, **88**, 3376 (1966).
275. N. L. Allinger, J. C. Tai, and M. A. Miller, *J. Am. Chem. Soc.*, **88**, 4495 (1966).
276. H. G. Adolf and M. J. Kamlet, *J. Am. Chem. Soc.*, **88**, 4761 (1966).
277. G. N. Lewis, *J. Franklin Inst.*, **226**, 293 (1938).

278. H. C. Brown, H. Bartholomay, Jr., and M. D. Taylor, *J. Am. Chem. Soc.*, **66**, 435 (1944).
279. W. v. E. Doering and A. K. Hoffman, *J. Am. Chem. Soc.*, **77**, 521 (1955).
280. A. Nickon and J. L. Lambert, *J. Am. Chem. Soc.*, **88**, 1905 (1966).
281. T. Birchall and W. L. Jolly, *J. Am. Chem. Soc.*, **88**, 5439 (1966).
282. J. Hine, R. D. Weimar, Jr., P. B. Langford, and O. B. Ramsey, *J. Am. Chem. Soc.*, **88**, 5522 (1966).
283. C. H. Langford and H. B. Gray, "*Ligand Substitution Processes,*" W. A. Benjamin, New York, 1965, 111 pp.
284. E. D. Hughes, F. Juliusberger, S. Masterman, B. Topley, and J. Weiss, *J. Chem. Soc.*, **1935**, 1525.
285. D. S. Matteson and R. A. Bowie, *J. Am. Chem. Soc.*, **87**, 2587 (1965).
286. P. D. Bartlett and S. T. Purrington, *J. Am. Chem. Soc.*, **88**, 3303 (1966).
287. G. M. Coppinger, *Tetrahedron*, **18**, 61 (1962).
288. A. J. Kirby and W. P. Jencks, *J. Am. Chem. Soc.*, **87**, 3217 (1965).
289. D. H. Hey, M. J. Perkins, and G. H. Williams, *J. Chem. Soc.*, **1965**, 110.
290. P. Kreienbuhl and H. Zollinger, *Tetrahedron Letters*, 1739 (1965).
291. P. B. D. de la Mare, L. Fowden, E. D. Hughes, C. K. Ingold, and J. D. H. Mackie, *J. Chem. Soc.*, **1955**, 3200.
292. T. T. Tidwell and T. G. Traylor, *J. Am. Chem. Soc.*, **88**, 3442 (1966).
293. C. G. Swain and C. B. Scott, *J. Am. Chem. Soc.*, **75**, 141 (1953).
294. J. O. Edwards, *J. Am. Chem. Soc.*, **78**, 1819 (1956).
295. J. O. Edwards and R. G. Pearson, *J. Am. Chem. Soc.*, **84**, 16 (1962).
296. K. H. Lohmann, quoted by C. G. Swain and L. E. Kaiser, *J. Am. Chem. Soc.*, **80**, 4089 (1958).
297. P. v. R. Schleyer, *J. Am. Chem. Soc.*, **89**, 699 (1967).
298. P. D. Bartlett and E. N. Trachtenberg, *J. Am. Chem. Soc.*, **80**, 5808 (1958).
299. D. W. Turner, *Advances in Phys. Org. Chem.*, **4**, 31 (1966).
300. J. D. Roberts and M. C. Caserio, "*Basic Principles of Organic Chemistry,*" W. A. Benjamin, New York, 1964, 1315 pp.
301. D. J. Cram and G. S. Hammond, "*Organic Chemistry,*" 2nd ed., McGraw–Hill Book Co., New York, 1964.
302. R. W. Gurney, "*Ionic Processes in Solution,*" McGraw–Hill Book Co., New York, 1953.
303. J. R. Partington, "*An Advanced Treatise on Physical Chemistry,*" Vol. 2, p. 2, Longmans, Green and Co., London, 1951.
304. D. Henderson, *Ann. Revs. Phys. Chem.*, **15**, 31 (1964).
305. P. Debye, "*Polar Molecules,*" Dover Publications, New York, 1945, 172 pp.
306. L. Onsager, *J. Am. Chem. Soc.*, **58**, 1486 (1936).
307. R. H. Cole, *Ann. Revs. Phys. Chem.*, **11**, 149 (1960).
308. J. G. Kirkwood, *J. Chem. Phys.*, **7**, 911 (1939).
309. F. E. Harris and B. J. Alder, *J. Chem. Phys.*, **21**, 1031 (1953).
310. R. A. Robinson and R. H. Stokes, "*Electrolyte Solutions,*" Butterworth Scientific Publications, London, 1959, 559 pp.
311. W. Fuller Brown, Jr., "*Dielectrics,*" in *Handbuch der Physik*, **17**, Springer–Verlag, Berlin, 1956.

312. J. G. Kirkwood and F. H. Westheimer, *J. Chem. Phys.*, **6**, 506 (1938).
313. F. H. Westheimer and J. G. Kirkwood, *J. Chem. Phys.*, **6**, 513 (1938).
314. C. P. Smyth, "*Dielectric Behavior and Structure*," Chapters II and IV, McGraw–Hill Book Co., New York, 1955.
315. C. P. Smyth, in "*Molecular Relaxation Processes*," pp. 1–14, Special Publ. No. **20**, Chem. Soc., London, 1966.
316. J. G. Kirkwood and J. B. Shumaker, *Proc. Nat'l. Acad. Sci., U.S.*, **38**, 855 (1952).
317. G. A. Jeffrey and R. K. McMullan, *Progress in Inorg. Chem.*, **8**, in press (1967).
318. J. A. Pople, W. G. Schneider, and H. J. Bernstein, "*High-Resolution Nuclear Magnetic Resonance*," McGraw–Hill Book Co., New York, 1959, 501 pp.
319. W. B. Moniz and H. S. Gutowsky, *J. Chem. Phys.*, **38**, 1155 (1963).
320. D. E. O'Reilly and G. E. Schacher, *J. Chem. Phys.*, **39**, 1768 (1963).
321. R. G. Gordon, *J. Chem. Phys.*, **43**, 1307 (1965).
322. P. G. Kohn, in "*State and Movement of Water in Living Organisms*," pp. 3–16, Academic Press, New York, 1965.
323. H. H. Hyman and J. J. Katz, R. J. Gillespie and E. A. Robinson, T. C. Waddingtin, R. S. Drago and K. F. Purcell, and W. J. Jolly and C. J. Hallada in "*Non-Aqueous Solutions*," T. C. Waddington, ed., Academic Press, 1965.
324. M. D. Danford and H. A. Levy, *J. Am. Chem. Soc.*, **84**, 3965 (1962).
325. S. W. Peterson and H. A. Levy, *Acta Cryst.*, **10**, 70 (1957).
326. Ref. 109, pp. 464–484.
327. M. v. Stackelberg and H. R. Muller, *Z. Elektrochem. Ber. Bunsenges. Physikal. Chem.*, **58**, 25 (1954); **62**, 130 (1958).
328. H. S. Frank and W. Y. Wen, *Discuss. Faraday Soc.*, **24**, 133 (1957).
329. G. Némethy and H. A. Scheraga, *J. Chem. Phys.*, **36**, 3382, 3401 (1962).
330. A. Ben-Naim, *J. Phys. Chem.*, **69**, 1922 (1965).
331. E. Wicke, *Angew. Chem. Intern. Ed.*, **5**, 106 (1966).
332. B. Kamb, *Science*, **150**, 205 (1965).
333. P. J. Brignell, U. Eisner, and P. G. Farrell, *J. Chem. Soc.*, **1966 B**, 1083.
334. A. Hartman and F. L. Hirshfeld, *Acta Cryst.*, **20**, 80 (1966).
335. J. L. Kavanau, "*Water and Solute-Water Interactions*," Holden–Day, San Francisco, 1964, 101 pp.
336. F. Franks, "*The Structural Properties of Water and Aqueous Solutions*," Heinemanns, London, in press (1967).
337. F. Franks and D. J. G. Ives, *Quart. Revs.*, **20**, 1 (1966).
338. E. Grunwald and S. Winstein, *J. Am. Chem. Soc.*, **70**, 846 (1948).
339. E. M. Kosower, J. A. Skorcz, W. M. Schwarz, Jr., and J. W. Patton, *J. Am. Chem. Soc.*, **82**, 2188 (1960).
340. E. M. Kosower, "*Molecular Biochemistry*," McGraw–Hill Book Co., New York, 1962, 304 pp.
341. C. J. F. Böttcher, "*Theory of Electric Polarization*," pp. 133–139, Elsevier, Amsterdam, 1952.

342. E. M. Kosower, unpublished results. See also Ref. 182.

343. Y. Wu and H. L. Friedman, *J. Phys. Chem.*, **70**, 501 (1966).

344. E. M. Kosower and G.-S. Wu, *J. Am. Chem. Soc.*, **83**, 3142 (1961).

345. J. E. Dubois and A. Bienvenue, *Tetrahedron Letters*, No. **17**, 1809 (1966).

346. J. A. Berson, Z. Hamlet, and W. A. Mueller, *J. Am. Chem. Soc.*, **84**, 297 (1962).

347. E. M. Kosower, *J. Am. Chem. Soc.*, **80**, 3261 (1958).

348. K. Dimroth, C. Reichardt, T. Siepmann, and F. Bohlmann, *Ann.*, **661**, 1 (1963).

349. C. Reichardt, *Angew. Chem. Intern. Ed.*, **4**, 29 (1965).

350. L. G. S. Brooker, A. C. Craig, D. W. Heseltine, P. W. Jenkins, and L. L. Lincoln, *J. Am. Chem. Soc.*, **87**, 2443 (1965).

351. L. G. S. Brooker, G. H. Keyes, and D. W. Heseltine, *J. Am. Chem. Soc.*, **73**, 5350 (1951).

352. A. H. Fainberg and S. Winstein, *J. Am. Chem. Soc.*, **78**, 2770 (1956).

353. Ref. 59, pp. 345–350.

354. S. Winstein and A. H. Fainberg, *J. Am. Chem. Soc.*, **79**, 5937 (1957).

355. J. B. Hyne, R. Wills, and R. E. Wonkka, *J. Am. Chem. Soc.*, **84**, 2914 (1962).

356. E. M. Arnett, W. G. Bentrude, J. J. Burke, and P. McC. Duggleby, *J. Am. Chem. Soc.*, **87**, 1541 (1965).

357. E. M. Arnett and D. R. McKelvey, *Rec. Chem. Progress*, **26**, 185 (1965).

358. J. B. Hyne and R. E. Robertson, *Can. J. Chem.*, **34**, 931 (1959).

359. E. M. Arnett, personal communication.

360. A. Allerhand and P. v. R. Schleyer, *J. Am. Chem. Soc.*, **85**, 371 (1963).

361. S. G. Smith, A. H. Fainberg, and S. Winstein, *J. Am. Chem. Soc.*, **83**, 618 (1961).

362. J. E. Dubois, E. Goetz, and A. Bienvenue, *Spectrochim. Acta*, **20**, 1815 (1964).

363. S. Brownstein, *Can. J. Chem.*, **38**, 1590 (1960).

364. J. B. Hyne, H. S. Golinkin, and W. G. Laidlaw, *J. Am. Chem. Soc.*, **88**, 2104 (1966).

365. J. F. King and R. G. Pews, *Can. J. Chem.*, **43**, 847 (1965).

366. T. G. Traylor, University of California, San Diego, private communication.

367. H. F. Herbrandson and F. R. Neufeld, *J. Org. Chem.*, **31**, 1140 (1966).

368. J. H. Hildebrand and R. L. Scott, "*Regular Solutions,*" Prentice–Hall, Englewood Cliffs, N.J., 1962.

369. A. H. Fainberg and S. Winstein, *J. Am. Chem. Soc.*, **79**, 1597 (1957).

370. A. H. Fainberg and S. Winstein, *J. Am. Chem. Soc.*, **79**, 1602 (1957).

371. S. Winstein, A. H. Fainberg, and E. Grunwald, *J. Am. Chem. Soc.*, **79**, 4146 (1957).

372. E. M. Kosower, *J. Am. Chem. Soc.*, **80**, 3267 (1958).

373. Ref. 1, pp. 379–388.

374. M. B. Robin, R. R. Hart, and N. A. Kuebler, *J. Chem. Phys.*, **44**, 1803 (1966).

375. D. E. Freeman and W. Klemperer, *J. Chem. Phys.*, **45**, 52 (1966).

376. W. D. Closson and P. Haug, *J. Am. Chem. Soc.*, **86**, 2384 (1964).

377. J. N. Murrell, "*The Theory of the Electronic Spectra of Organic Molecules*," John Wiley and Sons, New York, 1963, 328 pp.
378. L. Spialter, D. H. O'Brien, G. L. Untereiner, and W. A. Rush, *J. Org. Chem.*, **30**, 3278 (1965).
379. D. J. Severn, unpublished results.
380. E. M. Kosower and D. J. Severn, *Tetrahedron Letters*, No. **27**, 3125 (1966).
381. W. D. Closson, S. F. Brady, E. M. Kosower, and P.-k. C. Huang, *J. Org. Chem.*, **28**, 1161 (1963).
382. W. D. Closson, S. F. Brady, and P. J. Orenski, *J. Org. Chem.*, **30**, 4026 (1965).
383. H. Labhart and G. Wagnière, *Helv. Chim. Acta*, **42**, 2219 (1959).
384. E. M. Kosower, W. D. Closson, H. L. Goering, and J. C. Gross, *J. Am. Chem. Soc.*, **83**, 2013 (1961).
385. P. S. Wharton, *J. Org. Chem.*, **26**, 4781 (1961).
386. M. Ito, P.-k. C. Huang, and E. M. Kosower, *Trans. Faraday Soc.*, **57**, 1662 (1961).
387. K. Kimura and S. Nagakura, *Spectrochim. Acta*, **17**, 166 (1961).
388. J. Miller and A. J. Parker, *J. Am. Chem. Soc.*, **83**, 117 (1961).
389. A. J. Parker, *Quart. Revs.*, **16**, 163 (1962).
390. R. J. W. Le Fèvre, "*Dipole Moments*," Methuen, London, 1953.
391. "*Handbook of Organic Structural Analysis*," Y. Yukawa, ed., W. A. Benjamin, New York, 1965.
392. N. Tokura, T. Kawahara, and S. Ikeda, *Bull. Chem. Soc. Japan*, **37**, 138 (1964).
393. A. J. Parker, *J. Chem. Soc.*, **1961**, 1328.
394. J. Miller, *J. Am. Chem. Soc.*, **85**, 1628 (1963).
395. S. Winstein, L. G. Savedoff, S. Smith, I. D. R. Stevens, and J. S. Gall, *Tetrahedron Letters*, No. **9**, 24 (1960).
396. W. M. Weaver and J. D. Hutchsion, *J. Am. Chem. Soc.*, **86**, 261 (1964).
397. J.-J. Delpuech, *Tetrahedron Letters*, No. **25**, 211 (1965).
398. C. A. Kingsbury, *J. Org. Chem.*, **29**, 3262 (1964).
399. D. J. Cram, J. L. Mateos, F. Hauck, A. Langemann, K. R. Kopecky, W. D. Nielsen, and J. Allinger, *J. Am. Chem. Soc.*, **81**, 5774 (1959).
400. D. J. Cram and M. R. V. Sahyun, *J. Am. Chem. Soc.*, **84**, 1734 (1962).
401. E. W. Warnhoff, D. G. Martin, and W. S. Johnson, *Org. Syntheses*, **37**, 10 (1957).
402. D. R. Rosseinsky, *Chem. Revs.*, **65**, 467 (1965).
403. I. Lindqvist, "*Inorganic Adduct Molecules of Oxo-compounds*," Academic Press, New York, 1963, 129 pp.
404. S. G. Smith and S. Winstein, *Tetrahedron*, **3**, 317 (1958).
405. J. E. Gordon, *J. Am. Chem. Soc.*, **87**, 4347 (1965).
406. R. M. Diamond, *J. Phys. Chem.*, **67**, 2513 (1963).
407. C. A. Kraus, *J. Phys. Chem.*, **58**, 673 (1954).
408. T. L. Hill, "*Introduction to Statistical Thermodynamics*," pp. 321–331, Addison-Wesley Publ. Co., Reading, Mass., 1962.
409. C. W. Davies, *Progress in Reaction Kinetics*, **1**, 161 (1961).

410. B. E. Conway and R. G. Barrados, Editors, "*Chemical Physics of Ionic Solutions*," John Wiley and Sons, New York, 1966, 622 pp.

411. H. Bloom and J. W. Hastie, in Ref. 323, pp. 353–387.

412. J. Setschenow, *Ann. Chim. Phys.*, [6] **25**, 226 (1891).

413. G. A. Clarke and R. W. Taft, *J. Am. Chem. Soc.*, **84**, 2295 (1962).

414. D. R. Robinson and W. P. Jencks, *J. Am. Chem. Soc.*, **87**, 2470 (1965).

415. R. M. Noyes, *J. Am. Chem. Soc.*, **84**, 513 (1962).

416. J. Jortner and R. M. Noyes, *J. Phys. Chem.*, **70**, 770 (1966).

417. H. G. Hertz, *Nuclear Magnetic Resonance in Chemistry*, pp. 199–228, Academic Press, New York, 1965.

418. P. A. Leermakers, H. T. Thomas, L. D. Weis, and F. C. James, *J. Am. Chem. Soc.*, **88**, 5075 (1966).

419. R. K. Lyon and D. H. Levy, *J. Am. Chem. Soc.*, **83**, 4290 (1961).

420. R. M. Noyes, *Progress in Reaction Kinetics*, **1**, 129 (1961).

421. I. Amdur and G. G. Hammes, "*Chemical Kinetics: Principles and Selected Topics*," McGraw–Hill, New York, 1966, 268 pp.

422. W. A. Pryor, "*Free Radicals*," McGraw–Hill, New York, 1966, 354 pp.

423. N. J. Turro, "*Molecular Photochemistry*," W. A. Benjamin, New York, 286 pp.

424. G. S. Hammond, J. N. Sen, C. E. Boozer, *J. Am. Chem. Soc.*, **77**, 3244 (1955).

425. O. D. Trapp and G. S. Hammond, *J. Am. Chem. Soc.*, **81**, 4876 (1959).

426. H. P. Waits and G. S. Hammond, *J. Am. Chem. Soc.*, **86**, 1911 (1964).

427. P. S. Dixon, A. P. Stefani, and M. Szwarc, *J. Am. Chem. Soc.*, **85**, 2551 (1963).

428. W. G. Young, S. Winstein, and H. L. Goering, *J. Am. Chem. Soc.*, **73**, 1958 (1951).

429. M. Y. Shandala, E. S. Waight, and M. Weinstock, *J. Chem. Soc.*, **1966 B**, 590.

430. S. Winstein, E. Clippinger, A. H. Fainberg, and G. C. Robinson, *J. Am. Chem. Soc.*, **76**, 2597 (1954).

431. S. Winstein and E. Clippinger, *J. Am. Chem. Soc.*, **78**, 2784 (1956).

432. S. Winstein and G. C. Robinson, *J. Am. Chem. Soc.*, **80**, 169 (1958).

433. R. F. Kempa and W. H. Lee, *J. Chem. Soc.*, **1958**, 1936.

434. J.-J. Delpuech, *Bull. soc. Chim. France*, **1966**, 1624.

435. B. O. Coniglio, D. E. Giles, W. A. McDonald, and A. J. Parker, *J. Chem. Soc.*, **1966 B**, 152.

436. S. Winstein and D. Trifan, *J. Am. Chem. Soc.*, **74**, 1154 (1952).

437. D. J. Cram, *J. Am. Chem. Soc.*, **74**, 2129 (1952).

438. A. H. Fainberg and S. Winstein, *J. Am. Chem. Soc.*, **78**, 2780 (1956).

439. A. Ehret and S. Winstein, *J. Am. Chem. Soc.*, **88**, 2048 (1966).

440. S. Winstein, P. E. Klinedinst, Jr., and E. Clippinger, *J. Am. Chem. Soc.*, **83**, 4986 (1961).

441. F. C. Adam and S. I. Weissman, *J. Am. Chem. Soc.*, **80**, 1518 (1958).

442. J. W. Emsley, J. Feeney, and L. H. Sutcliffe, "*High Resolution Nuclear Magnetic Resonance Spectroscopy*," 2 Vols., Pergamon Press, Oxford, 1965, 1154 pp.

443. N. Hirota, *J. Phys. Chem.*, **71**, 127 (1967).
444. N. Hirota, *J. Chem. Phys.*, **37**, 1881 (1962).
445. G. Williams, *J. Phys. Chem.*, **63**, 534 (1960).
446. M. Davies and G. Williams, *Trans. Faraday Soc.*, **56**, 1619 (1960).
447. N. M. Atherton and S. I. Weissman, *J. Am. Chem. Soc.*, **83**, 1330 (1961).
448. N. Hirota and R. Kreilick, *J. Am. Chem. Soc.*, **88**, 614 (1966).
449. P. J. Zandstra and S. I. Weissman, *J. Am. Chem. Soc.*, **84**, 4408 (1962).
450. N. Hirota, *J. Am. Chem. Soc.*, **89**, 32 (1967).
451. M. C. R. Symons, *J. Phys. Chem.*, **70**, 172 (1967).
452. R. Chang and C. S. Johnson, Jr., *J. Am. Chem. Soc.*, **88**, 2338 (1966).
453. G. R. Luckhurst, *Mol. Phys.*, **9**, 179 (1965).
454. N. M. Atherton and A. E. Goggins, *Trans. Faraday Soc.*, **61**, 1399 (1965).
455. T. E. Hogen-Esch and J. Smid, *J. Am. Chem. Soc.*, **88**, 307 (1966).
456. D. N. Bhattacharya, J. Smid, and M. Szwarc, *J. Phys. Chem.*, **69**, 624 (1965).
457. H. L. Goering, M. M. Pombo, and K. D. McMichael, *J. Am. Chem. Soc.*, **85**, 965 (1963).
458. E. H. White and C. A. Elliger, *J. Am. Chem. Soc.*, **87**, 5261 (1965).
459. A. Iliceto, A. Fava, U. Mazzucato, and O. Rossetto, *J. Am. Chem. Soc.*, **83**, 2729 (1961).
460. H. M. Walborsky and A. E. Young, *J. Am. Chem. Soc.*, **86**, 3288 (1964) and previous papers.
461. G. D. Stucky and R. E. Rundle, *J. Am. Chem. Soc.*, **85**, 1002 (1963).
462. G. M. Whitesides, M. Witanowski, and J. D. Roberts, *J. Am. Chem. Soc.*, **87**, 2854 (1965).
463. G. M. Whitesides and J. D. Roberts, *J. Am. Chem. Soc.*, **87**, 4878 (1965).
464. L. J. Winters and E. Grunwald, *J. Am. Chem. Soc.*, **87**, 4608 (1965).
465. M. T. A. Behme and E. H. Cordes, *J. Am. Chem. Soc.*, **87**, 260 (1965).
466. M. T. A. Behme, J. G. Fullington, R. Noel, and E. H. Cordes, *J. Am. Chem. Soc.*, **87**, 266 (1965).
467. H. M. Koepp, H. Wendt, and H. Strehlow, *Z. Elektrochem.*, **64**, 483 (1960).
468. Ref. 4, pp. 74–86.
469. E. M. Arnett and G. W. Mach, *J. Am. Chem. Soc.*, **88**, 1177 (1966).
470. D. E. Freeman, J. R. Lombardi, and W. Klemperer, *J. Chem. Phys.*, **45**, 58 (1966).
471. H. H. Szmant and M. N. Roman, *J. Am. Chem. Soc.*, **88**, 4034 (1966).
472. E. M. Kosower and P.-k. C. Huang, *J. Am. Chem. Soc.*, **87**, 4645 (1965).
473. D. J. Cram, M. R. V. Sahyan, and R. R. Knox, *J. Am. Chem. Soc.*, **84**, 1734 (1962).
474. J. E. Nordlander S. P. Jindal, P. v. R. Schleyer R. C. Fort Jr., J. J. Harper, and R. D. Nicholas, *J. Am. Chem. Soc.*, **88**, 4475 (1966).
475. L. Friedman and F. M. Logullo, *J. Am. Chem. Soc.*, **85**, 1549 (1963).
476. M. Stiles and R. G. Miller, *J. Am. Chem. Soc.*, **82**, 3802 (1960).
477. J. H. Bayless, L. Friedman, J. A. Smith, F. B. Cook, and H. Schechter, *J. Am. Chem. Soc.*, **87**, 661 (1965).
478. A. T. Jurewicz and L. Friedman, *J. Am. Chem. Soc.*, **89**, 149 (1967).
479. A. Streitwieser, Jr., *J. Org. Chem.*, **22**, 861 (1957).

480. J. H. Bayless, F. D. Mendocino, and L. Friedman, *J. Am. Chem. Soc.*, **87**, 5790 (1965).

481. H. C. Brown and J. D. Cleveland, *J. Am. Chem. Soc.*, **88**, 2051 (1966).

482. P. v. R. Schleyer and G. W. Van Dine, *J. Am. Chem. Soc.*, **88**, 2321 (1966).

483. M. Vogel and J. D. Roberts, *J. Am. Chem. Soc.*, **88**, 2262 (1966).

484. G. A. Olah, C. U. Pittman, Jr., E. Namanworth, and M. B. Comisarow, *J. Am. Chem. Soc.*, **88**, 5571 (1966).

485. S. Winstein, E. Clippinger, R. Howe, and E. Vogelfanger, *J. Am. Chem. Soc.*, **87**, 376 (1965).

486. G. D. Sargent, *Quart. Revs.*, **20**, 301 (1966).

487. H. C. Brown, *Chemistry in Britain*, **2**, 199 (1966).

488. A. P. Krapcho and D. E. Horn, *Tetrahedron Letters*, No. **49**, 6107 (1966).

489. H. C. Brown and H. M. Bell, *J. Am. Chem. Soc.*, **86**, 5006 (1964).

490. P. v. R. Schleyer, W. E. Watts, R. C. Fort, Jr., M. B. Comisarow, and G. A. Olah, *J. Am. Chem. Soc.*, **86**, 5679 (1964).

491. S. Winstein, *J. Am. Chem. Soc.*, **87**, 381 (1965).

492. H. L. Goering and C. B. Schewene, *J. Am. Chem. Soc.*, **87**, 3516 (1965).

493. H. C. Brown and K. Takeuchi, *J. Am. Chem. Soc.*, **88**, 5336 (1966).

494. H. G. Richey, Jr., and J. M. Richey, *J. Am. Chem. Soc.*, **88**, 4971 (1966).

495. J. A. Berson and M. S. Poonian, *J. Am. Chem. Soc.*, **88**, 170 (1966).

496. D. C. DeJongh and S. R. Shrader, *J. Am. Chem. Soc.*, **88**, 3881 (1966).

497. S. Winstein and R. Buckles, *J. Am. Chem. Soc.*, **64**, 2780, 2787 (1942).

498. W. S. Trahanovsky, M. P. Doyle, and P. D. Bartlett, unpublished results.

499. M. Hanack, J. Häffner, and I. Herterich, *Tetrahedron Letters*, 875 (1965).

500. A. Lapworth, *J. Chem. Soc.*, **85**, 30 (1904).

501. M. L. Bender, *J. Am. Chem. Soc.*, **73**, 1626 (1951).

502. G. A. Olah, E. B. Baker, J. C. Evans, W. S. Tolgyesi, J. S. McIntyre, and I. J. Bastien, *J. Am. Chem. Soc.*, **86**, 1360 (1964).

503. G. A. Olah, M. B. Comisarow, C. A. Cupas, and C. U. Pittman, Jr., *J. Am. Chem. Soc.*, **87**, 2997 (1965).

504. G. A. Olah, J. M. Bollinger, C. A. Cupas, N. Friedman, and J. Lukas, *Abstracts*, 152nd National Meeting, *American Chemical Society*, U56, September, 1966.

505. G. A. Olah, W. S. Tolgyesi, S. J. Kuhn, M. E. Moffat, I. J. Bastien, and E. B. Baker, *J. Am. Chem. Soc.*, **85**, 1328 (1963).

506. G. A. Olah, S. J. Kuhn, W. S. Tolgyesi, and E. B. Baker, *J. Am. Chem. Soc.*, **84**, 2733 (1962).

507. P. v. R. Schleyer, W. E. Watts, R. C. Fort, Jr., M. B. Comisarow, and G. A. Olah, *J. Am. Chem. Soc.*, **86**, 5679 (1964).

508. M. Saunders, P. v. R. Schleyer, and G. A. Olah, *J. Am. Chem. Soc.*, **86**, 5680 (1964).

509. L. M. Jackman, "*Applications of Nuclear Magnetic Resonance Spectroscopy in Organic Chemistry*," Pergamon Press, 1959, 134 pp.

510. N. Muller and D. E. Pritchard, *J. Chem. Phys.*, **31**, 1471 (1959).

511. G. A. Olah and M. B. Comisarow, *J. Am. Chem. Soc.*, **88**, 1818 (1966).

512. G. A. Olah and M. B. Comisarow, *J. Am. Chem. Soc.*, **86**, 5682 (1964).

513. R. Breslow, H. Hover, and H. W. Chang, *J. Am. Chem. Soc.*, **84**, 3168 (1962).
514. T. J. Katz and E. H. Gold, *J. Am. Chem. Soc.*, **86**, 1600 (1964).
515. D. M. Hirst and J. W. Linnett, *J. Chem. Soc.*, **1962**, 1035.
516. M. Simonetta and E. Heilbronner, *Theoret. Chim. Acta*, **2**, 228 (1964).
517. T. S. Sorensen, *J. Am. Chem. Soc.*, **87**, 5075 (1965).
518. N. C. Deno, *Progress in Phys. Org. Chem.*, **2**, 129 (1964).
519. T. S. Sorensen, *Can. J. Chem.*, **42**, 2768 (1964).
520. T. Sorensen, *Can. J. Chem.*, **43**, 2744 (1965).
521. N. C. Deno, H. G. Richey, Jr., N. Friedman, J. D. Hodge, J. J. Houser, and C. U. Pittman, Jr., *J. Am. Chem. Soc.*, **85**, 2991 (1963).
522. J. D. Roberts and R. H. Mazur, *J. Am. Chem. Soc.*, **73**, 2509 (1951).
523. N. C. Deno, H. G. Richey, Jr., J. S. Liu, D. N. Lincoln, and J. O. Turner, *J. Am. Chem. Soc.*, **87**, 4533 (1965).
524. C. U. Pittman, Jr., and G. A. Olah, *J. Am. Chem. Soc.*, **87**, 2998 (1965).
525. L. Birladeanu, T. Hanafusa, B. Johnson, and S. Winstein, *J. Am. Chem. Soc.*, **88**, 2316 (1966).
526. G. A. Olah, S. J. Kuhn, W. S. Tolgyesi, and E. B. Baker, *J. Am. Chem. Soc.*, **84**, 2733 (1962).
527. F. P. Boer, *J. Am. Chem. Soc.*, **88**, 1572 (1966).
528. A. H. Gomes de Mesquita, C. H. MacGillavry, and K. Eriks, *Acta Cryst.*, **18**, 437 (1965).
529. M. Sundaralingam and L. H. Jensen, *J. Am. Chem. Soc.*, **85**, 3302 (1963).
530. H. Hart, T. Sulzberg, and R. R. Rafos, *J. Am. Chem. Soc.*, **85**, 1800 (1963).
531. G. A. Olah and M. B. Comisarow, *J. Am. Chem. Soc.*, **88**, 3313 (1966).
532. G. Merling, *Ber.*, **24**, 3108 (1891).
533. W. v. E. Doering and L. H. Knox, *J. Am. Chem. Soc.*, **76**, 3203 (1954).
534. H. J. Dauben, F. A. Gadecki, K. M. Harmon, and D. L. Pearson, *J. Am. Chem. Soc.*, **79**, 4557 (1957).
535. B. P. Dailey, A. Gawer, and W. C. Neikam, *Discuss. Faraday Soc.*, **34**, 18 (1962).
536. S. Meyerson, *Rec. Chem. Progress*, **26**, 257 (1965).
537. C. E. Keller and R. Pettit, *J. Am. Chem. Soc.*, **88**, 604 (1966).
538. C. E. Keller and R. Pettit, *J. Am. Chem. Soc.*, **88**, 606 (1966).
539. S. Winstein, C. G. Kreiter, and J. I. Brauman, *J. Am. Chem. Soc.*, **88**, 2047 (1966).
540. M. Brookhart, A. Diaz, and S. Winstein, *J. Am. Chem. Soc.*, **88**, 3135 (1966).
541. H. G. Richey, Jr., and R. K. Lustgarten, *J. Am. Chem. Soc.*, **88**, 3136 (1966).
542. M. Saunders, P. v. R. Schleyer, and G. A. Olah, *J. Am. Chem. Soc.*, **86**, 5680 (1964).
543. A. Streitwieser, Jr., and P. J. Stang, *J. Am. Chem. Soc.*, **87**, 4953 (1965).
544. E. J. Hart, ed., "*Solvated Electron*," Advances in Chemistry No. 50, American Chemical Society, Washington, 1965.
545. F. A. Cotton and G. Wilkinson, "*Advanced Inorganic Chemistry*," John Wiley and Sons, Interscience, New York, 1962.

546. T. J. Katz and P. J. Garratt, *J. Am. Chem. Soc.*, **86**, 5194 (1964).

547. E. A. LaLancette and R. E. Benson, *J. Am. Chem. Soc.*, **87**, 1941 (1965).

548. N. G. Krieghoff and D. O. Cowan, *J. Am. Chem. Soc.*, **88**, 1322 (1966).

549. G. M. Whitesides and J. D. Roberts, *J. Am. Chem. Soc.*, **87**, 4878 (1965).

550. R. R. Sauers and G. T. Kwiatkowski, *J. Org. Chem.*, **27**, 4049 (1962).

551. R. Waack, M. A. Doran, E. B. Baker, and G. A. Olah, *J. Am. Chem. Soc.*, **88**, 1272 (1966).

552. "*Handbook of Chemistry and Physics*," 45th ed., pp. E-41 and 42, Chemical Rubber Publishing Co., Cleveland, 1964.

553. M. Bersohn and J. C. Baird, "*An Introduction to Electron Paramagnetic Resonance*," W. A. Benjamin, New York, 1966, 274 pp.

554. A. Carrington and A. D. Maclachlan, "*Introduction to Magnetic Resonance*," Harper and Row, New York, 1967, 266 pp.

555. J. Hine, "*Divalent Carbon*," Ronald Press Co., New York, 1964, 206 pp.

556. W. Kirmse, "*Carbene Chemistry*," Academic Press, New York, 1964, 302 pp.

557. W. v. E. Doering and L. H. Knox, *J. Am. Chem. Soc.*, **78**, 4947 (1956).

558. R. W. Fessenden and R. H. Schuler, *J. Chem. Phys.*, **39**, 2147 (1963).

559. J. P. Freeman, in "*Free Radicals in Inorganic Chemistry*," p. 128, Advances in Chemistry No. 36, American Chemical Society, Washington, 1962.

560. P. P. Gaspar and G. S. Hammond, Chap. 12 in Ref. 556.

561. E. Wasserman, L. Barash, and W. A. Yager, *J. Am. Chem. Soc.*, **87**, 2075 (1965).

562. W. Lwowski and J. M. Conaghy, *Amer. Chem. Soc.* (*Abstracts*), Abstract S-129, 152nd Meeting, September, 1966.

563. L. H. Piette, R. C. Rempel, H. E. Weaver, and J. M. Flournoy, *J. Chem. Phys.*, **30**, 1623 (1959).

564. P. Kusch and H. Taub, *Phys. Rev.*, **75**, 1477 (1949).

565. M. L. Perl, I. I. Rabi, and K. Senitsky, *Phys. Rev.*, **98**, 611 (1955).

566. A. Dalgarno, T. Patterson, and W. Somerville, *Proc. Roy. Soc.*, **259A**, 100 (1960).

567. S. L. Miller and C. H. Townes, *Phys. Rev.*, **90**, 537 (1953).

568. J. J. Gallegher, F. D. Bedard, and C. M. Johnson, *Phys. Rev.*, **93**, 729 (1954).

569. H. E. Radford, *Phys. Rev.*, **136A**, 1571 (1962).

570. E. L. Cochran, F. J. Adrian, and V. A. Bowers, *J. Chem. Phys.*, **40**, 213 (1964).

571. T. R. Tuttle, Jr., and S. I. Weissman, *J. Am. Chem. Soc.*, **80**, 5342 (1958).

572. J. R. Bolton, *Mol. Phys.*, **6**, 219 (1963).

573. R. W. Fessenden and S. Ogawa, *J. Am. Chem. Soc.*, **86**, 3591 (1964).

574. T. J. Katz and H. L. Strauss, *J. Chem. Phys.*, **32**, 1873 (1960).

575. A Carrington and J. dos Santos-Veiga, *Mol. Phys.*, **5**, 21 (1962).

576. J. R. Bolton, A. Carrington, and J. dos Santos-Veiga, *Mol. Phys.*, **5**, 465 (1962).

577. B. L. Barton and G. K. Fraenkel, *J. Chem. Phys.*, **41**, 1455 (1964).

578. K. Kuwata and D. C. Geske, *J. Am. Chem. Soc.*, **86**, 2101 (1964).

579. R. D. Allendoerfer and P. H. Rieger, *J. Am. Chem. Soc.*, **87**, 2336 (1965).
580. E. T. Strom, G. A. Russell, and K. Konaka, *J. Chem. Phys.*, **42**, 2033 (1965).
581. T. M. McKinney and D. H. Geske, *J. Am. Chem. Soc.*, **87**, 3013 (1965).
582. M. Bersohn, as cited on p. 268, Ref. 553.
583. F. C. Adam and S. I. Weissman, *J. Am. Chem. Soc.*, **80**, 2057 (1958).
584. W. M. Tolles, D. W. Moore, and W. E. Thun, *J. Am. Chem. Soc.*, **88**, 3476 (1966).
585. P. Nordio, M. V. Pavan, and G. Giacometti, *Theoret. Chim. Acta (Berl.)*, **1**, 302 (1963).
586. K. W. Bowers, *Advances in Magnetic Resonance*, **1**, 317 (1965).
587. K. W. Bowers, G. J. Nolfi, Jr., T. H. Lowry, and F. D. Greene, *Tetrahedron Letters*, No. 34, 4063 (1966).
588. R.-M. Dupeyre and A. Rassat, *J. Am. Chem. Soc.*, **88**, 3180 (1966).
589. W. D. Blackley and R. R. Reinhard, *J. Am. Chem. Soc.*, **87**, 802 (1965).
590. S. P. Makarov, A. I. Iakubovitch, S. S. Dubov, and A. N. Medvedev, *Dokl. Akad. Nauk. SSSR*, **160**, 1319 (1965).
591. R. Brière, H. Lemaire, and A. Rassat, *Bull. Soc. Chim. France*, **1965**, 3273.
592. R. Brière, R.-M. Dupeyre, H. Lemaire, C. Morat, A. Rassat, and P. Rey, *Bull. Soc. Chim. France*, **1965**, 3290.
593. E. G. Rozantsev and V. A. Golubev, *Izvest. Akad. Nauk. SSSR, Ser. Khim.*, No. 4, pp. 718–720, April, 1965.
594. N. C. Yang and A. J. Castro, *J. Am. Chem. Soc.*, **82**, 6208 (1960).
595. P. D. Bartlett and T. Funahashi, *J. Am. Chem. Soc.*, **84**, 2596 (1962).
596. R. Kreilick, *J. Chem. Phys.*, **43**, 308 (1965).
597. M. C. R. Symons, *Advances in Physical Organic Chem.*, **1**, 284 (1963).
598. E. Wasserman, L. C. Snyder, and W. A. Yager, *J. Chem. Phys.*, **41**, 1763 (1964).
599. C. A. Hutchison and B. W. Mangum, *J. Chem. Phys.*, **29**, 952 (1958); **34**, 908 (1961).
600. J. H. van der Waals and M. S. de Groot, *Mol. Phys.*, **2**, 333 (1959); **3**, 190 (1960).
601. E. M. Kosower and Y. Ikegami, *J. Am. Chem. Soc.*, **89**, 461 (1967).
602. R. A. Bernheim, R. J. Kempf, J. V. Gramas, and P. S. Skell, *J. Chem. Phys.*, **43**, 196 (1965).
603. J. Higuchi, *J. Chem. Phys.*, **38**, 1237 (1963).
604. S. J. Fogel and H. F. Hameka, *J. Chem. Phys.*, **42**, 132 (1965).
605. G. Herzberg and J. Shoosmith, *Nature*, **183**, 1801 (1959).
606. E. Wasserman, L. Barash, and W. A. Yager, *J. Am. Chem. Soc.*, **87**, 2075 (1965).
607. G. Herzberg and D. N. Travis, *Can. J. Phys.*, **42**, 1658 (1964).
608. E. Ciganek, *J. Am. Chem. Soc.*, **87**, 652 (1965).
609. E. Wasserman and R. W. Murray, *J. Am. Chem. Soc.*, **86**, 4203 (1964).
610. E. Wasserman, L. Barash, A. M. Trozzolo, R. W. Murray, and W. A. Yager, *J. Am. Chem. Soc.*, **86**, 2304 (1964).
611. E. Wasserman, A. M. Trozzolo, W. A. Yager, and R. W. Murray, *J. Chem. Phys.*, **40**, 2408 (1964).

612. A. M. Trozzolo, R. W. Murray, and E. Wasserman, *J. Am. Chem. Soc.*, **84**, 4990 (1962).

613. R. W. Brandon, G. L. Closs, and C. A. Hutchison, Jr., *J. Chem. Phys.*, **37**, 1878 (1963).

614. A. M. Trozzolo, E. Wasserman, and W. A. Yager, *J. Am. Chem. Soc.*, **87**, 129 (1965).

615. R. N. Dixon, *Can. J. Chem.*, **37**, 1171 (1959).

616. E. Wasserman, G. Smolinsky, and W. A. Yager, *J. Am. Chem. Soc.*, **86**, 3166 (1964).

617. R. M. Moriarty, M. Rahman, and G. J. King, *J. Am. Chem. Soc.*, **88**, 842 (1966).

618. A. M. Trozzolo, R. W. Murray, G. Smolinsky, W. A. Yager, and E. Wasserman, *J. Am. Chem. Soc.*, **85**, 2526 (1963).

619. E. A. Chandross, *J. Am. Chem. Soc.*, **86**, 1263 (1964).

620. E. M. Kosower and H. P. Waits, unpublished results.

621. J. A. R. Coope, J. B. Farmer, C. L. Gardner, and C. A. McDowell, *J. Chem. Phys.*, **42**, 54 (1965).

622. R. Breslow, R. Hill, and E. Wasserman, *J. Am. Chem. Soc.*, **86**, 5349 (1964).

623. E. M. Kosower and J. L. Cotter, *J. Am. Chem. Soc.*, **86**, 5524 (1964).

624. R. H. Boyd and W. D. Phillips, *J. Chem, Phys.*, **43**, 2927 (1965).

625. C. A. Hutchison, Jr., A. Kowalsky, R. C. Pastor, and G. W. Wheland, *J. Chem. Phys.*, **20**, 1485 (1952).

626. R. K. Waring, Jr., and G. J. Sloan, *J. Chem. Phys.*, **40**, 772 (1964).

627. N. Hirota and S. I. Weissman, *J. Am. Chem. Soc.*, **86**, 2538 (1964).

628. P. S. Skell and R. C. Woodworth, *J. Am. Chem. Soc.*, **78**, 4496 (1956).

629. P. S. Skell and A. Y. Garner, *J. Am. Chem. Soc.*, **78**, 5430 (1956).

630. J. E. Dubois and G. Mouvier, *Tetrahedron Letters*, No. **20**, 1325 (1963).

631. J. E. Dubois and B. Barbier, *Tetrahedron Letters*, No. **17**, 1217 (1965).

632. D. E. Milligan and M. E. Jacox, *J. Chem. Phys.*, **45**, 1387 (1966).

633. P. S. Skell and R. R. Engel, *J. Am. Chem. Soc.*, **87**, 1135 (1965).

634. R. F. W. Bader and J. I. Generosa, *Can. J. Chem.*, **43**, 1631 (1965).

635. J. Hine, *J. Am. Chem. Soc.*, **72**, 2438 (1950).

636. J. Hine and P. B. Langford, *J. Am. Chem. Soc.*, **79**, 5497 (1957).

637. W. M. Wagner, H. Kloosterziel, and S. van der Ven, *Rec. Trav. Chim.*, **80**, 740 (1961).

638. J. Hine and D. C. Duffey, *J. Am. Chem. Soc.*, **87**, 1131 (1959).

639. K. R. Kopecky, G. S. Hammond, and P. Leermakers, *J. Am. Chem. Soc.*, **84**, 1015 (1962).

640. H. Kristinsson and G. W. Griffin, *J. Am. Chem. Soc.*, **88**, 1579 (1966).

641. W. Mahler, *Inorg. Chem.*, **2**, 230 (1963).

642. W. I. Bevan, R. N. Hazeldine, and J. C. Young, *Chem. and Ind.*, 789 (1961).

643. H. E. Simmons and R. D. Smith, *J. Am. Chem. Soc.*, **80**, 5323 (1958); **81**, 4256 (1959).

644. G. Köbrich and H. R. Merkle, *Chem. Ber.*, **99**, 1782 (1966).

645. W. T. Miller, Jr., and D. M. Whalen, *J. Am. Chem. Soc.*, **86**, 2089 (1964).

646. D. F. Hoeg, D. I. Lusk, and A. L. Crumbliss, *J. Am. Chem. Soc.*, **87**, 4147 (1965).
647. D. Seyferth, J. Y.-P. Mui, M. E. Gordon, and J. M. Burlitch, *J. Am. Chem. Soc.*, **87**, 681 (1965).
648. H. M. Frey, Chapter 11 in Ref. 556.
649. G. L. Closs and R. A. Moss, *J. Am. Chem. Soc.*, **86**, 4042 (1964).
650. W. v. E. Doering and W. A. Henderson, *J. Am. Chem. Soc.*, **80**, 5274 (1958).
651. J. E. Dubois and G. Mouvier, *Tetrahedron Letters*, No. **21**, 1629 (1965).
652. Footnote 9, Ref. 650.
653. W. v. E. Doering, R. G. Buttery, R. G. Laughlin, and N. Chaudhuri, *J. Am. Chem. Soc.*, **78**, 3224 (1956).
654. H. Meerwein, H. Rathjen, and H. Werner, *Ber.*, **75**, 1610 (1942).
655. W. v. E. Doering and H. Prinzbach, *Tetrahedron*, **6**, 24 (1959).
656. J. A. Berson, J. H. Hammons, A. W. McRowe, R. G. Bergman, A. Remanick, and D. Houston, *J. Am. Chem. Soc.*, **89**, 2590 (1967).
657. W. v. E. Doering and L. H. Knox, *J. Am. Chem. Soc.*, **83**, 1989 (1961).
658. W. v. E. Doering, unpublished results quoted on p. 39, Ref. 556.
659. L. Kaplan, *J. Am. Chem. Soc.*, **88**, 4531 (1966).
660. W. H. Urry and J. R. Eiszner, *J. Am. Chem. Soc.*, **74**, 5822 (1952).
661. M. L. Halberstadt and J. R. McNesby, *J. Chem. Phys.*, **45**, 1666 (1966).
662. A. G. Anastassiou, *J. Am. Chem. Soc.*, **88**, 2322 (1966).
663. A. G. Anastassiou, H. E. Simmons, and F. D. Marsh, *J. Am. Chem. Soc.*, **87**, 2296 (1965).
664. F. D. Marsh and M. E. Hermes, *J. Am. Chem. Soc.*, **86**, 4506 (1964).
665. Ref. 377, p. 296.
666. P-k.C. Huang and E. M. Kosower, *J. Am. Chem. Soc.*, **89**, 3910 (1967).
667. E. Ciganek, *J. Am. Chem. Soc.*, **88**, 1979 (1966).
668. I. B. M. Band, D. Lloyd, M. I. C. Singer, and F. I. Wasson. *Chem. Commun.*, No. **15**, 544 (1966).
669. S. I. Murahashi, I. Moritani, and M. Nishino, *J. Am. Chem. Soc.*, **89**, 1257 (1967).
670. W. B. DeMore, H. O. Pritchard, and N. Davidson, *J. Am. Chem. Soc.*, **81**, 5874 (1959).
671. W. v. E. Doering and E. A. Matzner, cited in W. v. E. Doering, "*Theoretical Organic Chemistry*," p. 35, Butterworth Scientific Publications, London, 1959.
672. P. S. Skell, L. D. Wescott, Jr., J.-P. Golstein, and R. R. Engel, *J. Am. Chem. Soc.*, **87**, 2829 (1965).
673. W. A. Chupka and M. G. Inghram, *J. Phys. Chem.*, **59**, 100 (1955).
674. P. S. Skell and R. R. Engel, *J. Am. Chem. Soc.*, **87**, 2493 (1965).
675. R. R. Engel and P. S. Skell, *J. Am. Chem. Soc.*, **87**, 4663 (1965).
676. M. S. Kharasch, H. Engelman, and F. R. Mayo, *J. Org. Chem.*, **2**, 288 (1937).
677. M. Stiles and R. G. Miller, *J. Am. Chem. Soc.*, **82**, 3802 (1960).
678. M. E. Schafer and R. S. Berry, *J. Am. Chem. Soc.*, **87**, 4497 (1965).

679. D. J. Cram and H. Steinberg, *J. Am. Chem. Soc.*, **73**, 5691 (1951).
680. R. H. Boyd, *Tetrahedron*, **22**, 119 (1966).
681. D. J. Cram and K. C. Dewhirst, *J. Am. Chem. Soc.*, **81**, 5963 (1959).
682. K. B. Wiberg, *Rec. Chem. Progress*, **26**, 143 (1965).
683. K. B. Wiberg and G. Lampman, *Tetrahedron Letters*, 2173 (1963).
684. D. Lemal, F. Menger, and G. Clark, *J. Am. Chem. Soc.*, **85**, 2529 (1963).
685. R. Srinivasan, *J. Am. Chem. Soc.*, **85**, 4045 (1963).
686. W. v. E. Doering and J. Coburn, Jr., *Tetrahedron Letters*, 991 (1965).
687. P. Eaton and T. W. Cole, Jr., *J. Am. Chem. Soc.*, **86**, 962, 3157 (1964).
688. J. C. Barborak, L. Watts, and R. Pettit, *J. Am. Chem. Soc.*, **88**, 1328 (1966).
689. M. S. Newman and D. Lednicer, *J. Am. Chem. Soc.*, **78**, 4765 (1956).
690. A. Moscowitz, *Tetrahedron*, **13**, 48 (1961).
691. K. E. Wilzbach and L. Kaplan, *J. Am. Chem. Soc.*, **87**, 4004 (1965).
692. R. Criegee and R. Askani, *Angew. Chem. Intern. Edn.*, **5**, 519 (1966).
693. G. S. Hammond, N. J. Turro, and A. Fisher, *J. Am. Chem. Soc.*, **83**, 4674 (1961).
694. W. Dauben and R. Cargill, *Tetrahedron*, **15**, 197 (1961).
695. N. J. Turro and W. B. Hammond, *J. Am. Chem. Soc.*, **87**, 3258 (1965).
696. R. B. Loftfield, *J. Am. Chem. Soc.*, **73**, 4707 (1951).
697. D. M. Lemal and K. S. Shim, *J. Am. Chem. Soc.*, **86**, 1550 (1964).
698. J. I. Brauman, L. E. Ellis, and E. E. van Tamelen, *J. Am. Chem. Soc.*, **88**, 846 (1966).
699. E. E. van Tamelen and S. P. Pappas, *J. Am. Chem. Soc.*, **84**, 3789 (1962); **85**, 3297 (1963).
700. R. Criegee and F. Zanker, *Chem. Ber.*, **98**, 3838 (1965).
701. Z. Maksic, L. Klasinc, and M. Randic, *Theor. Chim. Acta (Berl.)*, **4**, 273 (1966).
702. B. Nelander and S. Sunner, *J. Chem. Phys.*, **44**, 2476 (1966).
703. D. Seebach, *Angew. Chem.*, **77**, 119 (1965).
704. T. L. Cairns, R. A. Carboni, D. D. Coffman, V. A. Engelhardt, R. E. Heckert, E. L. Little, W. J. Middleton, R. M. Scribner, C. W. Theobald, and H. E. Winberg, *J. Am. Chem. Soc.*, **80**, 2775 (1958).
705. H. Weingarten and W. A. White, *J. Am. Chem. Soc.*, **88**, 2885 (1966).
706. R. L. Pruett, J. T. Barr, K. E. Rapp, C. T. Bahner, J. D. Gibson, and R. H. Lafferty, Jr., *J. Am. Chem. Soc.*, **72**, 3649 (1950).
707. H. E. Winberg, J. E. Carnahan, D. D. Coffman, and M. Brown, *J. Am. Chem. Soc.*, **87**, 2055 (1965).
708. R. W. Hoffmann, J. Schneider, and H. Hauser, *Chem. Ber.*, **99**, 1892 (1966).
709. R. West, A. Sado, and S. W. Tobey, *J. Am. Chem. Soc.*, **88**, 2488 (1966).
710. D. Lloyd, "*Carbocyclic Non-Benzenoid Aromatic Compounds*," Elsevier, Amsterdam, 1966, 220 pp.
711. J. M. Bollinger, C. A. Cupas, K. J. Friday, M. L. Woolfe, and G. A. Olah, *J. Am. Chem. Soc.*, **89**, 156 (1967).
712. R. S. Ely and R. T. Swindell, *J. Org. Chem.*, **30**, 10 (1965).
713. N. A. Hughes and P. R. H. Speakman, *Chem. Commun.*, 199 (1966).

714. W. D. Closson and S. A. Roman, *Tetrahedron Letters*, No. **48**, 6015 (1966).
715. Cited by P. D. Bartlett, *Chem. Engr. News*, p. 107, Oct. 3, 1966; P. D. Bartlett and McBride, *Pure and Applied Chem.*, in press (1967).
716. J. G. Calvert and J. N. Pitts, Jr., "*Photochemistry*," John Wiley and Sons, New York, 1966, 899 pp.
717. H. Kiefer and T. G. Traylor, *Tetrahedron Letters*, No. **49**, 6183 (1966).
718. P. D. Bartlett, E. P. Benzing, and R. E. Pincock, *J. Am. Chem. Soc.*, **82**, 1762 (1960).
719. A. J. Ihde, *Pure and Applied Chem.*, in press (1967).
720. M. Ballester, *Pure and Applied Chem.*, in press (1967).
721. C. Trapp, C.-S. Wang, and R. Filler, *J. Chem. Phys.*, **45**, 3472 (1966).
722. S. Hünig, *Pure and Applied Chem.*, in press (1967).
723. G. M. Coppinger, *J. Am. Chem. Soc.*, **79**, 501 (1957).
724. P. D. Bartlett and P. Gunther, *J. Am. Chem. Soc.*, **88**, 3288 (1966).
725. C. G. Overberger, H. Biletch, A. B. Finestone, J. Lilker, and J. Herbert, *J. Am. Chem. Soc.*, **75**, 2078 (1953).
726. H. C. Brown, R. S. Fletcher, and R. B. Johannesen, *J. Am. Chem. Soc.*, **73**, 212 (1951).
727. H. C. Brown and M. Borkowski, *J. Am. Chem. Soc.*, **74**, 1894 (1952).
728. J. P. Lorand and P. D. Bartlett, *J. Am. Chem. Soc.*, **88**, 3294 (1966).
729. W. L. Reynolds and R. W. Lumry, "*Mechanisms of Electron Transfer*," The Ronald Press Co., New York, 1966, 175 pp.
730. R. J. Beuhler, Jr., R. B. Bernstein, and K. H. Kramer, *J. Am. Chem. Soc.*, **88**, 5331 (1966).
731. P. R. Brooks and E. M. Jones, *J. Chem. Phys.*, **45**, 3449 (1966).
732. J. D. Bacha and J. K. Kochi, *J. Org. Chem.*, **30**, 3272 (1965).
733. C. Walling and P. J. Wagner, *J. Am. Chem. Soc.*, **86**, 3368 (1964).
734. R. W. Kreilick and S. W. Weissman, *J. Am. Chem. Soc.*, **88**, 2645 (1966).
735. C. Steel and T. F. Thomas, *Chem. Commun.* 900 (1966).
736. T. H. Fisher and J. C. Martin, *J. Am. Chem. Soc.*, **88**, 3382 (1966).
737. S. J. Cristol and R. V. Barbour, *J. Am. Chem. Soc.*, **88**, 4262 (1966).
738. R. E. Visco and E. A. Chandross, *J. Am. Chem. Soc.*, **86**, 5350 (1964).
739. D. M. Hercules, *Science*, **145**, 808 (1964).
740. K. S. V. Santhanam and A. J. Bard, *J. Am. Chem. Soc.*, **87**, 139 (1965).
741. E. A. Chandross, J. W. Longworth, and R. E. Visco, *J. Am. Chem. Soc.*, **87**, 3259 (1965).
742. Cf. G. A. Russell, *Pure and Applied Chemistry*, in press (1967) and previous references.
743. R. L. Strong, *J. Phys. Chem.*, **66**, 2423 (1962).
744. S. Proskow, H. E. Simmons, and T. L. Cairns, *J. Am. Chem. Soc.*, **85**, 2341 (1963).
745. N. Wiberg and J. W. Buchler, *Chem. Ber.*, **97**, 618 (1964).
746. S. Proskow, H. E. Simmons, and T. L. Cairns, *J. Am. Chem. Soc.*, **88**, 5254 (1966).
747. P. R. Story, R. W. Murray, and R. D. Youssefyeh, *J. Am. Chem. Soc.*, **88**, 4144 (1966).

748. R. W. Murray, R. D. Youssefyeh, and P. R. Story, *J. Am. Chem. Soc.*, **88**, 3143 (1966).

749. R. W. Murray, R. D. Youssefyeh, and P. R. Story, *J. Am. Chem. Soc.*, **88**, 3655 (1966).

750. J. E. Baldwin, G. V. Kaiser, and J. A. Romersberger, *J. Am. Chem. Soc.*, **87**, 4114 (1965).

751. C. G. Overberger, N. Weinshenker, and J.-P. Anselme, *J. Am. Chem. Soc.*, **87**, 4119 (1965).

752. W. J. Linn and R. E. Benson, *J. Am. Chem. Soc.*, **87**, 3657 (1965).

753. W. J. Linn, *J. Am. Chem. Soc.*, **87**, 3665 (1965).

754. J. H. Sullivan, *J. Chem. Phys.*, **46**, 73 (1967).

755. R. S. H. Liu, *J. Am. Chem. Soc.*, **89**, 112 (1967).

756. K. M. Shumate, P. N. Neuman, and G. J. Fonken, *J. Am. Chem. Soc.*, **87**, 3996 (1965).

757. D. M. Lemal and S. D. McGregor, *J. Am. Chem. Soc.*, **88**, 1335 (1966).

758. S. D. McGregor and D. M. Lemal, *J. Am. Chem. Soc.*, **88**, 2858 (1966).

759. W. L. Mock, *J. Am. Chem. Soc.*, **88**, 2857 (1966).

760. R. Hoffmann and R. B. Woodward, unpublished results.

761. R. Hoffmann, unpublished results.

762. A. T. Bottini, C. A. Grob, E. Schumacher, and J. Zergenyi, *Helv. Chim. Acta*, **49**, 2516 (1966).

763. E. L. Stogryn and S. J. Brois, *J. Org. Chem.*, **30**, 88 (1965).

764. E. Vogel, R. Erb, G. Lenz, and A. A. Bothner-by, *Ann.*, **682**, 1 (1965).

765. J. M. Brown, *Chem. Commun.*, 226 (1965).

766. G. Schröder, *Angew. Chem. Intern. Edn.*, **2**, 481 (1963).

767. W. v. E. Doering and J. W. Rosenthal, *J. Am. Chem. Soc.*, **88**, 2078 (1966).

768. A. Allerhand and H. S. Gutowsky, *J. Am. Chem. Soc.*, **87**, 4092 (1965).

769. G. Schröder, J. F. M. Oth, and R. Merenyi, *Angew. Chem. Intern. Edn.*, **4**, 752 (1965).

770. E. Gil-av and J. Herling, *Tetrahedron Letters*, No. **1**, 1 (1967).

771. D. M. Lemal and J. P. Lokensgard, *J. Am. Chem. Soc.*, **88**, 5934 (1966).

772. A. Maercker and J. D. Roberts, *J. Am. Chem. Soc.*, **88**, 1742 (1966).

773. D. J. Patel, C. L. Hamilton, and J. D. Roberts, *J. Am. Chem. Soc.*, **87**, 5144 (1965).

774. P. T. Lansbury, V. A. Pattison, W. A. Clement, and J. D. Sidler, *J. Am. Chem. Soc.*, **86**, 2247 (1964).

775. E. E. van Tamelen and T. L. Burkoth, *J. Am. Chem. Soc.*, **89**, 151 (1967).

776. F. R. Jensen and K. L. Nakamaye, *J. Am. Chem. Soc.*, **88**, 3437 (1966).

777. A. Streitwieser, Jr., and D. Holtz, *J. Am. Chem. Soc.*, **89**, 692 (1967).

778. M. Itoh and E. M. Kosower, *J. Am. Chem. Soc.*, **89**, 3655 (1967).

779. K. E. Wilzbach, J. S. Ritscher, and L. Kaplan, *J. Am. Chem. Soc.*, **89**, 1031 (1967).

780. G. D. Sargent and M. W. Brown, *J. Amer. Chem. Soc.* **89**, 2788 (1967).

781. I. Moritani, S. I. Murahashi, M. Nishino, Y. Yamamoto, K. Itoh, and N. Mataga, *J. Am. Chem. Soc.*, **89**, 1259 (1967).

782. R. Breslow, H. W. Chang, R. Hill, and E. Wasserman, *J. Am. Chem. Soc.*, **89**, 1112 (1967).

783. B. Dickens, *Chem. Commun.*, 246 (1967).

784. R. Alden, J. Kraut, and T. G. Traylor, *J. Phys. Chem.* **71**, 2379 (1967).

785. S. Winstein, to be published.

786. C. D. Ritchie and R. E. Uschold, *J. Am. Chem. Soc.*, **89**, 2752 (1967).

787. M. Itoh and S. Nagakura, *J. Am. Chem. Soc.*, **89**, in press (1967).

788. R. Huisgen, W. Scheer, and H. Huber, *J. Am. Chem. Soc.*, **89**, 1753 (1967).

789. L. B. Jones and V. K. Jones, *J. Am. Chem. Soc.*, **89**, 1880 (1967).

790. H. R. Ward and P. D. Sherman, Jr., *J. Am. Chem. Soc.*, **89**, 1962 (1967).

791. J. N. Murrell, S. F. A. Kettle, and J. M. Tedder, " *Valence Theory*," John Wiley and Sons, Ltd., London, 1965, 401 pp.

792. D. E. Applequist and R. Searle, *J. Am. Chem. Soc.*, **86**, 1389 (1964).

793. F. R. Jensen and L. H. Gale, *J. Am. Chem. Soc.*, **82**, 148 (1960).

Name Index

Subject Index